D0188413

Environmental Indicators for Agriculture

Methods and Results

Volume 3

2001

OECD

ORGANISATION FOR ECONOMIC CO-OPERATION AND DEVELOPMENT

ORGANISATION FOR ECONOMIC CO-OPERATION AND DEVELOPMENT

Pursuant to Article 1 of the Convention signed in Paris on 14th December 1960, and which came into force on 30th September 1961, the Organisation for Economic Co-operation and Development (OECD) shall promote policies designed:

- to achieve the highest sustainable economic growth and employment and a rising standard of living in Member countries, while maintaining financial stability, and thus to contribute to the development of the world economy;
- to contribute to sound economic expansion in Member as well as non-member countries in the process of economic development; and
- to contribute to the expansion of world trade on a multilateral, non-discriminatory basis in accordance with international obligations.

The original Member countries of the OECD are Austria, Belgium, Canada, Denmark, France, Germany, Greece, Iceland, Ireland, Italy, Luxembourg, the Netherlands, Norway, Portugal, Spain, Sweden, Switzerland, Turkey, the United Kingdom and the United States. The following countries became Members subsequently through accession at the dates indicated hereafter: Japan (28th April 1964), Finland (28th January 1969), Australia (7th June 1971), New Zealand (29th May 1973), Mexico (18th May 1994), the Czech Republic (21st December 1995), Hungary (7th May 1996), Poland (22nd November 1996), Korea (12th December 1996) and Slovak Republic (14th December 2000). The Commission of the European Communities takes part in the work of the OECD (Article 13 of the OECD Convention).

Publié en français sous le titre :
INDICATEURS ENVIRONNEMENTAUX POUR L'AGRICULTURE
Méthodes et résultatt
Volume 3

FOREWORD

The impacts of agriculture on the environment and the achievement of sustainable agriculture are of major public concern in the context of agricultural policy reform, trade liberalisation, and multilateral environmental agreements. This study is Volume 3 of the OECD project *Environmental Indicators for Agriculture*. It is a stocktaking of the environmental performance of agriculture considering a range of policy relevant agri-environmental issues in OECD countries. This Volume aims to review and take stock of progress in developing agri-environmental indicators in OECD countries; build on earlier OECD work in establishing standard definitions and methods of calculation for indicators; provide preliminary results of the state and recent trends of environmental conditions in agriculture across OECD countries; interpret indicator trends and highlight linkages between indicators; and outline the current limitations and key challenges for their future development.

Part I of the study, Agriculture in the broader economic, social and environmental context, outlines a set of contextual indicators which reveal the influence on agri-environmental relationships of macroeconomic forces, the viability of rural areas, biophysical processes, land use changes, and farm financial resources, including farm income and public and private expenditure on agri-environmental schemes. **Part II,** Farm management and the environment, examines different farming practices and systems and their impact on the environment, covering whole farm management, organic farming, as well as nutrient, pest, soil and irrigation management practices. **Part III,** Use of farm inputs and natural resources, tracks trends in farm input use, including nutrients, pesticides (including risks), and water use. **Part IV,** Environmental impacts of agriculture, monitors the extent of agriculture's impact on the environment including: soil quality, water quality, land conservation, greenhouse gases, biodiversity, wildlife habitats and landscape. A **Glossary**, list of **Websites**, and **Index** are also provided at the end of the study.

The study is the result of work carried out by the OECD Joint Working Party of the Committee for Agriculture and the Environment Policy Committee. These committees approved the study in August 2000, and agreed that it be published under the responsibility of the OECD Secretary-General. It is primarily aimed at policy makers and the wider public, in both OECD and non-OECD countries. Volume 1, *Concepts and Frameworks*, was released in 1997. Volume 2, *Issues and Design* was published in 1999 and provides the results of the OECD York Workshop (UK) which examined the design of suitable agri-environmental indicators. This study is accompanied by an *Executive Summary* published separately.

Acknowledgements

This study was prepared by the OECD Policies and Environment Division in the Food, Agriculture and Fisheries Directorate, with the participation of Member countries, especially through a questionnaire in 1999 which provided much of the data in the study. OECD wishes to acknowledge the many experts outside the Secretariat who have helped in preparing and editing draft chapters of the study, in particular, Richard Arnold, Ben Ten Brink, Frank Clearfield, Robert Koroluk, Jonathan Lloyd, Eiko Lubbe, Katsuyuki Minami, Jamie Morrison, Andrew Moxey, Leslie Russell, Jesper Schou, Nicola Shadbolt, Dirk Wascher, Daniel Zürcher and also Richard Pearce for editing the complete text. The following Secretariat staff, under the overall guidance of Wilfrid Legg, contributed to drafting this study: Kevin Parris, Yukio Yokoi, Outi Honkatukia, Seiichi Yokoi, Gérard Bonnis, Morvarid Bagherzadeh, Jeanne Richards, Dan Biller and Myriam Linster, and many other OECD staff provided comments on the study. Technical assistance was provided by Françoise Bénicourt, Theresa Poincet, Laetitia Reille, and Véronique de Saint-Martin, with the production and marketing of the publication provided by Mubeccel Valtat-Gevher, Colette Goldstein and Catherine Candea and their colleagues.

ACRONYMS AND ABBREVIATIONS

Acronyms

BMP	Best Management Practice
CAP	Common Agricultural Policy
CBD	Convention on Biological Diversity
COP	Conference of the Parties to the Convention
CVM	Contingent Valuation Method
DDT	Dichloro-diphenyl-trichloro-ethane
DSR	Driving force-state-response
EUROSTAT	Statistical Office of the European Communities
FAO	United Nations Food and Agriculture Organisation
GDP	Gross Domestic Product
GHG	Greenhouse Gas
GIS	Geographical Information System
GMOs	Genetically Modified Organisms
GPS	Global Positioning System
IPCC	Intergovernmental Panel on Climate Change
IPM	Integrated Pest Management
ISO	International Standardisation Organisation
MRF	Minimum Reference Flow
NCI	Natural Capital Index
NOPAT	Net Operating Profit After Tax
NVZ	Nitrate Vulnerable Zone
OFSF	Off-farm Sediment Flow
PNC	Potential Nitrate Concentration
PSE	Producer Support Estimate
SBI	Soil Biodiversity Indicator
UN	United Nations
UNFCCC	United Nations Framework Convention on Climate Change
USLE	Universal Soil Loss Equation
WRC	Water Retaining Capacity
WTP	Willingness-to-pay
WUE	Water Use Efficiency

For an explanation of technical terms, see the Glossary at the end of the Report

Abbreviations and symbols

µg	microgram	N	nitrogen
CH_4	methane	N_2O	nitrous oxide
CO_2	carbon dioxide	NH_3	ammonia
g	gram	NO_3	nitrate
ha	hectare	NO_x	nitrogen oxides
Kg	kilogram	P	phosphorus
Km	kilometre	ppbv	parts per billion by volume
l	litre	ppmv	parts per million by volume
m^3	cubic meter	t	metric tonne
mg	milligram	US$	United States dollar
mm	millimetre	yr/y	year

4

TABLE OF CONTENTS

Part I
Agriculture in the Broader Economic, Social and Environmental Context

Part II
Farm Management and the Environment

List of Boxes

Chapter 1

List of Tables

Chapter 1

List of Figures

Chapter 1

List of Tables

List of Figures

Part IV

Environmental Impacts of Agriculture

List of Boxes

List of Tables

EXECUTIVE SUMMARY

HIGHLIGHTS*

The impacts of agriculture on the environment are of major public concern, in the context of agricultural policy reform, trade liberalisation, international environmental agreements and the achievement of sustainable agriculture. Monitoring the environmental performance of agriculture and assessing the environmental effects of policies requires information on agri-environmental interactions.

This Report is a stocktaking of results in measuring the environmental performance of agriculture to address a range of agri-environmental areas considered of policy relevance to OECD member countries. The Report is primarily aimed at policy makers, other stakeholders and the wider public, including non-member OECD countries, interested in recent developments and trends in agri-environmental performance.

An improved capacity to assess agriculture's environmental performance has been a key outcome of the Report. This has been achieved by building on Member countries' experiences and earlier OECD work, and through helping to: establish a common framework, harmonised methodologies and data sets to calculate indicators; advance knowledge of agri-environmental interactions and linkages; and foster an exchange of national and international approaches and experiences in developing indicators.

Some positive developments can be observed. There has been a decrease of over 10 per cent in both nitrogen and pesticide use in many European countries and Japan, and associated improvements in water quality and lowering of greenhouse gas emissions, since the mid-1980s. Soil erosion rates have declined in Australia, Canada, and the United States, and progress has been made in adopting farming practices that enhance environmental performance, such as the shift to using nitrogen management plans, integrated pest management and conservation soil tillage.

The environmental performance of agriculture has deteriorated in some cases. This has been associated with the intensification of farm production in some areas and the regional concentration of activities, such as livestock farming. In turn, this has resulted in higher levels of nutrient surpluses, ammonia and greenhouse gas emissions, with consequent increases in water and air pollution, such as in regions of Canada, Europe, New Zealand and the United States. There is also growing competition for scarce water resources both between agriculture and other users and also meeting the water needs of aquatic ecosystems for recreational and environmental purposes, particularly in the drier regions of Australia, the United States and Southern Europe.

Overall agri-environmental indicator results over the last 10-15 years have been mixed. The overall indicator results suggest that for many agri-environmental issues, and regions within OECD countries, pollution levels are relatively high (*e.g.* nitrogen and pesticide loadings in water) and that various environmental risks persist (*e.g.* soil erosion, water resource depletion). Agriculture, however, does provide certain environmental benefits and services (*e.g.* providing wildlife habitat, acting as a sink for greenhouse gases, providing landscape amenity).

Interpreting the overall impact of agri-environmental trends can be complex. For example, the increase in agricultural production and total environmental emission levels has been offset, to some extent, by improvements in farm input and natural resource use efficiency. This is the case with the use of fertilisers, pesticides, and water in some countries, where improvements in technology and farm management practices have led to a reduction in the use of these inputs per unit volume of production.

---

*   The full *Executive Summary* of this Report is published separately.

HIGHLIGHTS (cont.)

Changes in the environmental performance of agriculture can be attributed to a wide range of factors. These include variations in agricultural production, structural and technological developments, the influence of public pressure and market forces on farming practices and systems, and changes in policy settings and priorities. The linkages between indicators observed in this Report suggest a sequence of causes and effects. Changes in market conditions or policy settings affect the level of financial resources available to farmers, which influence production decisions and farm practices, while agri-environmental measures and environmental regulations may constrain actions taken by farmers. This leads to different environmental outcomes depending on varying agro-ecological conditions.

These results need to be seen in a broader context. For most OECD countries agriculture's role in the national economy is small, but in terms of the use of natural resources is significant, accounting for around 40 per cent of total land use and 45 per cent of water use. Agricultural production has increased by around 15 per cent, resulting mainly from improvements in productivity with capital replacing labour helped by new technologies. The higher production has been achieved from increasing yields as the total agricultural land area has decreased, by 1 per cent, and the use of water has risen, by over 5 per cent. Agricultural employment has declined by about 8 per cent, while the farm population has aged. Farm numbers have declined with a corresponding increase in farm size.

OECD *agriculture continues to be characterised by high support*, which currently accounts for about 36 per cent of total farm receipts, although there are wide variations in the level, composition and trends in support among countries and commodities. Agricultural and trade policies have caused distortions in market input and output price signals, in some cases this has led to environmental damage. Policy reform should help improve agriculture's environmental performance but in some cases could reduce environmental benefits. As part of the reform process and in response to public pressure, many countries have introduced agri-environmental and environmental measures to help achieve environmental goals.

For some agri-environmental areas there is incomplete knowledge and data to establish trends. Information is incomplete, for example, concerning the degree of groundwater pollution or rate of depletion resulting from agricultural activities, and the human health and environmental risks associated with the use of pesticides. In other cases the linkages between different indicators are understood but are not easy to measure, such as between changes in farm management practices and environmental outcomes, or attributing the relative impact of agriculture and other activities, for example, on water pollution. Also for a number of areas, notably agriculture's impact on biodiversity, habitats and landscape, the understanding and measurement of these impacts is still at a preliminary stage of research, partly because of the high costs associated with monitoring programmes.

The future challenge to developing agri-environmental indicators is to meet the objectives of providing information on the current state and changes in the conditions of the environment in agriculture; and using indicators for policy monitoring, evaluation, and forecasting. This requires improving the analytical soundness and measurability of indicators, especially by overcoming conceptual and data deficiencies, and providing a better interpretation of indicator trends. This could contribute to understanding the linkages between indicators (*e.g.* water use, management and pricing) and to examining the synergies and trade-offs between the economic, social and environmental dimensions of sustainable agriculture. Developing a core set of integrated OECD agri-environmental indicators, complemented as necessary by other indicators, could help to achieve these objectives.

Background: Objectives and Scope of the Report

1. Introduction

The impacts of agriculture and agricultural policies on the environment are of major public concern, particularly in the context of agricultural policy reform, trade liberalisation and the achievement of sustainable agriculture. Understanding these impacts requires information on the relationship between agriculture, the environment, trade and sustainable development.

Agricultural policy reform in many OECD countries addresses environmental and natural resource issues. A number of recent international environmental agreements also have implications for agriculture, for example, the United Nations Conference on Environment and Development (UNCED) Rio Declaration and Agenda 21, the Convention on Biological Diversity, and the Kyoto Protocol commitments to reduce greenhouse gas emissions (Box 1).

Recent OECD ministerial meetings have emphasised the importance of examining agricultural and environmental policy issues supported by indicators and better information.[1]

- *The meeting of* OECD *Agriculture Ministers* (5-6 March 1998), identified a role for OECD to "foster sustainable development through analysing and measuring the effects on the environment of domestic agricultural and agri-environmental policies and trade measures".

- *The meeting of* OECD *Environment Ministers* (2-3 April 1998), recommended that OECD should "further develop and adopt a comprehensive set of robust indicators to measure progress toward sustainable development, in concert with sustainable development initiatives of other international agencies, to be used in country reviews and outlook reports...".

2. Objectives of the report

The audience for the Report is primarily policy makers and the wider public interested in the development, trends and the use of agri-environmental indicators for policy purposes. While the focus of the Report is on OECD countries, the discussion on indicator definitions and methodologies is of relevance to a much wider international readership. Many of the agri-environmental issues examined in the Report are of importance beyond OECD countries, for example, on issues covering soil and water quality, and the use of nutrients, pesticides and water by agriculture. For those readers wishing to pursue a particular issue in further detail each chapter provides a review of relevant literature, mainly drawn from government and non-government researchers. Also, where possible, details of relevant Internet Websites have been highlighted in the text and bibliography (a list of key websites is also provided at the end of the Report, following the Glossary).

The general objectives of OECD *work on agri-environmental indicators* is intended to contribute to the demands of policy makers and other stakeholders in a number of ways. First, by *providing information* to policy makers and the wider public on the current state and changes in the conditions of the environment in agriculture. Second, by *assisting policy makers* to better understand the linkages between the causes and impacts of agriculture, agricultural policy reform, trade liberalisation and environmental measures on the environment, and help to guide their responses to changes in environmental conditions. Third, by *contributing to monitoring and evaluating* the effectiveness of policies addressing agri-environmental concerns and promoting sustainable agriculture (OECD, 1999a).

The objectives of the Report, against this general background, are to:
- review and take stock of progress in developing indicators across OECD countries;
- build on earlier OECD work in establishing standard definitions and methods of calculation for indicators (OECD, 1997; and OECD, 1999a);
- provide preliminary results of the state and recent trends of environmental conditions in agriculture across OECD countries;
- interpret indicator trends and highlight linkages between indicators; and,
- outline limitations and the key challenges for the future development of indicators.

19

Box 1. **Selected International and Regional Environmental Agreements Relevant to OECD Agri-environmental Indicators**[1]

Indicator areas	International agreements[2]	Regional agreements[2]
Water quality, Water use, Nutrient use, Pesticide use and risks	• Convention on the Protection and Use of Transboundary Watercourses and International Lakes *www.unece.org/env/water/* • Montreal Protocol on Substances that Deplete the Ozone Layer (related to the use of the methyl bromide pesticide) *www.unep.org/ozone/*	• Convention for the Prevention of Marine Environment of the North-East Atlantic (OSPAR Convention) *www.ospar.org/* • Convention on the Protection of the Marine Environment of the Baltic Sea Area *www.helcom.fi/oldhc.html* • EU Directives: Water Framework, Nitrate, and Drinking Water *www.europa.eu.int/water/* • Great Lakes Water Quality Agreement (North America) *www.ijc.org/*
Soil quality	• Convention to Combat Desertification in those Countries Experiencing Serious Drought and/or Desertification *www.unccd.ch/*	
Greenhouse gases	• Framework Convention on Climate Change *www.unfccc.org/*	
Biodiversity, Wildlife Habitat, Landscape	• Convention on the Conservation of Migratory Species of Wild Animals *www.wcmc.org.uk/cms/* • Convention on Long-Range Transboundary Air Pollution *www.unece.org/env/irtap* • Convention on International Trade in Endangered Species of Wild Fauna and Flora (CITES) *www.cites.org/* • Convention on Wetlands of International Importance especially as Waterfowl Habitat (Ramsar Convention) *www.ramsar.org/* • Convention on Biological Diversity *www.biodiv.org/* • Convention Concerning the Protection of the World Cultural and Natural Heritage *www.unesco.org/whc/*	• Canada-United States Migratory Birds Convention *www.fws.gov/r9mbmo/intrnltr/tblcont.html* • EU Habitat and Wild Birds Directive *www.europa.eu.int/comm/environment/nature/legis.htm*

1. For other international and regional agreements related to the environment, see the Environmental Treaties and Resource Indicators (ENTRI) website: *www.sedac.ciesin.org/pidb/*. See also the list of key websites provided at the end of this Report, following the Glossary.
2. For each listed agreement, the respective website is indicated.
Source: OECD Secretariat.

3. Structure of the report

The complete list of indicators covered in the Report is summarised in Box 2 and a technical *Glossary of Terms* is provided at the end of the Report, together with an *Index* of countries and main agri-environmental themes. The Report is structured into four parts.

Box 2. Complete list of OECD Agri-environmental Indicators[1]

I. AGRICULTURE IN THE BROADER ECONOMIC, SOCIAL AND ENVIRONMENTAL CONTEXT

1. Contextual Information and Indicators		2. Farm Financial Resources

• *Agricultural GDP*
• *Agricultural output*
• *Farm employment*
• *Farmer age/gender distribution*
• *Farmer education*
• *Number of farms*
• *Agricultural support*
	• Land use
	  – Stock of agricultural land
	  – Change in agricultural land
	  – Agricultural land use
		• *Farm income*
		• *Agri-environmental expenditure*
		  – Public and private agri-environmental
		    expenditure
		  – Expenditure on agri-environmental research

II. FARM MANAGEMENT AND THE ENVIRONMENT

1. Farm Management

• *Whole farm management*
  – Environmental whole
    farm management plans
  – Organic farming
	• *Nutrient management*
	  – Nutrient management plans
	  – Soil tests
	• *Pest management*
	  – Use of non-chemical pest control
	    methods
	  – Use of integrated pest management
		• *Soil and land management*
		  – Soil cover
		  – Land management practices
		• *Irrigation and water management*
		  – Irrigation technology

III. USE OF FARM INPUTS AND NATURAL RESOURCES

1. Nutrient Use	2. Pesticide Use and Risks	3. Water Use

• *Nitrogen balance*
• *Nitrogen efficiency*
	• *Pesticide use*
	• *Pesticide risk*
		• *Water use intensity*
		• *Water use efficiency*
		  – Water use technical efficiency
		  – Water use economic efficiency
		• *Water stress*

IV. ENVIRONMENTAL IMPACTS OF AGRICULTURE

1. Soil Quality	3. Land Conservation	4. Greenhouse Gases
• *Risk of soil erosion by water* • *Risk of soil erosion by wind*	• *Water retaining capacity* • *Off-farm sediment flow*	• *Gross agricultural greenhse gas emissions*
2. Water Quality		
• *Water quality risk indicator* • *Water quality state indicator*		

5. Biodiversity	6. Wildlife Habitats	7. Landscape

• *Genetic diversity*
• *Species diversity*
  – Wild species
  – Non-native species
 	
• *Eco-system diversity*
  (see Wildlife Habitats)
	• *Intensively-farmed agricultural habitats*
	• *Semi-natural agricultural habitats*
	• *Uncultivated natural habitats*
	• *Habitat matrix*
		• *Structure of landscapes*
		  – Environmental features and
		    land use patterns
		  – Man-made objects (cultural features)
		• *Landscape management*
		• *Landscape costs and benefits*

1. This list includes all the agri-environmental indicators covered in the Report. For a detailed description of each indicator, see the Annex to this chapter.
Source: OECD Secretariat.

- **Part I: Agriculture in the broader economic, social and environmental context** sets the discussion in a broader context by considering *contextual information and indicators*, that is the influence on agri-environmental relationships of: economic forces (*e.g.* farm production, employment), societal preferences (*e.g.* rural viability), environmental processes (*e.g.* interaction of agriculture with biophysical conditions) and land use changes (*e.g.* agricultural land use). One of the key contextual issues discussed concerns *farm financial resources* and their relation to environmental outcomes in terms of farm level income and public and private agri-environmental expenditure.

- **Part II: Farm management and the environment**, examines the relationship between different farming practices and systems and their impact on the environment, covering *whole farm management* practices that encompass overall trends in farming methods, including organic farming, as well as *nutrient, pest, soil* and *irrigation management* practices.

- **Part III: Use of farm inputs and natural resources**, tracks trends in the use of farm inputs, covering *nutrients* (*e.g.* fertilisers, manure), *pesticides* (including risks), and *water use* intensity, efficiency, stress and the price of water paid by farmers relative to other users in the economy.

- **Part IV: Environmental impacts of agriculture**, monitors the extent of agriculture's impact on the environment covering: *soil quality, water quality, land conservation* (*i.e.* the soil and water retaining capacity of agriculture), *greenhouse gases, biodiversity, wildlife habitats* and *landscape*.

For each agri-environmental indicator area shown in Box 2, except for contextual indicators, the Report has a common structure.

- **Highlights** – provides a summary of the chapter (the highlights section of each chapter are also published separately in the *Executive Summary* of the Report).

- **Background** – discusses the *policy context* at domestic and international level, and the *environmental context* by outlining the key environmental and scientific processes that underpin the indicator area.

- **Indicators** – describes the *definition* for each respective indicator, outlines the *method of calculation*, examines *recent trends* showing time series data across countries, discusses the *interpretation and links to other indicators*, including indicator limitations, and outlines specific country and other *related information*.

- **Future challenges** – sets out the areas where refining and developing indicators may help overcome current limitations and relate physical indicators to a common economic framework.

4. Developing the indicators

Definitions of indicators, particularly specific indicators, vary widely as a concept (Moxey, 1999). The *definition of an agri-environmental indicator*, used in this Report, is a summary measure combining raw data of something identified as important to OECD policy makers (*e.g.* soil erosion rates). Indicators form part of a continuum from raw data through to calculated indicators, formalised models and established knowledge, which includes validated information around which a broad consensus has formed.

Some of the indicators in this Report are closer to the raw data end of this continuum, such as the change in agricultural land use area, while others vary in the degree they summarise data. This ranges from simpler formulations, for example, the share of the agricultural land under organic farming systems, to more complex calculations, such as the nitrogen balance indicator, which is calculated using a complete input-output equation.

The common theme running through the indicators in this Report is that they are a vehicle for communicating information in a summary form about issues important to OECD policy makers. Hence, information is elevated to the status of an indicator by its user(s), which implies that the choice of indicators involve public and political acceptability as well as scientific rigour (Moxey, 1999).

OECD (1997) has identified a number of general criteria which agri-environmental indicators need to meet. These include the requirements that they are:

- *policy-relevant* – they should address the key environmental issues faced by governments and other stakeholders in the agriculture sector;

- *analytically sound* – based on sound science, but recognising that their development involves successive stages of improvement;
- *measurable* – feasible in terms of current or planned data availability and cost effective in terms of data collection;
- *easy to interpret* – the indicators should communicate essential information to policy makers and the wider public in a way that is unambiguous and easy to understand.

Development of the indicators in this Report has involved five steps outlined below, taking into account the general criteria discussed previously.

Identifying policy relevant issues which indicators should address

The agri-environmental areas, listed in Box 2, have been identified by OECD Member countries as the current priority areas to address. This choice represents a consensus amongst OECD countries that has emerged over time (OECD, 1997 and 1999*a*). Each area, however, does not have the same relevance across all OECD countries in view of differences in agro-ecological conditions and domestic concerns.

The choice of indicators is an evolving process depending on societal pressures and political choices. Some environmental areas are gaining in importance as new issues emerge (*e.g.* soil greenhouse gas sinks), while others are diminishing in the context where agricultural impacts on the environment have been reduced (*e.g.* prohibition of certain pesticides). However, it is evident that a considerable effort is taking place to develop agri-environmental indicators to help assess the current state and trends in the environment and provide a tool for policy makers, as summarised in Box 3.

Developing a common framework to structure the development of indicators

A common framework has been developed by OECD to help in the process of developing indicators. The OECD **Driving Force-State-Response (DSR) framework** identifies three main types of agri-environmental indicators (OECD, 1997 and 1999*a*):

- *driving force indicators*, addressing the issue of what is causing environmental conditions in agriculture to alter, such as, changes in the availability of farm management practices and the use of nutrients, pesticides, land and water;
- *state indicators*, highlighting what are the effects of agriculture on the environment, such as covering impacts on soil, water, air, biodiversity, habitats and landscapes;
- *response indicators*, measuring what actions are being taken to respond to the changes in the state of the environment, for example, variation in agri-environmental expenditure.

The DSR framework recognises explicitly that agri-environmental interactions and linkages are complex and multi-faceted, while providing a structure within which individual indicators can be placed in context (Moxey, 1999). The boundaries between driving forces, state and response are unclear in some cases as certain indicators can be considered as both driving forces and responses, for example, changes in the management practices and systems adopted by farmers.

The DSR framework builds on the Pressure-State-Response model used by OECD to develop its set of environmental indicators (OECD, 1998*a* and 1999*b*). OECD is also undertaking work to examine the appropriate measurement frameworks to structure and establish a broader set of sustainable development indicators (OECD, 2000*a*).

Establishing indicator definitions and methods of measurement

The Report's *indicators cover the linkages between primary agriculture and the environment*, and do not address those related to the agro-food chain (*e.g.* pesticide manufacturing, food processing) or the impact of the environment on agriculture (*e.g.* impact of climate change and acidification on agriculture).

While the indicators cannot be considered as indicators of "sustainability", many of them can be useful inputs for illustrating the environmental dimension. Some attention is paid to the economic and

---

Box 3. Development of Agri-environmental Indicators in OECD Countries and Internationally[1]

A growing number of **national initiatives** are seeking to assess the environmental performance of agriculture, including in Canada (McRae et al., 2000), Denmark (Simonsen, 2000), France (IFEN, 1997, and 2000), New Zealand (New Zealand MAF, 1995), the Netherlands (Brouwer, 1995), Switzerland (OFAG, 2000) and the United States (USDA, 1997). For other countries the approach is to examine progress toward sustainable agriculture, including the balance between economic, environmental and social needs, for example, reports completed by Australia (Commonwealth of Australia, 1998), Finland (Aakkula, 2000) and the United Kingdom (MAFF, 2000).

At the **regional country level** various European institutions are involved in the process of establishing agri-environmental indicators. Most importantly is the recent request from the European Union Council Summit meeting in Helsinki, December 1999, to establish indicators for the integration of environmental concerns into the Common Agricultural Policy (Commission of the European Union, 2000). An initial response to this request has been a joint Report by the European Commission and EUROSTAT to provide statistical information on agriculture, environment and rural development (European Commission, 1999; and EUROSTAT, 1999). The European Environment Agency is involved with developing environmental indicators, which include an agricultural focus (European Environment Agency, 2000).

Under the auspices of the North American Free Trade Agreement (NAFTA), the Commission for Environmental co-operation is developing an analytical framework to address environmental concerns, including issues related to agriculture (CEC, 1999). Major components of the framework are indicators for assessing how NAFTA-associated processes generate environmental pressures and responses that affect air, water, land and biodiversity.

Australia and New Zealand have a collaborative effort to oversee the process of defining, promoting and monitoring progress toward sustainable agriculture (Agricultural Council of Australia and New Zealand, 1996).

Concerning **international governmental organisations**, environmental indicators are being developed by the UN Commission on Sustainable Development, as a follow-up to the UN Conference on Environment and Development (UNCED) Rio Declaration and Agenda 21 (UNCSD, 1996). Included in this work is the development of a set of indicators related to sustainable agriculture and rural development (SARD) under the guidance of the Food and Agricultural Organisation (FAO).

The FAO's inter-governmental Commission on Genetic Resources for Food and Agriculture is also establishing a monitoring system to track the state of the world's plant and animal genetic resources (FAO, 1996 and 1998). The FAO activity is linked with the broader concerns of the Secretariat to the Convention on Biological Diversity, and their development of biodiversity indicators including agro-biodiversity indicators.

The World Bank is actively engaged in developing environmental indicators, some of which are relevant to agriculture (World Bank et al., 2000a; 2000b, and 2000c; and the website: www-esd.worldbank.org/eei/). In addition, the World Bank has been working for several years with Land Quality Indicators (World Bank, 1997).

A considerable number of **non-governmental organisations** (NGOs) are also involved in developing environmental indicators, both at the national and international level, which in some cases focus on agri-environmental issues, such as recent work by the European Centre for Nature Conservation (2000), Worldwatch Institute (see Brown et al., 1999), the World Resources Institute (1995) and the World Wide Fund for Nature (1995; and 2000).

---

1. This Box provides a selective review of recent efforts to develop agri-environmental indicators in OECD countries and by international governmental and non-governmental organisations.
Source: OECD Secretariat.

social dimensions of sustainable agriculture in the context of farm financial resources and rural viability (see the Contextual Indicators chapter). Indicators on farm management practices might be considered as being indicators of sustainability in so far as changes in management practices could be predictors of future improvements or deterioration in the capital base. Changes in water use and soil quality also provide information on the capacity (potential) of agriculture to meet future demands for food and other agricultural products.

The *indicator definitions and methods of calculation* described in the Report have mainly been drawn from OECD countries' own experiences and approaches (Box 3). Also the OECD has held several Expert Workshops to help refine and develop indicator definitions and calculation methodologies, most notably the York Workshop held in the United Kingdom in 1998 which marked an important step forward in the work (OECD, 1999a). The OECD has also made its own research of relevant literature to contribute to the process of establishing indicators, and held various Joint Expert Working Groups with EUROSTAT (Statistical Office of the European Communities), to develop nutrient balance indicators, for example.

Indicators need to be based on a consistent methodology in order to provide a common "benchmark" across countries, and be transparent so that all stakeholders can understand the indicators and the policy implications based on them. For some indicator areas, such as biodiversity, wildlife habitats and landscape, indicator definitions allow some degree of flexibility to enable countries to adapt overall indicator methodologies to suit specific agricultural, economic, social and environmental circumstances.

The *spatial coverage* of indicators in the Report is confined mainly to revealing the state and trends at the national level, although the regional dispersion around the national average trend has been highlighted in a number of cases. For many of the indicator methodologies outlined, these can be applied at different scales ranging from the farm to the national level, although data collection by the OECD Secretariat have only, so far, been at the national scale. Even so, nearly all the national level indicators reported here have been calculated by aggregating regional information to estimate a national average value.

Concerning the *temporal coverage*, for the majority of indicators in the Report the time period covered is from the mid-1980s to the late 1990s. The mid-1980s is used by OECD as a base period because in 1987 the OECD Council Meeting at Ministerial level adopted a set of policy principles for agricultural policy reform, which have underpinned much of subsequent OECD work on agricultural policy monitoring and evaluation.[2] The mid/late-1980s also represents a period when a growing number of OECD countries began to implement agri-environmental measures. Associated with the introduction of these measures countries also started to establish databases and indicators to help track environmental conditions in agriculture and monitor and evaluate related measures (Box 3).

Collecting data and calculating indicators

The main basis for the data sources and indicator calculations shown in the Report are derived from OECD Member country responses to an *Agri-environmental Indicator Questionnaire* circulated in 1999, but not published. The Questionnaire provided valuable information on the extent and detail of basic agri-environmental data and related indicators currently available or being developed in countries.

While all OECD countries responded to the Questionnaire and/or provided relevant information, the coverage and quality of responses varied considerably, which can largely be explained by two key reasons.[3] First, some agri-environmental areas are of little or no relevance to particular countries and as a result information on such issues is either absent or extremely limited (*e.g.* the issue of water use tends to be unimportant for countries without agricultural irrigation). Second, data deficiencies exist even where certain issues are important to a country, because systematic collection of basic data and construction of indicators has only begun relatively recently in many OECD countries (*e.g.* biodiversity).

In addition to the OECD Questionnaire, calculation of indicators has been supplemented by *data from other sources*. These additional sources mainly include the OECD's existing databases and work in the area, in particular, the nitrogen balance database (OECD, 2001), the OECD environmental database and indicators work (OECD, 1999b, and 1998a), and the Working Group on Pesticides' activity on developing pesticide risk indicators.[4] In addition, OECD has drawn on other international databases, especially that of FAO for agricultural land use data; the EUROSTAT database covering EU member States; and the UN Framework Convention on Climate Change (UNFCCC) for greenhouse gas emission data.

Interpreting indicators

The indicators in this Report should be viewed as an integrated preliminary set, with caution needed in interpreting trends in individual indicators for a number of reasons discussed in this section.

Definitions of indicators are standardised in most cases, but not all. For example, there is no unique internationally agreed definition for organic farming or integrated pest management.

Calculation methodologies are at varying stages of development, with work on some areas having a longer history of research, such as nutrient use and soil quality, while for other areas, such as land conservation, biodiversity, wildlife habitats and landscape, quantification is at a very early stage of development. There is also a lack of knowledge about causalities and linkages between indicators in some cases. For example, explaining the causes of changes in wild species distribution and populations on farm land is complex as it can relate to changes in farming practices and factors, such as the influence of climate or alteration to other habitats in proximity to agriculture, for example, forests and aquatic ecosystems.

Data quality and comparability have been ensured as far as possible, in terms of the consistency, coherence and harmonisation of data, but deficiencies remain. These include, for example, the absence of data series (*e.g.* biodiversity), variability in data coverage (*e.g.* pesticide use/sales), and differences in how data were obtained (*e.g.* calculation of agricultural water use).

Spatial aggregation shows indicator trends at the national level, although in many cases national averages can mask significant variations at the regional level. Where possible regionally disaggregated data are highlighted (*e.g.* nitrogen balances and soil erosion). At this stage of the work it is not yet possible to provide a comprehensive set of data revealing regional variation around national averages. Moreover, care is needed in comparing "small" with "large" countries for some indicators, for example, there is a tendency for the number and population sizes of wild species to be greater in larger countries than in smaller countries.

Temporal scales over which indicators provide information on changes in environmental conditions are variable. Nutrient and pesticides run-off from agricultural land into rivers, lakes and marine waters can occur rapidly (hours/days), but over much longer periods into groundwater (months/years). Moreover, understanding the environmental impacts of changes that occur over longer periods can be highly complex, such as those involving changes in land use and greenhouse gases. In addition, some agri-environmental interactions involve processes that are irreversible (*e.g.* removal of tropical rainforests, wetlands), lead to an unexpected chain of events in the environment (*e.g.* the effects of using the now widely prohibited DDT pesticide on wildlife), and sometimes are affected by a sudden or violent change in environmental conditions, such as from flooding, drought and fires.

Trends and ranges in indicators are important for comparative purposes across countries rather than absolute levels for many indicators, especially as local site specific conditions vary considerably within and across countries. Tolerable rates of soil erosion, for example, can vary from 1-5 tonnes/hectare/year depending on site specific soil, topography and climatic conditions. However, in some cases absolute levels are significant where they are above clearly defined scientific limits, such as nitrate levels in water, and/or where changes in trends are being measured from a very low base. An illustration of this latter point is national agri-environmental expenditure, which has risen substantially over the 1990s, but from a near zero base at the beginning of the decade for many countries (see Figures 2 to 5 in the Farm Financial Resources chapter).

Contribution of agriculture to specific environmental impacts is sometimes difficult to identify, especially for water quality, soil quality, and biodiversity, where other factors can play an important role. These factors may include, other economic activities (*e.g.* forestry, industry, households), the "natural" state of the environment (*e.g.* water may contain high levels of naturally occurring salts, nitrates, organic components), and natural environmental processes (*e.g.* fires, floods, droughts).

The direction of change of indicators in the Report is unambiguous in most cases in terms of the impact on the environment of an increase/decrease in the specific indicator (*e.g.* changes in agricultural greenhouse gas emissions). However, for some indicators it is not always clear as to what constitutes an environmental improvement or deterioration (*e.g.* changes in the levels of agri-environmental expenditure or some landscape indicators). Moreover, it is preferable not to interpret indicators in isolation, but rather use them together in clusters, such as the links between nitrogen management, nitrogen use and nitrates in water. Also the interpretation of some indicators raise important trade-off questions. These cannot easily be interpreted without considering the indicators in a broader framework of assessment, such as determining the overall socio-economic and environmental costs and benefits associated with converting agricultural land to other uses, such as to forestry or for urban housing.

Baselines, threshold levels and/or targets for indicators are not used to assess indicator trends in the Report. Where such benchmarks have been developed or used by OECD Member countries, however, these have been described. In general there is no analysis of what factors have caused indicator trends to alter, although where changes diverge significantly from overall OECD trends then some explanation has been provided. Illustrative are the significant reductions in nitrogen surpluses and pesticide use over the last decade for the *Czech Republic*, *Hungary* and *Poland*. This was mainly associated with the transition to a market economy triggering a collapse in agricultural support levels, the elimination of fertiliser/pesticide input subsidies, and increasing debt levels in the farm sector limiting farmers ability to purchase inputs.

While it is necessary to take care in interpreting trends in agri-environmental indicators, they should also be considered in the context of assessing changes in other indicators of broader economic, social and environmental trends for three main reasons. *First*, it is only relatively recently that work started on establishing agri-environmental indicators and associated data collection efforts. Inevitably the process of development will be iterative as indicators are tried and tested by users until a consensus forms around a core set, as has occurred over the much longer historical record of developing, for example, economic performance indicators such as measures of inflation and gross domestic product.

Second, to capture through indicators the interface between the biophysical "natural" environment and agricultural activities is often more complex and difficult than monitoring trends in purely economic (*e.g.* incomes) and social (*e.g.* education) activities. Also some agri-environmental outputs and effects are not valued in conventional markets and have no monetary values (*e.g.* the carbon sink function of agricultural soils) nor are they easily measured in physical terms (*e.g.* landscape). *Third*, many of the issues related to the limitations of interpreting agri-environmental indicators, apply equally to other indicators. With many economic and social variables, for example, there can be a wide regional variation around national averages (*e.g.* employment levels), and definitional, methodological and data deficiency issues are not uncommon (*e.g.* the measurement of poverty and wealth distribution).

5. Future challenges

The future challenge for developing OECD *agri-environmental indicators* is to meet the objectives of: providing information on the current state and changes in the environmental performance of agriculture; and using indicators for policy monitoring, evaluation and forecasting purposes. This requires addressing a number of issues, including: identifying "new" agri-environmental areas for which indicators may need to be developed; improving the analytical soundness, measurability and ease of interpreting indicators; and, developing linkages between indicators.

This Report has identified a number of *"new" agri-environmental areas*, for which some OECD countries have begun to establish indicators to address these issues, such as soil biodiversity and the greenhouse gas sink function of agricultural land. In addition, there is a growing interest in expressing changes in eco-efficiency, for example, indicators showing changes in agricultural production efficiency in using various inputs and natural resources such as nutrients, pesticides, energy and water.[5]

OECD countries have begun the process of using indicators for policy purposes, although this is still a new field of activity for most countries (Box 3). Also indicators are being used by policy makers as a tool to help monitor compliance with international obligations, for example, greenhouse gases (Box 1). 27

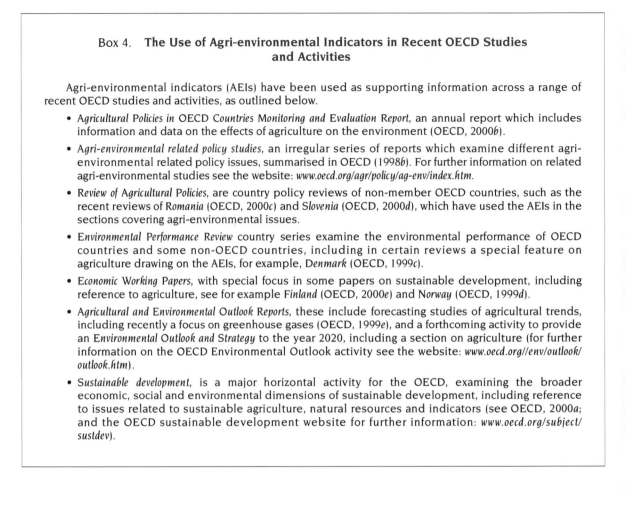

The OECD, through its various studies and activities, is also exploring a range of applications for better using indicators for policy purposes, as summarised in Box 4 (see also OECD, 1999a).

There are various *methodological issues* that need to be addressed to help improve indicators for agri-environmental areas where work is less advanced, in particular, biodiversity, habitats and landscape. Related to this is the need to develop understanding of the interactions and linkages between agriculture and the environment and changes in farm financial resources available to farmers, socio-economic factors (rural viability) and farm management practices.[6]

Data deficiencies are also an impediment to indicator development, including issues related to incomplete data series, poor quality and non-validated data, and in some cases no systematic collection of data to calculate indicators. There are encouraging signs, however, that many countries are beginning to make progress in overcoming data deficiencies (Box 3). This progress is being facilitated by drawing on existing data, extending their use through using new information technologies, and also improving the co-operation and co-ordination between different national and international agencies developing indicators.

To eliminate some of the methodological and data impediments requires a *step-by-step approach in developing indicators.* This implies initially developing indicators at a fairly rudimentary level and moving toward more rigorous indicators as understanding of issues improves, methodological problems are overcome, and more basic data becomes available. The OECD nitrogen balance is illustrative of developing indicators by an evolutionary process, by first including all sources of nitrogen farm inputs (*e.g.* fertilisers, manure) and nitrogen uptake by crops, which is more robust than using an indicator of inorganic nitrogen fertiliser per hectare of farm land. However, the nitrogen balance can be gradually replaced by more sophisticated approaches, such as the farm gate approach, once data becomes available.

Improving the interpretation of indicators involves further attention to spatial and temporal considerations, and use of benchmarks against which to assess performance. Also, where possible, moving from physical to a common unit of measure, such as money or energy, to help examine various questions related to linkages and trade-offs, for example, the links and trade-offs between changes in agricultural production, farm input use and environmental outcomes.

National averages can mask the *spatial variance* of an indicator, and to overcome this problem it can be important to reveal the variation around the national average, for example, the percentage of the total agricultural land area experiencing low, moderate or high soil erosion rates. Statistical measures might also be used to more accurately determine the significance of variation around national averages. Developing and measuring indicators for a range of spatial scales, however, can be constrained by the ability to extrapolate data from the field/farm level to higher levels and the trade-offs that occur with gains in coverage at higher levels but loss of detail and variation at lower scales.[7]

The variations in the *temporal dimensions* of different environmental effects of agriculture range from the short term, such as the impact on water quality in rivers from pesticide use to the long term, which may involve decades in the case of greenhouse gas emissions and climate change. The impacts on the environment from agricultural policies, economic and societal pressures may also have different time lags and consequences. While this issue is not uncommon to socio-economic indicators, a key focus of sustainable development is the intergenerational impact. Most indicators, however, use a time series approach showing current trends, which ignores the trade-off between the present and the future. Developing forward-looking indicators may need further research and analysis.

Developing appropriate *baselines, threshold levels and targets* can be useful to help assess the performance of indicator trends. Some OECD countries, for example *The Netherlands*, have established environmental targets by which to monitor and evaluate policy performance (OECD, 2000f). Given the difficulties in determining suitable benchmarks across OECD countries, it may be more useful for policy makers to track progress with indicators towards nationally agreed targets for different agri-environmental areas.

The use of a *common indicator measure* (*e.g.* money or energy values) would allow for trends to be evaluated on a common basis (*e.g.* cost-benefit approaches). For policy purposes, it is necessary that agri-environmental information is provided in a form that enables policy makers to evaluate the performance of the sector, the effects of policies on environmental outcomes, and to weigh up the (marginal) changes in the environment with other outcomes (*e.g.* social, economic, agricultural production). While placing money values on environmental outputs and services has a role to play for policy purposes, especially in considering the trade-offs between economic, social and environmental demands in society, there still remains considerable constraints to estimating these values and trade-offs.

Developing *linkages between different indicators* can help contribute to a better understanding of under-lying cause and effect relationships. For example, there are links between the price of water charged to farmers, the rate of expansion in irrigated area, the efficiency of water use management, and the impact of the use of water resources on aquatic environments and groundwater reserves.

In broader terms the *sustainable agriculture* concept emphasises the *links between the economic, social and environmental dimensions*. The OECD agri-environmental indicators recognise the three dimensions of sustainable agriculture, such as through farm financial resources (economic); rural viability (social) and water quality (environmental) indicators, but the linkages between them are not developed. For example, measures of resource productivity (*e.g.* nutrient and water use efficiency) illustrate economic-environmental linkages, while the health consequences of agri-environmental impacts (*e.g.* the impact of pesticide use on human health) highlight social-environmental linkages.[8]

Establishing a *core set of* OECD *agri-environmental indicators*, complemented as necessary by other infor-mation and indicators, could help to achieve the overall future objectives for developing the OECD indicators, that is, providing information on the environmental performance of agriculture and using indicators for policy purposes.

Annex

COMPLETE LIST OF OECD AGRI-ENVIRONMENTAL INDICATORS

Issue	Indicators	Definitions
I. AGRICULTURE IN THE BROADER ECONOMIC, SOCIAL, AND ENVIRONMENTAL CONTEXT		
1. Contextual Information and Indicators	*Agricultural* GDP	Share of agriculture in total Gross Domestic Product
	Agricultural output	Change in the value of final agricultural output
	Farm employment	Share of agriculture in total civilian employment
	Farmer age/gender distribution	Share of new farmers entering agriculture by age and gender categories
	Farmer education	Educational level of farmers
	Number of farms	Change in total number of farms
	Agricultural support	Change in the Percentage Producer Support Estimate
	Land use	
	– Stock of agricultural land	Share of agricultural land use in total national land area
	– Change in agricultural land	Change in the agricultural land area
	– Agricultural land use	Share of agricultural area by land use categories
2. Farm Financial Resources	*Farm income*	Net farm income defined as the difference between the value of gross output and all expenses, including depreciation at the farm level from agricultural activities
	Agri-environmental expenditure	
	– Public and private agri-environmental expenditure	Public and private expenditure, both investment and current, on agri-environmental goods, services and conservation for improving environmental quality
	– Expenditure on agri-environmental research	Share of public and private sector expenditure, on agri-environmental research in total agricultural research expenditure
II. FARM MANAGEMENT AND THE ENVIRONMENT		
1. Farm Management	*Whole farm management*	
	– Environmental whole farm management plans	Share of the total number of farms or total agricultural area under environmental whole farm management plans
	– Organic farming	Share of farms or the total agricultural area under a certified organic farming system or in the process of conversion to such a system
	Nutrient management	
	– Nutrient management plans	Share of farms or cultivated area with nutrient management plans
	– Soil tests	Use and frequency of soil tests expressed as the proportion of farms conducting soil tests at different frequencies or share of crop area tested
	Pest management	
	– Use of non-chemical pest control methods	Area of cultivated crops not treated with chemical pesticides
	– Use of integrated pest management	Area of cultivated agricultural land under integrated pest management
	Soil and land management	
	– Soil cover	Number of days in a year that the soil (agricultural land) is covered with vegetation
	– Land management practices	Share of the total crop area under environmental land management practices
	Irrigation and water management	
	– Irrigation technology	Share of irrigation water applied by different forms of irrigation technology

Issue	Indicators	Definitions
III. USE OF FARM INPUTS AND NATURAL RESOURCES		
1. Nutrient Use	Nitrogen balance	Physical difference (surplus/deficit) between nitrogen inputs into, and outputs from, an agricultural system, per hectare of agricultural land
	Nitrogen efficiency	Ratio of total nitrogen uptake (output) to the total nitrogen available (input) in an agricultural system
2. Pesticide Use and Risks	Pesticide use indicator	Trends over time of pesticide sales and/or use data
	Pesticide risk indicators	Trends in pesticide risks over time by combining information on pesticide toxicity and exposure with information on pesticide use
3. Water Use	Water use intensity	Share of agriculture water use in national total water utilisation
	Water use efficiency	
	– Water use technical efficiency	For selected irrigated crops, the mass of agricultural production (tonnes) per unit volume of irrigation water utilised
	– Water use economic efficiency	For all irrigated crops, the monetary value of agricultural production per unit volume of irrigation water utilised
	Water stress	Proportion of rivers subject to diversion or regulation for irrigation without defined minimum reference flows
IV. ENVIRONMENTAL IMPACTS OF AGRICULTURE		
1. Soil Quality	Risk of soil erosion by water	Agricultural area subject to water erosion, that is the area for which there is a risk of degradation by water erosion above a certain reference level
	Risk of soil erosion by wind	Agricultural area subject to wind erosion, that is the area for which there is a risk of degradation by wind erosion above a certain reference level
2. Water Quality	Water quality risk indicator	Potential concentration of nitrate (or phosphorus) in the water flowing from a given agricultural area, both percolating water and surface run-off
	Water quality state indicator	Nitrate (or phosphorus) concentration in water in vulnerable agricultural areas: the proportion of surface water and groundwater above a national threshold value of nitrate concentration (NO_3 mg/l) or phosphorus (P_{total} mg/l)
3. Land Conservation	Water retaining capacity	Quantity of water that can be retained in the short term, in agricultural soil, as well as on agricultural land where applicable (e.g. flood storage basins) and by agricultural irrigation or drainage facilities
	Off-farm sediment flow	1. The estimated risk of the quantity of soil sediments transferred from farm to off-farm areas and water bodies
		2. The actual (or state) quantity of soil sediments transferred from farm to off-farm areas and water bodies
4. Greenhouse Gases	Gross agricultural greenhouse gas emissions	Change in the gross total agricultural emissions of carbon dioxide (CO_2), methane (CH_4) and nitrous oxide (N_2O) expressed in CO_2 equivalents
5. Biodiversity	Genetic diversity	1. For the main crop/livestock categories (e.g. wheat, rice, cattle, pigs) the total number of crop varieties/livestock breeds that have been registered and certified for marketing
		2. Share of key crop varieties in total marketed production for individual crops (e.g. wheat, rice, rapeseed, etc.)
		3. Share of the key livestock breeds in respective categories of livestock numbers (e.g. the share of Friesian, Jersey, Charolais, etc., in total cattle numbers)
		4. Number of national crop varieties/livestock breeds that are endangered
	Species diversity	
	– Wild species	Trends in population distributions and numbers of wild species related to agriculture
	– Non-native species	Trends in population distributions and numbers of key "non-native" species threatening agricultural production and agro-ecosystems
	Ecosystem diversity	See Wildlife Habitat Indicators
6. Wildlife Habitats	Intensively farmed agricultural habitats	1. Share of each crop in the total agricultural area
		2. Share of organic agriculture in the total agricultural area
	Semi-natural agricultural habitats	Share of the agricultural area covered by semi-natural agricultural habitats
	Uncultivated natural habitats	1. Net area of aquatic ecosystems converted to agricultural use
		2. Area of "natural" forest converted to agricultural use
	Habitat matrix	A habitat matrix identifies and relates the ways in which wild species use different agricultural habitat types

Issue	Indicators	Definitions
	IV. ENVIRONMENTAL IMPACTS OF AGRICULTURE (*cont.*)	
7. Landscape	*The structure of landscape*	
	– Environmental features and land use patterns	1. Environmental features, encompassing mainly landscape habitats and ecosystems 2. Land use patterns, including changes in agricultural land use patterns and distributions
	– Man-made objects	Key indicative man made objects (cultural features) on agricultural land resulting from human activity
	Landscape management	Share of agricultural land under public and private schemes committed to landscape maintenance and enhancement schemes
	Landscape costs and benefits	1. Cost of maintaining or enhancing landscape provision by agriculture 2. Public valuation of agricultural landscapes

1. This list includes all the agri-environmental indicators covered in this Report. For a detailed description of each indicator, see the respective agri-environmental indicator chapter.
Source: OECD Secretariat.

NOTES

1. For the full text of these various OECD Ministerial Communiqués see the OECD News Releases at: *www.oecd.org/media/release/*.

2. OECD Agriculture Ministers in 1998 adopted a set of policy principles building on the agricultural reform principles agreed by OECD Ministers in 1987, see OECD (2000*b*) for relevant Ministerial Communiqués.

3. The tables and figures in the Report show all OECD countries for which information was obtained through the OECD Questionnaire and or related information, so that the absence of specific countries in the Report's tables and figures implies that data are not available and/or not collected.

4. Details of the OECD Working Group on Pesticides activities on pesticide risk indicators is provided in the Pesticide Use and Risks chapter.

5. The issue of agricultural efficiency in using farm inputs and natural resources is briefly examined in the Report, see in particular the chapters on nutrient use, pesticide use, water use and greenhouse gases.

6. Brouwer and Crabtree (1999) explore in depth some of the methodological issues concerning agri-environmental indicators.

7. For a discussion of developing agri-environmental indicators at the farm level, see, for example, Rigby *et al.* (2000); and at a sub-national regional level, see the example of the County of Hampshire in the United Kingdom (Hampshire County Council, 2000).

8. There is now a growing literature on sustainable agriculture and related indicators, most recently see, for example, Pannell and Glenn (2000).

BIBLIOGRAPHY

Aakkula, J. (ed.) (2000),
Sustainable Development in Agriculture: Indicators, Agri-environmental Programmes and Demonstrations, Final Report of the SUSAGRI-project, Agricultural Research Centre of Finland, Helsinki, Finland.

Agricultural Council of Australia and New Zealand (1996),
Indicators for Sustainable Agriculture: Evaluation of Pilot Testing. Report prepared for the Sustainable Land and Water Resources Management Committee, Standing Committee on Agriculture and Resource Management, CSIRO Publications, Victoria, Australia.

Brouwer, F.M. (1995),
Indicators to Monitor Agri-environmental Policy in the Netherlands, Agricultural Economics Research Institute, The Hague, The Netherlands.

Brouwer, F.M. and B. Crabtree (eds.) (1999),
Environmental Indicators and Agricultural Policy, CAB International, Wallingford, United Kingdom.

Brown, L.R., M. Renner and B. Halweil (1999),
Vital Signs 1999: The Environmental Trends that are Shaping Our Future, Worldwatch Institute, Washington, DC., United States.

CEC [Commission for Environmental Cooperation] (1999),
"Environmental Impacts and Indicators", Chapter V of Issue Study 1, pp. 153-167, in CEC, *Assessing Environmental Effects of the North American Free Trade Agreement (NAFTA): An Analytic Framework (Phase II) and Issue Studies*, Montreal, Canada. Available at: *www.cec.org/* [English > Publications and Information Resources > CEC Publications > Environment, Economy and Trade].

Commission of the European Union (2000),
Communication from the Commission to the Council and the European Parliament – Indicators for the Integration of Environmental Concerns into the Common Agricultural Policy, COM(2000)20Final, 26 January, Brussels, Belgium.

Commonwealth of Australia (1998),
Sustainable Agriculture – Assessing Australia's Recent Performance, A Report to the Standing Committee on Agriculture and Resource Management (SCARM) of the National Collaborative Project on Indicators for Sustainable Agriculture, SCARM Technical Report No. 70, CSIRO Publishing, Victoria, Australia.

European Centre for Nature Conservation [ECNC] (2000),
Agri-environmental Indicators for Sustainable Agriculture in Europe, Edited by D.M. Wascher, ECNC Publication Technical report series, Tilburg, The Netherlands. Available at: *www.ecnc.nl/* .

European Environment Agency (2000),
Environmental Signals 2000, Environmental Assessment Report No. 6, Copenhagen, Denmark. Available at: *themes.eea.eu.int/* [> all available reports].

European Commission (1999),
Agriculture, Environment, Rural Development: Facts and Figures – A Challenge for Agriculture, Office for Official Publications of the European Communities, Luxembourg. Available at: *www.europa.eu.int/comm/dg06/envir/report/en/index.htm*.

EUROSTAT [Statistical Office of the European Communities] (1999),
Towards Environmental Pressure Indicators for the EU, Environment and Energy Paper Theme 8, Luxembourg. The background documentation is available at: *www.e-m-a-i-l.nu/tepi/* and *www.esl.jrc.it/envind/*.

FAO [United Nations Food and Agriculture Organisation] (1996),
Report on the State of the World's Plant Genetic Resources for Food and Agriculture, prepared for the International Technical Conference on Plant Genetic Resources, Leipzig, Germany, 17-23 June. Available at: *www.193.43.36.6/wrlmap_e.htm*.

FAO (1998),
  The State of the World's Animal Genetic Resources for Food and Agriculture, First Session, 8-10 September of the International Technical Working Group on Animal Genetic Resources for Food and Agriculture, Rome, Italy. Available at: *www.fao.org/ag/cgrfa/docs8.htm*.

Hampshire County Council (2000),
  Investigating Appropriate Indicators for Local Biodiversity, Winchester, Hampshire, United Kingdom. Available at: *www.hants.gov.uk/TC/biodiversityindicators/*.

IFEN [Institut français de l'environnement] (1997),
  Agriculture et environnement: les indicateurs (only in French, "Agriculture and the Environment: Indicators"), édition 1997-1998, Orléans, France. Available at: *www.ifen.fr/* [> Publications].

IFEN (2000),
  Aménagement du territoire et environnement: Politiques et indicateurs (Bilingual report "Spatial Planning and Environment: Policies and Indicators"), Orléans, France. Available at: *www.ifen.fr/* [> Publications].

MAFF [Ministry of Agriculture, Fisheries and Food] (2000),
  Towards Sustainable Agriculture – A Pilot Set of Indicators, London, United Kingdom. Available at: *www.maff.gov.uk/* [Farming > Sustainable Agriculture].

McRae, T., C.A.S. Smith and L.J. Gregorich (eds.) (2000),
  Environmental Sustainability of Canadian Agriculture: Report of the Agri-Environmental Indicator Project, Agriculture and Agri-Food Canada (AAFC), Ottawa, Ontario, Canada. Available at: *www.agr.ca/policy/environment/publications/list.html*.

Moxey, A. (1999),
  "Cross-Cutting Issues in Developing Agri-Environmental Indicators", pp. 113-130, in OECD, *Environmental Indicators for Agriculture, Volume 2: Issues and Design – The York Workshop*, Paris, France.

New Zealand MAF (1995),
  Proceedings of the Indicators for Sustainable Agriculture Seminar, Ministry of Agriculture and Forestry (MAF), Policy Technical Paper 95/7, August, Wellington, New Zealand.

OECD (1997),
  Environmental Indicators for Agriculture, Volume 1: Concepts and Framework, Paris, France.

OECD (1998a),
  Towards Sustainable Development: Environmental Indicators, Paris, France.

OECD (1998b),
  Agriculture and the Environment: Issues and Policies, Paris, France.

OECD (1999a),
  Environmental Indicators for Agriculture, Volume 2: Issues and Design – The York Workshop, Paris, France.

OECD (1999b),
  OECD *Environmental Data Compendium* 1999, Paris, France.

OECD (1999c),
  Environmental Performance Reviews: Denmark, Paris, France.

OECD (1999d),
  Sustainable Economic Growth: Natural Resources and the Environment in Norway, Economics Department Working Papers No. 218, General Distribution paper [ECO/WKP(99)10], Paris France. Available at: *www.oecd.org/* [Documentation > 1999 > Reference Components > ECO].

OECD (1999e),
  The Agricultural Outlook 1999-2004, Paris, France.

OECD (2000a),
  Frameworks to Measure Sustainable Development, Paris, France.

OECD (2000b),
  Agricultural Policies in OECD Countries: Monitoring and Evaluation 2000, Paris, France.

OECD (2000c),
  Review of Agricultural Policies: Romania, Paris, France.

OECD (2000d),
  Review of Agricultural Policies: Republic of Slovenia, Paris, France.

OECD (2000e),
  Enhancing Environmentally Sustainable Growth in Finland, Economics Department Working Papers No. 229, General Distribution document [ECO/WKP(2000)2], Paris, France. Available at: *www.oecd.org/* [Documentation > 2000 > Reference Components > ECO].

OECD (2000f),
    "Agriculture/Environment Indicators – The Experience of the Netherlands, pp. 279-288, in OECD, *Towards Sustainable Development – Indicators to Measure Progress*, Paris, France.

OECD (2001),
    OECD *National Soil Surface Nitrogen Balances: Preliminary Estimates 1985-1997*, Paris, France. Available at: *www.oecd.org/agr/ env/indicators.htm*.

OFAG [Office fédéral de l'agriculture] (2000),
    Rapport Agricole 2000 (only in French, German and Italian "Agriculture Report 2000"), Berne, Switzerland.

Pannell, D.J. and N.A. Glenn (2000),
    "A framework for the economic evaluation and selection of sustainability indicators in agriculture", *Ecological Economics*, Vol. 33, No. 1, pp. 135-149.

Rigby, D., P. Woodhouse, M. Burton and T. Young (2000),
    Constructing a Farm Level Indicator of Agricultural Sustainability , paper presented at the Agricultural Economics Society Annual Conference, Manchester, 14-17 April, United Kingdom.

Simonsen, B. (ed.) (2000),
    How Can Agricultural Statistics Meet Environmental Information Needs?, Proceedings of a Seminar hosted by Statistics Denmark, June/July, Copenhagen, Denmark. Available at: *www.dst.dk//dst/search_frame_uk.asp*.

UNCSD [United Nations Commission on Sustainable Development] (1996),
    Indicators of Sustainable Development Framework and Methodologies, New York, United States.

USDA [United States Department of Agriculture] (1997),
    Agricultural Resources and Environmental Indicators, 1996-97, Agricultural Handbook No. 712, Natural Resources and Environment Division, Economic Research Service, Washington, DC., United States. Available at: *www.ers.usda.gov/* [Briefing Rooms > Agricultural Resources and Environmental Indicators].

World Bank (1997),
    Expanding the Measure of Wealth – Indicators of Environmentally Sustainable Development, Environmentally Sustainable Development Studies and Monographs Series, No. 17, Washington, DC., United States.

World Bank (2000a),
    The Little Green Data Book, Development Data Group and Environmental Economics and Indicators Unit, Washington, DC., United States.

World Bank (2000b),
    World Development Indicators 2000, Washington, DC., United States. Text and samples of tables are available at: *www.worldbank.org/data/wdi2000/*.

World Bank (2000c),
    Rural Development Indicators Handbook, Rural Development Department, Washington, DC., United States.

World Resources Institute (1995),
    Environmental Indicators: A Systematic Approach to Measuring and Reporting on Environmental Policy Performance in the Context of Sustainable Development, Washington, DC., United States.

World Wide Fund for Nature [WWF] (1995),
    Measuring Progress Toward Bio-Intensive IPM: A Methodology to Track Pesticide Use, Risks and Reliance, WWF International, Gland, Switzerland.

World Wide Fund for Nature (2000),
    Living Planet Report 2000, WWF International, Gland, Switzerland.

Part I

AGRICULTURE IN THE BROADER ECONOMIC, SOCIAL AND ENVIRONMENTAL CONTEXT

1. CONTEXTUAL INFORMATION AND INDICATORS
2. FARM FINANCIAL RESOURCES

Chapter 1

CONTEXTUAL INFORMATION AND INDICATORS

HIGHLIGHTS

To set the discussion on agri-environmental indicators in this Report in a broader economic, social and environmental context, this Chapter examines the impact on agri-environmental relationships of economic forces, societal preferences, environmental processes, and land use changes.

Economic forces shape the performance of the agricultural sector and its role in the national economy. *Agriculture's contribution to gross domestic product* is under 4 per cent for most OECD countries, with the role of agriculture in the economy declining in all countries during the last decade. The real *value of agricultural output* has risen for most countries over the past 10 years attributed to higher production, the latter almost entirely due to increases in productivity. Nevertheless, over a 30-year period the value of output has declined, mainly because of a decrease in real commodity prices. Trends in *real net farm incomes* from agricultural activities have been variable over the last 10 years, rising for many countries but sharply declining over recent years in some cases, largely reflecting changes in macroeconomic conditions, farm costs and support levels.

The growing world *demand for food and industrial crops* will continue to present a challenge to world agricultural production, especially as some of the future demand will continue to be met by OECD cereal and livestock product exporters. But the future expansion in production may heighten the pressure on the environment through intensification and growth in farm output, particularly for exporting countries.

Agricultural employment as a share of total employment is now less than 7 per cent for most OECD countries, and the *age distribution* of farmers often shows a major share to be over 55 years old. There are very few countries where the majority of new entrants into agriculture are less than 35 years old. A younger, well-educated workforce is more likely to be able to respond rapidly to changing economic and environmental conditions. In addition, there are only a small number of countries where more than 40 per cent of farmers receive even basic agricultural training.

Farm numbers have declined in most OECD countries with a corresponding increase in *farm size*, leading to the concentration of production in a small number of larger farms. The share of small farms in total farm numbers is, at the same time, increasing. Research suggests that the trend toward increasing farm size usually entails field consolidation with the loss of boundary features, as well as intensification as capital replaces labour and the use of inputs per hectare increases.

Changes in farm structures have been influenced by *technological developments*, some of which have damaged the environment, such as the use of certain pesticides. An increasing focus in research of new technologies relates to *eco-efficiency and environmentally cleaner technologies*, which can increase profitability and reduce environmental harm, for example precision farming.

Agricultural and trade policies in many cases have caused environmental harm by distorting price signals through, for example, linking support to agricultural commodities and encouraging farming on environmentally fragile land, and lowering the costs of inputs, such as energy and water. Support to OECD agriculture is high, but with wide variations in the level, composition and trends among countries and commodities. OECD average share of support to producers in total gross farm receipts, the percentage producer support estimate (PSE), has declined from 40 to 36 per cent between 1986-88 to 1997-99.

The *reform of agricultural policies* should improve the allocation of resources and reduce the negative impacts of agriculture on the environment, but reform can also lower performance where agriculture is providing environmental benefits. As part of the reform process OECD countries have introduced *measures to address environmental issues*, mainly focusing on altering farm management practices and land use patterns incompatible with achieving environmental goals. There is at present insufficient information to provide a full assessment of these changes, but while some improvements have been made, they have been more costly than would have been the case without production enhancing policies. Also, the negative environmental impacts resulting from farming still remain at relatively high levels in many cases.

HIGHLIGHTS (*cont.*)

The reform of agricultural policies should improve the allocation of resources and reduce the negative impacts of agriculture on the environment, but reform can also lower performance where agriculture is providing environmental benefits. As part of the reform process OECD countries have introduced *measures to address environmental issues*, mainly focusing on altering farm management practices and land use patterns incompatible with achieving environmental goals. There is at present insufficient information to provide a full assessment of these changes, but while some improvements have been made, they have been more costly than would have been the case without production enhancing policies. Also, the negative environmental impacts resulting from farming still remain at relatively high levels in many cases.

Societal preferences affect agriculture and the environment across a range of issues. There is *growing public concern about agriculture's impact on the environment* in terms of reducing pollution and enhancing benefits, mainly in response to rising incomes, increasing leisure time, heightened public knowledge of these issues, and the desire for the space offered by rural areas.

Rural viability relates to issues such as farmer age structures, educational and managerial skills, and access to key services. The retention of a skilled workforce in rural areas and having an appropriate rural community infrastructure, will affect the capacity of farming to adjust and manage their enterprises to changing economic and environmental conditions and the sustainability of agriculture.

Environmental processes relate to the interaction between agriculture and natural environmental processes. Particularly relevant in this respect, is that farming forms a part of the ecosystem rather than being external to it, unlike most other economic activities. Agri-environmental relationships are often complex, site specific and non-linear, with a wide range of biophysical conditions within and across OECD countries, reflecting, for example, variations in climate, soils, availability of water resources, and land use patterns.

Land use changes represent the integrating element between the economic, societal and environmental influences on agriculture. For most OECD countries *agricultural land* occupies over 50 per cent of the total land area, with only a small reduction in area over the past 10 years, mainly through agricultural land being converted to forests in marginal farming areas. The change of *marginal farming land* to other land uses has raised concerns related to the associated harmful environmental and socio-economic impacts in some countries, but equally the conversion of this land may enhance its biodiversity and related amenity values.

The *pattern of agricultural land use* change within countries has mainly involved a growing share of permanent pasture in agricultural land, largely because of the adoption of land diversion schemes. Changes in farm land use from arable crops to pasture, more to less intensive cropping systems, and in terms of different cropping patterns can have major environmental effects, such as through altering soil erosion rates.

1. Background

The primary aim for agriculture is to produce food and industrial crops efficiently and safely, to meet a growing world demand without degrading natural resources and the environment. While agricultural productivity has improved substantially, it has often led to environmental degradation, such as soil erosion, water depletion and pollution. But agriculture also maintains landscapes and habitats for wildlife on agricultural land, acts as a sink for greenhouse gases, provides soil and water filtering and retention functions, and contributes to rural employment.

Differences in economic, social and environmental conditions account for the variation in the importance of particular environmental issues and impacts from agriculture within and between countries, and has implications for the long-term sustainability of agriculture. This chapter sets the discussion of agri-environmental indicators in a broader context by addressing the following issues:

- *economic forces* shaping the performance of the agricultural sector and its role in the national economy, including levels and changes in farm production, incomes, employment, education, and structures, and the impact of technological changes and government policies on the sector;

- *societal preferences* affecting agriculture, especially in terms of the public's demand for a secure and safe food supply; the increasing societal preference for agriculture to maintain and enhance recreational, cultural, scenic and other related amenity functions and values associated with agriculture; and the desire by rural communities that agriculture contribute to rural viability;

- *environmental processes* relating to the interaction between agricultural activity and natural biophysical processes, such as climate, soils, and water;

- *land use changes* representing the integrating element between the economic, societal and environmental influences on agriculture, and their impact on the level, type and intensity of agricultural land use.

2. Agriculture and economic forces[1]

Agricultural production and farm incomes

While the volume of agricultural production has increased significantly over the past ten years, *agriculture's contribution to gross domestic product* (GDP) is under 4 per cent for most OECD countries (Figure 1). The share of agriculture in GDP has fallen in all OECD countries during the last decade. For a large number of countries, however, the agro-food chain, which depends on farm output, contributes a significantly higher share to economic activity, especially the food processing sector and input manufacturing, such as pesticides, fertilisers and farm machinery. Agriculture also accounts for a major share of merchandised exports, in excess of 15 per cent of total exports for a number of countries.

The growing world *demand for food and industrial crops* will continue to present a challenge to world agricultural production. World population grew by 1.4 per cent in 1998, more than double the average population growth for OECD countries of 0.6 per cent, but world population growth is slowing down. This implies that most of the future increase in food demand will originate from non-OECD countries, while some of the future growth global food demand will continue to be supplied by OECD countries, especially cereals and livestock products. The future expansion in agricultural production may heighten the pressure on the environment through the intensification and growth in farm output, especially for OECD agricultural exporting countries.

Over the past decade the real *value of agricultural output* has risen for most OECD countries, measured in terms of US dollars using constant purchasing power parities (Figure 2). This can be attributed to the substantial expansion in the volume of production, almost entirely due to increases in productivity (*i.e.* the efficiency by which farming converts inputs into outputs, see OECD, 1995). Labour productivity is likely to continue to rise more rapidly than total factor productivity (*i.e.* a productivity measure including fixed capital and labour) given the potential for substituting capital for labour and the increasing use of mechanical and chemical inputs (MAFF, 2000).

41

Figure 1. **Share of agriculture in Gross Domestic Product: mid-1990s**

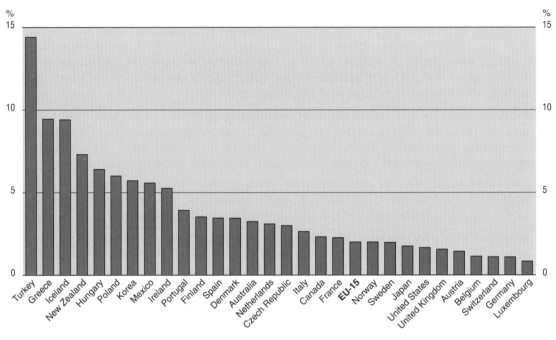

Note: See Annex Table 1.
Sources: OECD Secretariat; European Commission (1999).

Figure 2. **Value of final agricultural output in constant 1990 US dollars
Purchasing Power Parities: 1985-87 to 1995-97**

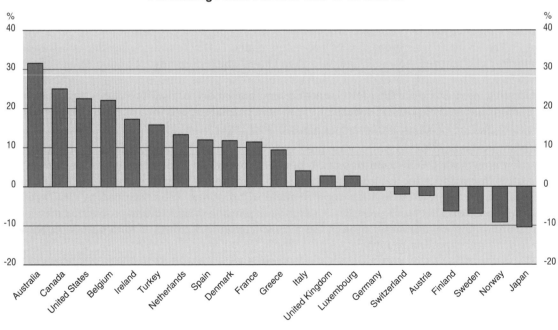

Note: See Annex Table 1.
Source: OECD Secretariat.

Examined over a longer period of 30 years, however, the real value of agricultural production has declined in most countries. During this period there has been a continuous decrease in real agricultural commodity prices, despite the growth in world population and demand for food and industrial crops. Moreover, the improvements in agricultural productivity should also be interpreted with caution, as they do not always take into account the environmental costs and benefits associated with agricultural activity.

Developments in annual average real net **farm incomes** from agricultural activity have been variable over the past 10 years for a large number of OECD countries, steadily rising for many countries over most of this period, but showing a sharp decline over the past 2-3 years in a number of cases. These developments in farm incomes have largely reflected changes in macroeconomic conditions (*e.g.* interest and exchange rates), farm costs and support levels. The importance of off-farm income has increased in most OECD countries as farm households have diversified to include activities such as rural tourism. Also for some countries, the income of agricultural households is higher than the income of other households, although in all countries there are periods and pockets of low income (the issue of farm incomes is further discussed in the Farm Financial Resources chapter).

Farm employment and education

The declining role of agriculture in overall economic activity is also reflected in the decrease in **farm employment**. The share of agricultural employment in total civilian employment is now less than 7 per cent for most countries, although for some countries with relatively large agricultural sectors the figure exceeds 15 per cent (Figure 3). Agriculture continues to account for the major share of employment in most rural areas, while indirectly it also contributes to employment in other sectors, especially the food processing and input manufacturing industries (OECD, 1998b).

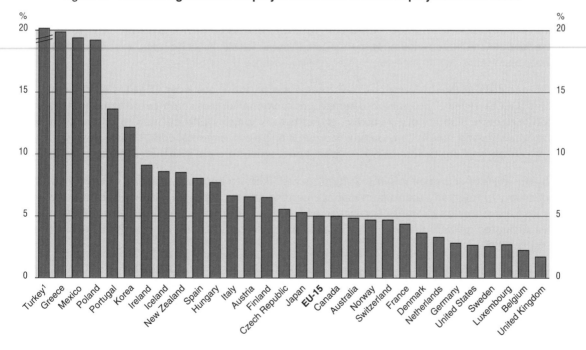

Figure 3. **Share of agricultural employment in total civilian employment: late 1990s**

1. Percentage equals 42%.
Note: See Annex Table 1.
Sources: OECD Secretariat; European Commission (1999).

Figure 4. **Share of new farmers entering agriculture by age
and gender categories: late 1990s**

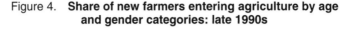

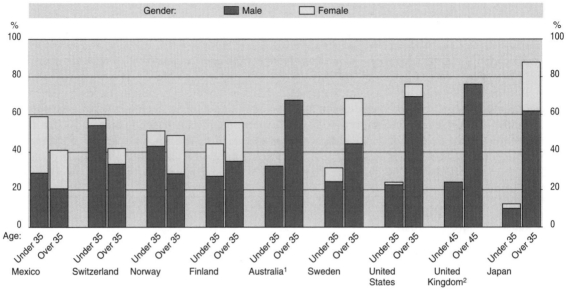

1. Both male and female.
2. Categories under and over 45 including both male and female.
Note: See Annex Table 1.
Sources: OECD Agri-Environmental Indicators Questionnaire, 1999; Commonwealth of Australia (1998); MAFF (2000).

In most OECD countries, the number of farmers has declined mainly through retirement and migration to urban areas, which was not offset by new entrants into agriculture. The overall rate of decline in farm employment has varied considerably across countries over the past ten years, with sharp reductions in farm employment in the *Czech Republic, Iceland, Italy* and *Japan*, a more modest decrease in *Australia* and *Mexico*, but an increase in *New Zealand* and the *United States*.

The *age distribution* of farmers shows that a major share are over 55 years old in many OECD countries (OECD, 1998*a*). The entry into agriculture of young farmers can provide some indication of the potential long-term viability of agriculture, given that a younger well-educated workforce is more likely to be able to respond rapidly to changing economic and environmental conditions.[2] However, there are very few countries where the majority of entrants into agriculture are less than 35 years old (Figure 4).

Higher *levels of education* mean that farmers are likely to be more aware of environmental issues and adopt environmentally sound farm management practices. Although further education provides the potential for greater environmental awareness, much will also depend on farmers' own personal motives, attitudes towards risk and other factors driven by socio-economic conditions (Commonwealth of Australia, 1998).

There are only a relatively small number of OECD countries where more than 40 per cent of farmers have even basic agricultural training, although there are wide variations in the educational attainment levels of farmers across countries (Figure 5). This low level of training could reduce farmers' adaptability to new economic, social and environmental conditions in the future.

In the *United States* it was found that farmers with some formal training were more likely to adopt conservation tillage practices than a farmer with no training (Huffman, 2000). Evidence from *Australia* and *Germany* show that farmers with a university degree usually participate in training to improve their farm

Figure 5. **Educational level of farmers: mid/late 1990s**

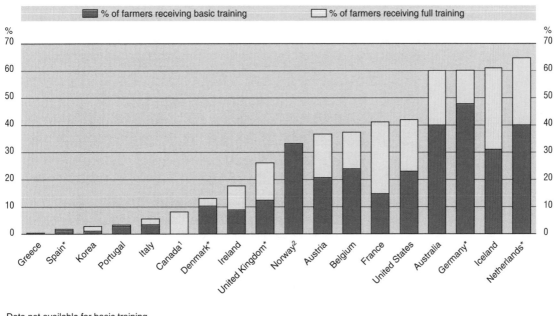

1. Data not available for basic training.
2. Value refers to both basic and full training.
* 1990 data.
Note: See Annex Table 1.
Sources: OECD Agri-environmental Indicators Questionnaire, 1999; Commonwealth of Australia (1998).

management skills, adopt best management practices and are more likely to have a farm plan compared with farmers with no formal education (Mues *et al.*, 1998; Nieberg and Isermeyer, 1994).

Farm structures

With higher levels of agricultural productivity related to the contraction of the agricultural labour force, *farm numbers* have declined in nearly all OECD countries (Figure 6). This has led to a corresponding increase in *farm size*. These developments have had two related effects, first, the increasing concentration of production in a relatively small number of larger farms, and second, the growing proportion of small farms in total farm numbers, partly reflecting the growth in off-farm employment and interest in hobby farming. The tendency toward greater concentration in production has led to the replacement of mixed farming by more specialised enterprises (*i.e.* livestock or arable based farms), not only at the individual farm level but for whole regions.[3]

The impact of the changing structure of agriculture for the environment is an issue raised in many chapters of this Report, but especially the chapters on Nutrient Use, Biodiversity, Wildlife Habitats and Landscape. In general, research suggests that the trend toward increasing farm size usually entails the consolidation of fields with the loss of boundary features, such as hedges and small trees, and the intensification of operations, as capital replaces labour, which enables farmers to produce a higher output from the land.

The complexities involved in determining the environmental effects of changing farm structures can be illustrated by two examples: the adoption of Integrated Pest Management (IPM) on vegetable farms, and the environmental implications of structural changes in the pig industry. Research in the *United States* found that farm size affects the adoption of IPM by vegetable growers, with larger farms being more likely to adopt such practices (Hrubovcak *et al.*, 1999). IPM requires a substantial amount of

Figure 6. **Change in the number of farms: 1985-87 to 1995-97**

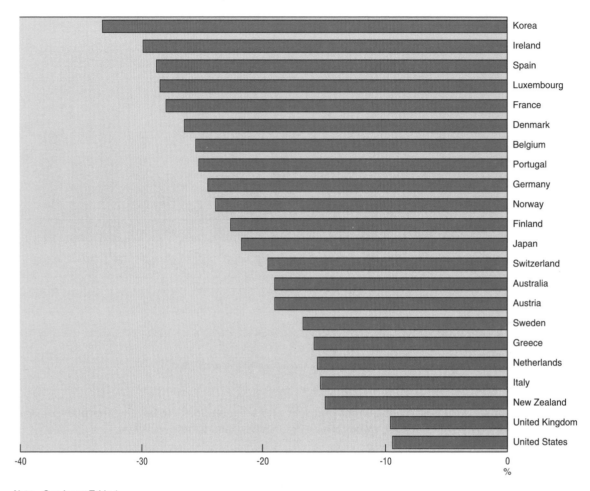

Note: See Annex Table 1.
Source: OECD Secretariat.

farmer time that may compete with off-farm employment opportunities, and the availability of unpaid family labour time has been found to be positively associated with IPM adoption.

In the case of the pig industry trends, in *Canada*, the *United States* and parts of *Europe* over the past 10 years, reveal a substantial increase in the number of pigs raised on a single operation, facilitated by developments in pig raising technologies and management systems. With the trend toward a larger and more regionally concentrated pig industry, this has raised environmental concerns with respect to the effects of pig manure on water quality, greenhouse gas and ammonia emissions.[4]

Technology

Assessing the **impact of technological change on environmental conditions in agriculture**, as with structural changes, is complex. Technologies that have altered the nature and scale of agriculture range through greater mechanisation, development of farm chemicals to genetic modification and biotechnology (OECD, 1995). This technological progress has shifted agriculture from a mainly physical based to a more knowledge based industry (MacGregor and McRae, 2000).

The use of some technologies by farmers, however, has had unanticipated and serious effects on the environment, such as the use of the insecticide DDT, now banned in most OECD countries (see the Pesticide Use and Risks chapter). In other cases the consequences of heavy farm machinery on soil compaction have had damaging consequences on soil quality resulting in yield and financial losses for farmers (see the Soil Quality chapter).

An increasing focus in research of new technologies relates to the concept of *eco-efficiency and environmentally cleaner technologies* ("green technologies"). In a number of OECD countries the share of total agricultural research expenditure devoted to agri-environmental issues is expanding and forms a major share of total research outlays (see the Farm Financial Resources chapter).

"Green technologies", for example integrated pest management, conservation tillage, and precision farming are important because they can increase farm profitability while reducing environmental degradation and conserving natural resources (Hrubovcak *et al.*, 1999). Precision agriculture, for example, can reduce adverse environmental impacts by using advanced technology, such as the global positioning system, to collect data at exact locations and the geographical information system, to map more precisely fertiliser and pesticide requirements across a field.

Policies

The environmental implications of farmers' production decisions are not always incorporated in farming costs and revenues. For example, fertilisers, animal waste and pesticides can leach into groundwater, and thus increase the cost of purifying drinking water, but farms may not be charged for this pollution. Unless market or policy mechanisms are in place to compensate farmers for the extra costs associated with providing additional environmental services to society, farmers are unlikely to provide these services.

In many cases environmental problems have been aggravated by *agricultural and trade policies* that distort price signals, by linking support to agricultural production, or by lowering or disguising the costs of inputs. The distortions created by such policies can lead to inappropriate use of inputs and location of production, with environmentally harmful outcomes. These policies can also discourage the development and use of farming technologies less stressful on the environment (OECD, 1998c).

Agricultural support in OECD countries has been mainly delivered through higher market price support for commodities, direct payments to farmers, and subsidised prices for inputs such as fertiliser, pesticides, water and energy, and subsidised credit, structural investment and infrastructure development. Support to OECD agriculture is high, but with wide variations in the level, composition and trends among OECD countries and across commodities. The trend in the OECD average share of support to producers in total gross farm receipts (the percentage producer support estimate – PSE) has declined only slightly from 40 per cent in 1986-88 to 36 per cent in 1997-99 (Figure 7).[5]

The reform of agricultural policies should improve the domestic and international allocation of resources, reduce incentives to use polluting chemical inputs and to farm environmentally sensitive land. Such reforms would tend to reverse the harmful environmental impacts associated with commodity and input specific policy measures. But in those cases where current agricultural policies are associated with farming activities providing environmental benefits, policy reform can reduce environmental performance. OECD has recognised, therefore, that agricultural policy reform is a necessary, but not always a sufficient condition to improve the environmental performance of agriculture (OECD, 1998c).

As part of the agricultural policy reform process many OECD countries started to introduce *measures to address environmental issues in agriculture,* beginning around the late 1980s/early 1990s. While the nature of these measures varies greatly across countries, they have mainly focused on altering inappropriate farm management practices incompatible with achieving environmental objectives in agriculture, the latter sometimes encouraged by high price support levels.

The implementation of these measures has included the provision of payments if certain practices are adopted, such as area payments for adoption of low-input or organic farming systems. A few countries have used taxes to limit the pollution from the use of pesticides and fertilisers. Some countries have

47

Figure 7.   **Percentage Producer Support Estimate:[1] 1986-88 to 1997-99**

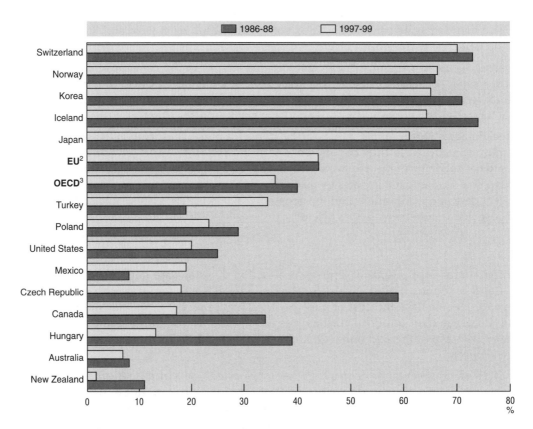

1.   The Producer Support Estimate (PSE) is an indicator of the annual monetary value of gross transfers from consumers and taxpayers to agricultural producers, measured at farm gate level, arising from policy measures which support agriculture, regardless of their nature, objectives or impacts on farm production or income. The percentage PSE measures the share of support to producers in total gross farm receipts.
2.   EU-12 for 1986-88; EU-15 for 1997-99. PSEs are not caculated by the OECD Secretariat for individual EU Member states.
3.   OECD includes the most recent Member countries for both periods (date of OECD membership in brackets): Czech Republic (1995), Hungary (1996), Korea (1996), Mexico (1994) and Poland (1996).
Note: See Annex Table 1.
Source: OECD (2000).

enforced restrictions on farmers to meet certain minimum environmental standards, such as the disposal of animal waste into watercourses. In addition, land diversion schemes, although in most cases originally introduced to achieve supply control objectives, are increasingly including environmental conditions, such as diverting land to develop semi-natural habitats so helping to reduce soil erosion and encourage wildlife. A number of countries also use voluntary efforts, including farm advisory services and information exchange, to address local and community related issues, and raise environmental awareness amongst farmers.

While evidence is still limited, the introduction of these measures has in some regions of certain countries contributed to altering farm management practices and changing agricultural land use patterns. For example, the conservation of certain "high nature value" habitats on agricultural land and the reduction of diffuse pollution (see the discussion in various chapters of this Report). However, there is at present insufficient information in many cases to be sure about the extent and permanence of these changes within or across OECD countries. While in some cases improvements have been made, they have been more costly than would have been the case in the absence of production enhancing policies. Moreover, the negative environmental impacts resulting from agricultural activity still remain at relatively high and damaging levels in many OECD countries (OECD, 2000).

3. Agriculture and societal preferences

In most OECD countries there has been *growing public awareness and concern about agriculture's impact on environmental quality*, both in terms of reducing the pollution and enhancing the benefits resulting from agricultural activity. This change in societal preferences has been mainly in response to rising incomes, increasing leisure time, and greater personal mobility. Also there is heightened public knowledge of environmental and food safety issues resulting from better education and greater media coverage of these issues, and the desire from the highly urbanised society in most OECD countries for the tranquillity and space offered by rural areas. A recent *Canadian* survey provides an illustration of the range and evolution of the Canadian public perception of agriculture and the environment (Box 1).

Box 1.   Public perceptions of agriculture and the environment in Canada

Overall, Canadians have a relatively favourable environmental image of the agriculture and food industry. When asked to rate the degree of environmental damage caused by 12 industries, agriculture was rated 11th, followed only by the computer software industry. Compared with other resource industries (energy, fisheries, and forestry), Canadians see agriculture as being the closest to sustainability.

When it comes to the impacts of agricultural activities on the environment, Canadians (60%) are most concerned about the use of chemical fertilisers and pesticides. A much smaller share of people are most concerned about water pollution from livestock wastes (19%), the impact on wildlife habitat and wetlands (13%), and odours from livestock operations (4%). There is some regional variation in these responses. For example, a higher proportion (8%) of people in Quebec, Saskatchewan, and Alberta expressed concern about livestock odours.

Public perceptions about agriculture and the environment have evolved. Ten years ago, loss of farmland to urban development was cited as the most important agri-environmental issue. Concern about this issue has decreased steadily as attention has shifted to the use of farm chemicals.

Source: MacGregor and McRae (2000, p. 24).

In some cases changing societal preferences are also creating pressure on agriculture, especially in terms of competition for land. The demand for improved housing, better communications infrastructure, and land for commercial development, for example, is increasing competition for agricultural land, especially close to urban centres. While in other cases greater leisure time has increased demand for golf courses and nature parks, often involving converting agricultural land to these uses.

An area of growing interest in OECD countries relates to concern for *rural viability*, particularly in creating rural employment and maintaining rural communities (Box 2). This is part of a broader concern in terms of developing social capital, such as building social relationships. Rural viability relates to issues such as the age structure of the agricultural workforce, the educational and managerial skills of farmers, and access to key services (Commonwealth of Australia, 1998), with some of these issues discussed in this and other chapters of the Report. Retaining a skilled workforce in rural areas and having an appropriate rural community infrastructure, will affect the capacity of farming communities to adjust and manage their enterprises to changing economic and environmental conditions and, over the longer term, contribute to the sustainability of agriculture.

4. Agriculture and environmental processes

Agricultural activity is closely linked to natural environmental processes and is a part of ecosystems rather than external to them, unlike most other economic activities. The relationship between agricultural activities and the environment is often complex, site specific and non-linear. Viewed both within and

---

Box 2. **Rural viability**

Traditionally rural economies have depended heavily on agricultural activities, which have affected and shaped the social life of local communities. In many OECD countries this dependency has weakened and, consequently, there is increasing recognition that problems in rural areas, such as depopulation, poverty, unemployment, and amenity loss, are best addressed in a broader rural development context and not through agricultural policy measures.

Structural adjustment allows agricultural producers to use more advanced farming practices and to derive benefits from economies of scale by reducing the number of farms and increasing average farm size in a particular region. On the other hand, it leaves those parts of the population that cease their previous farming activities searching for alternative sources of income.

Where the rural economy does not provide sufficient non-agricultural employment opportunities, increases in unemployment, poverty, and emigration might ensue. OECD countries have addressed these adverse impacts of structural change on rural viability through policy measures such as education and retraining, assistance for early retirement, and investment in rural infrastructure and social organisations (OECD, 1998b).

There are different approaches to measuring rural viability, such as assessing demographic characteristics, income changes and distribution, the number of people entering or leaving agriculture, and the level of education, social interactions, attitudes and structures in rural areas. In addition, the interest in assessing *social capital* in the context of sustainable agriculture and rural viability has increased recently (see for example Schuller, 2000; and Webster, 1999). Social capital measures the social dimension of sustainable development and is of considerable relevance to rural viability. Social capital reflects social relationships or "trust" within a community that make the community viable, socially progressive, and economically vigorous. Low social capital implies low trust, community disagreements, and difficulties in solving problems or achieving goals.

Rural viability issues are closely related to several agri-environmental indicators. For example, rural amenities relate to landscape, biodiversity, and wildlife habitat; education levels are associated with farm management practices; and social capital issues may be discussed in conjunction with farm management in a community context (OECD, 1999, pp.107-109; OECD, 1997, pp.33-34). Moreover, there are other aspects that are generally perceived as relevant to rural viability, such as spatial isolation, costs of service delivery, and delays in communication, which some countries are considering integrating into a broad set of indicators to track sustainable agriculture (for example, see Commonwealth of Australia, 1998).

Note: For a recent OECD review of agriculture and the rural economy in OECD countries, see OECD (1998b), and also the related publications of the OECD Territorial Development Service (TDS) detailed on the TDS website at: *http://web.oecd.org/tds/frames1.htm*. Kilpatrick (1999) is investigating the elements of social capital and developing a set of indicators to show changes in social capital relevant to agriculture.

Source: OECD Secretariat.

across OECD countries there are a wide range of biophysical conditions, reflecting, for example, variations in underlying climatic conditions, topography, soils, availability of water resources, and land use patterns.

Farming manipulates the natural environment to produce agricultural commodities, through a range of different practices and systems, such as draining land, tilling soil, diverting natural watercourses, using irrigation, and applying nutrients and pesticides (Smith and McRae, 2000). The agro-ecosystem, like natural ecosystems, is dynamic with a constant cyclical flow of inputs entering the system (*e.g.* land, water, energy, nutrients, pesticides), and outputs leaving the system (*e.g.* crops, livestock, fibre, waste). At the same time natural cycles of climate and biodiversity, for example, affect agriculture, while agriculture also impacts on these cycles (*e.g.* greenhouse gas emissions). These various environmental processes and natural cycles are briefly described in the "*Environmental Context*" sections in each indicator chapter of this Report (see also Norberg, 1999).

There is now a better understanding of the limits and potential of the productive capacity of the natural resource base in agriculture, notably soils and water. Moreover, knowledge has improved on the impacts of inappropriate farming practices and systems on the degradation of natural resources and the environment (Commonwealth of Australia, 1998, pp. 9-10). Less well known are the processes by which agriculture provides environmental benefits, such as those related to wildlife habitat provision, the soil and water retaining capacity of agriculture, or the function of agricultural soils to act as a sink for greenhouse gases by storing carbon (Smith and McRae, 2000).

5. Land use changes

Overview

Land use patterns and changes provide the integrating element between the economic, social and environmental influences on agriculture examined in the previous sections of this chapter. Although the agricultural sector is relatively small in OECD countries when measured in terms of the share in GDP or employment, it is important in terms of land use, accounting for nearly 40 per cent of the OECD total land area (Figure 8). This is significant, as any activity accounting for the major share of the total land area has potential for creating widespread environmental impacts (Pearce, 1999).

Land use describes the functional aspects of land, characterised by some identifiable purpose or function (such as land used for agricultural, forestry or urban purposes), leading to tangible (food, industrial crops and biodiversity) or intangible products (landscape) or values.[6] Land use changes are driven by economic and technological developments, demographics, environmental factors and government policies, which alter the type and intensity of land use (Darwin *et al.*, 1996).

Evaluating the environmental impacts of changes in land use needs to take into account the trade-offs between competing economic, societal and environmental demands for land. Competition for land occurs because land used for one purpose can prevent or reduce its use for other purposes, although land can also provide joint products, such as food and landscape. For example, a decrease in the area of agricultural land area due to urban development depends on whether priority, expressed through land prices in private markets, is given to retaining agricultural land or providing residential housing.

Defining priorities for land use may not be easy and countries may have contradictory policies in place. Land diversion policies, for example, may encourage the conversion of low lying agricultural land to saltmarsh, while simultaneously policies to maintain sea defences have the opposite effect (Moxey, 1999). A further difficulty arises when interpreting land use changes, in that not all values attributed to land are embodied in land market prices. This is because private markets do not always recognise the externalities associated with land, such as the provision of habitat, ecological and amenity services (Tweeten, 1997).

Agricultural land use

For the majority of OECD countries agricultural land occupies over 50 per cent of the total land area (Figure 8).[7] Where the *share of agriculture in the total land area* is small, this is usually explained by climatic or physical factors, for example, in Canada, Finland, Iceland, Japan, Korea, Norway and Sweden. The total OECD area of agricultural land has shown only a modest reduction over the past 10 years, largely reflecting an increase in the agricultural land base, particularly in Mexico and Turkey, offset by a decrease, notably in the European Union, Japan, Korea and the United States (Figure 9).[8]

In those countries where the supply of agricultural land has been declining over the past decade, most of this land has been converted to forests and open land (uncultivated land), particularly in marginal farming areas (*i.e.* land less suitable for agricultural production), with the rest converted for urban, commercial and infrastructure use (see Figure 8 in the Wildlife Habitat chapter). The *conversion of marginal farming land* to other uses, especially forest or uncultivated land, is of concern to some OECD countries in terms of both the environmental and socio-economic implications of these land use changes.

In certain situations taking marginal farmland out of production can cause environmental degradation, such as soil erosion, reduction in water retaining capacity, loss of landscape and wildlife

Figure 8. **Share of agricultural land use in the total national land area: 1995-97**

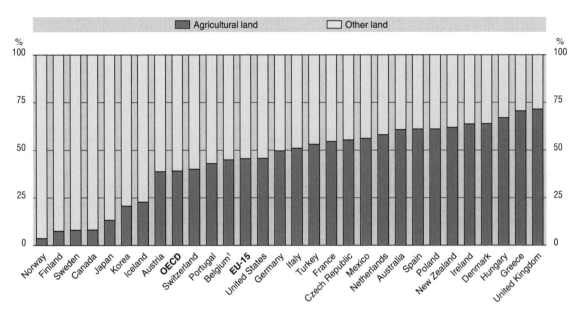

1. Including Luxembourg.
Note: See Annex Table 2.
Source: FAO Database, 1999.

Figure 9. **Change in the agricultural land area: 1985-87 to 1995-97**

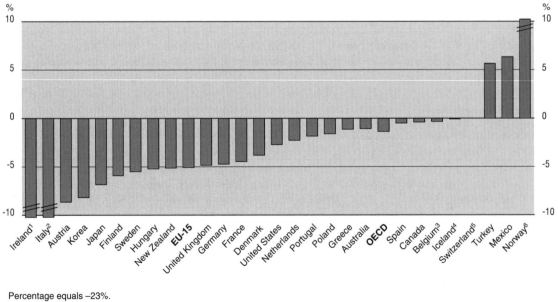

1. Percentage equals –23%.
2. Percentage equals –12%.
3. Including Luxembourg.
4. Percentage is close to zero.
5. Percentage equals 0.
6. Percentage equals +14%.
Note: See Annex Table 3.
Source: FAO Database, 1999.

Figure 10. **Agricultural land area by different use categories: 1995-97**

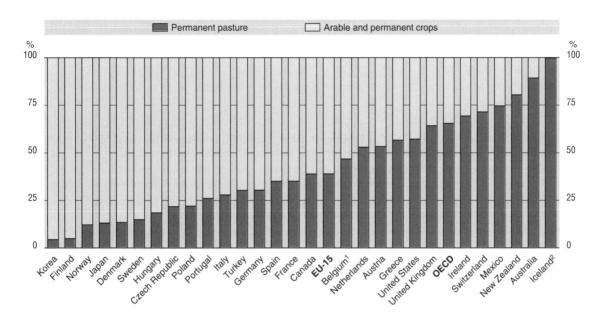

1. Including Luxembourg.
2. Percentage for arable and permanent crops equals 0.3%.
Note: See Annex Table 2.
Source: FAO Database, 1999.

habitats, and disappearance of local varieties.[9] The reversion of agricultural land to uncultivated "natural" habitat may, over time, however, lead to environmental improvements, such as enhancing the biodiversity, habitat and recreational functions and values of previously cultivated land, and improved soil conservation (*i.e.* reduced erosion). Moreover, in some countries policies have been introduced, for example, to encourage the conversion of agricultural to aquatic habitats, especially wetlands (see the Wildlife Habitat chapter).

Important changes have also occurred in terms of the *pattern of agricultural land use* within OECD countries. For a large number of OECD countries the major use of agricultural land is for permanent pasture (Figure 10). In some countries the share of permanent pasture in agricultural land has increased over the past ten years, mainly because of the introduction of land diversion schemes (see Annex Table 2 in this chapter; and Box 2 on land diversion schemes in the Wildlife Habitat chapter).

Changes in the pattern of agricultural land use from arable crops to pasture, from more to less intensive cropping systems, and in terms of different cropping patterns can have considerable environmental effects. Some examples include: exploiting the potential of agricultural land as a source of renewable energy from biomass production, enhancing the biodiversity and habitat functions provided by different cropping systems, and altering the sink functions of farm land affecting the net emissions of greenhouse gases from agriculture. These and other agri-environmental issues related to changes in land use are examined in many of the chapters in this Report, in particular, those chapters covering Soil Quality, Land Conservation, Greenhouse Gases, Biodiversity, Wildlife Habitats and Landscape.

NOTES

1. For a more detailed discussion of the historical trends discussed in this section see OECD (1998a) and the annual OECD *Agricultural Policies in OECD Countries: Monitoring and Evaluation Report*.

2. The development of indicators relevant to the age structure of agriculture in the context of sustainable agriculture is being examined by *Australia* (Commonwealth of Australia, 1998) and the *United Kingdom* (MAFF, 2000).

3. The structural trends in farm size and numbers discussed here are documented in more detail for the *European Union* in: European Commission (1999); and for the *United States* in: USDA (1997).

4. The increasing concentration of the pig and other livestock sectors and its environmental implications is discussed in the Nutrient Use chapter, but also see MacGregor and McRae (2000, pp. 27) in the case of the *Canadian* pig industry; and the European Commission (1999, pp.89-92) for a similar discussion on the pig industry in the European Union context.

5. The PSE data draws from OECD (2000), with numbers for the PSE per full time farmer equivalent shown in Annex Table 1.

6. The various functions and values associated with agricultural land/landscape are shown in Figure 3 of the Landscape chapter.

7. The OECD average is heavily distorted by Canada, which accounts for over a quarter of the total OECD land area, and where agricultural land occupies only 8 per cent of the total land area (see Annex Table 2).

8. For a recent analysis of agricultural land use trends in the *European Union* see Commision of the European Union (2000).

9. There is extensive literature on the damaging environmental impacts associated with the conversion of marginal agricultural land to other uses, see for example, Baldock *et al.*(1995), JIAC (1997), Sumelius (1997), Swiss Federal Office of Agriculture (1997), and Tikof (1997). For an examination of both the gains and losses to biodiversity from changing land use, including agricultural land, see Mac *et al.* (1998, pp.37-61). In some literature uncultivated marginal land is referred to as abandoned land.

Annex Table 1. **Key agricultural[1] indicators**

	Employment in agriculture[2]	Agriculture in GDP[3]	Change in final agricultural output[4]	Annual change in real net farm income[5]
	%	%	%	%
	1998	Mid-1990s	1985-87 to 1995-97	Mid-1980s to mid-1990s
Australia	5	3	32	−1.6
Austria	7	1	−2	4.3
Belgium	2	1	22	0.7
Canada	5	2	25	−1.3
Czech Republic	6	3	..	..
Denmark	4	3	12	4.9
Finland	7	4	−6	−4.0
France	4	2	11	7.9
Germany[6]	3	1	−1	..
Greece	20	9	9	−3.9
Hungary	8	6	..	..
Iceland	9	9	..	..
Ireland	9	5	17	..
Italy	7	3	4	−0.1
Japan	5	2	−10	2.8
Korea	12	6	..	−2.5
Luxembourg	3	1	3	..
Mexico	19	6	..	..
Netherlands	3	3	13	0.4
New Zealand	9	7	..	..
Norway	5	2	−9	−1.7
Poland	19	6	..	..
Portugal	14	4	..	..
Spain	8	3	12	..
Sweden	3	2	−7	..
Switzerland	5	1	−2	..
Turkey	42	14	16	..
United Kingdom	2	2	3	..
United States	3	2	23	0.7
EU-15	5	2	..	..
OECD	..	..	..	..

.. Not available.
1. Agriculture is defined as primary agriculture (*i.e.* excluding upstream/downstream activities, forestry, fishing and hunting) unless otherwise indicated.
2. Employment in agriculture, including hunting, forestry and fishing as a percentage of total civilian employment. Percentages refer to 1997 for Greece and Portugal and to 1995 for Luxembourg.
3. Agriculture, including hunting, forestry and fishing as a percentage of Gross Domestic Product (GDP).
4. Agricultural output in million US dollars converted using constant 1990 Purchasing Power Parities (PPPs).
5. Details of real net farm income are provided in the Farm Financial Resources chapter of this Report. The period mid-1980s refers to the early 1990s for Finland, France, Korea and the United States.
6. The change in final agricultural output refers to the period 1990-92 to 1995-97.

Annex Table 1. **Key agricultural[1] indicators** (*cont.*)

	Change in the number of farms[7]	New farmers[8]		Educational level of farmers[9]	
	%	% under 35 years	% over 35 years	% basic training	% full training
	1985-87 to 1995-97	Late 1990s		Mid/late 1990s	
Australia	−19	32	68	40	20
Austria	−19	..	..	21	16
Belgium	−25	..	..	24	13
Canada	..	..	..	..	8
Czech Republic	..	..	..	..	..
Denmark	−26	..	..	10	3
Finland	−23	44	56	..	..
France	−28	..	..	15	26
Germany[10]	−24	..	..	48	12
Greece	−16	..	..	< 1	< 1
Hungary	..	..	..	..	..
Iceland	..	..	..	31	30
Ireland	−30	..	..	9	9
Italy	−15	..	..	3	2
Japan	−22	12	88	..	..
Korea	−33	..	..	1	2
Luxembourg	−28	..	..	..	..
Mexico	..	59	41	..	..
Netherlands	−15	..	..	40	25
New Zealand	−15	..	..	..	..
Norway	−24	51	49	33	..
Poland	..	..	..	..	..
Portugal	−25	..	..	3	< 1
Spain	−29	..	..	1	< 1
Sweden	−17	32	68	..	..
Switzerland	−20	58	42	..	..
Turkey	..	..	..	..	..
United Kingdom	−10	24	76	12	14
United States	−9	24	76	23	19
EU-15	..	..	..	..	..
OECD	..	..	..	..	..

.. Not available.

7. For Austria and Korea, data for the period 1985-87 refer to the year 1980. For Finland, the percentage covers the period 1990-95. For the United States, data for the period 1995-97 refer to the year 1994. For Portugal, data for the period 1985-87 refer to the year 1989 (new statistical methodology) and data for the period 1995-97 refer to the year 1995.

8. For the United Kingdom, the categories refer to under 45 years old and over 45 years old.

9. Basic training includes any training course completed after school at an agricultural college, such as an agricultural apprenticeship. Full training includes any training course for at least two years after school at an agricultural college, such as that completed at a university.

10. The change in the number of farms covers eastern and western Germany.

Annex Table 1. **Key agricultural[1] indicators** (*cont.*)

	Producer Support Estimate[11]		Producer Support Estimate per Full-time Farmer Equivalent[12]	
	%		Thousand US$	
	1986-88	1997-99	1986-88	1997-99
Australia	8	7	3	3
Austria	n.c.	n.c.	n.c.	n.c.
Belgium	n.c.	n.c.	n.c.	n.c.
Canada	34	17	12	8
Czech Republic[13]	59	18	8	4
Denmark	n.c.	n.c.	n.c.	n.c.
Finland	n.c.	n.c.	n.c.	n.c.
France	n.c.	n.c.	n.c.	n.c.
Germany	n.c.	n.c.	n.c.	n.c.
Greece	n.c.	n.c.	n.c.	n.c.
Hungary	39	13	3	2
Iceland	74	64	26	33
Ireland	n.c.	n.c.	n.c.	n.c.
Italy	n.c.	n.c.	n.c.	n.c.
Japan	67	61	15	23
Korea	71	65	8	22
Luxembourg	n.c.	n.c.	n.c.	n.c.
Mexico	8	19	n.c.	1
Netherlands	n.c.	n.c.	n.c.	n.c.
New Zealand	11	2	4	1
Norway	66	66	24	32
Poland	29	23	1	1
Portugal	n.c.	n.c.	n.c.	n.c.
Spain	n.c.	n.c.	n.c.	n.c.
Sweden	n.c.	n.c.	n.c.	n.c.
Switzerland	73	70	33	33
Turkey	19	34	n.c.	n.c.
United Kingdom	n.c.	n.c.	n.c.	n.c.
United States	25	20	17	18
EU-15[14]	44	44	11	17
OECD	40	36	11	11

n.c.   Not calculated.

11. The Producer Support Estimate (PSE) is an indicator of the annual monetary value of gross transfers from consumers and taxpayers to agricultural producers, measured at farm gate level, arising from policy measures which support agriculture, regardless of their nature, objectives or impacts on farm production or income.
12. Full-time Farmer Equivalent (FFE) numbers are calculated on the basis of the European Union Annual Work Unit (2 200 hours of working time in agriculture each year); EU-12 for 1986-88; EU-15 for 1997-99.
13. PSE data before 1993 covers the Czech part of the former Czechoslovakia.
14. EU-12 for 1986-88; EU-15 for 1997-99. PSEs are not caculated by the OECD Secretariat for individual EU Member states.
Sources: OECD Secretariat; European Commission (1999); Commonwealth of Australia (1998).

Annex Table 2. **National and agricultural land area: 1985-87 to 1995-97**

	Total national land area	Total national land area of which:		Agricultural land area of which:			
		Agricultural land area*	Other land area*	Arable and permanent crop area*		Permanent pasture area*	
	Million hectares	%		%		%	
	1995-97	1995-97	1995-97	1985-87	1995-97	1985-87	1995-97
Australia	768	61	39	10	11	90	89
Austria	8	39	61	43	47	57	53
Belgium[1]	3	45	55	50	53	50	47
Canada	922	8	92	61	61	39	39
Czech Republic[2]	8	55	45	81	78	19	22
Denmark	4	64	36	92	86	8	14
Finland	30	7	93	95	95	5	5
France	55	55	45	62	65	38	35
Germany[3]	35	50	50	68	70	32	30
Greece	13	71	29	43	43	57	57
Hungary	9	67	33	81	81	19	19
Iceland	10	23	77	< 1	< 1	100	100
Ireland	7	64	36	18	31	82	69
Italy	29	51	49	71	72	29	28
Japan	38	13	87	88	87	12	13
Korea	10	21	79	96	96	4	4
Mexico	191	56	44	25	25	75	75
Netherlands	3	58	42	43	47	57	53
New Zealand	27	62	38	21	20	79	80
Norway	31	4	96	90	88	10	12
Poland	30	61	39	79	78	21	22
Portugal	9	43	57	79	74	21	26
Spain	50	61	39	67	65	33	35
Sweden	41	8	92	84	85	16	15
Switzerland[4]	4	40	60	27	29	73	71
Turkey	77	53	47	71	70	29	30
United Kingdom	24	71	29	39	36	61	64
United States	916	46	54	44	43	56	57
EU-15	313	45	55	60	61	40	39
OECD	3 354	39	61	35	35	65	65

Percentages may include rounding errors.
* **Definitions drawn from FAO:**
  Agricultural land area:
  Arable crops, permanent crops and permanent pasture.
  Other land area:
  Forest and woodland, urban areas, infrastructure, open land, etc.
  Arable crop area:
  Land under temporary crops (double-cropped areas are counted only once), temporary meadows for mowing or pasture, land under market and kitchen gardens and land temporarily fallow (less than five years).
  Permanent crop area:
  Land cultivated with crops that occupy the land for long periods and need not be replanted after each harvest, such as cocoa, coffee and rubber; this category includes land under flowering shrubs, fruit trees, nut trees and vines, but excludes land under trees grown for wood or timber.
  Permanent pasture area:
  Land used permanently (five years or more) for herbaceous forage crops, either cultivated or growing wild (wild prairie or grazing land).
1. Including Luxembourg.
2. National data for 1985-87 refer to 1980-82 and cover the Czech part of the former Czechoslovakia.
3. Data cover western and eastern Germany.
4. National data were used.
Source: FAO Database, 1999.

Annex Table 3. **Agricultural land use: 1985-87 to 1995-97**

Thousand hectares

	Agricultural land area*		Arable and permanent crop area*		Permanent pasture area*	
	1985-87	1995-97	1985-87	1995-97	1985-87	1995-97
Australia	471 622	466 556	47 130	50 223	424 491	416 333
Austria	3 503	3 201	1 517	1 493	1 986	1 707
Belgium[1]	1 476	1 471	745	784	731	687
Canada	74 960	74 667	46 010	45 667	28 950	29 000
Czech Republic[2]	4 370	4 279	3 523	3 348	847	931
Denmark	2 817	2 710	2 602	2 344	215	366
Finland	2 407	2 265	2 276	2 153	130	112
France	31 397	30 001	19 334	19 474	12 062	10 527
Germany[3]	18 192	17 336	12 412	12 062	5 780	5 274
Greece	9 196	9 091	3 941	3 941	5 255	5 150
Hungary	6 524	6 186	5 290	5 038	1 234	1 148
Iceland	2 281	2 280	7	6	2 274	2 274
Ireland	5 689	4 387	1 008	1 347	4 681	3 040
Italy	17 050	15 010	12 094	10 821	4 956	4 189
Japan	5 359	4 994	4 733	4 336	626	658
Korea	2 223	2 041	2 143	1 951	80	90
Mexico	100 833	107 200	25 333	27 300	75 500	79 900
Netherlands	2 016	1 970	873	927	1 143	1 044
New Zealand	17 472	16 579	3 615	3 262	13 857	13 317
Norway	965	1 099	865	965	100	134
Poland	18 887	18 586	14 827	14 484	4 060	4 103
Portugal	3 997	3 924	3 159	2 900	838	1 024
Spain	30 641	30 491	20 409	19 807	10 232	10 684
Sweden	3 475	3 285	2 907	2 793	568	492
Switzerland[4]	1 580	1 580	432	452	1 148	1 128
Turkey	38 680	40 854	27 647	28 476	11 033	12 378
United Kingdom	18 141	17 266	7 025	6 183	11 115	11 083
United States	429 915	418 250	189 125	179 000	240 791	239 250
EU-15	149 997	142 408	90 303	87 029	59 694	55 379
OECD	1 325 669	1 307 559	460 983	451 537	864 686	856 022

* **Definitions drawn from FAO:**
   Agricultural land area:
   Arable crops, permanent crops and permanent pasture.
   Arable crop area:
   Land under temporary crops (double-cropped areas are counted only once), temporary meadows for mowing or pasture, land under market and kitchen gardens and land temporarily fallow (less than five years).
   Permanent crop area:
   Land cultivated with crops that occupy the land for long periods and need not be replanted after each harvest, such as cocoa, coffee and rubber; this category includes land under flowering shrubs, fruit trees, nut trees and vines, but excludes land under trees grown for wood or timber.
   Permanent pasture area:
   Land used permanently (five years or more) for herbaceous forage crops, either cultivated or growing wild (wild prairie or grazing land).
1. Including Luxembourg.
2. National data for 1985-87 refer to 1980-82 and cover the Czech part of the former Czechoslovakia.
3. Data cover western and eastern Germany.
4. National data were used.
Source: FAO Database, 1999.

BIBLIOGRAPHY

Baldock, D., G. Beaufoy and J. Clark (1995),
The Nature of Farming, Low Intensity Farming Systems in Nine European Countries, Institute for European Environmental Policy, London, United Kingdom.

Commission of the European Union (2000),
From Land Cover to Landscape Diversity in the European Union, Office for Official Publications of the European Communities, Luxembourg. Available at: *http://europa.eu.int/comm/dg06/publi/landscape/index.htm*.

Commonwealth of Australia (1998),
Sustainable Agriculture – Assessing Australia's Recent Performance, A Report to the Standing Committee on Agriculture and Resource Management (SCARM) of the National Collaborative Project on Indicators for Sustainable Agriculture, SCARM Technical Report No. 70, CSIRO Publishing, Victoria, Australia.

Darwin, R., M. Tsigas, J. Lewandrowski and A. Raneses (1996),
"Land use and cover in ecological economics", *Ecological Economics*, Vol. 17, No. 3, pp. 157-181.

European Commission (1999),
Agriculture, Environment, Rural Development: Facts and Figures – A Challenge for Agriculture, Office for Official Publications of the European Communities, Luxembourg. Available at: *http://europa.eu.int/comm/dg06/envir/report/en/index.htm*.

Hrubovcak, J., U. Vasavada and J.E. Aldy (1999),
Green Technologies for a More Sustainable Agriculture, Resource Economics Division, Economic Research Service, US Department of Agriculture, Agricultural Information Bulletin No. 752, Washington, DC., United States.

Huffman, W.E. (2000),
"Human Capital: Education and Agricultural Productivity", Part 1, Volume 1, in B.L. Garnder and C. Rausser (eds.), *Handbook of Agricultural Economics*, Elsevier Science, Amsterdam, The Netherlands.

JIAC [Japan International Agriculture Council] (1997),
"Let's Support the Movement to Preserve Terraced Paddy Fields", *Japan Agrinfo Newsletters*, Vol. 14, No. 11, Tokyo, Japan.

Kilpatrick, S (1999),
How social capital facilitates learning outcomes for small family businesses, Centre for Research and Learning in Regional Australia, University of Tasmania, Australia. Available at: *www.crlra.utas.edu.au/discussion/d2-2000.shtml*.

Mac, M.J., P.A. Opler, C.E.P. Haecker and P.D. Doran (1998),
Status and Trends of the Nation's Biological Resources, Two Volumes, United States Department of the Interior, United States Geological Survey, Reston, Virginia, United States. Available at: *http://biology.usgs.gov/pubs/execsumm/page2.htm*.

MacGregor, R.J. and T. McRae (2000),
"Driving Forces Affecting the Environmental Sustainability of Agriculture", Chapter 3, in T. McRae, C.A.S. Smith and L.J. Gregorich (eds.), *Environmental Sustainability of Canadian Agriculture: Report of the Agri-Environmental Indicator Project*, Agriculture and Agri-Food Canada (AAFC), Ottawa, Ontario, Canada. Available at: *www.agr.ca/policy/environment/publications/list.html*.

MAFF [Ministry of Agriculture, Fisheries and Food] (2000),
Towards Sustainable Agriculture – A Pilot Set of Indicators, London, United Kingdom. Available at: *www.maff.gov.uk/* [Farming > Sustainable Agriculture].

Moxey, A. (1999),
"Cross-Cutting Issues in Developing Agri-Environmental Indicators", pp. 113-130, in OECD, *Environmental Indicators for Agriculture, Volume 2: Issues and Design – The York Workshop*, Paris, France.

Mues, C., L. Chapman and R. van Hilst (1998),
Promoting Improved Land Management practices on Australian Farms: A Survey of Landcare and Land Management Related Programmes, Australian Bureau of Agriculture and Resource Economics, Research Report 98.4, Canberra, Australia.

Nieberg, H. and F. Isermeyer (1994),
   The Use of Agri-environmental Indicators in Agricultural Policy, unpublished paper presented to the OECD Meeting of Experts on Agri-environmental Indicators, Paris, 8-9 December 1994.

Norberg, J. (1999),
   "Linking nature's services to ecosystems: some general ecological concepts", *Ecological Economics*, Vol. 29, No. 2, pp. 183-202.

OECD (1995),
   Technological Change and Structural Adjustment in OECD Agriculture, Paris, France.

OECD (1997),
   Environmental Indicators for Agriculture, Volume 1: Concepts and Framework, Paris, France.

OECD (1998a),
   Agricultural Policy Reform: Stocktaking of Achievements, A discussion paper for the meeting of the OECD Committee for Agriculture at Ministerial level, 5-6 March, Paris, France. Available at: *www.oecd.org/agr/ministerial/* [Documentation > Discussion papers for the meeting].

OECD (1998b),
   Agricultural Policy Reform and the Rural Economy in OECD Countries, Paris, France.

OECD (1998c),
   The Environmental Effects of Reforming Agricultural Policies, Paris, France.

OECD (1999),
   Environmental Indicators for Agriculture, Volume 2: Issues and Design – The York Workshop, Paris, France.

OECD (2000),
   Agricultural Policies in OECD Countries: Monitoring and Evaluation 2000, Paris, France.

Pearce, D. (1999),
   "Measuring Sustainable Development: Implications for Agri-environmental Indicators", pp. 29-45, in OECD, *Environmental Indicators for Agriculture, Volume 2: Issues and Design – The York Workshop*, Paris, France.

Schuller, T. (2000),
   "Social Capital, Human Capital and Sustainable Development", pp. 51-64, in OECD, *Frameworks to Measure Sustainable Development*, Paris, France.

Smith, C.A.S. and T. McRae (2000),
   "Understanding and Assessing the Environmental Sustainability of Agriculture", Chapter 2, in T. McRae, C.A.S. Smith and L.J. Gregorich (eds.), *Environmental Sustainability of Canadian Agriculture: Report of the Agri-Environmental Indicator Project*, Agriculture and Agri-Food Canada (AAFC), Ottawa, Ontario, Canada. Available at: *www.agr.ca/policy/environment/publications/list.html*.

Sumelius, J. (1997),
   Concerns Related to Possibly Effects of Trade Liberalisation on Landscape and Biodiversity in the Nordic Countries, Paper presented at the NJF-seminar on Agriculture, Trade and the Environment, Greve, Denmark, 22-24 May.

Swiss Federal Office of Agriculture (1997),
   "Switzerland: Government Policy to Stimulate Environmental Benefits", pp. 159-167, in OECD, *Helsinki Seminar on Environmental Benefits from Agriculture, Country Case Studies*, OECD General Distribution document [OCDE/GD(97)110], Paris, France. Available at: *www.oecd.org/* [Documentation > 1997 > Reference Components > OCDE > OCDE/GD].

Tikof, M. (1997),
   "Greece: Policy Measures and Practices, and Environmental Benefits from Agriculture", pp. 95-112, in OECD, *Helsinki Seminar on Environmental Benefits from Agriculture, Country Case Studies*, OECD General Distribution document [OCDE/GD(97)110], Paris, France. Available at: *www.oecd.org/* [Documentation > 1997 > Reference Components > OCDE > OCDE/GD].

Tweeten, L. (1997),
   Competing for Scarce Land: Food Security and Farmland Preservation, paper presented to the American Agricultural Law Association meeting 17 October at Minneapolis, Minnesota, United States.

USDA [United States Department of Agriculture] (1997),
   Agricultural Resources and Environmental Indicators, 1996-97, Agricultural Handbook No. 712, Natural Resources and Environment Division, Economic Research Service, Washington, DC., United States. Available at: *www.ers.usda.gov/* [Briefing Rooms > Agricultural Resources and Environmental Indicators].

Webster, P. (1999),
   "The Challenge of Sustainability at the Farm Level: Presidential Address", *Journal of Agricultural Economics*, Vol. 50, No. 3, pp. 371-387.

61

Chapter 2

FARM FINANCIAL RESOURCES

HIGHLIGHTS

Context

Financial resources are a key driving force behind farmers' actions, but are not directly related to environmental performance. The relationship between farm financial resources and environmental outcomes is complex, as farms can remain profitable at the expense of environmental degradation, at least over the medium term. Profitable farms, however, can better afford to take the environment into account in their investment and farm management decisions.

The availability of financial resources influences farming practices; the ability to acquire new technologies; as well as the type, level and intensity of input use and of production. They also affect the degree of adoption of environmentally benign production methods, including farmers' attitude towards environmental risks; rates of structural adjustment, including farm amalgamation; and the exit and entry of farmers into the sector.

The two main sources of farm financial resources in OECD countries include returns from the market and government support (farm household income can also include non-farm sources of income). The type and level of support provided to farmers varies widely across the OECD. Since the late 1980s many countries have introduced agri-environmental measures, and land diversion schemes with environmental objectives, mainly aimed at: changing farming practices (*e.g.* raising environmental awareness through farm advisory services or voluntary farm groups); developing agri-environmental research (*e.g.* on soil carbon changes); providing payments to farmers for reducing environmental damage (*e.g.* animal waste treatment facilities) and enhancing environmental services (*e.g.* laying hedgerows). In addition, farmers also have to comply with environmental standards and regulations, especially with regard to the use of pesticides and inorganic fertilisers.

Indicators and recent trends

OECD indicators on farm financial resources reflect the financial health of the farm and cover two areas: first, net farm income from agricultural activities, and second, public and private agri-environmental expenditure, including agri-environmental research expenditure.

Net farm income is calculated as the difference between gross output and all expenses, including depreciation at the farm level. While nominal net farm incomes have risen for most OECD countries over the past 10 years, the performance in real terms has been variable and over recent years net farm incomes have sharply declined for some countries. Agricultural households also obtain a substantial share of their income from non-agricultural activities in many countries, and in some countries the total average income of agricultural households exceeds that of non-agricultural ones.

Public and private agri-environmental expenditure is aimed at both mitigating the negative impacts of agriculture on the environment and also enhancing the benefits. For a large number of OECD countries there has been a very rapid increase in public agri-environmental expenditure over the 1990s, associated with the introduction of many new environmental measures related to agriculture. The use of this expenditure varies widely across countries, reflecting differences in agri-environmental concerns and priorities.

A significant share of *public agricultural research expenditure* in many countries is spent on addressing agri-environmental concerns, and in some cases this share has been increasing since the mid-1980s. While in a few countries *private agri-environmental expenditure* is important, there is little systematic collection of this expenditure data.

1. Background

The link between financial resources and environment is complex as farms can remain profitable at the expense of environmental degradation, but on the other hand, only profitable farms can afford to take the environment into account in their actions. Farmers thus require sufficient financial resources (*i.e.* be financially sustainable) in order to operate profitably and use environmentally sound farming technology[1] and management practices.

In addition to financial resources, there are other factors influencing the adoption of environmentally sound management practices, such as education and attitudes to risk and the environment, and "external" factors, such as farm size and type, topography and climate (see Contextual Indicators chapter). Farmers' skills and ability to manage the financial resources at their disposal also include their adaptability to respond to changes in their financial situation, and whether a farmer is part-time, full time, tenant, or owner, and engages wage labour (Culver and Seecharan, 1986).

In most OECD countries, farm financial resources or farm income consist of market returns on agricultural production, loan and equity capital, and transfers due to agricultural policies from taxpayers (government budgetary support) and consumers (through market price support).[2] Although fluctuations in farm income reflect uncertainties and risks in the economy, short-term fluctuations can lead to bankruptcy for normally viable farmers. Hence governments often introduce policies to reduce fluctuations in farm income including disaster relief, insurance schemes and income safety net or stabilisation programmes.

The timing, certainty and level of financial resource flows affect farmers' ability and actions with respect to the type, level and intensity of input use and of production and with respect to the acquisition of new technologies. Uncertainty and a short planning horizon may cause difficulties in achieving financial sustainability through, for example, a lack of investment in measures that reduce soil degradation, which may ultimately lead to higher costs and reduction of profitability.

At a broader level, the availability of financial resources influences the rate of structural adjustment in agriculture, including farm amalgamation and the exit and entry of farmers into the agricultural sector. The latter can lead to pressures for policy interventions (Lockie *et al.*, 1995; Supalla *et al.*, 1995). A farm that is well-managed, efficiently farmed and able to meet debt servicing requirements also has the ability to adapt and react to changes in a timely way (Shadbolt *et al.*, 1997).

Farmers for whom farming is not the main source of livelihood can have different attitudes towards farming and risk, and consequently may be more likely to take environmental quality into account in their farm management decisions. At the same time, part-time farmers may substitute farm chemicals for labour, which can have adverse environmental effects. Ownership patterns also influence farmers' attitudes towards the environment, as these patterns not only reflect present cultivation rights and obligations, but also embody a mixture of historical traditions and events.

Where markets are not considered to give correct signals regarding the level of environmental quality demanded by society, in some countries payments are given to farmers for the provision of environmental benefits or services or to reduce actions that have harmful environmental effects. Regulatory measures are also used, in particular relating to the use of pesticides, fertilisers and treatment of livestock manure through applying the polluter pays principle in all countries. All these policy measures have an impact on farm financial resources.

It is useful to identify drivers for both short-term (viability) and long-term (sustainability) goals. Farmers need to achieve a balance over time between the cost of capital and the benefits realised from agriculture's use of natural resources and the environment. This balance provides a link between the environmental, economic and social dimensions of sustainable development.

Within the Driving Force-State-Response (DSR) framework (see Background chapter), financial parameters are both driving forces and state indicators. As driving forces, they influence the decisions and behaviour of farmers in relation to the environment. In other words, they determine the "responses" farmers will make. As state indicators, they indicate the financial health of the farming operation.

2.   Indicators

Farm income

Definition

Trends in net farm income defined as the difference between the value of gross output and all expenses, including depreciation at the farm level from agricultural activities.

Method of calculation

Gross output is the sum of receipts from sales of crop and livestock products, direct payments, and receipts from agricultural activities. *Expenses* include expenditure on intermediate consumption (goods and services consumed in the production process, such as, seeds, animal feed, fertilisers, pesticides, repair and maintenance), taxes, compensation of employees (wages and salaries), rent, interest and depreciation (consumption of fixed capital). Net farm income from agricultural activities is calculated by subtracting the expenses from the gross output.

Recent trends

Over the past ten years net farm incomes have increased in many OECD countries, although for some countries farm incomes have decreased over recent years, and declined for most countries when adjusted for inflation in real terms (Figure 1). Annual changes in net farm income from agricultural activities, however, only provide a part of the farm income picture, as it is also important to examine farm household income, which takes into account income received from non-agricultural sources. This can include income received, for example, from non-commodity related farming activities, such as rural tourism, or include, income generated from non-agricultural investments (*e.g.* on the stockmarket) or by other members of the farm household not involved with the farm (*e.g.* a farmer's children living on the farm but working outside agriculture).

In *Australia* and *New Zealand*, long-term real net farm income is one of the key indicators for assessing sustainable agriculture (Commonwealth of Australia, 1998). The real net farm income is calculated by subtracting the real value of farm costs (marketing expenses, purchases of inputs, taxes, interest and other charges and wages paid by the business) from the real value of farm income (receipts from agricultural production, rents, interest and other revenues). The resulting real net farm income is the amount available to give a return on financial capital and human resources as well as maintain the productive capacity of the natural resource base.

An improvement to the real net farm income indicator being developed by *Australia* and *New Zealand* is the profit at full equity indicator. This indicator takes account of the depreciation costs of farm capital and the value of farm and partnership labour, but is difficult to calculate due to lack of data (Commonwealth of Australia, 1998). In *Australia*, over the 1990s there has been a slight downward trend in real net farm income, caused by the net effect of a declining terms of trade but higher productivity and declining farm numbers (Commonwealth of Australia, 1998).

Interpretation and links to other indicators

The net farm income indicator tracks financial viability, so that if financial returns are consistently negative any farming system will be unsustainable. Net farm income shows whether the farmer has made adjustments to the operating profit, cost of capital or both, in order to maintain financial sustainability. In addition to varying agricultural prices and policies, changes in farm income over time are affected by farm size, changes in technology and management practices, all of which affect input use, output levels and the productivity of resources.

Net farm income measures profitability and is one of the key indicators of sustainability in agriculture: it reflects the economic viability of the agricultural sector. Profitability is very important in environmental farm management decisions, evidence shows that farmers who believe they could do

Figure 1. **Nominal and real net farm income from agricultural activities: mid-1980s to mid-1990s**

Annual change in real net farm income

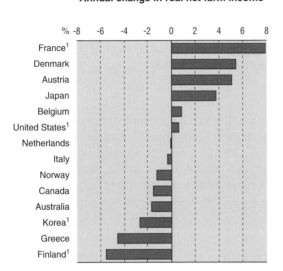

Percentage annual change in net farm income

	Period	Nominal income	Real income
France	1990-1995	10.3	7.9
Denmark	1985-1997	7.8	5.4
Austria	1985-1997	7.4	5.1
Japan	1985-1998	4.9	3.7
Belgium	1987-1994	2.9	0.8
United States	1991-1998	2.5	0.6
Netherlands	1988-1994	0.5	-0.1
Italy	1987-1995	4.5	-0.3
Norway	1985-1997	1.8	-1.2
Canada	1985-1997	1.2	-1.5
Australia	1988-1996	1.2	-1.6
Korea	1990-1998	1.2	-2.6
Greece	1986-1995	8.2	-4.6
Finland	1991-1996	-4.1	-5.6

1. Mid-1980s refer to early 1990s.
Note: See Annex Table 1.
Sources: OECD (1995*a*, 1995*b*, 1998, 1999); EUROSTAT (1998).

more to preserve the environment often feel too constrained by economic considerations to do so (see, for example, Beedell and Rehman, 1996; Rauniyar and Parker, 1996). If net income has not changed significantly this may not mean operating profits have not changed, because interest payments may have reduced as farm businesses repay debt to reduce commitments. Returns for owners' capital will also have decreased.

The standard way to calculate financial profit does not take into account the environmental externalities of farming (*e.g.* cost of water pollution, soil erosion, damage to biodiversity and habitat). Nor does it indicate the degree to which changes in technology or the quality of the resource base are responsible for changes in agricultural output and the efficiency of resources used in production. Assessing sustainability would be simplified if the value of land reflected its true productive potential, but often the degradation of the natural resource base of the farm is not recognised or included in short-term financial indicators of a farm's profitability (Agricultural Council of Australia and New Zealand, 1993; Hrubovcak *et al.*, 1995). Similarly, changes in farming practices that improve the resource base are not widely reflected in most farm financial indicators.

While the consumption of physical capital is deducted from the net farm income calculation, a similar deduction is not made for other types of capital, including farmland or natural resource stocks such as water quality and quantity. In addition, it is not adjusted for externalities associated with agricultural production, such as the degradation of water quality through farm nutrient and pesticide run-off. Research in the United States shows that the environmentally adjusted agricultural net income would be 6 to 8 per cent lower than the conventional income measurement (Hrubovcak *et al.*, 1995). In Australia, the production equivalent of degradation, *i.e.* the estimated decline from the value of production obtainable from current land uses had there been no degradation, is between 5 to 6 per cent of agricultural production or around A\$ 1.1 to 1.5 billion annually (US\$0.8-1.1 billion in 1994-95 values) (Commonwealth of Australia, 1995; and Industry Commission, 1996).

Measuring trends in farm income is of limited use unless they are compared with families' income expectations. If lifestyle expectations have been increasing at a faster rate than farm income, as would appear to be the case in New Zealand, then the financial equilibrium is at risk (Shadbolt, 2000). According to research carried out in New Zealand, the trend in farm income has, almost without exception, been positive, but it has not matched farmers' expectations. In addition, if more than half of household income comes from off-farm sources, as it does in many OECD countries, then it could be that off-farm income is financing unprofitable farming businesses.

The links between farm financial resources, farm management and environmental outcomes are shown in Figure 1 of the Farm Management chapter. Farm financial indicators must be seen in conjunction with indicators for other agri-environmental areas, especially farm management indicators, in order to assess the overall sustainability of the farm.

Related information

Farm household income

In many OECD countries a substantial share of farm household income is derived from off-farm activities. In some countries, even households whose main occupation is farming get a significant share of their income from non-agricultural activities. Off-farm income mainly includes wages from non-agricultural employment of household members, capital income and social transfers.

For a number of OECD countries, the average income of agricultural households exceeds that of the non-agricultural households (OECD, 1995a; OECD, 1998). In some cases, however, farm household incomes are substantially below, the average non-agricultural household income, such as in regions of Southern Europe, Mexico and Turkey.

Comparisons with non-farming incomes, however, can be misleading if recognition is not made of the amount of capital the owners have invested in the business. A notional cost of that capital (say 3 per cent) should be deducted from net farm income if comparisons are made to take into account the opportunity cost of that capital. Moreover, the information on farm household incomes does not account for possible differences in the size of agricultural relative to non-agricultural households, and it does not provide information on the composition of farm household income, which in part comes from non-agricultural sources.

Farm real estate values

Farm real estate values are indicators of the general economic health of the agricultural sector. Farm real estate consists of farmland and attached buildings and dwellings. In the United States, farm real estate accounts for more than 75 per cent of total farm assets (USDA, 1997). In addition to being the largest single investment item in a typical farmer's portfolio, farm real estate is the principal source of collateral for farm loans, enabling farmers to finance the purchase of additional farmland and equipment, or to finance current operating expenses. Large variations in farm real estate values alter the equity positions, creditworthiness, and borrowing capacity of those farm operators and landowners that hold a large proportion of their assets in farmland. It is not only to farmers that farm real estate values are important, they are also important to other landowners, prospective buyers, lenders, and the government.

Farm real estate values are affected by agricultural and non-agricultural factors. Net returns from agricultural use of farmland are a principal determinant of farmland values. Farmland values are also influenced by, for example, capital investment in farm structures, non-agricultural demand for farmland, interest rates, and government agricultural policies. In the United States, the value of buildings account for about 22 per cent of total farm real estate value, but the regional variations are significant (USDA, 1997). Trends in the value of farmland and buildings suggest that since 1989, the per-farm value of farmland and buildings has increased slightly more than the corresponding per-hectare value, on account of the increase in average farm size (Table 1).

Table 1. **Value of farmland and buildings: United States, 1989 to 1996**

	1989	1990	1991	1992	1993	1994	1995	1996	% change 1989-1996
Average per-hectare value of farmland and buildings in nominal dollars	1 649	1 684	1 736	1 760	1 817	1 931	2 054	2 198	33
Average per-hectare real (inflation adjusted) value of farmland and buildings, dollars	1 331	1 304	1 286	1 252	1 262	1 306	1 358	1 417	6
Average per-farm value of farmland and buildings in nominal dollars	304 260	313 668	325 855	330 818	345 098	368 659	390 581	417 761	37

Source: USDA (1997).

The potential to convert farmland to non-agricultural uses can increase the price of farmland well above its value in agricultural use. Various government policies influence the income derived from farmland, and hence its value. In addition to government commodity support programmes, farm credit programmes, zoning regulations, habitat protection laws, infrastructure development (such as roads and dams), environmental regulations, and property and income tax policy are also important (USDA, 1997). Research has shown that commodity programmes have increased farmland values relative to what they would have been in the absence of such programmes (Featherstone and Baker, 1988; Herriges *et al.*, 1992).

Agri-environmental expenditure

Public and private agri-environmental expenditure

Definition

Trends in public and private expenditure, both investment and current, on agri-environmental goods, services and conservation for improving environmental quality.

Method of calculation

The indicator, measured annually in nominal terms, takes account of: public expenditure on agri-environmental programmes/measures; existing financial support programmes for farmers adopting environmental farm management practices (cost-share programmes) and private financial resources from farmers and private groups directed at the environment. Since the government budget is generally available for public scrutiny, it is easier to obtain data on public expenditure on agri-environmental goods and services than on private expenditure.

Agri-environmental expenditure is defined as public and private expenditure aimed at changing farming practices (such as moving towards extensive or organic methods of production, or establishing voluntary community actions and groups), subsidising environmental investments (such as animal waste treatment facilities) or paying farmers for the provision of environmental benefits (such as landscape provision and for providing field margins to improve biodiversity). Public agri-environmental expenditure includes expenditure by federal/central, state/provincial and local governments.

Private agri-environmental expenditure includes expenditure by farmers and private groups, such as industry and environmental pressure groups. For example, the agro-food industry and supermarket-chains may compensate contract farmers for using environmentally sound production methods, while some companies producing mineral water pay farmers for using environmentally sound management practices to ensure that groundwater is not contaminated. Some environmental pressure groups also purchase land, which they rent out to farmers with the requirement that they use environmentally sound production methods.

Recent trends

New agri-environmental programmes were introduced in many OECD countries in the late 1980s and early 1990s and consequently the trend in *public* agri-environmental expenditure has shown a significant increase in most cases (Figure 2). Although the level of *private* agri-environmental expenditure is significant in several OECD countries, information on these expenditure items is seldom collected systematically. The distribution of agri-environmental expenditure across different areas varies between OECD countries (Figure 3). The differences in the distribution reflect environmental and policy priorities in the countries, so cross-country comparisons should be avoided.

Figure 2. **Public expenditure on agri-environmental goods, services and conservation: 1993 to 1998**

Index 1993 = 100

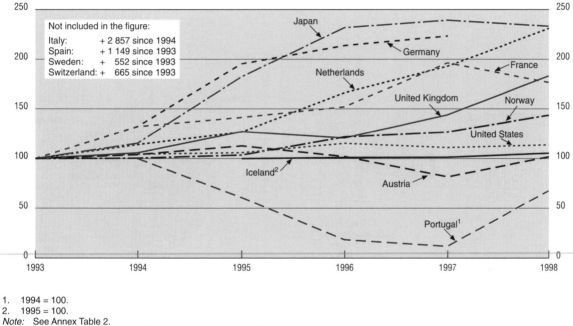

1.   1994 = 100.
2.   1995 = 100.
Note: See Annex Table 2.
Source: OECD Agri-environmental Indicators Questionnaire, 1999.

The expenditure on environmental payments in relation to the total expenditure under the Common Agricultural Policy (CAP) has been increasing in the United Kingdom (Figure 4). Shifts in the composition of CAP expenditure towards environmental payments is likely to be a move towards a more sustainable and better targeted method of support for rural areas. Although the share of environmental expenditure is still low, it is increasing rapidly.

Interpretation and links to other indicators

Total agri-environmental expenditure provides a general indication of the ability and preferences of a country's financial efforts to address environmental quality in agriculture. The expenditure figures must be interpreted carefully as expenditure may increase because environmental problems are being recognised, or because more environmental benefits are being provided.

Figure 3. **Shares of the main items in total agri-environmental expenditure: late 1990s**

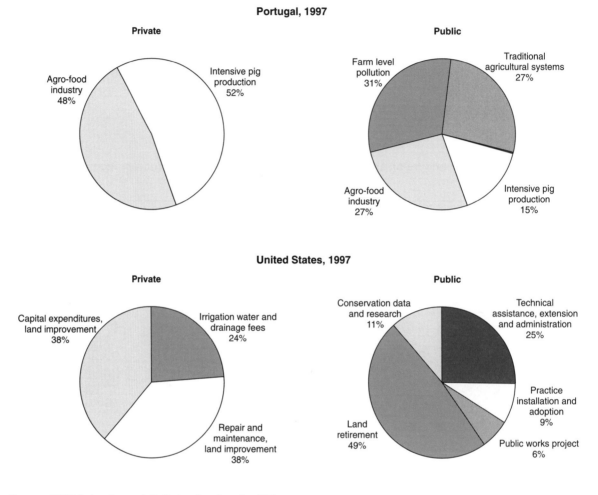

Portugal, 1997

Private

Agro-food industry 48%

Intensive pig production 52%

Public

Farm level pollution 31%

Traditional agricultural systems 27%

Agro-food industry 27%

Intensive pig production 15%

United States, 1997

Private

Capital expenditures, land improvement 38%

Irrigation water and drainage fees 24%

Repair and maintenance, land improvement 38%

Public

Conservation data and research 11%

Technical assistance, extension and administration 25%

Land retirement 49%

Practice installation and adoption 9%

Public works project 6%

Source: OECD Agri-environmental Indicators Questionnaire, 1999.

Moreover, for some countries agri-environmental expenditure may not include expenditure provided to farmers under environmental measures.

Low agri-environmental expenditure can be associated both with poor environmental quality (indicating lack of political concern and awareness of environmental issues), or with high environmental quality (indicating that there is no need for agri-environmental expenditure). In some cases high agri-environmental expenditure levels may also mean that farmers are being over-remunerated. Agri-environmental expenditure is not the equivalent to the cost of environmental damage.

Public agri-environmental expenditure is often directed to farmers to reduce harmful environmental effects, and to remunerate them for providing additional environmental goods and services. Private agri-environmental expenditure refers to expenditure by economic entities implementing pollution control measures and undertaking compliance activities. A description of public/private expenditure on biodiversity, habitat and landscape conservation in agriculture is provided in the Landscape chapter.

Figure 3. **Shares of the main items in total agri-environmental expenditure: late 1990s** *(cont.)*

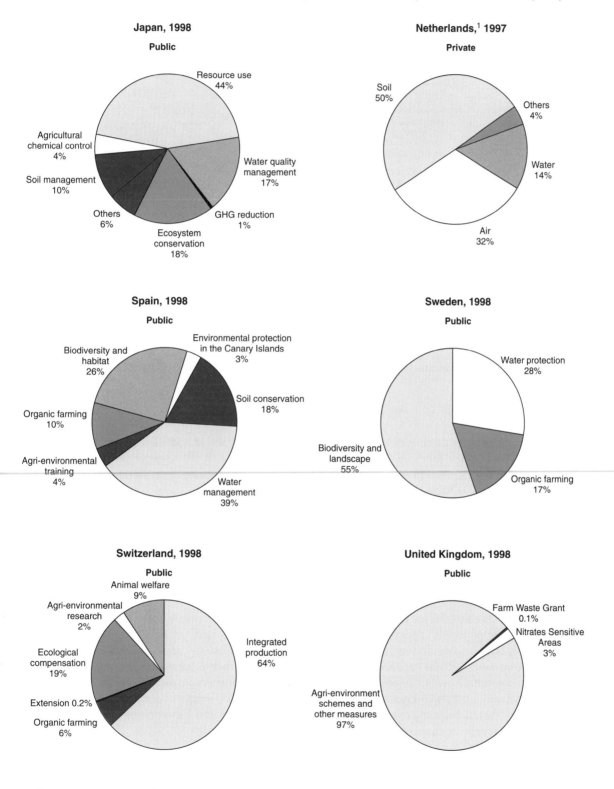

Japan, 1998

Public

Resource use
44%

Water quality
management
17%

GHG reduction
1%

Ecosystem
conservation
18%

Others
6%

Soil management
10%

Agricultural
chemical control
4%

Netherlands,[1] 1997

Private

Soil
50%

Others
4%

Water
14%

Air
32%

Spain, 1998

Public

Environmental protection
in the Canary Islands
3%

Biodiversity and
habitat
26%

Soil conservation
18%

Organic farming
10%

Agri-environmental
training
4%

Water
management
39%

Sweden, 1998

Public

Water protection
28%

Biodiversity and
landscape
55%

Organic farming
17%

Switzerland, 1998

Public

Animal welfare
9%

Agri-environmental
research
2%

Integrated
production
64%

Ecological
compensation
19%

Extension 0.2%

Organic farming
6%

United Kingdom, 1998

Public

Farm Waste Grant
0.1%

Nitrates Sensitive
Areas
3%

Agri-environment
schemes and
other measures
97%

1. Only concerns management for landscape, and not expenditure covered under environmental pressures.
Source: OECD Agri-environmental Indicators Questionnaire, 1999.

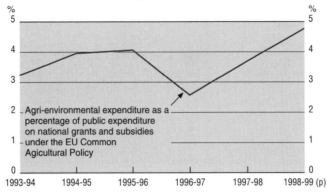

Figure 4. **Payments to farmers for agri-environmental purposes:**
United Kingdom, 1993 to 1999

p: Provisional.
Source: MAFF (2000).

Expenditure on agri-environmental research

Definition

Share of public and private sector expenditure on agri-environmental research in total agricultural research expenditure.

Method of calculation

Agri-environmental research is defined as research primarily aimed at addressing environmental issues in agriculture. This includes, for example, research aimed at ameliorating the negative impacts of agriculture on the environment (*e.g.* pollution of water from pesticides), or at enhancing agricultural activities that have positive environmental impacts (*e.g.* habitat conservation).

Public sector agri-environmental research expenditure includes, for most countries, research funding by central, state and local governments, and publicly funded universities and research institutes. Private sector research expenditure covers research mainly by the agro-food industry, private research institutes and universities, although few countries have data on private research expenditure.

Recent trends

For those OECD countries for which data are available, the share of public agri-environmental research expenditure in relation to total agricultural research expenditure has been relatively stable since the early 1990s, generally with a share above 20 per cent. A significant increase in the share of agri-environmental research expenditure in total research expenditure has occurred in *Japan* and *Switzerland* (Figure 5). There are some country specific differences in these data, *Japan*, for example, only includes expenditure by the central government. The composition of agri-environmental research expenditure also varies across OECD countries, but in general cover research on soil, land, water and biodiversity. There is very little information on private sector expenditure on agri-environmental research.

Interpretation and links to other indicators

Historically, new technologies developed through agricultural research and development have increased productivity and output, and been essential in meeting the growing demand for food and

Figure 5. **Share of public agri-environmental research expenditure in total agricultural research expenditure: 1985 to mid/late 1990s**

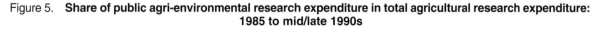

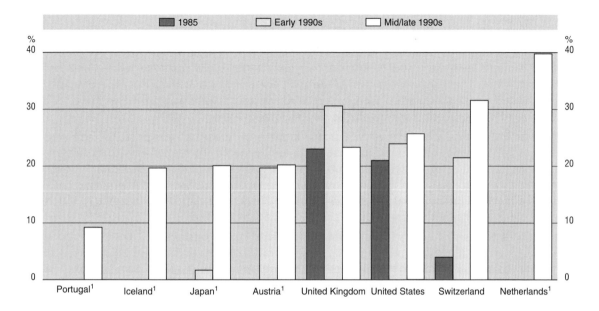

1. Data not available for all periods.
Note: Early 1990s: 1991 (United Kingdom, United States and Switzerland); 1993 (Japan); 1994 (Austria).
Mid/late 1990s: 1995 (United Kingdom); 1996 (United States); 1997 (Switzerland, Portugal); 1998 (Austria, Iceland, Japan, Netherlands).
Source: OECD Agri-environmental Indicators Questionnaire, 1999.

industrial crops. The objective of agri-environmental research, on the other hand, is to improve the environmental performance in agriculture.

Agri-environmental research includes a wide range of topics, such as research on environmentally sound farm management practices (*e.g.* integrated pest management, conservation tillage, enhanced nutrient management and precision farming), and the environmental effects of farm management practices (*e.g.* effect on non-target species, soil erosion and nutrient leaching). Agri-environmental research expenditure measures investment in the capacity of the agricultural sector to build and transfer knowledge to improve on-farm management practices. Although it can be assumed that more agri-environmental research is beneficial for the environment, some caution is necessary with this assumption.

A more precise definition of agri-environmental research would help to improve the interpretation of the indicator. Definitions of what constitutes environmental expenditure vary across countries, for example, some include animal welfare and research expenditure on genetically modified organisms. Research funding levels do not necessarily reveal the relevance of particular agri-environmental issues. For example, it is not always apparent if research outcomes support sustainable agriculture objectives, whether the research is of high quality, or whether farmers will accept and apply the research findings. The indicator could be further developed to reflect at least some of these aspects, particularly by linking them to farm management indicators.

3. Future challenges

Net farm income does not reveal whether the farm business is financially sustainable or not in the long term. In order to assess financial sustainability, it is important to look at the *farm financial equilibrium*, which is the equilibrium between net operating profit after tax (NOPAT) and the extracted cost of

73

capital.[3] The total net returns from a farmland-based business include those generated from the farming business (NOPAT) and those generated by the property market (capital gains/losses). In reality, a non-farming agricultural land owner would require a cash rental return in addition to any capital gain and a tenant farmer would expect to pay a rent for the farmland operated. The rent can only be paid if net operating profits after tax are generated by the farming business.[4]

Total net returns must at least meet the weighted average cost of capital (WACC) of that business. The WACC is made up of the cost of debt (net of any tax credits if such costs are tax deductible) and the cost of equity. The cost of equity consists of the cash component, extracted from the business by the owners over and above that paid to them as a reward for labour and management in the calculation of the NOPAT, and the non-cash component, the capital gains or losses.

If the NOPAT is consistently negative but the farming business has an operating cash surplus the business is unable to meet the imputed value of its family labour. This is unlikely to be sustainable as at some point either the next generation returning to the farm, or its new owners when it is sold, will not be prepared to work for less than they are worth. If the cash, or "extracted" cost of equity is consistently negative the family is removing less for its labour and management than it is worth. While this is logical in the short term to ensure the cost of debt is met, it is not sustainable.

If the extracted cost of equity is zero then the farmland-based business can be redefined as a farm household. That is a place from which income is generated, either on or off-farm, but from which no equity return is required from the capital invested other than capital gain. There is a risk implicit in relying only on capital gain for a return on equity. This risk may not be acceptable to future generations or new owners of the property.

Research reported by *Switzerland* explored varying options of how indicators on farm financial resources could be developed, recognising the difficulties involved in comparing countries for items such as the debt/equity ratio, when definitions vary so much according to accountancy rules, type of farm and country. The particular problem areas identified were definitions concerning the farm, valuation and depreciation. The research also pointed out the difficulties that would arise from attempting to draw a direct link between similar environmental indicators (*e.g.* a decrease in phosphorous surplus) and net farm and off-farm income in a comparison between countries. The use of financial indicators to measure the effect of participation in environmentally relevant programmes could be helpful in this respect.

Adjusting for changes in agriculture natural resource use and pollution could help to further develop the indicator on farm financial resources. This might include, for example, monetary estimates of the cost of groundwater reserve depletion and nutrient pollution from agricultural activities. The indicator would then have the potential to show whether the farm is maintaining its financial resources at the cost of resource depletion or pollution. A similar adjustment could be made for environmental benefits, although this is at present more difficult than quantifying resource depletion. This sustainable cost approach extends farm financial equilibrium to include resource management. A positive trend would indicate that the farm is not only maintaining financial and environmental resources but also reinvesting for growth.

Developing the farm financial resource indicators to take into account natural resource depletion, pollution, and environmental goods and services provided by agriculture, would help in research to estimate agricultural productivity indices net of these environmental externalities. This work could also help toward adjusting national agricultural economic accounts for the environmental costs and benefits generated by agricultural activities.[5]

NOTES

1. The use of environmentally sound farming technology, such as precision farming, can reduce adverse environmental impacts. Precision farming uses advanced technology, such as the global positioning system (GPS) to collect data at precise locations, optical scanners to detect soil organic matter and the geographical information system (GIS) (Hrubovcak *et al.*, 1999).

2. For an examination of support provided to farmers through agricultural policies, see OECD (2000).

3. The net operating surplus approach used, for example, in the OECD Agricultural Accounts (1997) is the same as the net operating profit after tax approach, when the reward for family labour and management is included in the compensation for employees as an imputed cost.

4. Research on the farm financial equilibrium approach has been developed in New Zealand, see Shadbolt *et al.* (1997); Shadbolt and Stewart (1998); and Shadbolt (2000).

5. The issue of adjusting agricultural productivity measures and national agricultural economic accounts for environmental externalities generated by agriculture is explored by Ball and Nehring (1994); and Gray (1993).

Annex Table 1. Nominal net farm income from agricultural activities: 1984 to 1998

US$, Calendar year

	1984	1985	1986	1987	1988	1989	1990	1991	1992	1993	1994	1995	1996	1997	1998
Australia[1]	..	..	..	..	36 120	26 663	4 308	6 378	10 464	16 951	11 989	32 589	29 517	..	..
Austria	..	10 229	..	18 981	..	20 943	..	26 805	..	26 340	30 776	40 470	34 015	28 197	..
Belgium	..	..	..	29 927	44 388	38 208	46 561	45 389	47 993	45 938	43 064	..	..	..	..
Canada	7 502	7 532	7 888	9 648	7 948	8 494	8 136	8 607	8 352	10 814	8 493	9 626	9 257	9 791	..
Czech Republic	..	..	..	..	..	3 877	..	..	2 645	..	..	..	..	..	..
Denmark[1]	16 807	13 736	17 082	17 392	21 242	27 615	28 598	29 219	26 785	26 750	32 043	39 117	42 530	37 295	..
Finland	..	..	..	..	..	..	..	23 216	20 953	15 568	16 393	21 044	18 814	..	..
France	..	..	..	..	..	..	31 063	..	..	..	..	50 705	..	..	..
Germany[1]	5 876	..	..	..	..	..	11 543	..	14 246	13 103	31 195	37 664	37 094	33 254	..
Greece	..	..	7 059	..	9 663	..	..	..	..	..	15 404	18 579	..	..	..
Hungary	..	..	..	..	..	..	..	..	..	..	..	86	58	..	..
Iceland	..	..	..	..	..	..	..	..	..	..	..	..	..	..	..
Ireland	11 723	..	..	19 643	..	..	24 296	30 104	29 689	25 036	26 710	31 893	..	..	..
Italy	4 484	4 465	6 002	6 526	7 435	8 057	8 033	8 329	11 291	11 615	15 584	15 331	12 754	9 942	8 913
Japan	..	4 247	..	..	..	..	8 848	9 595	9 431	10 502	12 838	13 571	13 471	10 735	6 394
Korea	..	..	..	..	..	..	..	..	..	..	..	..	..	..	..
Luxembourg	..	..	..	..	..	..	..	..	..	..	..	..	..	..	..
Mexico	..	..	..	..	..	..	..	..	..	..	..	..	..	..	..
Netherlands	..	..	..	..	58 931	66 058	77 157	77 420	72 921	59 206	76 566	83 547	..	..	..
New Zealand	..	..	..	..	..	..	..	..	..	..	..	..	..	..	..
Norway	19 754	19 351	22 119	26 437	27 129	29 551	34 882	32 804	32 119	30 630	26 146	28 877	29 068	25 791	..
Poland	..	..	..	..	..	..	..	..	..	..	..	..	..	..	..
Portugal	3 411	3 128	3 612	3 770	2 666	3 044	..	..	..	..	..	..	..	..	..
Spain	..	..	..	..	..	..	23 453	..	..	..	..	..	..	..	..
Sweden	..	..	..	..	..	..	..	..	..	..	..	..	..	..	..
Switzerland	..	..	..	..	..	..	..	..	..	45 809	47 113	47 453	49 607	..	..
Turkey	..	..	..	..	..	..	..	..	..	..	..	..	..	..	..
United Kingdom	..	..	..	..	..	..	..	..	..	..	..	..	..	..	..
United States	..	..	..	..	..	..	..	5 810	7 180	4 815	4 376	4 720	7 906	6 205	7 106

.. Not available.

1. Data are for fiscal year (July to June).

Source: OECD (1995a, 1995b, 1998, 1999); EUROSTAT (1998).

Annex Table 2. **Public expenditure on agri-environmental goods, services and conservation:[1] 1985 to 1998**

Million US$

	1985	1986	1987	1988	1989	1990	1991	1992	1993	1994	1995	1996	1997	1998
Austria	..	..	..	..	..	..	55	228	292	309	380	328	228	279
France	..	..	1	1	0	1	4	9	194	260	310	325	368	328
Germany	..	..	..	..	..	10	35	72	264	357	596	621	563	543
Iceland[2]	..	..	..	..	..	..	..	..	..	..	3	3	3	3
Italy	..	..	..	..	..	..	..	..	..	27	196	349	459	724
Japan	..	..	..	..	..	..	..	..	74	93	159	175	162	146
Netherlands	1	2	3	5	5	8	9	11	11	13	17	21	21	25
Norway	..	..	..	..	2	212	286	436	415	419	481	555	527	560
Portugal	..	..	..	..	..	..	..	..	..	37	25	7	4	23
Spain	..	..	..	..	..	..	..	..	16	20	39	73	101	152
Sweden[3]	..	..	..	3	7	16	34	47	40	40	137	246	182	217
Switzerland[4]	..	1	1	2	1	12	4	27	74	125	232	503	506	504
United Kingdom[5]	..	..	..	..	15	20	104	132	143	154	191	179	224	289
United States	1 398	1 364	1 390	1 436	2 143	2 728	3 021	3 467	3 631	3 793	3 843	4 183	4 027	4 121

.. Not available.
1. Research expenditure are not included.
2. Only includes expenditures on soil conservation.
3. From 1995 onwards, the data include programmes co-financed by EU.
4. Expenditures on agri-environmental research is only available every two years.
5. Data are for financial year (April to March).
Source: OECD Agri-environmental Indicators Questionnaire, 1999.

BIBLIOGRAPHY

Agricultural Council of Australia and New Zealand (1993),
Sustainable Agriculture: Tracking the Indicators for Australia and New Zealand, Standing Committee on Agriculture and Resource Management (SCARM), CSIRO Publications, Victoria, Australia.

Ball, E. and R. Nehring (1994),
"Building a Better Agricultural Productivity Index", *Agricultural Outlook* AO-205, pp. 2-12.

Beedell, J.D.C. and T. Rehman (1996),
"A Meeting of Minds for Farmers and Conservationists? Some Initial Evidence on Attitudes towards Conservation from Bedfordshire", *Farm Management*, Vol. 9, No. 6, pp. 305-313.

Commonwealth of Australia (1995),
Sustaining the Agricultural Resource Base, 12th Meeting of the Prime Minister's Science and Engineering Council, Office of the Chief Scientist, Department of the Prime Minister and Cabinet, Canberra, Australia.

Commonwealth of Australia (1998),
Sustainable Agriculture – Assessing Australia's Recent Performance, A Report to the Standing Committee on Agriculture and Resource Management (SCARM) of the National Collaborative Project on Indicators for Sustainable Agriculture, SCARM Technical Report No. 70, CSIRO Publishing, Victoria, Australia.

Culver, D. and R. Seecharan (1986),
"Factors that influence the adoption of soil conservation technologies", *Canadian Farm Economics*, Vol. 20, No. 2, pp. 9-13.

EUROSTAT [Statistical Office of the European Communities] (1998),
Income of the Agricultural Households Sector, 1997 Report, Luxembourg.

Featherstone, A.M. and T.G. Baker (1988),
"Effects of Reduced Price and Income Supports on Farmland Rent and Value", *North Central Journal of Agricultural Economics*, Vol. 10, pp. 177-190.

Gray, R. (1993),
Accounting for the Environment: Green Accounting, The Cromwell Press Ltd, Melksham, United Kingdom.

Herriges, J., N.E. Barickman and J.F. Shogren (1992),
"The Implicit Value of Corn Base Acreage", *American Journal of Agricultural Economics*, February, pp. 50-58.

Hrubovcak, J., M.L. Blanc and B.K. Eakin (1995),
Accounting for the Environment in Agriculture, Natural Resources and Environment Division, Economic Research Service, US Department of Agriculture, Technical Bulletin No. 1847, Washington, DC., United States.

Hrubovcak, J., U. Vasavada and J.E. Aldy (1999),
Green Technologies for a More Sustainable Agriculture, Resource Economics Division, Economic Research Service, US Department of Agriculture, Agricultural Information Bulletin No. 752, Washington, DC., United States.

Industry Commission (1996),
Land Degradation and the Australian Agricultural Industry, Staff Information Paper, Australian Government Publishing Service, Canberra, Australia.

Lockie, S., A. Mead, F. Vanclay and B. Butler (1995),
"Factors Encouraging the Adoption of More Sustainable Crop Rotations in South-East Australia: Profit, Sustainability, Risk and Stability", *Journal of Sustainable Agriculture*, Vol. 6, No. 1.

MAFF [Ministry of Agriculture, Fisheries and Food] (2000),
Towards Sustainable Agriculture – A Pilot Set of Indicators, London, United Kingdom. Available at: *www.maff.gov.uk/* [Farming > Sustainable Agriculture].

OECD (1995a),
"A Review of Farm Household Incomes in OECD Countries", in OECD, *Adjustment in OECD Agriculture: Issues and Policy Responses*, Paris, France.

OECD (1995*b*),

A *Review of Farm Household Incomes in* OECD *Countries*, General Distribution document [OCDE/GD(95)97], Paris, France. Available at: *www.oecd.org/* [Documentation > 1995 > Reference Components > OCDE > OCDE/GD].

OECD (1997),

Economic Accounts for Agriculture – 1997 *Edition*, Paris, France.

OECD (1998),

Agricultural Policy Reform: Stocktaking of Achievements, A discussion paper for the meeting of the OECD Committee for Agriculture at Ministerial level, 5-6 March, Paris, France. Available at: *www.oecd.org/agr/ministerial/* [Documentation > Discussion papers for the meeting].

OECD (1999),

Distributional Effects of Agricultural Support in Selected OECD *Countries*, General Distribution document [AGR/CA(99)8/FINAL], Paris, France. Available at: *www.oecd.org/* [Documentation > 1999 > Reference Components > AGR].

OECD (2000),

Agricultural Policies in OECD *Countries: Monitoring and Evaluation 2000*, Paris, France.

Rauniyar, G.P. and W.J. Parker (1996),

Constraints to farm level adoption of new sustainable technologies and management practices in New Zealand pastoral agriculture, Research Report by the Ministry of Agriculture and Forestry, Wellington, New Zealand. Available at: *www.maf.govt.nz/MAFnet/publications/susconst/constraints.htm*.

Shadbolt, N.M. (2000),

Sustainable Business Growth, Brochure, Ministry of Agriculture and Forestry, Wellington, New Zealand.

Shadbolt, N.M. and A. Stewart (1998),

Indicators Of Sustainability For Farming Businesses And Families: An Examination Of The Issues Relating To Land Tenure And Their Effect On Sustainable Management Practices, Policy Publication, Ministry of Agriculture and Forestry, Wellington, New Zealand.

Shadbolt, N.M., S.D. Morriss and T.C. Kelly (1997),

Financial indicators of sustainability for farming businesses and families: a conceptual model to relate these indicators to those used for environmental and social sustainability, Policy Publication, Ministry of Agriculture and Forestry, Wellington, New Zealand.

Supalla R.J., R.A. Selly, S. Bredeweg and D. Watts (1995),

"Adoption of nitrogen and water management practices to improve water quality", *Journal of Soil and Water Conservation*, Vol. 50, No. 1, pp. 77-82.

USDA [United States Department of Agriculture] (1997),

Agricultural Resources and Environmental Indicators, 1996-97, Agricultural Handbook No. 712, Natural Resources and Environment Division, Economic Research Service, Washington, DC., United States. Available at: *www.ers.usda.gov/* [Briefing Rooms > Agricultural Resources and Environmental Indicators].

Part II

FARM MANAGEMENT AND THE ENVIRONMENT

1. FARM MANAGEMENT

Chapter 1

FARM MANAGEMENT

HIGHLIGHTS

Context

Environmental conditions and farming systems vary within and across OECD countries and, consequently, best farm management practices vary from one region to another. Farm management decisions are influenced by environmental regulations, agricultural support measures, investments in research, education and extension services and site-specific environmental conditions. Information on farm management practices, and how these practices affect the environment and meet compulsory, regulatory or voluntary standards, is an important tool for policy makers.

There can be trade-offs in implementing environmentally sound management practices. Reducing soil erosion, for example, whereby farmers move from conventional to reduced or no-tillage in crop production, can be achieved if weeds are controlled with herbicides. An environmental side-effect of these practices is a likely change in water movement in the soil, with no-tillage leading to increasing infiltration and percolation of nutrients such as nitrate to the water table compared with conventional tillage. In addition, the increase in herbicide use may cause pesticide leaching. Thus, the objective of lowering soil erosion through no-tillage may lead to some negative environmental effects.

Indicators and recent trends

Farm management indicators have the potential to help policy makers take into account the linkages and trade-offs between different management practices and their impact on the environment, including: whole farm management involving the overall farming system; and farm management aimed at specific practices related to nutrients, pests, soils, and irrigation.

Concerning *whole farm management indicators*, the share of farms with environmental *whole farm plans* is increasing, but cross-country data is limited. Also the share of agricultural area under *organic farming* has increased significantly over the past ten years, but from a very low base and with wide variations among OECD countries. Many countries now encourage conversion to and maintenance of organic farming by providing financial compensation to farmers for any losses incurred during conversion.

Nutrient management indicators include the share of farms with nutrient management plans and the frequency of soil nutrient tests. Although many countries have developed nutrient management plans, there is little quantitative information available, however, and soil tests are conducted in most OECD countries at regular intervals.

Pest management indicators measure the share of cultivated agricultural area that is not treated with pesticides and the share of cultivated agricultural area under integrated pest management. Based on limited information, for a few countries it appears both practices have been used more widely during the 1990s.

Soil and land management indicators measure the number of days in a year that the soil is covered with vegetation. The greater the cumulative soil cover, the greater the protection from soil erosion, compaction and run-off and the contribution, in general, to biodiversity. Many OECD countries have policy initiatives to increase soil cover and promote environmental land management practices. In a number of countries, soil cover days have increased since the mid-1980s and now exceed 250 days per year, but in a few countries days of soil cover has decreased.

Irrigation and water management indicators measure the share of irrigation water applied by different irrigation technologies, from the least efficient methods (*e.g.* flooding) to technologies (*e.g.* drip-emitters) that use water more efficiently. For the few countries where information on changes in irrigation technologies exist, this suggests a shift toward technologies that use water more efficiently. Moreover, water is not considered a scarce resource in many OECD countries and consequently issues related to irrigation efficiency are of less importance in those countries.

1. Background

Policy context

Farm management decisions are influenced by environmental regulations, agricultural support measures, investments in research, education and extension services and site-specific environmental conditions. Information on farm management practices, how these practices affect the environment, and how they compare with recommended (or legislated) practices and standards can contribute to policy making.

Many OECD countries have developed guidelines for farmers on best management practices (BMP) and other reference material as a way of encouraging environmentally sound farm management. Countries also conduct research and provide extension advice and programme support to encourage the adoption of BMPs. In some countries (e.g. Switzerland) payments to farmers are linked to adoption of specific management practices (e.g. integrated pest management, maintenance of semi-natural habitats and minimum soil cover). In others (e.g. the United States), cross-compliance provisions are in place which withhold financial support from producers who do not comply with certain management practices, such as restrictions on ploughing erodible cropland or draining sensitive wetlands.

In addition to public sector bodies, voluntary groups and private professional farm organisations have established guidelines on best management practices in many OECD countries. Other private sector initiatives include schemes instigated by the agro-food industry and supermarket-chains, which sometimes have self-generated standards that require contract farmers to use environmentally sound farm management practices, such as integrated pest management.

There can be trade-offs in policies to encourage environmentally sound management practices. For example, a policy objective to reduce soil erosion by encouraging farmers to move from conventional tillage to reduced or no-tillage in crop production, can be achieved if weeds are controlled with herbicides. An environmental side-effect of these tillage practices is a likely change in water movement in the soil, with no-tillage increasing infiltration and percolation of nutrients such as nitrate leaching to the watertable when compared with conventional tillage. In addition, the increase in herbicide use may cause pesticide leaching. Thus the objective of lowering soil erosion through no-tillage may lead to some negative environmental effects.

Environmental conditions and farming systems vary within and across countries, and best farm management practices vary from one region to another. Consequently, it is difficult to compile an exhaustive list of best management practices that would be valid across OECD countries.

Certain international environmental agreements have implications for farm management practices, for example, the UN Framework Convention on Climate Change to reduce greenhouse gas emissions from agriculture, and the Convention on Biological Diversity. Within the European Union organic farming is harmonised under Regulation 2092/91, while under the International Organic Agriculture Movements, (IFOAM) guidelines have been established for marketing organic products internationally[1] Also important in an international context are the International Organisation for Standardisation (ISO) series of voluntary management standards ISO 9000 (quality management) and 14000 (environmental management). These standards are being developed to improve management standards internationally, including agricultural management practices.[2]

Farm management indicators are closely linked to indicators on farm financial resources and rural viability. They capture the broader economic and social elements of sustainable agriculture, in addition to the environment. Farm management capacity (covering the institutional aspects of agriculture) and on-farm management practices cover the environmental dimension of sustainable agriculture; farm financial resources are related to the economic dimension; while rural viability covers mainly the social dimension. Issues related to farm management capacity, farm financial resources and rural viability are discussed in other chapters of this report. The linkages between these indicator areas in the context of environmental farm management plans and their impact on the environment are illustrated in Figure 1.

List of Figures

BACKGROUND:
OBJECTIVES AND SCOPE OF THE REPORT

Figure 1.   **Linkages between OECD agri-environmental indicator areas
related to farm management**

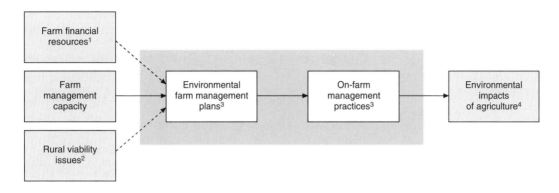

1.   See Farm Financial Resources chapter of this Report.
2.   See Box 2 in the Contextual Information and Indicators chapter of this Report.
3.   Management plans and practices are discussed in this chapter.
4.   See the following chapters of this Report: Nutrient Use, Pesticide Use and Risks, Water Use, Soil Quality, Water Quality, Land Conservation, Greenhouse Gases, Biodiversity, Wildlife Habitats and Landscapes.
Source: OECD Secretariat.

Farm management indicators can provide an early indication of likely changes in the direction of environmental impacts sometimes well before they can be measured by other indicators, such as those pertaining to soil and water quality. They can also serve as a proxy for "state" indicators where the latter are difficult or costly to monitor. Measuring farming practices is often more practical and cheaper than measuring actual changes in the environment. Monitoring the trends in management practice indicators alongside appropriate "state" indicators, such as water quality, can also help policy makers to evaluate directly the success of policies aimed at environmental improvement.

Environmental context

Farm management practices have a direct impact on the environment, both on and off the farm.[3] For example, switching from continuous maize or maize-soyabean rotation to maize-alfalfa rotation may reduce soil erosion by 40 per cent. Similarly, maize-soyabean rotation may reduce nitrogen run off by 10-30 per cent relative to the continuous maize alternative. Some case studies have shown that herbicide run-off can be reduced by about 70 per cent with no-till and mulch-till practices whereas over 40 per cent reduction can be obtained with ridge-till.

The key environmental and scientific processes underpinning each of the farm management areas discussed below, are elaborated in greater detail in many other chapters of this Report. Only a brief outline of the environmental impacts of each farm management area is described in this section, and summarised in Table 1.

Whole farm management focuses on the long-term, comprehensive view of the use of farm resources, including land, water, biological and atmospheric resources. It enables a farmer to view the farm operation as a system whose management explicitly takes into account not only the diverse elements of the operation, but also their linkages and relationships covering all those elements – soil, water, air, biodiversity, habitat and landscape – shown in Table 1. Whole farm management can include conventional and organic farming systems.

An adequate supply of nutrients is required to grow crops and livestock fodder. Sound **nutrient management** involves understanding crop needs and nutrient availability at different growth stages, in

Table 1.   **Environmental impacts of farm management practices**

Soil and land	Environmental impacts:
Nutrient management	– Improving soil quality requires adequate fertility. – Crop and residue cover enhanced. – Soil erosion and compaction reduced by soil cover.
Pest management	– Reducing pesticide residues left in soil, by lowering the quantity of pesticides applied and using less toxic and less persistent pesticides.
Soil and land management	– Wind and water erosion from tillage, through inadequate crop or residue cover. – Increased water erosion from failure to maintain terraces and other erosion control structures. – Soil translocation downslope by tillage equipment. – Compaction from loss of organic matter, excessive tillage. – Reduced infiltration and increased run-off as a result of compaction. – Less soil cover when yields reduced by erosion and compaction. – Lower organic matter, increased run-off, erosion and compaction when soil cover is reduced. – Field consolidation removes hedgerows, walls and woodlots which serve as windbreaks and can have value as landscape features
Irrigation and Water management	*Irrigation*: – Increases crop yields, soil cover and residues. – Increases water erosion if poorly applied to uneven fields. – Decreases wind erosion. – Causes waterlogging if excess water is applied on poorly drained soils. – Leads to salinity on poorly drained saline soils, or if using saline water. *Drainage*: – Leads to more intensively cultivated crops and less soil cover. – Surface drainage increases water erosion.

Water	Environmental impacts:
Nutrient management	– Eutrophication from nitrogen (N) and phosphorus (P) in run-off into surface waters. – Ammonia/acid rain deposition of N into surface waters. – Nitrate (NO_3) leaching into groundwater can occur under poorly managed irrigation.
Pest management	– Pesticides carried by run-off/sediment into surface water after application. – Aerosol and vapour drift into surface water. – Spraying over drainage channels. – Spillage during filling and cleaning of spray equipment – Pesticides leached into groundwater.
Soil and land management	– Increased run-off and water erosion carries nutrients, pesticides and sediment into surface water causing eutrophication and contamination. – Wind erosion deposits soil and contaminants into water. – Livestock in riparian zones contaminate water with manure and sediment. – Buffer strips along watercourses trap sediments and contaminants.
Irrigation and water management	*Irrigation*: – Return flows carry pesticides and nutrients into surface and groundwater, depending on nutrient and pest management practices. – Increases leaching of nitrate (NO_3) to groundwater. – Leaches salts from saline soils into drainage waters. *Drainage*: – Surface methods increase erosion and run-off of nutrients and pesticides. – Subsurface drains intercept leached nitrate and pesticides and divert them to surface water. – Construction and maintenance of open drains leads to turbidity and sedimentation downstream.

Air	Environmental impacts:
Nutrient management	– Denitrification adds to greenhouse gas emissions and ozone depletion. – Volatilisation of ammonia (NH_3) into air from fertilisers and manure. – Odours from manure storage and spreading.
Pest management	– Vapour from volatilisation of spray materials, which can be long-range. – Spray drift. – Wind erosion of soil particles contaminated with pesticide residues.
Soil and land management	– Denitrification increased in compacted and moist soils, NO_x and greenhouse effects. – Reduced air quality from wind-blown soil can aggravate human respiratory conditions and allergies.

Table 1.　**Environmental impacts of farm management practices** (*cont.*)

Air (*cont.*	Environmental impacts:
Irrigation and water management	*Irrigation*: – Increases denitrification, NO_x and greenhouse effects. – Reduces volatilisation of ammonia (NH_3) and wind erosion. *Drainage*: – Reduces denitrification. – Increases volatilisation of NH_3 and wind erosion.

Biodiversity, Habitat and Landscape	Environmental impacts:
Nutrient management	– Eutrophication affects fish and aquatic plant species. – Minimum nutrient supply necessary for productivity of aquatic ecosystems. – Species diversity in low-intensity production, for example, high use of N fertilisers may reduce rare wild flowers in meadows.
Pest management	– Direct alteration of mix of species as a result of elimination of target pest. – Direct alteration of species from pesticide effect on non-target organisms. – Effect on biodiversity of development of pesticide-resistant mutants. – Habitat and feed for organisms that rely on target species.
Soil and land management	– Eroded sediments damage fish spawning areas. – Turbidity of water affects aquatic species competition and survival. – Soil cover by vegetation and residues provides habitat for many species. – Crop rotation incorporating forages provides habitat for many species. – Hedgerows and trees provide corridors for wildlife between larger habitats.
Irrigation and water management	*Irrigation*: – Increases soil cover, habitat and food for variety of organisms. – Reservoirs and canals provide habitat for waterfowl and fish. – Wetlands created by seepage and drainage from canals provide habitat. – Pumping from ponds and wells can damage or destroy aquatic habitats. *Drainage*: – Encourages cultivated field crops with less soil cover and habitat. – Construction and maintenance of outlets lower water tables and reduce habitat by draining wetlands.

Note:　Whole farm management covers all the elements shown in this table.
Source:　OECD Secretariat.

order to match nutrient applications efficiently to absorption by the crop roots. It also requires a good understanding of the costs of different nutrient sources and handling options.

The environmental effects associated with nutrient management stem from "shortage" of nutrients or from "surplus" nutrient losses from agriculture (Table 1). Nutrient "shortage" means that nutrient supply does not match crop uptake, which can reduce, for example, soil quality. Nutrient "surplus", on the other hand, can result in nutrient leaching. Nutrient management decisions with potential environmental impacts include timing, placement, forms and rates of fertiliser and manure applications; crop rotations; manure storage and handling; and soil tests to provide accurate readings of soil nutrient levels.

Losses of agricultural production due to pests can jeopardise farm economic viability (Table 1). Pesticides are generally used when the financial benefit, measured by the value of increased yield or crop quality, exceeds the cost of applying the pesticide. **Pest management** decisions mainly involve applying the mix of pesticides more efficiently and choosing between biological pest control methods and pesticides. Where pesticides are used, the objective of reducing the cost of pesticide use is achieved through decisions which involve selecting the most appropriate pesticides, and the timing and method of application.

Insect monitoring is widely used to determine the timing and frequency of insecticide application, and the same method can be applied for fungal diseases. Fungicides are also often applied to seed as an insurance against subsequent cool, wet conditions that would encourage fungal disease of the seedlings. The decision to use these fungicides is often made by the seed producer, and it can be difficult to obtain untreated seeds.

87

Examples of non-chemical pest control methods include crop rotation; use of crop plants that are allopathic (plants whose roots and residues produce exudates that suppress the growth of many other plants, including weeds) and antagonistic (plants that produce compounds that repel many insect and other pest organisms); and encouragement of predatory organisms.

Integrated pest management (IPM) uses a combination of practices to reduce the need for chemical pesticides, including crop rotation; scouting and monitoring the presence and growth stage of pests, and the use of allopathic, antagonistic and parasitic organisms, and biological pesticides. Rotating crops between those that host a particular pest, or are especially vulnerable to particular weeds, reduces the need for pest control.

Monocultures in arable production often increase pest problems and the risk of strains of insects and weeds developing resistance to pesticides. Inclusion of forage crops with grain or horticultural crops in regular crop rotation, is likely to reduce the need for pest control. Allopathic crops and residues release natural compounds that discourage some weeds. Some insect pests are repelled by certain plants and materials made from naturally occurring hormones.

Soil and land management encompasses the range of decisions farmers make regarding when and how to till the soil, how much crop residue to keep on the soil surface, whether to clear land or leave it in rangeland or woodland, whether to construct terraces, and whether to remove hedgerows and walls (Table 1). These decisions also affect other farm management issues, including pesticide and nutrient use. For example, reduced tillage or no-till systems rely on herbicides to replace tillage energy for the control of weeds. They also reduce erosion and compaction. As a consequence, farmers need to compare the costs and the benefits of tillage practices with herbicide use. Financial considerations are also important in retention or removal of woodland, hedges and walls, unless the farmer is retaining them deliberately for wildlife habitat or aesthetic reasons.

Soil erosion is often not recognised by farmers, because the short-term effects on crops and performance on-farm are usually insignificant compared to the effects of erosion off-farm. It is a problem on tilled soils, especially those left barren, and without residue or plant cover during winter. Because of the combined effect of erosion by wind and water, and soil displacement by machinery, cropping systems on sloping land are seldom stable or sustainable if heavy tillage equipment is used.

Reduced tillage and no tillage practices will generally improve soil structure through reduced compaction, but often result in the need for higher herbicide use and can cause leaching losses (Topp et al., 1995). Other methods to improve soil structure involve crop rotation with forage grasses and/or legumes, and the application of manure. The application of these practices, however, will be limited in areas where agriculture is largely crop based without livestock.

Reduced and no tillage result in greater soil cover. Winter cover crops provide protection from soil erosion over winter and add organic matter to the soil when they are ploughed under in the spring. Reduced tillage also reduces the loss of organic matter by oxidation.

Irrigation may be undertaken for a variety of crops in drier regions where it is economically feasible, or support is provided to farmers to lower the cost of irrigation water and irrigation systems. In more humid regions, irrigation might only be viable for high value crops, such as tobacco, fruit, vegetables and fibre crops. Irrigation systems can also provide environmental benefits by stabilising river flows, thus reducing floods and landslides, and improving groundwater reservoir recharging (see Land Conservation chapter).

The environmental impacts associated with **irrigation and water management** are soil degradation and problems associated with surface and groundwater contamination, due to inappropriate irrigation and water management practices (Table 1). Management practices that apply *irrigation* water only as and when required, and only to the root zone, will have the least environmental impact. This is best achieved by methods such as automated drip irrigation, which is used for high value crops like fruit and vegetables. Low-pressure centre-pivot sprinkler systems can offer an efficient method for water application for field crops.

Efficient water use can also be achieved in the irrigation systems in paddy fields, with uniform water supply and rotational irrigation among plots. On the other hand, flood irrigation used on steeply sloping agricultural land, can lead to poor uniformity of water application and excessive run-off, with detrimental environmental effects. Soil moisture and application rates need to be monitored to minimise impacts of irrigation. Properly graded land is also essential for uniform surface irrigation without run-off and pond formation.

Improved drainage is essential for field crops in humid regions with slowly permeable soils. Where growing seasons are short, irrigation may be the only way to complete seeding early enough, and harvesting late enough, for a cultivated crop to be successfully grown. Initial costs vary greatly with the type of drainage (surface or subsurface) and maintenance, which must be carried out every few years.

Maintenance of vegetative cover in surface and outlet channels is necessary to minimise erosion and sedimentation caused by *drainage*. Properly installed subsurface drainage outlets prevent erosion in the receiving channel, or in the field around the drainage pipe. Drainage channels need to be routed around wetlands, unless the wetland is the end point of the drainage works. Leaching of nitrogen into subsurface drains may cause problems, as can highly soluble and easily leached pesticides. Livestock should be kept out of drainage channels and ditches that are constructed in order to protect riparian vegetation and avoid erosion of the channel banks. Keeping livestock out of riparian areas will also help preserve vegetation along watercourses and reduce water contamination and loss of aquatic habitat.

2. Indicators

A distinction needs to be made between the advisory and information inputs into farm decision making, such as formulation of plans, strategies and schemes for the farm, and the environmental consequences of farming activities and practices. The key farm management concepts and related indicators, which are oriented towards the achievement and monitoring of environmentally sustainable agriculture, include (Figure 1):

- farm management capacity (based on data at the aggregated agriculture sector level); and

- farm management practices (based on data measured at the farm level, but aggregated to the national level).

Indicators of *farm management capacity* concern the investment in the capacity of the agricultural sector to build and transfer knowledge to improve on-farm management practices leading to a more environmentally sustainable agriculture. This covers a broad range of elements to encourage environmentally sound farm management practices and farming systems, in particular investment into research (see Farm Financial Resources chapter) and farmer education (see Contextual Indicators chapter).

Indicators of *farm management practices* encompass overall trends of farming methods (see Table 1 and Figure 10). They address whole farm management and organic farming, discussed in the following section, including the development of appropriate institutions and standards, as well as various aspects of farm management which have significant effects on the environment. These include nutrient management, pest management, soil and land management, and irrigation and water management, examined in this chapter.

Whole farm management

Environmental whole farm management plans

Definition

The share of the total number of farms or total agricultural area under environmental whole farm management plans.

Method of calculation

The indicator includes a calculation of the number of farms (or total agricultural area) under environmental whole farm management plans divided by the total national number of farms (or total agricultural area). There is no rigorous international definition of what constitutes an environmental whole farm management plan and, consequently, countries have adopted different approaches. Some countries use the International Organisation for Standardisation (ISO) 14000 certification of agricultural operations (see previous section), while others employ certified organic farming and more specific farm management plans, such as integrated pest management and nutrient management plans.

Recent trends

While the elements included in environmental whole farm plans vary across countries, there are a number of common features, as for example illustrated by *Austria* (see Box 1). Many countries do not have precise information on the number of farms with environmental whole farm management plans, but for the limited number of countries where data is available the adoption of whole farm plans increased over the 1990's (Figure 2).

Box 1.   **Whole Farm Management and Organic Farming under the Austrian Agri-environmental Programme**

After joining the European Union in 1995, the prices for agricultural commodities in Austria decreased rapidly. As a consequence of this development a further intensification of Austrian agriculture was expected. However, the country's agriculture is small scale with 70 per cent of agricultural holdings less than 20 hectares.

To prevent the process of intensification, Austria established an *Agri-Environmental programme* according to EU Regulation 2078/92. This programme is top-down oriented and effective across the whole country. It consists of 36 measures, tailored to national and regional requirements, while each farmer can select and combine certain measures according to their particular needs.

Farmers have to sign a contract under the programme and are obliged to comply with the various conditions and restrictions under the measures of the programme for at least 5 years. The *main objectives* of the programme include the promotion of environmentally compatible farming; reduction of the harmful environmental impacts of agriculture; the extensification, maintenance and development of farming in marginal (or abandoned) and less favoured agricultural areas; and the long term set-aside of arable land.

The key measures under the programme cover limitations on livestock density, maintenance and care of landscape elements, adoption of farm management practices and systems which do not increase yield on arable land and grassland, prohibition of the conversion of grassland into arable land, restrictions on the use of fertilisers, adoption of integrated pest management, and measures to protect soil and water quality.

In 1997 about 70 per cent of all domestic farms and 85 per cent of Austria's utilised agricultural area are included under this programme (Figure 2). The efficiency and effectiveness of the programme are under constant monitoring, with the results of this evaluation transmitted to the EU Commission.

Within the scope of this programme agricultural holdings under a certified *organic farming* system are provided support. To obtain financial support under this scheme, farmers have to comply with the rules for organic farming stipulated under EU Regulation 2092/91. With organic farming accounting for 9 per cent of all agricultural holdings, and 10 per cent of the utilised agricultural area, this is amongst the highest share across OECD countries (Figure 3). In addition, more than half of Austria's organic farms are members of various organic farming associations, with stricter guidelines than defined under the corresponding EU Regulation 2092/91.

Source: Federal Ministry of Agriculture and Forestry, Vienna, Austria (unpublished).

Figure 2. **Share of farms with environmental whole farm plans: 1993 and 1997**

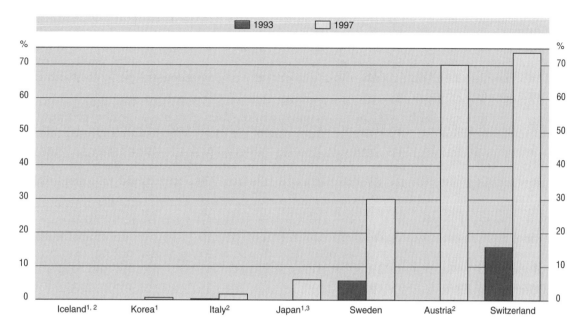

1. Data for 1993 are not available.
2. Percentages are zero or close to zero per cent for Iceland (1997), Italy (1993), and Austria (1993).
3. Data for 1997 refer to 1996 and only apply to rice production.
Source: OECD Agri-environmental Indicators Questionnaire, 1999.

In *Australia*, 36 per cent of broadacre and dairy farmers had a farm plan in 1995-96, that addressed the existing farm situation and included future management and development plans. The plans cover various issues. For example, 69 per cent of plans (or 25 per cent of all farmers) include information on soil and land capabilities; 61 per cent (22 per cent) on existing or proposed Landcare projects; and 49 per cent (18 per cent) on areas of conservation value (Mues *et al.*, 1998). The total productivity of Australian farmers grew by 2.7 per cent annually over the 1980's and 1990's, which is partly due to improved management planning. This includes best practices for the minimisation or avoidance of adverse impacts on the natural resource base and associated ecosystems, and the amelioration of any adverse impacts which do occur (Craik, 1998).

The share of farms with environmental whole farm management plans, in *Canada*, includes farms that are involved in farm conservation clubs (a Québec-based initiative), or have an environmental farm plan (available only to producers in Ontario or the Atlantic provinces). During the mid-1990s 17 per cent of farms had environmental whole farm plans in Canada.[4]

The central government in *Japan* encourages local governments (prefectures and municipalities) to make plans to promote environmental conservation in agriculture (Figure 2). It is also considering a new scheme in which each prefecture would establish guidelines on sustainable agricultural practices and certify farmers who develop farm plans under the guidelines.

Based on the inputs used in crop production, *Korea* divides farms with environmental whole farm plans into three groups: 1) organic producers, with no synthetic pesticides or fertilisers applied and "appropriate" water and soil management; 2) producers not using pesticides and with "appropriate" water and soil management; and 3) producers using low quantities of synthetic pesticides and with "appropriate" water and soil management. The share of Korean farms with whole farms, however, is small (Figure 2).

In the *European Union*, nearly 15 per cent of farms and over 20 per cent of agricultural area are under agri-environmental programmes, which require farmers to meet various environmental criteria and include restrictions on farm management practices within the context of EU Regulation 2078/92 (Fay, 1999). These agri-environmental programmes are close to being a whole farm plan as outlined, for example, in the case of *Austria* (Box 1). The EU agri-environmental programmes have reduced the use of nitrogen fertilisers (see Figure 5, Nutrient Use chapter) and improved application techniques, as well as enhanced nature protection and the conservation of landscape features. While the share of agricultural area covered by the programmes is not an indicator of environmental quality, in countries where the share has been particularly low, the impact of agri-environmental policies is also likely to have been low (Fay, 1999).

Most of the farms in *Sweden* with an environmental whole farm plan use a national certification system which was introduced in 1996 with over 50 per cent of the total cultivated area covered (and 30 per cent of farms) by whole farm plans (Figure 2). In order to be certified, the farmers have to answer questions on plant and animal production, handling of materials, waste products, etc. Based on the answers, the system proposes suitable management practices for the farm. A few farmers also take part in the International Organisation for Standardisation (ISO) 14000 and ISO 9002 certification (see previous section).

Over 70 per cent of the cultivated area and farms in *Switzerland* are covered by whole farm, that is farms which have to meet ecological performance criteria (Figure 2). This covers animal welfare and nutrient balances (phosphate balance, nitrogen restrictions), with a minimum of 7 per cent of the agricultural area kept as semi-natural habitat (*i.e.* ecological compensation area), and regulations for "appropriate" crop rotations, a minimum soil cover, and the use and method of pesticide application.

Interpretation and links to other indicators

It is assumed that the greater the number or area of farms covered by environmental whole farm plans, the better this is for the environment, through superior farmer knowledge and awareness of the environment, and the implementation of best management practices. Whole farm management enables a producer to view the farm operation as a system whose management explicitly takes into account not only the diverse elements of the operation, but also their linkages and relationships. Environmental whole farm plans aim at optimising the use of commercial pesticides and fertilisers.

Environmental whole farm plans are an indicator of farmer awareness of environmental issues. In a number of countries farmers are being encouraged to develop whole farm plans by reviewing potential environmental problem areas on the farm and developing action plans to address issues that do not meet various environmental standards. Integrated pest management (IPM) and nutrient management plans can be part of a whole farm plan. As the implementation of the plan is the farmers' responsibility, this is not necessarily a precise indicator of "actual" implementation, rather an indicator of intent. The exception is where the particular practice or plan is compulsory (*e.g.* farm waste disposal regulations), or obligatory as part of receiving payments under particular programmes (*e.g.* land set aside).

The existence of an environmental whole farm plan does not indicate the quality of the plan or whether the plan is implemented, and these aspects need to be assessed to improve the validity of the indicator. It will also be necessary to link these farm plans to actual environmental outcomes, for example, as measured through other indicators such as soil and water quality, biodiversity and wildlife habitats. In addition, it should be emphasised that, from the environmental point of view, the total area under these plans is more important than the total number of farms.

Related information

Environmental conditions and farming systems vary within and across OECD countries and, consequently, optimal farm management practices and environmental farm management standards also vary. Farm management standards are often developed at the sub-national level resulting in great variations even within a country Environmental farm management standards, regulations, codes of good agricultural practice, etc., are established by public agencies, standards are also defined by voluntary groups, professional farm organisations, and the agro-food industry.

Voluntary codes of practice are widely used, while compulsory standards and regulations are particularly important for pesticides and nutrients (Table 2). In *Germany* and *Spain* compulsory standards and regulations are also in place for soil and water. Examples of voluntary codes of practice include best management practice guides for livestock and poultry waste management, field crop production, horticultural crops and habitat management.

Table 2. **Environmental farm management standards: late 1990s**

	Farm management area					
	Whole farm	Nutrients	Pesticides	Soil	Water	Others
Number of OECD countries with:						
– Compulsory standards	3	8	9	5	5	2
– Regulations	3	11	11	8	7	6
– Voluntary codes of practice	12	13	12	11	7	7
– Other standards	3	2	4	2	0	1

Note: This table shows the farm management areas addressed by environmental farm management standards for 19 out of 29 OECD Member countries.
Source: OECD Agri-environmental Indicators Questionnaire, 1999.

The year in which farm management standards were introduced also varies considerably across countries, although in most cases standards were introduced in the early or mid-1990s. In some countries, however, standards were introduced much earlier. In the *United States*, for example, compulsory standards for pesticide management were introduced in 1947, and voluntary codes of practice covering whole farm, nutrient, soil, water and animal waste management in 1935. Moreover, in *Switzerland* environmental legislation was introduced covering pesticide management in 1951; nature and landscape in 1966; and water and nutrient management in 1971. The interval between the revision of standards varies too, the compulsory standards and regulations on nutrients, for example, are revised annually in *Denmark*.

The establishment of professional standards indicates the intention to develop farm practices that are environmentally sound, reliable and valid (see MAFF, 1991; 1992; and 1993, for examples of Codes of Good Agricultural practice).[5] An increasing trend toward raising environmental farm management standards would potentially imply a greater desire (or intention) to move towards a more environmentally sustainable agriculture. The role of sub-national jurisdictions and the private sector in developing and enforcing regulations, codes of practice, etc., may be greater, in certain cases, than that of national governments. For example, the agro-food industry and supermarket-chains can require farmers to use environmentally sound farm management practices, such as integrated pest management or organic farming practices, in order to remain as contract farmers.

The optimal measurement point (from an indicator perspective) for assessing a given farming system or management practice is to measure actions or practices actually undertaken by farmers, rather than intentions, especially as it is often difficult to measure environmental outcomes. That is, measure what farmers actually do, not what they say they intend to do. The existence of environmental farm management standards does not necessarily mean that the actual standards have a firm scientific basis or are implemented, monitored and effective as well as efficient. Hence, tracking the extent of environmental farm management standards as a measure of "intent" for some, but not all, countries would need to be linked closely with those indicators on "actual" implementation of farm management practices, as defined in the indicators in the following sections of this chapter.

Organic farming

Definition

The share of farms or the total agricultural area under a certified organic farming system or in the process of conversion to such a system.

Method of calculation

The indicator is calculated by measuring the number of farms (or total agricultural area) under certified organic systems or in the process of converting to organic farming divided by the total national number of farms (or total agricultural area). At present there is no unique international definition for "organic" farming practices, and consequently differences in definitions and standards exist between countries, although IFOAM has developed guidelines for trading in organic products (see previous section). In general, by accepting the rules of "organic" registration, farmers are committed to use mechanical weed control (*i.e.* plough and cultivator), to use biological control of other pests, and to forego the use of all synthetic pesticides (Macey, 1992). Different authorities are responsible for certifying organic farms in OECD countries. Often both government and private sector bodies are involved in certification.

Recent trends

The cultivated area under organic farming has increased significantly in OECD countries over the past ten years (Figure 3). In the *United States*, the area under certified organic farming systems increased by over 60 per cent over the period 1995 to 1997 (Figure 3, and Welsh 1999)

The importance of organic farming varies within the *European Union*, where just under 2 per cent of the total agriculture area is under organic farming, which corresponds to over 1 per cent of farms (Hau and Joaris, 1999). Organic farms are larger than the EU average farm size, although the situation varies considerably between countries. Production of grass as fodder is by far the most important use of organic land, though organic horticulture is important in Southern Europe (Hau and Joaris, 1999). The European Union encourages conversion to and maintenance of organic

Figure 3. **Share of the total agricultural area under organic farming: early 1990s and mid/late 1990s**

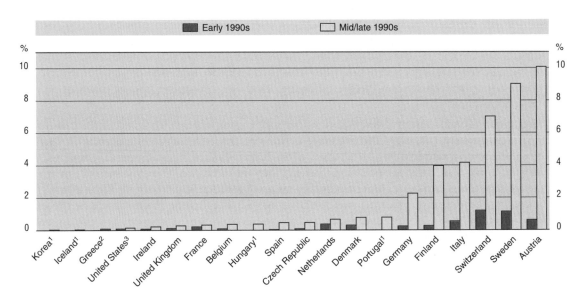

1. Data for the early 1990s are not available.
2. Percentage for the early 1990s equals 0.003%.
3. Data for the United States are taken from Welsh (1999).
Sources: OECD Agri-environmental Indicators Questionnaire, 1999; EEA (1998); Welsh (1999).

farming, by providing financial compensation to farmers for any losses incurred during conversion (see Austria, for example, Box 1).

In the European Union, regulations restrict the range of products that can be used to fertilise soil and control pests and diseases on organic farms. In addition, countries are required to set up an inspection system to certify compliance with organic farming regulations (Hau and Joaris, 1999). For example, in *Denmark*, the Danish Ministry of Food, Agriculture and Fisheries is responsible for the administration and control of organic farms. All farms are controlled annually and, in addition, random checks are carried out on 25 per cent of the farms. The Danish Association of Organic Agriculture is a growers organisation, which requires its members to meet a set of requirements that are in some ways stricter than government requirements, as in the case in *Austria* (Box 1).

Two private sector inspection bodies have been approved by the *Swedish* government to monitor organic farming (KRAV and Svenska Demeterförbundet), and the Swedish Board of Agriculture is responsible for supervising these private bodies. They ensure that producers comply with the European Union regulations, but also have their own stricter requirements on crop production and animal husbandry. Producers wanting to label their products not only as organic but also with the stricter private body label are inspected according to the additional criteria. The Swedish consumers are familiar with these labels and have confidence in their reliability.

For many OECD countries, organic farms are certified by private sector bodies, which have been accredited by the government. In the *United Kingdom* for example, seven private sector bodies are in charge of certification. Certification inspections are made annually and the government monitors the inspections by selecting a proportion for further assessment by government-appointed officials.

A case study from the United Kingdom shows that for a specific farm converting from conventional to organic farming, the gross margins fell by almost £100 (US$ 150) per hectare in the conversion years, of which the then Organic Aid Scheme in the United Kingdom would have offset only about a third. The Organic Aid Scheme was replaced in 1999 by the Organic Farming Scheme and rates of aid were increased. Once fully converted, gross margins on organic farms were up to 15 per cent higher than for a similar conventional farm (Cobb *et al.*, 1998; and MAFF, 2000).[6]

The *Norwegian Agriculture Inspection Service* (Statens landbrukstilsyn) is the control authority for organic agricultural production, and has appointed Debio as the control and inspection body. Debio is the only *Norwegian* control and certification body for organic production, while the Norwegian Food Control Authority (Statens næringsmiddeltilsyn) is the authority for processing, trading and the import of organic products. Debio co-operates with the local Food Control Authorities.

Interpretation and links to other indicators

This indicator reflects the move towards the elimination of the use of chemicals, some of which are of environmental concern. Under certain climatic conditions, however, this increases the risk of soil erosion unless control measures, such as contour strip cropping, are adopted and rigorously applied. Organic farming practices also have important implications for biodiversity by altering habitat conditions. (see Figure 5, Wildlife Habitat chapter)

Organic producers are usually registered and inspected, and must agree to use no pesticides or fertiliser materials other that those that are approved as "organic." Any manure that is used should preferably come from registered organic livestock farms. Limited quantities of manure from non-organic farms may be used provided the stock are managed in a non-intensive system. The system requires an entirely different approach to farm management compared to "conventional" methods, but there are constraints. These include possible difficulties in obtaining crop insurance, the rules of which require that all feasible methods, including pesticides, must be used by participating farmers to protect their crops from yield loss.

Nutrient management

Nutrient management plans

Definition

Share of farms or cultivated area with nutrient management plans.

Method of calculation

The method of calculation involves measuring the number of farms or cultivated area with nutrient management plans as a share of the total number of farms or total cultivated area. Nutrient management plans normally include restrictions on the :

- periods when the application of fertiliser is inappropriate;
- application of fertiliser to steeply sloping ground;
- application of fertiliser to water saturated, flooded, frozen or snow-covered ground;
- conditions for application of fertiliser near water courses; and
- capacity and construction of storage containers for livestock manure, including measures to prevent water pollution by run-off and seepage into the groundwater of liquids containing livestock manure and effluents from stored plant materials such as silage.

Nutrient management plans also usually include requirements for the:

- application of nutrients, including the rate and uniformity of spreading, of both chemical fertiliser and livestock manure, to restrict nutrient losses to water to an acceptable level;
- timing and method of application for the land application of livestock manure and other organic materials to encourage efficient crop recovery of nutrients to minimise losses to water and air;
- maintenance of a minimum quantity of vegetative cover during (rainy) periods that will take up the nitrogen from the soil that would otherwise cause nitrate pollution of water;
- establishment of fertiliser plans on a farm-by-farm basis and the keeping of records on fertiliser use; and
- prevention of water pollution from run-off and the downward water movement beyond the reach of crop roots in irrigation systems.

In addition, nutrient management plans may include land management elements, such as the use of crop rotation systems, and the proportion of the land area devoted to permanent crops relative to annual tillage crops.

Recent trends

Many OECD countries have developed and use nutrient management plans, but only a few collect information on the number of farms or the agricultural area under these plans (Figure 4). Nutrient management plans generally cover most if not all the restrictions and requirements listed above.

In *Germany*, for example, some of the restrictions and requirements are included in fertiliser legislation (Düngeverordnung; from 1996) with which all German farmers must comply. The legislation requires, for example, that farmers keep records on fertiliser use and calculate nutrient balances. The EU Nitrate Directive requires countries to identify areas vulnerable to contamination by nitrogen (see the Nutrient Use and Water Quality chapters).

Virtually all *Danish* farms now have nutrient management plans, in view of the country's high stocking density and intensive agricultural production system (Figure 4). In addition, a significant share of farms have nutrient management plans in *Norway* (Figure 4) and the *Netherlands*.

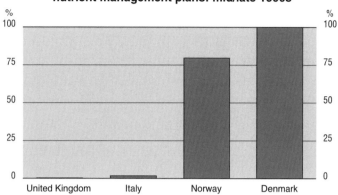

Figure 4. **Share of the total number of farms with nutrient management plans: mid/late 1990s**

Source: OECD Agri-environmental Indicators Questionnaire, 1999.

Interpretation and links to other indicators

A nutrient management plan is an indicator of farmer awareness of environmental issues, but nutrient plans are also introduced in response to legislation (*e.g.* the EU Nitrate Directive, see Nutrient Use and Water Quality chapters). The existence of a nutrient management plan does not necessarily mean that the plan is followed, thus, it is the implementation of the plan that should be measured. This indicator is closely linked to nutrient use, water and soil quality and other farm management areas.

Soil tests

Definition

Use and frequency of soil tests expressed as the proportion of farms conducting soil tests at different frequencies or share of crop area tested

Method of calculation

The indicator is calculated as the share of farms conducting soil tests on agricultural land or share of the crop area which is regularly sampled and analysed for nutrient content. The soil test frequency may range form every year or at intervals of every 2 to over 5 years.

Recent trends

Soil nutrient tests are carried out in almost all OECD countries. As both public and private bodies are involved in these tests, data on the share of farms or crops covered by soil tests are not generally available unless explicitly requested in government farm surveys. Most countries include both nitrogen and phosphorous in soil tests and some countries test for other soil nutrients and trace elements.

For major *United States'* field crops (maize, soyabeans, cotton, winter wheat and autumn potatoes) the share of the crop area that is tested annually for nutrient content has increased since the late 1980s (Table 3). Research on the economic and environmental benefits of soil/water nitrogen testing in Central Nebraska, United States, has shown that adoption of such nutrient management practices would result in increased economic benefits to farmers and reduced nitrate levels in groundwater (Kim *et al.*, 1999). In *France* the share of crop area annually tested would appear to lower than in the United States (Table 3), while in *Canada*, 60 per cent of farms took soil samples in 1995 (Table 4). Regular soil testing has also increased substantially in *Australia* over the 1990s (Commonwealth of Australia, 1998).

97

Table 3. **Share of annual crop area tested for nutrient content: France and United States**

Crop	France	United States	
	1994	1988-89	1990-94 (average)
	%	%	
Autumn potatoes	..	..	83
Barley	8	..	..
Cotton	..	29	30
Maize	..	33	41
Rapeseed	5	..	..
Soybeans	..	26	28
Wheat	13[1]	16[2]	20[2]

.. Not available.
1. Soil test on nitrogen.
2. Data refer to winter wheat.
Sources: OECD Agri-environmental Indicators Questionnaire, 1999; USDA (1997).

Table 4. **Share of farms conducting soil tests: Canada, 1995**

Frequency of tests	% share of the total number of farms conducting soil tests
Every year	35
2-3 years	40
4-5 years	14
Over 5 years	11

Sources: OECD Agri-environmental Indicators Questionnaire, 1999; McRae *et al.* (2000).

Interpretation and links to other indicators

Soil testing is a useful tool for nutrient management, as it provides an accurate gauge of nutrient levels in the soil and enables farmers to match nutrient application to crop needs. The greater the frequency of soil testing, the greater the likelihood that application rates match crop needs, hence soil tests at least once every three years may avoid over, or under, fertilisation. This is an indicator of interest and awareness, even if recommended fertiliser application rates are not always followed.

Nutrient management practices need to be linked with soil and water quality indicators. Infrequent soil tests can leave problems undetected and lead to problems of underfertilisation, and thus damage soil quality, or overfertilisation which may increase nutrient leaching to ground and surface water (see the Soil and Water Quality chapters).

Related information

In addition to nutrient soil tests, the United States also monitors changes for other nutrient management practices for major field crops. All indicators are reported as a share of planted area on which the practice is applied and the data are derived from probability-based surveys of farm operators. The indicator trends for maize are shown in Table 5, while indicators are also calculated for cotton, soyabeans, winter wheat and autumn potatoes (USDA, 1997).

Canada has also developed other indicators for fertiliser and manure management. These include, for fertilisers, the method of fertiliser application; the timing of nitrogen application; and the reduction of fertilisers applied to offset the nutrient content of manure. For manure, the indicators include, the storage method for solid and liquid manure, the liquid manure storage capacity and the manure application method. These indicators suggest that fertilisers are generally applied with methods that reduce nutrient losses, and that although nitrogen fertilisers are usually applied before planting, farmers are more likely to apply them after planting in ecozones where leaching is a problem.[7] The results also show that manure management needs to be improved (McRae *et al.*, 2000).

Table 5. **Nutrient management practices on planted maize area: United States,[1] 1990 to 1995**

Activities and practices	1990	1991	1992	1993	1994	1995
	Percentage of planted area					
Nutrient sources						
– Previous crop was legume, hay or pasture	8	7	8	5	7	7
– Only manure applied	1	1	1	1	1	1
– Both commercial fertilisers and manure applied	16	18	15	17	15	13
	Percentage of planted area					
Commercial fertilisers and manure						
– Applied at the recommended rate	..	..	85	87	84	78
– Applied above the recommended rate	..	..	5	3	7	7
– Applied below the recommended rate	..	..	10	10	9	14
	Percentage of area receiving commercial fertilisers					
Timing of nitrogen application[2]						
– Autumn before planting	27	26	23	20	27	30
– Spring before planting	57	50	53	51	54	52
– At planting	44	48	47	48	43	42
– After planting	26	31	31	35	27	29
	Percentage of area receiving commercial fertilisers					
Nutrient placement						
– Broadcast (ground)	71	72	69	71	72	73
– Broadcast (air)	..	..	1	1	1	1
– Chemigation	1	2	1	1	1	1
– Banded	43	41	42	42	41	40
– Foilar	1	0	0	0	0	0
– Injected (knifed in)	55	53	54	47	53	51

.. Not available.
1. Includes data for ten major maize producing States.
2. Data also available on phosphate timing.
Source: USDA (1997).

Norway has minimum area requirements for manure spreading, with a farmer needing to have at least 0.4 hectares of land per livestock manure unit. Failure to comply with the requirements are monitored and result in the loss of certain agri-environmental payments. The area of agricultural land that did not meet the minimum requirement fell from 1 381 hectares in 1996 to 1 076 hectares in 1997.

In *Switzerland* nutrient management practices are also monitored by using a farm level soil surface balance for phosphorous. In addition, restrictions are applied on the maximum nitrogen fertilisation (including farmyard manure) per farm. Soil nutrient analysis is also obligatory for all farmers who benefit from direct payments, and spreading livestock manure is illegal on soils that are waterlogged, frozen, covered with snow or dry.

The *United Kingdom* is also developing indicators on nutrient management practices. These indicators cover agricultural land which is regularly sampled and analysed for phosphorus content; the timing of slurry application; the length of available storage on the farm; and the types of machinery or techniques used to apply manure and slurry to land which reduce polluting emissions (MAFF, 2000).

Pest management

Use of non-chemical pest control methods

Definition

The area of cultivated crops not treated with chemical pesticides.

Method of calculation

The crop area not treated with chemical pesticides is divided by the total cultivated agricultural area to calculate the indicator. The cultivated agricultural area includes the total arable and permanent cropland and assumes that pesticides are not used on temporary or permanent pasture. Non-chemical pest control methods include, for example, tillage (*e.g.* ploughdown of allopathic residues, that is plants whose roots and residues can suppress the growth of many other plants, including weeds), crop rotation, biological control (*e.g.* parasitic organisms for control of insect pests), pheromones and hand weeding.

Recent trends

Synthetic pesticides are not used in organic farming, hence, the share of agricultural land under organic farming can also be considered to reflect trends in the area where only non-chemical pest control methods are used (Figure 3). Organic farming systems also include many other requirements and, consequently, the area where chemical pesticides are not used often exceeds the area under organic farming. Examples of such countries include *Germany*, *Spain* and the *United Kingdom*.

About two-thirds of *Canadian* farms (and field crop area) use non-chemical pest control methods (Table 6). In addition to the use of non-chemical pest control methods, Canada has developed other indicators for pesticide management, including the timing of herbicide, insecticide and fungicide applications, and sprayer calibration (McRae *et al.*, 2000). These indicators suggest that: *a*) herbicide application was triggered by the level of economic injury to the crop on about 20 per cent of treated cropland; *b*) farmers were more likely to apply herbicides at a certain stage of crop growth or to use the first sign of pests to time pesticide applications; and *c*) nearly 70 per cent of farmers calibrated sprayers only at the beginning of the crop season (McRae *et al.*, 2000).

Table 6. **Pest control methods used by farmers excluding the use of chemical pesticides:[1] Canada, 1995**

Pest Control Method	Number of farms	% of farm numbers	% of field crop area treated
Tillage	53 805	26	28
Crop rotation	99 970	49	56
Biological control	4 570	2	2
Pheromones	495	< 1	< 1
Hand weeding	14 900	7	4
Other	2 605	1	1
No non-chemical method	80 510	39	34

1. Percentages may exceed 100% where more than one practice is used on the same crop area.
Source: McRae *et al.* (2000).

Interpretation and links to other indicators

The pest management practices included in the indicator are assumed to pose fewer risks to human health and the environment than "conventional" pesticide application methods and they can potentially be applied to manage pest pressures without affecting farm profitability. The definitions of practices could be harmonised to improve international comparability and the data availability could also be improved.

In general it can be assumed that an increase in agricultural area under non-chemical pest control methods is beneficial to human health and the environment. However, some caution is required with such an interpretation, as it will be necessary to link these farm management practices to actual environmental outcomes, or outcomes measured through other indicators such as soil and water quality, biodiversity and wildlife habitats.

Use of integrated pest management

Definition

The area of cultivated agricultural land under integrated pest management (IPM).

Method of calculation

The indicator measures the area under IPM divided by the total cultivated agricultural area. The cultivated agricultural area includes the total arable and permanent cropland and assumes that pesticides are not used on temporary or permanent pasture. IPM is a knowledge-intensive and farmer based management approach that encourages natural control of pest populations by anticipating pest problems and preventing pests from reaching economically damaging levels. Activities under IPM include, for example, the enhancement of natural enemies, planting pest-resistant crops, adapting crop management, and "judicious" use of pesticides.

Recent trends

In view of the limited information that exists, it is difficult to be clear if more or less farmers are now using IPM than in the 1980s (Figure 5).[8]

In the *United States*, IPM was applied on over 50 per cent of the fruit, vegetable and major field crop (maize and soybeans) area in the early 1990s (Vandeman *et al.*, 1994).[9] Scouting for insects and diseases is already used on 75 per cent of fruit crops and nearly 75 per cent of vegetable crops (OECD, 1997). A number of these farmers also used pest-resistant crops, crop management, and other non-chemical

Figure 5. **Share of the total arable and permanent crop land area under integrated pest management: mid/late 1980s and late 1990s**

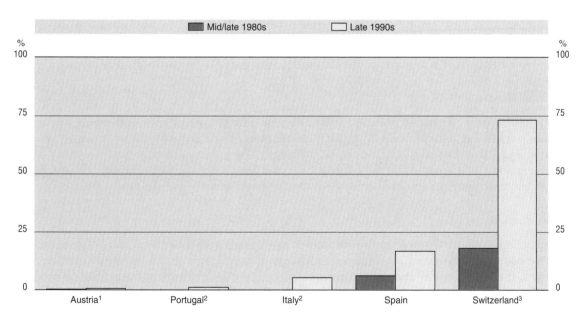

1. Data for mid/late 1980s refers to 1991.
2. Data are not available for mid/late 1980s.
3. Data for mid/late 1980s refers to 1993.
Source: OECD Agri-environmental Indicators Questionnaire, 1999.

techniques. The United Kingdom does not record the IPM area separately, but a recent survey in 1997 estimated that 50 per cent of farmers use IPM techniques on their farms.

Interpretation and links to other indicators

New pesticide products generally pose lower environmental risks, but may still have an impact on non-targeted species and water quality. The pest management practices included in these indicators are assumed to pose fewer risks to human health and the environment than "conventional" pesticide application methods and they can potentially be applied to manage pest pressures without affecting farm profitability.

The cultivated area under IPM is an indicator of comprehensive pest management, reduced pesticide risk, and optimal timing of pesticide use (as measured by the number or area of farms/crops where IPM is used). It addresses all pests and pest control methods, and it attempts to optimise the use of pesticides, not to replace them. It may be the best indicator of farm pest management efficiency, but it probably has a lower sensitivity to environmental concerns than the indicator on the use of non-chemical pest control methods.

As with non-chemical pest control methods, it can be assumed in general that an increase in agricultural area under IPM is beneficial for human health and the environment. However, some caution is required with such an interpretation, as it will be necessary to link these farm management practices to actual environmental outcomes, or outcomes measured through other indicators such as soil and water quality, biodiversity and wildlife habitats.

It is necessary to distinguish between certain herbicides and other pesticides. This is partly because herbicides are frequently used to reduce tillage, which has considerable environmental benefits. Herbicide materials can be divided into those that are used in forage or close-grown crops, where there is no benefit from reduced tillage, and those used primarily in wide-row crops, and in reduced or no-tillage systems, as an alternative to tillage.

Soil and land management

Soil cover

Definition

The number of days in a year that the soil (agricultural land) is covered with vegetation.

Method of calculation

The indicator is calculated from agricultural census data showing the period during any one year when the soil has a vegetative cover. By making assumptions on soil cover for different crops, the number of days in a year that the soil is covered can be calculated. The indicator incorporates the effects of tillage and crop rotation, and accounts for the effectiveness of different management practices in protecting the soil from processes that are environmentally negative, especially water and wind erosion.

Recent trends

Many OECD countries have policy initiatives to increase soil cover, and for some countries soil cover exceeds 250 days per year (Figure 6). Although the indicator shows an improvement in some countries, the trend could change if farmers, for economic or other reasons, shift to crops that provide less soil cover. There is therefore scope for policies to promote soil cover and to develop new methods and equipment to provide it, especially in areas of intensive farming of row crops (McRae et al., 2000).

Canada uses an index of bare-soil days to estimate the number of days in a year that soil is bare under specific cropping and tillage practices (McRae et al., 2000). The indicator suggests that

Figure 6. **Number of days in a year that agricultural soils are covered with vegetation: mid/late 1980s and mid/late 1990s**

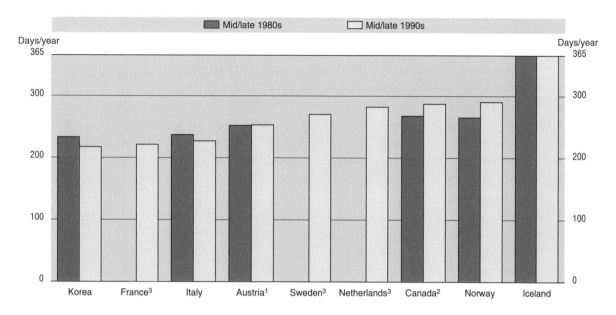

1. Data for mid/late 1980s and mid/late 1990s refer respectively to 1994 and 1997.
2. Data for mid/late 1980s refer to 1981.
3. Data are not available for mid/late 1980s.
Source: OECD Agri-environmental Indicators Questionnaire, 1999.

between 1981 and 1996 the number of bare-soil days different agricultural regions dropped by 20 per cent, from 98 to 78 per cent, indicating an improvement in soil cover during this period (McRae *et al.*, 2000).

Interpretation and links to other indicators

Plant and crop residue cover protects soils from erosion, reduces run-off of nutrients and pesticides and provides habitat for biodiversity. An increase in the cumulative soil cover, the greater the protection from soil erosion, compaction and run-off, and the greater the contribution to biodiversity. Hence, soil coverage for the whole year is the ideal target.

The indicator could be subdivided by the percentage of soil cover provided by vegetation and crop residues. The relative efficiency of different soil cover types in terms of nutrient and pesticide run-off, for example, could then be further evaluated. This indicator is closely linked to indicators of soil and water quality, indicators of biodiversity, as well as to other areas within farm management, especially land management (see following section).

Related information

Switzerland has developed an index to measure winter soil cover, where the values depend on the type of soil cover. For example, the index values for fallow land planted before September, rapeseed and winter wheat, are 100, 80 and 40 respectively. The index value for bare soil is 0. The individual values are then combined into an aggregate index. The risks of soil erosion and nutrient leaching are considered to be at acceptable levels when the index values are above 50. Preliminary results from the pilot project show that winter soil cover has increased (Figure 7).

103

Figure 7. **Agricultural soil cover index: Switzerland,[1] 1991 to 1996**

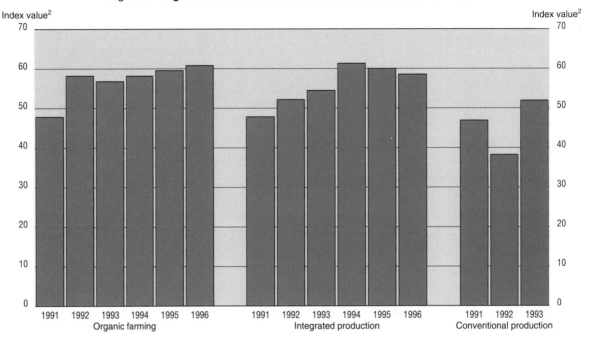

1. The data refer to a pilot farm network and cannot be considered to be representative for Switzerland nationally.
2. The index measures winter soil cover, the lowest acceptable index value is 50, with the index value for bare soil equal to zero.
Source: Federal Office for Agriculture, 1999 (unpublished).

Land management practices

Definition

The share of the total crop area under environmental land management practices.

Method of calculation

The indicator is calculated as the crop area under environmental land management practices divided by the total crop area. Environmental land management practices include conservation and no-till practices. These include practices other than conventional tillage methods that incorporate most of the crop residue (remaining after harvest into the soil), and other best land management practices including crop rotations and winter cover crops. Crop areas under the following land management practices are included in the indicator:

- Conservation tillage, also called mulch tillage, minimum tillage, and reduced tillage. These are tillage methods that leave most of the crop residue (*i.e.* plant material remaining after harvest) on the surface of the soil to provide protection against erosion, reduce soil crusting, and increase the organic matter content of surface soils.

- No-till, also called zero-tillage. This is a tillage method where the soil is not disturbed between harvesting one crop and planting the next. It includes direct seeding into stubble or sod, and ridge tillage.

- Crop rotation, that is planting different crops successively in the same field.

- Winter cover crops. These are crops, for example, autumn rye and winter barley, which are planted after the autumn harvest as a means of soil protection.

- Contour cultivation. This includes cultivation that follows the contour of a field, at angles to the slope of the field.

- Grassed waterways. These are grassy strips in run-off depressions of cultivated fields that provide a channel for excess water.

- Strip-cropping. For example, alternating strips of crop and summer-fallow, or alternating two crops, across a field.

- Windbreak, also called shelterbelt. This is a natural or planted line of trees, bushes, or hedge at the border or within a field.

Recent trends

Most OECD countries promote sustainable land management practices, and include many of the practices listed above. For certain OECD countries the crop area under environmental land management practices has increased significantly. In *Austria* (Box 1), *Norway* and *Switzerland*, for example, these practices are now used in over 70 per cent of the crop area (Figure 2). Reduced and no-till systems are recognised in *Norway* as ways to reduce nutrient run-off from agricultural land. This has been monitored in Norway by measuring the share of the total grain area where all soil preparations are completed in the spring, with the share increasing from 16 per cent to 36 per cent in 1997/98.

In both *Canada* and the *United States* there has been a shift in tillage practices from conventional tillage to conservation and no-till systems. For *Canada* there has also been an increase in crop rotation, and these changes have led to an overall improvement in the quality of Canadian soils (Table 7). Similarly in the *United States*, the impact of soil conservation programmes, especially the increase in area under conservation and no-till systems, has led to a significant reduction in soil erosion rates (Table 8 and see the Soil Quality chapter). Research in the United States, however, has found that farmers perceptions of what constitutes no-till and their actual use of this practice may not always be consistent (Uri, 2000). Farmers have adopted conservation tillage on a voluntary basis and in response to incentives provided under the Conservation Compliance Program (Hrubovcak *et al.*, 1999).

Australia and *New Zealand* Landcare groups have been established to encourage environmentally sound land management practices (Commonwealth of Australia, 1998; Ministry for the Environment, 1996; and Mues *et al.*, 1998). In 1995-96, 34 per cent of Australian broadacre and dairy farmers belonged

Table 7. **Land and soil management practices: Canada, 1991 and 1996**

	1991	1996
	Percentage of total planted area	
Reduced tillage practices		
– Tillage retaining most crop residues on soil surface	24	31
– No tillage prior to seeding	7	16
	Percentage of total farm numbers	
Other land and soil management practices[1]		
– Crop rotation	37	57
– Permanent grass cover	..	29
– Winter cover crops for spring plough-down	9	3
– Contour cultivation	9	5
– Strip-cropping	8	4
– Grassed waterways	11	9
– Windbreaks or shelterbelts	..	13

.. Not available.
1. Percentages may exceed 100% where more than one practice is used on the same crop area.
Source: McRae *et al.* (2000).

Table 8. **Environmental land management practices: United States, 1985-89 to 1990-94**

Management practice	1985-89		1990-94		% change
	Years	Area in 000 ha	Years	Area in 000 ha	
Conservation tillage	1989	23 310	1990-94	24 144	4
Zero tillage	1989	5 706	1990-94	11 283	98
Crop rotation	..	..	1990-92, 1994	54 226	..
Winter cover crops	1985-89	58	1990-94	53	−9
Contour cultivation	1987	12 726	1992	12 611	−1
Grassed waterways	1988-89	79	1990-94	86	9
Strip-cropping	1988-89	53	1990-94	42	−21
Windbreaks	1988-89	243	1990-94	91	−63
Grass cover establishment	1988-89	2 609	1990-94	643	−75
Grazing land protection	1988-89	1 492	1990-94	1 395	−7
Terraces and diversions	1988-89	405	1990-94	282	−30

.. Not available.
Sources: OECD Agricultural Environment Indicators Questionnaire, 1999; USDA (1997).

Table 9. **Share of total sown crop area using different land management practices: Australia, 1995 to 1996**

Management practices	Landcare group members	Non-landcare group members	Total Australia
	% of sown crop area		
Direct drilling (single pass in previously uncultivated field)	22	15	18
Minimum/reduced tillage	31	29	30
Conventional tillage	46	57	52

Source: Mues *et al.* (1998).

Table 10. **Environmental agricultural land management practices: France, 1989, 1994 and 1998**

Management practice	Area			1989 to 1998
	1989	1994	1998	
	Million hectares			% change
Crop rotation	14.3	12.8	12.8	−10.9
Winter cover crops	7.3	6.4	8.0	10.3

Source: OECD Agricultural Environment Indicators Questionnaire, 1999.

to a Landcare group and, in general, Landcare members used more environmentally friendly farm management practices than non-Landcare members (Table 9).

Environmental land management in *France* over the period 1989 to 1998 reveals a reduction in the area under crop rotation, but an increase in the use of winter crop coverage (Table 10).

Interpretation and links to other indicators

This is an indicator of the use of best management practices in crop production to minimise soil erosion, pesticide and nutrient run-off, etc. The higher the adoption rate of such practices on land areas at risk, the lower the risks of various environmental impacts. The relative efficiency of different practices in reducing soil erosion, for example, can be further evaluated and the practices weighted to calculate an index. This indicator is closely associated with the indicator on soil cover, but only considers the adoption of different soil management practices, rather than the actual effect of soil management, such as the extent of soil cover.

Irrigation and water management[10]

Definition

The share of irrigation water applied by different forms of irrigation technology.

Method of calculation

The indicator is calculated as the share of irrigation water used under different irrigation technologies and systems (such as, flooding, high-pressure rain guns, low-pressure sprinklers, and drip-emitters) divided by the total quantity of water used for irrigation. Water is a scarce resource in some OECD countries, but not in others (see the Water Use chapter). Consequently, monitoring of irrigation practices is not important in all countries.

Recent trends

Scientific and well managed irrigation methods (drip-emitters, booms and pivots) have facilitated a reduction in water use to the minimum levels required by the crop in some countries. However, this reduction in water use is often accompanied by an increase in irrigated area, so that the overall quantity of water utilisation remains the same. In addition, the booms and pivots, which are capable of irrigating tens of hectares at a time, have greatly changed the size and shape of agricultural fields (crops arranged in circles or in islands around capture points, consolidation, etc., Poiret, 1999). For a few countries for which data are available, flooding and high pressure rain guns are the technologies most commonly used to provide irrigation water except for *Poland* (Figure 8).

Figure 8. **Share of total irrigated crop area using different irrigation systems: mid/late 1990s**

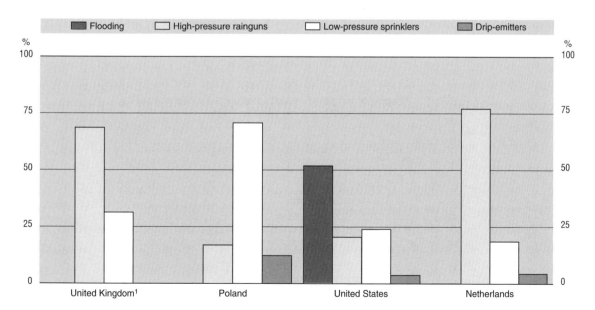

1. Calculations based on the number of holdings using irrigation. Data on drip-emitters are not available.
Source: OECD Agri-environmental Indicators Questionnaire, 1999.

Interpretation and links to other indicators

The greater the percentage of irrigation water applied by high-efficiency appliances (*e.g.* drip-emitters), compared with low-efficiency appliances (*e.g.* flooding), the less the amount of water wasted and the lower the risk of adverse environmental effects. It is necessary to clearly define the hierarchy of the technical efficiency of different irrigation systems. Also it is important to take into account the share of irrigated area when interpreting the indicator, as the larger the share of the irrigated area in the total agricultural area the larger the potential environmental impacts of irrigation technologies The indicator provides supportive information to the water use efficiency indicators by showing the share of irrigated area under different irrigation systems (see Water Use chapter).

Monitoring water use efficiency has the potential to identify opportunities for increased production of more food and fibre from existing or reduced water allocation. This is important in terms of being able to accommodate (to a degree) growing demands for food and fibre without additional demands on a limited water resource; and to shift production away from land with a low production potential. It may also help ease the pressure of increasing water withdrawals on natural processes and aquatic ecosystems, and on aquaculture enterprises (see Water Use chapter).

Related information

Another irrigation management indicator used in the *United States* is based on the methods used to decide when to irrigate. Farmers are asked whether their decision to irrigate is based on the condition of the crop; the soil conditions; readings from soil moisture sensing devices; commercial scheduling services; media reports on plant water use; calendar schedules; the schedules of water delivery organisations (no choice by water user); or other factors.[11] The indicator is calculated as the share of farms using advanced decision methods (soil moisture sensing devices, commercial scheduling services, media reports on plant water use) in relation to other methods. In 1988, 16 per cent of farms used advanced decision methods compared with 19 per cent in 1994.

In the *United Kingdom* irrigation management practices are also measured by the volume of water stored as a percentage of water applied. In the UK, the amount of water abstracted in winter when flows are abundant and stored in reservoirs for use during the irrigation season, has increased. The results for the indicator show that 39 per cent of irrigation water was stored in 1995 compared with 22 per cent in 1987 (Figure 9).

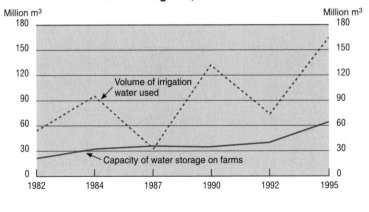

Figure 9. **Volume of irrigation water used and storage capacity: United Kingdom, 1982 to 1995**

Source: MAFF (2000).

3. Future challenges

Data availability is the main barrier to wider use of these indicators, as many OECD countries do not have reliable information on the extent to which environmental farm management practices are used. Certain central concepts, such as whole farm management and environmental farm management plans, should be defined more precisely and linkages between the various farm management practices need to be identified.

Environmental conditions and farming systems vary within and across OECD countries and, consequently, best farm management practices vary from one region to another. For example, a detailed nutrient management plan is not a priority in areas without nutrient surplus or leaching problems. Nor is there a need to change pest control practices if pesticide use is already at a low level for climatic or other reasons. Thus, identifying and developing a standard set of indicators on farm management practices across the OECD is not straightforward. A matrix of farm management practices which allows the diversity of country situations to be reflected, is one tool which may be developed to accommodate this variability (Figure 10).

The matrix should include an issue substructure (nutrients, soil, pesticides, water, etc.) and specified management practices under each, with countries reporting on the level of adoption or "actual" use of

Figure 10. **Matrix of sustainable farm management practices and the implementation index**

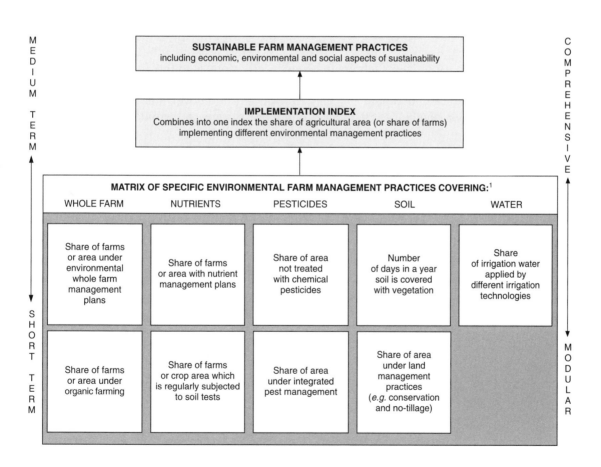

1. Other relevant practices, such as farm practices to protect biodiversity, habitat and landscape could be added to this matrix.
Source: OECD Secretariat.

those practices most relevant to their specific national and regional situations. Other relevant practices, such as farm practices to protect biodiversity, habitat, could be added to the matrix, in addition to the practices included in Figure 10.

As a means to express the results of the matrix in a comprehensive manner for a given country, an Implementation Index could be used to measure the extent to which environmental farm management practices are actually used by farmers (Figure 10). The Implementation Index (II) could be calculated as follows:

$$II = \sum_{i=1}^{n} \frac{[(\text{adoption rate of practice i at time 2}) - (\text{adoption rate of practice i at time 1})]}{\text{Total number of practices monitored}}$$

where: i is a management practice; i = 1,2,...n and

$$\text{adoption rate of practice i} = \frac{\text{agricultural area (or number of farms) under practice i}}{\text{total agricultural area (or total number of farms)}}$$

The adoption rate of a particular practice would thus be a sub-index showing the change over time in the ratio for each practice in a country or agro-ecological region. A simple summation over different farm management practices would be an over-simplification, as some practices are better for the environment than others. Different management practices would therefore need to be weighted in the Implementation Index to reflect their varying environmental impacts. Although it is more meaningful from the environment point of view to look at the area rather than the number of farms using different farm management practices, it may be sometimes easier to obtain information on the number of farms.

A key challenge to establishing farm management indicators, is to link these indicators to other indicator areas. For example, changes in the nutrient management indicator could be linked to nutrient use changes and the indicator of nitrate concentration in water. Moreover, it is also important to better understand the net environmental consequences of relative changes in the different farm management indicators.

NOTES

1. The IFOAM guidelines are available online from the IFOAM website: *www.ifoam.org*.

2. For further details of the ISO 9 000 and 14 000 standards see the ISO web page online at: *www.iso.ch/9000e/9k14ke.htm*.

3. For an examination of the impact of farm management practices on the environment see, for example, Fawcett *et al.* (1994); Insensee and Sadeghi (1993); Jones *et al.* (1990); Mellerowics *et al.* (1994); Phillips *et al.* (1993); and Putman and Alt (1987).

4. For a survey of experiences with whole farm planning in Canada and the United States, see Higgins (1998).

5. For a survey of the uptake of the Codes of Good Agricultural Practices in the *United Kingdom*, see MAFF (2000).

6. For a comparison of the profitability between organic and conventional farming in *France* and the *Netherlands* see OECD (2000*a*; and 2000*b*).

7. The injection method was used on 22 per cent of cropland receiving fertiliser, banding on 43 per cent, and application with seed on 55 per cent.

8. The OECD recently held a Workshop in 1999 in Switzerland on Integrated Pest Management (for further details, see the OECD website at: *www.oecd.org/ehs/* [Pesticide Programme > Pesticide Risk Reduction]). For a discussion on the economics and policy analysis of IPM see Swinton and Day (2000).

9. Farmers were considered to be using IPM "if, before making pesticide application decisions, they monitored pest populations (scouting) in order to determine when a pest population had reached an economically damaging threshold". For a recent study on pest management, including IPM, in the United States, see Fernandez-Cornejo and Jans (1999).

10. For further research related to irrigation and water management see the International Commission on Irrigation and Drainage, with information available on line at: *www.icid.org*.

11. The use of irrigation scheduling is also important in *Australia*, see Commonwealth of Australia (1998).

BIBLIOGRAPHY

Cobb, D., R. Feber, A. Hopkins and L. Stockdale (1998),
   Organic Farming Study, Global Environmental Change Programme Briefings No. 17, March, University of Sussex, United Kingdom. Available at: *www.susx.ac.uk/Units/gec/pubs/briefing/briefs.htm*.

Commonwealth of Australia (1998),
   Sustainable Agriculture – Assessing Australia's Recent Performance, A Report to the Standing Committee on Agriculture and Resource Management (SCARM) of the National Collaborative Project on Indicators for Sustainable Agriculture, SCARM Technical Report No. 70, CSIRO Publishing, Victoria, Australia.

Craik, W. (1998),
   "Sustainable Agriculture and Pesticide Reduction", in P. Rowland and D. Branford (eds.), *Proceedings of the Australian National Pesticide Risk Reduction Workshop*, Bureau of Rural Sciences, Department of Primary Industry, Canberra, Australia.

EEA [European Environment Agency] (1998),
   Europe's Environment: The Second Assessment, Office for Official Publications of the European Communities, Luxembourg. Available at: *http://themes.eea.eu.int/* [> all available reports].

Fawcett, R.S., B.R. Christiansen and D.P. Tierney (1994),
   "The Impact of Conservation Tillage on Pesticide Run-off into Surface Water", *Journal of Soil and Water Conservation*, Vol. 49, No. 2, pp. 126-135.

Fay, F. (1999),
   "Impact of agri-environment measures", in European Commission, *Agriculture, Environment, Rural Development: Facts and Figures – A Challenge for Agriculture*, Office for Official Publications of the European Communities, Luxembourg. Available at *http://europa.eu.int/comm/dg06/envir/report/en/index.htm*.

Fernandez-Cornejo, J. and S. Jans (1999),
   Pest Management in US Agriculture, Agricultural Handbook No. 717, Resource Economics Division, Economic Research Service, US Department of Agriculture, Washington DC., United States. Available at: *www.ers.usda.gov/* [Publications > Inputs and Technology > Fertilizer and Pesticides].

Hau, P. and A. Joaris (1999),
   "Organic Farming", in European Commission, *Agriculture, Environment, Rural Development: Facts and Figures – A Challenge for Agriculture*, Office for Official Publications of the European Communities, Luxembourg. Available at: *http://europa.eu.int/comm/dg06/envir/report/en/index.htm*.

Higgins, E. (1998),
   Whole Farm Planning – A Survey of North American Experiments, Policy Studies Report No. 9, Henry A. Wallace Institute for Alternative Agriculture, Greenbelt, Maryland, United States. Available at: *www.hawiaa.org/hawiaa.htm*.

Hrubovcak, J., U. Vasavada and J.E. Aldy (1999),
   Green Technologies for a More Sustainable Agriculture, Resource Economics Division, Economic Research Service, US Department of Agriculture, Agricultural Information Bulletin No. 752, Washington, DC., United States.

Insensee A.R. and A.M. Sadeghi (1993),
   "Impact of Tillage Practice on Run-off and Pesticide Transport", *Journal of Soil and Water Conservation*, Vol. 48, No. 6, pp. 523-527.

Jones, A.J., R.A Selley and L.N. Mielke (1990),
   "Cropping and Tillage Options to Achieve Erosion Control Goals and Maximum Profit on Irregular Slopes", *Journal of Soil and Water Conservation*, Vol. 45, No. 6, pp. 648-653.

Kim, C.S., H. Taylor, and C. Sandretto (1999),
   Economic and Environmental Benefits of Soil/Water Nitrogen Testing: The Case of Central Nebraska, paper presented at the Western Agricultural Economics Association Annual Meeting, July 11-14, Fargo, North Dakota, United States.

Macey, A. (ed.) (1992),
   Organic Field Crop Handbook, Canadian Organic Growers Inc., Ottawa, Canada.

MAFF [Ministry of Agriculture, Fisheries and Food] (1991),
 Code of Good Agricultural Practice for the Protection of Water, London, United Kingdom.

MAFF (1992),
 Code of Good Agricultural Practice for the Protection of Air, London, United Kingdom.

MAFF (1993),
 Code of Good Agricultural Practice for the Protection of Soil, London, United Kingdom.

MAFF (2000),
 Towards Sustainable Agriculture – A Pilot Set of Indicators, London, United Kingdom. Available at: *www.maff.gov.uk/* [Farming > Sustainable Agriculture].

McRae, T., C.A.S. Smith and L.J. Gregorich (eds.) (2000),
 Environmental Sustainability of Canadian Agriculture: Report of the Agri-Environmental Indicator Project, Agriculture and Agri-Food Canada (AAFC), Ottawa, Ontario, Canada. Available at: *www.agr.ca/policy/environment/publications/list.html*.

Mellerowics, K.T., H.W. Rees, T.L. Chow and I. Gnahem (1994),
 "Soil Conservation at the Watershed Level Using the Universal Soil Loss Equation with GIS and Microcomputer Technologies: A Case Study", *Journal of Soil and Water Conservation*, Vol. 49, No. 2, pp. 194-200.

Ministry for the Environment (1996),
 Sustainable Land Management: A Strategy for New Zealand, Wellington, New Zealand.

Mues, C., L. Chapman and R. van Hilst (1998),
 Promoting Improved Land Management practices on Australian Farms: A Survey of Landcare and Land Management Related Programmes, Australian Bureau of Agriculture and Resource Economics, Research Report 98.4, Canberra, Australia.

OECD (1997),
 Agriculture, Pesticides and the Environment: Policy Options, Paris, France. This document is accompanied by an OECD General Distribution document: Agriculture, Pesticides and the Environment: Policy Options – Annexes, [OCDE/GD(97)157]. Available at: *www.oecd.org/* [Documentation > 1997 > Reference Components > OCDE > OCDE/GD].

OECD (2000a),
 Comparing the profitability of organic and conventional farming: The impact of support on arable farming in France, General Distribution document, [ENV/EPOC/GEEI(99)5/FINAL], Paris France. Available at: *www.oecd.org/* [Documentation > 1999 > Reference Components > ENV > ENV/EPOC/GEEI].

OECD (2000b),
 The effects of support measures on the profitability of organic farming relative to conventional farming: A Case Study for the Netherlands, General Distribution document [ENV/EPOC/GEEI(99)4/FINAL], Paris, France. Available at: *www.oecd.org/* [Documentation > 1999 > Reference Components > ENV > ENV/EPOC/GEEI].

Phillips, D.L., P.D. Harding, V.W. Benson and J.V. Baglio (1993),
 "Non-point Source Pollution Impacts of Alternative Agricultural Management Practices in Illinois: A Simulation Study", *Journal of Soil and Water Conservation*, Vol. 48, No. 5, pp. 449-457.

Poiret, M. (1999),
 "Specialised Holdings And More Intensive Practices", in European Commission, *Agriculture, Environment, Rural Development: Facts and Figures – A Challenge for Agriculture*, Office for Official Publications of the European Communities, Luxembourg. Available at: *http://europa.eu.int/comm/dg06/envir/report/en/index.htm*.

Putman, J. and K. Alt (1987),
 "Erosion Control: How does it change farm Income?", *Journal of Soil and Water Conservation*, Vol. 42, No. 4, pp. 265-267.

Swinton, S.M. and E. Day (2000),
 Economics in the design, assessment, adoption, and policy analysis of I.P.M., Staff Paper 00-02, Department of Agricultural Economics, Michigan State University, East Lansing, Michigan, United States. Available at: *http://agecon.lib.umn.edu/msu/sp00-02.html*.

Topp, G.C., K.C. Wires, D.A. Angers, M.R. Carter, J.L.B. Culley, D.A. Holmstrom, B.D. Kay, G.P. Lafond, D.R. Langille, R.A. McBride, G.T. Patterson, E. Perfect, V. Rasiah, A.V. Rodd and K.T. Webb (1995),
 "Changes in Soil Structure", pp. 51-60, in D.F. Acton and L.J. Gregorich (eds.), *The Health of our Soils – Toward sustainable agriculture in Canada*, Agriculture and Agri-Food Canada (AAFC), Ottawa, Canada. Available at: *www.agr.ca/* [English > Site Index > Environment and Resource Management].

Uri, N.D. (2000),
 "Perceptions on the use of no-till farming in production agriculture in the United States: an analysis of survey results ", *Agriculture, Ecosystems and Environment*, Vol. 77, pp. 263-266.

USDA [United States Department of Agriculture] (1997),
 Agricultural Resources and Environmental Indicators, 1996-97, Agricultural Handbook No. 712, Natural Resources and Environment Division, Economic Research Service, Washington, DC., United States. Available at: *www.ers.usda.gov/* [Briefing Rooms > Agricultural Resources and Environmental Indicators].

113

Vandeman, A., J. Fernandez-Cornejo, S. Jans and B. Lin (1994),
   Adoption of Integrated Pest Management in US Agriculture, Agricultural Handbook No. 707, Economic Research Service, US Department of Agriculture, Washington, DC., United States.

Welsh, R. (1999),
   The Economics of Organic Grain and Soyabean Production in the Midwestern United States, Policy Studies Report No. 13, Henry A. Wallace Institute for Alternative Agriculture, Greenbelt, Maryland, United States. Available at: *www.hawiaa.org/hawiaa.htm*.

Part III

USE OF FARM INPUTS AND NATURAL RESOURCES

1. NUTRIENT USE
2. PESTICIDE USE AND RISKS
3. WATER USE

Chapter 1

NUTRIENT USE

HIGHLIGHTS

Context

Inputs of nutrients, such as nitrogen and phosphorus, are essential to agricultural production, and integral to raising productivity. At the same time, a surplus of nutrients in excess of immediate crop needs can be a source of potential environmental damage to surface and ground water (eutrophication), air quality (acidification) and contribute to global warming (greenhouse effect). If soils are farmed and nutrients not replenished, this can lead to declining soil fertility and may impair agricultural sustainability through "soil mining" of nutrients.

Many OECD countries have established goals to reduce nutrient emissions from agriculture. These are closely linked to the need for agriculture to comply with national standards for nitrate and phosphate emissions into aquatic environments. A number of international conventions and agreements also have the objective of limiting and reducing transboundary emissions into the environment, including nutrient emissions from agriculture into surface and ground water, marine waters and the atmosphere.

Indicators and recent trends

The OECD *soil surface nitrogen balance indicator* measures the difference between the nitrogen available to an agricultural system (inputs, mainly from livestock manure and chemical fertilisers) and the uptake of nitrogen by agriculture (outputs, largely crops and forage).* A persistent surplus indicates potential environmental pollution, while a persistent deficit indicates potential agricultural sustainability problems. The indicator provides information on the potential loss of nitrogen to the soil, the air, and to surface or groundwater. However, nitrogen loss through the volatilisation of ammonia to the atmosphere from livestock housing and stored manure is excluded from the calculation.

The trend with regard to surpluses in national nitrogen soil surface balances over the last decade is downward or constant for most OECD countries, which suggests that the potential environmental impact from agricultural nitrogen emissions is decreasing or stable. Some countries with a relatively high nitrogen surplus have reported significant reductions, although for a few countries surpluses have risen.

The spatial variation of nitrogen surpluses within a country can be considerable. Regional data suggests that even in countries with a relatively low national nitrogen surplus, nitrate pollution is experienced in some localities, while soil nutrient deficits occur in others

A second nutrient use indicator, the *efficiency of nitrogen use in agriculture*, measures the physical nitrogen input/output ratio. This indicator has shown an improvement in nitrogen use efficiency for most countries over the past decade. However, there is considerable variation across countries in the efficiency of using nitrogen in agriculture, and in some cases the efficiency of nitrogen use has deteriorated.

---

* For a detailed description of the OECD soil surface nitrogen balance indicator, including related data series for all OECD Member countries, 1985-1997, see the OECD website: *www.oecd.org/agr/env/indicators.htm*.

1. Background

Policy context

Many OECD countries have established goals to reduce emissions of nitrogen and phosphorous from agriculture into the environment, particularly from livestock farming. These goals are closely linked to the need for agriculture to comply with national standards for nitrate and phosphate emissions into drinking water and aquatic environments, such as rivers, lakes and marine waters. Policy measures to reduce nutrient emissions usually involve a mixture of economic incentives (or taxes), advisory support and regulatory compulsion (Abrahams and Shortle, 1997; USDA, 1997, pp. 304-224).

The *European Union*'s Nitrate Directive (EU Council Directive 676/91), for example, is one of the measures introduced to comply with EU drinking water standards and operates by limiting the usage of nitrogen inputs within designated nitrate vulnerable zones (see Water Quality chapter). Many countries have also introduced programmes to limit acidification, including agricultural ammonia emissions into the atmosphere resulting from livestock farming and the use of inorganic fertilisers. An example includes the *Netherlands* Priority Programme on Acidification (Lekkerkerk *et al.*, 1995).

Environmental emissions resulting from agricultural use of nutrients also have an international dimension, because of transboundary agricultural nutrient emissions into rivers, lakes, marine waters and the atmosphere, and their contribution to global warming. A number of international conventions and agreements have the objective to limit and reduce transboundary emissions into the environment, including, for example, the 1992 Helsinki Convention on the Protection and use of Transboundary Water Courses and Lakes, and the Oslo and Paris Conventions for the Prevention of Marine Pollution (OSPARCOM; see also Box 1 below). The latter Convention agreed to aim for a 50 per cent reduction of nitrogen and phosphorous emissions into the marine environment of the Baltic and North Seas between 1985 and 1995. Also under the Convention on Long-Range Transboundary Air Pollution, the Protocol to Abate Acidification, Eutrophication and Ground-level Ozone, requires signatory countries to take measures to control ammonia emissions from agriculture.[1]

Environmental context[2]

An adequate supply of nutrients in the soil is essential to crop growth. Some nutrients are required in large amounts, for example nitrogen, phosphorus and potassium, whilst others are needed in small quantities, such as magnesium and iron. As crops grow and are harvested or consumed by livestock, nutrients are removed from the farming system when crop or livestock products are moved off-farm. However, some nutrients will be recycled on the farm as crop residues or through using livestock manure (Figure 1). If these are not replenished, a nutrient deficiency may develop, leading to declining soil fertility and yields. In the long term, this leads to soil degradation ("soil mining") and may impair agricultural sustainability.

A build up of surplus nutrients in excess of immediate crop and forage needs can lead to nutrient emissions, which at certain levels are sources of environmental pollution. This represents a possible cause of technical and economic inefficiency in the use of nutrients, but also a source of potential environmental damage to surface water, groundwater, marine waters and the atmosphere.

Surface water and marine water pollution into rivers, lakes and coastal waters, particularly from phosphates, can accelerate the process of eutrophication (*i.e.* algae growth and oxygen shortages in water). This can impair the use of surface water for drinking, and damage the biodiversity of these aquatic environments and harm their use for fishing and recreational purposes.[3]

Groundwater pollution (*e.g.* of aquifers) from nitrates can be damaging to human health. Pollution of groundwater is more problematic than that of surface water since groundwater, once polluted, may remain contaminated for many years, whereas surface water is refreshed relatively rapidly.

Air pollution, through the volatilisation of ammonia in livestock excreta, leads to limited direct effects on plant foliage and wider indirect effects as a result of both dry (*i.e.* particulate) and wet (*i.e.* rain) re-deposition,

Figure 1. **The nitrogen cycle**

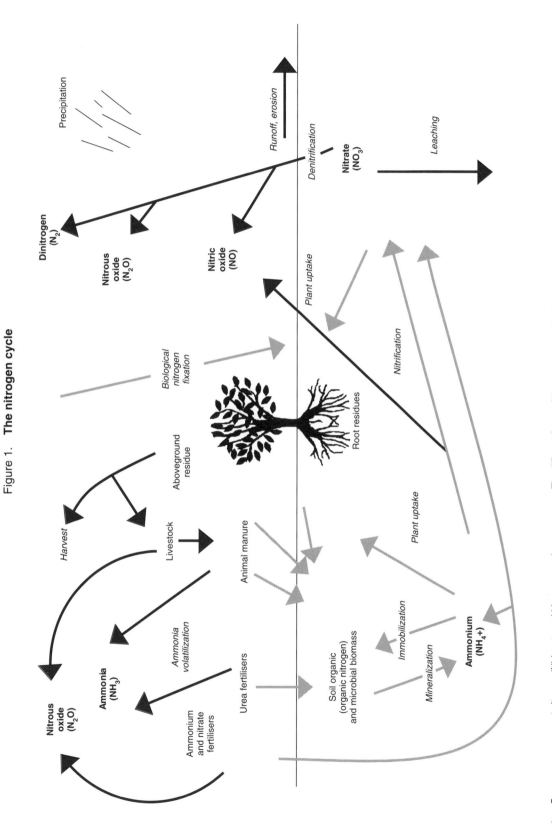

Note: Grey arrows represent nitrogen (N) inputs and blue arrows nitrogen outputs. The different forms of N are represented in bold text and the processes of N transformation are shown in italics.
Source: Adapted from Cavigelli *et al.* (1998).

contributing to soil acidification and water eutrophication. These processes also contribute as a secondary consequence, to greenhouse gas emissions (see Greenhouse Gas chapter).

Three main processes affect nutrient supplies in an agricultural system. These are described below, and shown in Figure 1.

- *Direct input of nutrients*: these are mainly supplied from *i*) inorganic or chemical fertilisers; *ii*) organic manures, mainly livestock manure, crop residues and sewage sludge;[4] *iii*) biological nitrogen fixation, largely from legume crops (*e.g.* soyabeans, rice paddies) and legume pastures (*e.g.* clover);[5] and *iv*) atmospheric deposition of dust and rain containing nitrogen, which mainly originates from industrial activities, but also from agriculture.

- *Nutrient availability and susceptibility to loss* largely occurs through the following processes: *i*) mineralisation, which makes soil nutrients available for plant uptake and growth; *ii*) immobilisation, which renders nutrients unavailable to plants; *iii*) volatilisation of ammonia to the atmosphere, from stored manure, livestock housing or when manure and ammonium fertilisers are spread on the soil; and *iv*) nitrification and denitrification of soil nitrate into nitrogen gas and nitrous oxide, a greenhouse gas.

- *Net losses of nutrients* occur as a result of: *i*) denitrification and leaching, the physical downward movement of soluble nutrients through the soil; *ii*) erosion and runoff, the lateral transportation of nutrients in soil sediment or solution; and *iii*) the net uptake of nutrients by crops and grassland, which varies with different crops, pasture conditions and the growing season.

The extent to which these processes lead to a net nutrient surplus or deficit from agricultural activities will depend on a combination of factors including:

- *the type of nutrient*: for example, phosphates are easily absorbed by soil particles and, hence, are leached at very slow rates, whereas nitrates are very soluble and not absorbed, and are therefore, very susceptible to being leached from the soil;

- *the efficiency* with which different crops use nutrients, which can vary between different crops (see section below on the nitrogen efficiency indicator);

- *the type of cropping/livestock system*, for example, the pattern of disposal of manure from livestock farms has become more problematic, because intensive agricultural production systems have typically led to the separation of crop and livestock farming;

- *the environmental assimilative capacity of an agro-ecosystem*, which influences the environmental fate of surplus nutrients and is affected by soil type, organic matter content, degree of aeration, moisture, temperature, topography and climatic conditions;

- *naturally occurring nutrient levels*, which may be influenced by underlying geology and atmospheric deposition of nitrogen, although in most OECD countries atmospheric nitrogen has an anthropogenic origin, mainly industry; and,

- *farm management practices*, including the timing and method of nutrient application and storage (see the nutrient management section in the Farm Management chapter).

2. Indicators

Nitrogen balance

Definition

The physical difference (surplus/deficit) between nitrogen inputs into, and outputs from, an agricultural system, per hectare of agricultural land.

Method of calculation

The nitrogen balance indicator is measured by the soil surface balance, which is calculated as the difference between the total quantity of nitrogen inputs entering, and the quantity of nitrogen outputs leaving, the soil over one year. Calculation of a soil surface balance for other nutrients, *e.g.* phosphorous or potassium, is similar.[6] The annual total **quantity of inputs** for the soil surface nitrogen balance, includes the summation of the following elements (see Figure 2):

- *inorganic or chemical nitrogen fertiliser*: quantity consumed by agriculture;

- *net livestock manure nitrogen production*: total numbers of livestock categorised according to species (*e.g.* chickens, turkeys), gender, age, purpose (*e.g.* milk cows, beef cattle) and weight/milk yield of animal (*e.g.* the manure production of a dairy cow varies considerably according to its annual average milk yield), multiplied by coefficients describing the quantity of nitrogen contained in the manure generated per animal per year, net of the nitrogen loss through the volatilisation of ammonia to the atmosphere from livestock housing and stored manure;[7]

- *biological nitrogen fixation*: area of harvested legume crops and legume pasture systems (*e.g.* soybeans, alfalfa) multiplied by coefficients of nitrogen fixation, plus the nitrogen fixation by free living soil organisms computed from the total agricultural land area multiplied by a single coefficient of nitrogen fixation;

- *atmospheric deposition of nitrogen*: total agricultural land area multiplied by a single coefficient of nitrogen deposited/kg/hectare;[8]

- *nitrogen from recycled organic matter*: quantity of sewage sludge applied to agricultural land multiplied by a single coefficient of nitrogen content of sewage sludge;

- *nitrogen contained in seeds and planting materials*: quantity of seeds and planting materials (*e.g.* cereals, potato tubers) multiplied by coefficients of nitrogen content of seeds and planting materials.

The annual total **quantity of outputs** , or nitrogen uptake, for the nitrogen balance includes:

- *crop and fodder production*: quantity of harvested crop production (*e.g.* cereals, root crops, fruit and vegetables); harvested fodder crops (*e.g.* fodder beets, silage maize); and grass from temporary

Figure 2. **The main elements in the OECD soil surface nitrogen balance**

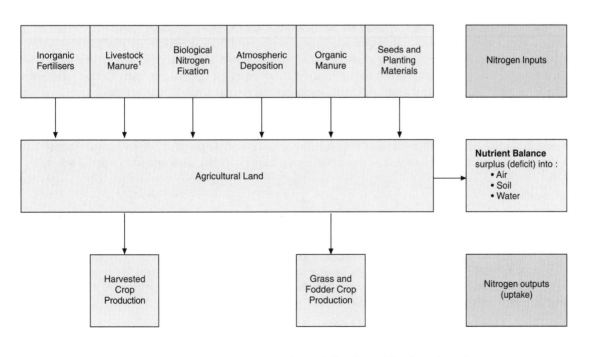

1. Livestock manure excludes nitrogen losses through volatilisation of ammonia from livestock housing and stored manure.
Source: OECD Secretariat.

and permanent pasture, respectively multiplied by coefficients of nitrogen uptake to produce a kilogram of output.[9]

The calculation of the soil surface balance provides information about the surplus (deficit) of nitrogen in the soil, water and air from an agricultural system. A large number of researchers, OECD countries and international organisations are using modified versions of the so-called *"soil surface balance"* across a range of agricultural nutrients, but typically nitrogen, phosphorous and potassium.[10]

The OECD calculation is a modified "gross balance" as it excludes nitrogen loss through the volatilisation of ammonia to the atmosphere from livestock housing and stored manure (Figure 1), as the key issue for many OECD countries is the potential impact of excess nitrogen on water, rather than air, pollution. Even so, nitrogen air emissions from agriculture are important within the context of many OECD countries national air pollution emission limits and also international conventions, such as the UN Long-Range Transboundary Air Pollution Convention.

Much of the basic data required to calculate a national soil surface nitrogen balance (*i.e.* fertiliser use, livestock numbers, areas and quantities of crop and forage production) are available annually from official agricultural census data. In the case of the coefficients required to convert livestock and crop production data into nitrogen equivalents, normative estimates are available from agricultural research institutes and published literature, although for some countries further work is required to refine and develop these coefficients.

The soil surface nitrogen balance indicator has the attribute of simplicity: information can be collected through official agricultural censuses for the basic data, and field level research and surveys for coefficients. In addition, the methodology is transparent, and consequently the underlying assumptions and approximations may be easily refined as and when additional information becomes available.

The explanatory potential of nutrient balances are enhanced when they are related to agricultural land area or to the total input of nutrients. The choice of a suitable denominator partly depends on the kind of indicator required. For example, as a measure of the risk of ground and surface water pollution or soil nutrient depletion, the nutrient surplus (deficit) per hectare of total agricultural land may be appropriate. This is the indicator described here.

Other denominators, however, may be appropriate, for example nutrient surplus per unit of input (Bomans *et al.*, 1996). The latter allows comparisons between different regions or production systems. It is also possible to provide a physical measure of nitrogen use efficiency in agriculture from the soil surface balance, from the calculation of the ratio of total nitrogen uptake (output) to the total nitrogen available (input), as described in the section below on the nitrogen efficiency indicator.

It is also necessary to consider the appropriate spatial scale at which to express national average nutrient balances, in order to capture regional variations. Oppenshaw (1984) demonstrated the sensitivity of numerical measures to their spatial measurement unit, and Antle *et al.*, (1999) suggest that careful attention needs to be paid to spatial scales when evaluating economic and environmental trade-offs.

Recent trends

The nitrogen balance estimates reveal that for most OECD countries the **key sources of nitrogen** input in agricultural systems are from livestock manure – mainly from cattle and to a lesser extent pigs, poultry, sheep and goats – and from inorganic nitrogen fertiliser (Annex Table 2). In general, inorganic commercial fertiliser is by far the major source of nitrogen applied to crops (and in some cases to forage), because transport costs usually inhibit the more widespread use of manure other than in the immediate vicinity of livestock farms (USDA, 1997, pp. 97-115).

Other important nitrogen inputs in agricultural systems include atmospheric deposition and biological nitrogen fixation. Only a minor role is played in most countries by sewage sludge, manure imports and nitrogen in seeds and planting materials. Those countries with a more extensive form of agriculture (*e.g.* Australia, Canada, Mexico, New Zealand and the United States) tend to have a higher share of total nitrogen inputs provided from atmospheric deposition and biological nitrogen fixation, compared with the more intensive systems of farming, common in *Europe*, *Japan* and *Korea*.

The *absolute levels and trends of soil surface nitrogen balances* vary considerably across OECD member countries (Figure 3). This mainly reflects differences in agricultural systems, underlying biophysical conditions, and the policy environment in which agriculture operates, although some of the variability can be explained by differences in the nitrogen coefficients (see endnote 7, for example, in the case of ammonia emission estimates). In general, countries with high livestock densities and intensive farming systems have the highest nitrogen surpluses, and for most, but not all, countries the trend in nitrogen surplus is in a downward direction.

Figure 3.   **Soil surface nitrogen balance estimates: 1985-87 to 1995-97**

Change in the nitrogen balance
kg/ha of total agricultural land

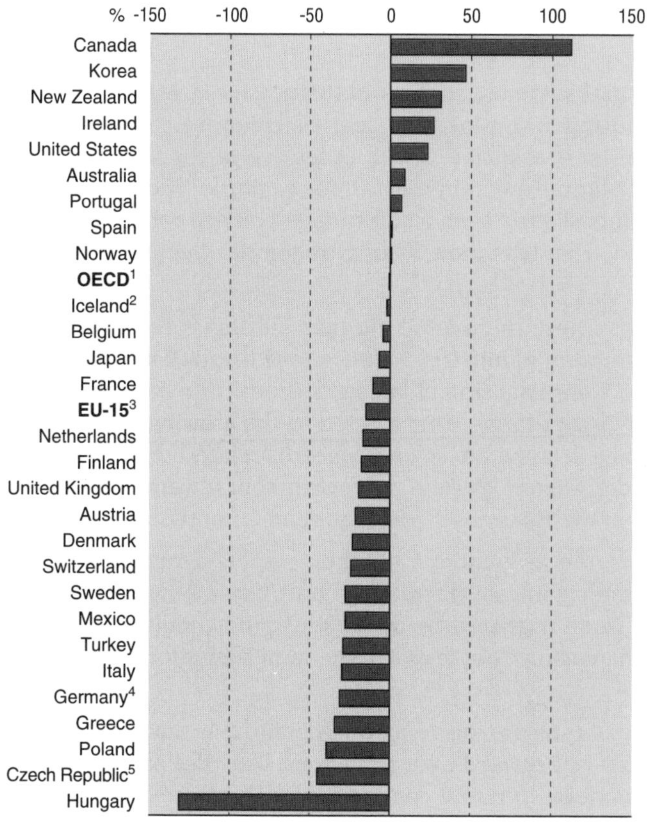

Nitrogen balance
kg/ha of total agricultural land

	1985-87	1995-97
Canada	6	13
Korea	173	253
New Zealand	5	6
Ireland	62	79
United States	25	31
Australia	7	7
Portugal	62	66
Spain	40	41
Norway	72	73
OECD	23	23
Iceland	7	7
Belgium	189	181
Japan	145	135
France	59	53
EU-15	69	58
Netherlands	314	262
Finland	78	64
United Kingdom	107	86
Austria	35	27
Denmark	154	118
Switzerland	80	61
Sweden	47	34
Mexico	28	20
Turkey	17	12
Italy	44	31
Germany	88	61
Greece	58	38
Poland	48	29
Czech Republic	99	54
Hungary	47	-15

1.   OECD averages, excluding Luxembourg.
2.   The 1995-97 average refers to 1995.
3.   EU-15 averages, excluding Luxembourg.
4.   Including eastern and western Germany for the whole period 1985-97.
5.   Data for the period 1985-92 refer to the Czech part of the former Czechoslovakia.
Notes: See Annex Tables 1 and 2. While these calculations have been derived from using an internationally harmonised methodology, nitrogen conversion coefficients can differ between countries, which may be due to a variety of reasons. For example, differing agro-ecological conditions, varying livestock weight/yield, and differences in the methods used to estimate these coefficients. Also one part of the calculation is the atmospheric deposition of nitrogen which is mostly independent from agricultural activities.
Source: OECD (2000).

Figure 4. **Regional distribution of a nitrogen balance:**[1] **Canada, 1996**

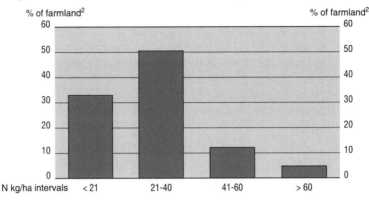

1. The nitrogen balance shown in this figure uses a different methodology than that used by OECD to calculate the balances shown in Figure 3.
2. Farmland area comprises British Columbia, Alberta, Saskatchewan, Manitoba, Ontario, Quebec and Atlantic Provinces.
Source: MacDonald (2000).

Countries with more extensive agricultural systems, such as *Australia, Canada, Mexico, New Zealand, Turkey* and the *United States*, have the lowest nitrogen surpluses. In nearly all of these countries, however, there are typically both environmental problems associated with excessive nitrogen emissions from agriculture, and nitrogen deficits affecting plant growth. In *Canada*, for example, recent estimates of residual nitrogen from agriculture (which differs slightly from a soil surface balance calculation) reveal a range of residual nitrogen across the country from less than 20 kg nitrogen per hectare (kgN/ha) to in excess of 60 kgN/ha (Figure 4).[11]

A notable trend in some of the countries where the overall nitrogen surplus is relatively low compared to the OECD average, is the growing problem of *nutrient pollution from livestock manure*. In *Canada, New Zealand* and the *United States*, for example, the expansion of livestock production over the past 10-15 years has been paralleled by a decline in livestock farms. This has led to the growing concentration of livestock production, higher livestock densities in some areas, and concerns related to the environmental and health impacts of disposing of livestock waste.[12] A similar development toward concentration of livestock operations is beginning to emerge in the *European Union* (European Commission, 1999).

For the *Czech Republic, Hungary* and *Poland*, the reduction in nitrogen surplus over the past 10 years has been substantial, particularly linked to the significant decrease in both cattle numbers and the use of inorganic fertilisers (Figure 3).[13] This has been triggered by the collapse in agricultural support levels, the elimination of input subsidies and increasing debt levels in the farm sector following the transition toward a market economy (OECD, 1998a).

Most other OECD European countries have also experienced substantial reductions in nitrogen surpluses over the past decade, most notably in *Denmark, Germany, Greece, Italy,* the *Netherlands, Sweden, Switzerland* and the *United Kingdom*.[14] This has been due to a combination of factors, varying in degree across different countries, including the reduction in dairy cattle numbers linked to milk supply control policies; removal of arable land under the *European Union's* (EU) set-aside scheme; and specific policies aimed at reducing nitrogen surpluses from livestock farms and at limiting inorganic fertiliser use (see Romstad, 1997a).

It is also noticeable that in the *European Union* the overall decline in total nitrogen surplus from 1985 to 1997, both in absolute terms and as a share of the total agricultural area, was mainly due to the reduction in inorganic fertiliser use (nitrogen input), while the production of harvested crops (nitrogen output, *e.g.* cereals, oilseed crops, etc.) increased (Figure 5). These diverging trends might also indicate the improving efficiency in the use of fertilisers per unit volume of crop output, partly revealed through the

Figure 5. **Decomposition of changes in the European Union[1] nitrogen balance:[2] 1985-87 to 1995-97**

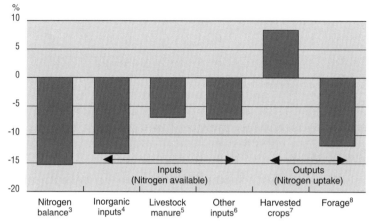

	1985-87	1995-97
	kg/ha	
Nitrogen balance	69	58
	million tonnes	
Inorganic inputs	11.1	9.6
Livestock manure	6.7	6.2
Other inputs	4.2	3.9
Harvested crops	5.3	5.8
Forage	6.8	6.0

1. EU-15 averages, including western and eastern Germany, but excluding Luxembourg.
2. Preliminary estimates, see text for method of calculation.
3. Nitrogen balance: nitrogen in kilograms per hectare.
4. Inorganic inputs: includes inorganic nitrogen fertiliser.
5. Livestock manure: nitrogen content of manure production minus volatilisation of ammonia from livestock housing and manure storage.
6. Other inputs: includes biological nitrogen fixation, atmospheric deposition, organic fertiliser, seeds and planting materials.
7. Harvested crops: includes nitrogen uptake from annually harvested cereals, oil crops, pulses, industrial crops, other crops and permanent crops (*e.g.*, apples).
8. Forage: includes nitrogen uptake from harvested forage crops (*e.g.*, silage maize) and pasture.
Source: OECD (2000).

improvement in the EU's nitrogen use efficiency (Annex Table 1). Over the same period, the downward trend in livestock manure production (nitrogen input) revealed a much lower rate of decline relative to inorganic fertiliser (Figure 5). This development was mainly attributed to the fall in EU cattle numbers, with some reduction in pig numbers, partly offset by increasing poultry, sheep and goat populations.

In some countries the nitrogen surplus has risen over the last decade, and this is a cause of some concern where levels of nitrogen surplus are already high relative to the potential for environmental pollution. In the case of *Ireland*, for example, a recent Report (Environmental Protection Agency, 1999*a*) indicates that the problem of eutrophication remains a major challenge and that a large number of private water supplies fail Drinking Water Regulations due, to a large extent, to emissions from agriculture. Recent calculations in Ireland show that savings of £25 million Irish Punts (US$32 million) could be made by reducing the unnecessary use of artificial phosphorus fertiliser. In some soils phosphorous levels are high enough to permit optimum crop production for a number of years without further additions (Environmental Protection Agency, 1999*b*).

For *Korea* an OECD (1998*b*) study notes that increasing livestock production and use of inorganic fertilisers has had a detrimental effect on water quality. The accumulation of phosphorus in soils arising from the over use of phosphorus fertiliser also has been reported. For example, the level of phosphorus in crop land (other than rice paddy fields) has been recorded as 51 per cent in excess of the optimum for crop growth.[15]

While the problems of excessive nutrient emissions from agriculture are widespread amongst OECD countries, in some sub-national regions *nutrient deficits* are also of concern. Estimates of soil fertility in *Australia* show one third of the total harvested cereal area is seriously deficient in nitrogen with no gain in yields for 40 years (Commonwealth of Australia, 1995, pp. 33-34).[16] Even so, since the 1960s much of Australia's agricultural land has consistently received applications of phosphate fertilisers in excess of plant uptake (Hooper *et al.*, 2000).

Canada also reports problems of under-fertilisation of soils, especially in the Prairie Provinces. In the United States it has been estimated that one-third of the maize area and a higher proportion of the wheat area in the top five cereal producing states suffer from acute nitrogen deficiency (USDA, 1994, pp. 71-74). High levels of calculated phosphate deficiency were also reported for these areas.

Interpretation and links to other indicators

Nutrient or mineral balances establish links between agricultural nutrient use, changes in environmental quality, and the sustainable use of soil nutrient resources. A persistent surplus indicates potential environmental problems; a persistent deficit indicates potential agricultural sustainability problems. With respect to environmental impacts, however, the main determinant is the absolute size of the nutrient surplus/deficit linked to local farm nutrient management practices and agro-ecological conditions, such as soil types and climatic features.

A nutrient balance surplus or deficit, at least over the short term, does not unambiguously indicate a beneficial or harmful environmental or resource impact. A nutrient balance can only show the potential for environmental damage or unsustainable use of soil resources, not actual pollution or resource depletion. Nutrient balances do, however, provide a practical and relatively low cost, if indirect, estimate of potential environmental and resource sustainability effects.

While the nitrogen balance calculation does provide an indication of potential pollution and identifies those agricultural areas and systems with very high nitrogen loadings, it does not provide a measure of the extent of pollution nor indicate the pollution pathways which are influenced by other factors, such as rainfall, land cover and on-farm nitrogen management practices. A further limitation to the current set of OECD calculations is that not all coefficients are fully harmonised (*e.g.* estimates of the volatilisation of ammonia from livestock housing vary widely which might be a source of error), and there are differences between countries in methods of calculating nitrogen uptake by crops (*e.g.* derivation of the nitrogen uptake by pasture). Moreover, for some countries, Sweden for example, using agricultural land as the denominator to calculate the nitrogen surplus per hectare could be misleading as large areas of semi-natural grassland receive little if any nitrogen fertiliser.

In establishing a **reference level** against which to monitor and assess changes in nitrogen surpluses, some studies suggest that the figure of 50 kg N/ha annually, including variations between 30 to 70 kg N/ha, should be taken as a baseline when assessing the risk of possible nitrate leaching in ground and surface waters (Eckert *et al.*, 1999). However, other studies suggest the appropriate reference level may vary considerably, particularly according to the type of soil, climatic conditions and other factors. In New Zealand, for example, guidelines for nutrient loadings vary from 30 kg N/ha on sandy soils to 300 kg N/ha on clayey soils (Cameron and Trenouth, 1999).

In cases of nutrient deficits it may be more difficult to establish reference levels or baselines to monitor changes in nutrient depletion and declining soil fertility (Agricultural Council of Australia and New Zealand, 1993, p. 39). Such information might possibly be derived from existing soil surveys to establish baseline values of soil nutrients, which might not only be used to gauge changes in soil nutrient status, but could also be used to identify regions requiring further monitoring and investigation.[17]

Whilst an annual national nutrient balance provides an overall impression of the performance of the agricultural sector in its use and management of agricultural nutrients, there is usually significant **spatial and temporal variation in nutrient balances**. This is due to regional variations in farming systems and biophysical conditions caused by, for example, changing weather conditions, technological variations, and the economic and policy context.

The data required to calculate soil surface balances are generally available at the sub-national scale. A soil surface balance can therefore be used to generate regional indicators, thereby identifying the degree of regional variation around a national average. An example of the regional variation in the Canadian national nitrogen balance is shown in Figure 4.

A study by Brouwer, *et al.* (1999) also provides information of sub-national variation in nitrogen balances across the European Union countries. This study suggests that nitrogen surpluses remain below

50 kg nitrogen per hectare (kg N/ha) on almost 50 per cent of the agricultural land in the EU, exceeds 100 kg N/ha on a further 22 per cent, and is in excess of 200 kg N/ha on only 2 per cent of agricultural land, with the EU average in the late 1990s nearly 60 kg N/ha (Figure 3). While in *France*, for example, the range of nitrogen surpluses is between 6 kg N/ha in Limousin up to 120 kg N/ha in Brittany, with the national average just over 50 kg N/ha (Figure 3).

Recent research has also shown that considerable potential exists to combine nutrient balances with other spatial information. This can be achieved by using statistical, mathematical and geographical information system (GIS) techniques to estimate more accurately areas where ground and surface waters are at greatest risk from agricultural nutrient pollution (see Allanson *et al.*, 1993; Cook and Norman, 1996). A study in *Ireland* has used such an approach and suggests that about 10 per cent of the total land area is highly vulnerable to groundwater pollution (EUROSTAT, 1996).

The information derived from nutrient balances can be enhanced when used in conjunction with knowledge and indicators regarding other influences on the production system, such as soil and climatic conditions, the type and density of livestock, crop production systems, farm management practices and the quality of soil and water.

Nitrogen efficiency

Definition

The ratio of total nitrogen uptake (output) to the total nitrogen available (input) in an agricultural system.

Method of calculation

This indicators provides a physical measure of nitrogen use efficiency in agriculture by calculating the ratio of total nitrogen uptake (output) to the total nitrogen available (input). The indicator draws data from the nitrogen soil surface balance indicator described in the previous section.

Recent trends

The efficiency of nitrogen use reveals marked differences across OECD countries (Figure 6). On average OECD countries utilise over 60 per cent of the annual nitrogen available (input) into the agricultural system. It is also important to note that some countries with a relatively low national average nitrogen surplus per hectare (*e.g. Australia* and the *United States*), have nearly the same nitrogen efficiency levels comparable to countries with much higher average nitrogen surplus levels (*e.g. European Union* average, *Norway* and *Switzerland*).[18]

A modified version of the nitrogen efficiency indicator relates agricultural nutrient inputs to outputs of protein, providing an indicator that reflects agriculture's contribution to both the economic and environmental aspects of sustainable development. Work in the *United Kingdom* on such an indicator reveals that between 1985 and 1994 nitrogen inputs relative to protein production have been generally constant (UK Department of the Environment, 1996, pp. 136-37).

Interpretation and links to other indicators

It important to emphasise that this an indicator of physical and not economic efficiency of nitrogen use in agriculture. Also the indicator measures the use efficiency of all sources of nitrogen used in agriculture and not just inorganic nitrogen fertilisers. Moreover, the efficiency with which different crops use nutrients varies. For example, nitrogen, is usually used less efficiently in rice cultivation than in most other major crop production systems, although efficiency of use has increased as a result of improvements in technology, such as side root fertilisation.[19]

127|

Figure 6. **Nitrogen efficiency[1] based on the soil surface nitrogen balance: 1995-97**

Percentage of nitrogen uptake (output) to nitrogen input

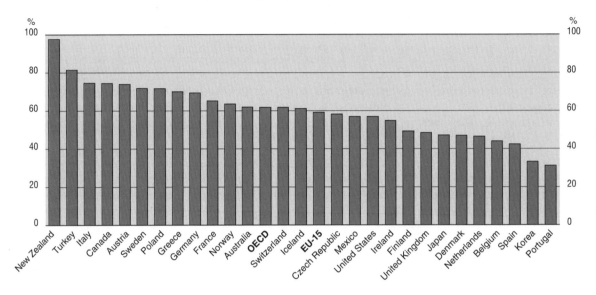

1. Nitrogen use efficiency measured as the percentage ratio of total nitrogen uptake (output) to the total nitrogen available (input).
Notes: See Annex Table 1. Hungary is not included in the figure.
Source: OECD (2000).

3. Related information

Water pollution from nutrients

Agriculture is not the only sector which burdens the environment with emissions of nitrogen, phosphates, and other nutrients, although for most OECD countries it is a major contributor. It accounts for around two-thirds of nitrogen emissions into surface and marine waters and about one-third for phosphorus (see Water Quality chapter). Estimates suggest that nitrate losses into the soil may be up to 50 times higher in areas with intensive agriculture where chemical fertilisers and livestock manure are applied, compared with losses from uncultivated areas with a similar soil type (EEA, 1995, p. 335). The extent of groundwater pollution from agricultural nutrients is less well documented than for surface and marine waters, partly because it can take many years for nutrients to leach through overlying soils into aquifers.

Air pollution from nutrient emissions

While agricultural activity contributes to emissions of acidifying substances, mainly ammonia (NH_3), the major sources of acidifying emissions, sulphur dioxide (SO_2) and nitrous oxide (N_2O), derive from coal and fuel combustion by industry, power stations and motor vehicles. Evidence for some European countries indicates that around 95 per cent of ammonia (NH_3) emissions into the air result from agricultural activity, with about 60 per cent from animal manure (particularly cattle) and much of the remainder from the use of inorganic nitrogen fertilisers (European Commission, 1999). However, although agriculture contributes to problems of acidification, it is also adversely affected by the impact of acidifying air deposition on agricultural land, from agricultural and other sources.

In the late 1990s about 7 per cent of global greenhouse gas emissions were accounted for by nitrous oxide, with 48 per cent of this total derived from agricultural sources (see Table 2 in the Greenhouse Gas chapter).

Comparison of the OECD and OSPARCOM nitrogen balance calculations

There are various approaches to calculate nitrogen balances used by different national agencies and international organisations. One comparison that it is of particular interest at the international level is between that developed by OECD described in this chapter and that used by Oslo and Paris Conventions for the Prevention of Marine Pollution (OSPARCOM, see above). A brief comparison of the two approaches, using the Swiss nitrogen balance data for the early 1990s as an example, is provided in Box 1.

4. Future challenges

The current soil surface nitrogen balance calculations could be improved by verifying basic data and *nitrogen conversion coefficients*, as well as ensuring that nitrogen fertiliser usage data applies only to agriculture, and does not include other uses such as for urban gardens. In addition, harmonising definitions of terminology would allow, for example, the distinction to be made between temporary and permanent grassland and the interpretation of rough grazing.

Improving the expression of the *spatial variation* in national nitrogen balances through the calculation of regional level balances, would permit a clearer picture of where nitrogen surplus/deficit problems exist at a sub-national level. The example of *Canada* (Figure 4), demonstrates the possibility that exists to reveal regional variations in national calculations.

Using the same methodology, soil surface balances could also be calculated for phosphates and potassium, while the indicator could be improved by a re-examination of the assumptions made regarding volatilisation of ammonia from livestock housing, biological nitrogen fixation, nitrogen deposition and denitrification. Also consideration might be given to how crop residues left in the field after harvesting might be included in the calculations.

One way in which some of these issues might be resolved would be to calculate a *gross nitrogen balance*, that takes account of all nitrogen losses into the environment (*i.e.* soil, water and air). This would involve, in particular, adding the volatilisation of ammonia from livestock housing and stored manure to the nitrogen input side of the calculation, which is a source of air pollution in some cases (see OSPARCOM approach Box 1).

Weaknesses in the calculation arising from insufficient attention to the handling of livestock feedstuffs and waste products could be addressed by the *farm gate balance approach*. Work by Brouwer *et al.* (1994, p. 22), however, suggests that it is likely to be of marginal importance in the calculation of regional balances.

The farm gate balance calculates the difference between the quantity of nutrient inputs into the agricultural system from both crop and livestock farming and the nutrient content of agricultural output. It is fixed at the boundary between primary agriculture and the agro-food chain (van Eerdt and Fong, 1998). Sources of inputs are chemical fertilisers, purchased live animals, feed, and organic material such as sewage sludge. Outputs include both crop and livestock products. However for many countries, implementation of this approach is currently hampered by incomplete and missing data relating to livestock feedstuffs and waste products.[20]

Ascertaining which factors account for annual changes in nutrient balance calculations would also be a useful area to explore, particularly the extent to which variable climatic conditions are responsible for these changes (Pirttijarvi *et al.*, 1999). Establishing linkages with other environmental issues, particularly soil and water quality, biodiversity and farm management practices might be undertaken to enhance the explanatory potential of different indicators. The possibility of achieving this could be advanced by using GIS techniques.

Box 1. **Comparison of the OECD and OSPARCOM nitrogen balance calculations**

The OECD soil surface nitrogen balance calculation is similar to the OSPARCOM farm gate balance approach. Even so, a key difference between these two approaches is that while OECD excludes losses through volatilisation of ammonia from livestock housing and stored manure, OSPARCOM includes them. Thus, the OSPARCOM method can be described as a "gross" nitrogen balance that takes into account all nitrogen loss to the environment (*i.e.* soil, water and air).

The calculation of nitrogen input (availability) in the OSPARCOM calculation includes, the import on-farm (or purchase) of forage and seeds, the use of chemical fertilisers and sewage sludge, and biological nitrogen fixation and atmospheric deposition. Concerning the calculation of nitrogen output (uptake) this includes livestock (*e.g.* milk, meat and eggs) and crop products. This method takes into account the flows of nitrogen on and off-farm, unlike the OECD approach, which focuses on nitrogen flows into the soil.

Comparison of the OECD and OSPARCOM Methods,
Based on Data for Switzerland, early 1990s

	1 000 tonnes of nitrogen (N) per year	
A	Imported forage	25
B	Chemical fertiliser	70
C	Sewage sludge	5
D	Atmospheric deposition	36
E	Biological nitrogen fixation	45
F	Livestock products	26
G	Crop products	15
H	Change in soil nitrogen stock	−1
I	Ammonia losses: livestock housing and manure	20
J	Ammonia losses: from fields	26
K	Denitrification	52
L	Soil erosion	2
M	Run-off	1
N	Leaching	40
O	Other losses	< 1
P	Animal feed	12
Q	Livestock manure	149
R	Losses in feeding forage	46
S	Forage	150
T	Seeds	< 1

OSPARCOM Method	1 000 tonnes N/year
Input: A + B + C + D + E =	181
Output: F + G=	41
Surplus: =	140
Losses: (H) + (I + J + K + L + M + N + O) =	140

OECD Method (according to the nitrogen flows used in the OSPARCOM calculation)

Input: B + C + D + E + (Q − I) + T =	285
Output: G + S=	165
Balance: =	120

The results for Switzerland show similar trends using the two methods. The difference of 20 000 tonnes between the two methods is explained by the ammonia losses from livestock housing and stored manure.

Source: Federal Office for Agriculture, Berne, Switzerland (unpublished).

Up to the present, work has been directed at developing physical indicators of changes in nutrient use. However, an approach that takes into consideration economic and policy dimensions would be useful.[21] This might be achieved by developing a "cost-benefit" approach that analyses the relationship between the environmental and health costs associated with nutrient use, and the benefits derived from nutrients in terms of helping to raise agricultural productivity.[22] Currently the scale of the costs relative to the benefits of nutrient use in agriculture are unclear, and it is this relative assessment which is needed to better inform policy makers and other stakeholders, and prioritise different measures to reduce nitrogen surpluses.

NOTES

1. Details of OSPARCOM are available at: *www.ospar.org/eng/html/welcome.html*. Concerning the Protocol to abate acidification, eutrophication and ground-level ozone, see details at: *www.unece.org/env/lrtap/*.

2. This section draws on the work of Follett (1995); Lekkerkerk *et al.* (1995); Shaffer (1995); Sharpley (1995); Sharpley (2000); and van der Hoek *et al.* (1998).

3. The focus of this section is mainly on the use of nitrogen in agriculture, but for a recent review of the use of phosphorus in agriculture and phosphate losses into the environment see Sharpley (2000).

4. With increasing quantities of urban sewage sludge and municipal waste there is interest in using this as a source of fertiliser in agriculture, see for example, Bonnieux and Rainelli (1997); and USDA (1997, pp. 99-100; 111). For a review of the use of sewage as a fertiliser in agriculture across Europe and in Canada and the United States, see ADEME (1999).

5. The role of biological nitrogen fixation in agriculture is discussed by Galloway (1998).

6. The methodology to develop soil surface balances described here draws, in particular, from the work of Bomans *et al.* (1996). For a more detailed description of the OECD soil surface nitrogen balance methodology, information is available on the OECD web site, see OECD (2001).

7. In the OECD soil surface nitrogen balances, assumption/estimates of the volatilisation of ammonia from livestock housing and stored manure range from 15 to 40 per cent of the total nitrogen contained in livestock manure production, with the majority of OECD countries using an assumption/estimate of about 15 per cent. For details of these assumptions/estimates, see OECD (2001).

8. It should be noted that the atmospheric deposition of nitrogen includes all sources, from agricultural and non-agricultural activities.

9. In general the coefficients of nitrogen uptake by harvested and forage crops used here cover the nitrogen contained in the harvested grains, fruit and vegetables, etc., and the nitrogen contained in stems, leaves, straw, roots and other crop residues if they are removed from the field, see OECD (2001). However, crop residues remaining in the field are not included in the balance at present, and this aspect of the balance still requires further research.

10. For a discussion of nutrient balances see for example Brouwer and Kleinhanss (1997); Lankoski (1996); Romstad *et al.* (1997a); Schleef and Kleinhanb (1994); Simonsen (1996); Slak *et al.* (1998); van Eerdt and Fong (1998); in various government publications see, for example, Hamblin (1998, pp. 78-82); Ministry for the Environment (1997, pp. 111-113); and USDA (1997, pp. 204-209); and for international organisations see, for example, EEA (2000); EUROSTAT (1999); International Fertiliser Industry Association (1998); OSPARCOM (1994); and the World Bank (1997, pp. 107-108).

11. For an extensive review of the impact of agricultural nutrients in the Canadian Environment see Chambers (2000).

12. For more information on structural changes in the livestock industries of Canada, New Zealand and the United States, including the policy response to these developments with respect to limiting environmental pollution see, for example, Cameron and Trenouth (1999); and the United States Senate Committee on Agriculture, Nutrition and Forestry (1997).

13. A recent estimate of the Polish national nitrogen balance (Sapek, 1999a) suggests a similar trend to that observed for phosphorus, see Sapek (1999b).

14. For a discussion of trends in phosphorus in agricultural land of the UK, see MAFF (2000).

15. This information is provided by the Korean Ministry of Agriculture and Forestry which, through the National Institute of Agriculture, Science and Technology, has completed balances for phosphates and potassium, which have also increased over the period 1985 to 1997.

16. For a discussion of national phosphorus and potassium balances for Australia, see Commonwealth of Australia (1998).

17. Bindraban *et al.* (1998), has proposed another indicator approach for situations of nutrient deficits, by matching yield gaps to soil nutrient balances.

18. The issue of nutrient losses and efficiency is discussed, for example, by the International Fertiliser Industry Association (1998, pp. 23-28). For an economic analysis of nitrogen efficiency in agriculture, applied to Dutch dairy farms, see Reinhard (1999).

19. The issue of the efficiency of nitrogen use in rice production is discussed by Ghosh and Bhat (1998).

20. A further development of the farm gate balance approach, the complete balance, which considers all nitrogen inputs and outputs entering/leaving a farm has been examined by Legard *et al.* (1999).

21. There are a number of attempts to use nutrient balance information for economic and policy analysis of agri-environmental linkages, see for example, Brouwer and Kleinhanss (1997); and Meudt (1999); and modelling nitrate losses from agriculture at national and catchment scales, see, for example, Lord (1999); and Romstad *et al.* (1997*b*). The Finish Agricultural Economic Research Institute has also examined the impact of environmental policies on nitrate and phosphorus emissions from agriculture (see Statistics Finland, 1999, pp. 20-21).

22. Drake (1997) provides a monetary valuation of eutrophication costs from agricultural nitrogen leaching.

Annex Table 1. **Soil surface nitrogen balance estimates: 1985-87 to 1995-97**

	Nitrogen input		Nitrogen output		Nitrogen efficiency (output/input)		Nitrogen balance			
	1 000 tonnes		1 000 tonnes		%		1 000 tonnes		Kg/ha of total agricultural land	
	1985-87	1995-97	1985-87	1995-97	1985-87	1995-97	1985-87	1995-97	1985-87	1995-97
Australia	8 417	8 667	5 306	5 361	63	62	3 111	3 306	7	7
Austria	411	364	288	269	70	74	123	95	35	27
Belgium	457	443	194	196	42	44	263	247	189	181
Canada	3 124	3 818	2 660	2 843	85	74	464	976	6	13
Czech Republic[1]	836	558	407	325	49	58	429	233	99	54
Denmark	716	611	280	287	39	47	435	323	154	118
Finland	318	272	129	134	41	49	189	138	78	64
France	4 753	4 550	2 908	2 965	61	65	1 845	1 585	59	53
Germany[2]	4 401	3 442	2 836	2 390	64	69	1 565	1 052	88	61
Greece	777	653	444	457	57	70	333	195	58	38
Hungary	943	446	636	537	67	120	307	−91	47	−15
Iceland[3]	36	34	22	21	62	61	14	13	7	7
Ireland	770	878	457	480	59	55	312	397	62	79
Italy	2 239	1 909	1 466	1 424	65	75	773	485	44	31
Japan	1 466	1 275	690	601	47	47	775	674	145	135
Korea	652	764	267	254	41	33	385	511	173	253
Mexico	5 429	5 016	2 628	2 854	48	57	2 801	2 162	28	20
Netherlands	1 084	960	461	447	43	47	623	513	314	262
New Zealand	3 598	3 455	3 532	3 371	98	98	66	83	5	6
Norway	198	206	129	131	65	63	69	75	72	73
Poland	2 701	1 881	1 808	1 348	67	72	894	533	48	29
Portugal	393	384	111	120	28	31	282	264	62	66
Spain	2 160	2 086	926	885	43	42	1 234	1 202	40	41
Sweden	405	373	248	268	61	72	158	105	47	34
Switzerland	277	251	151	155	54	62	127	96	80	61
Turkey	2 712	2 716	2 046	2 216	75	82	666	500	17	12
United Kingdom	3 135	2 865	1 319	1 387	42	48	1 816	1 478	107	86
United States	27 916	30 596	17 048	17 400	61	57	10 868	13 196	25	31
EU-15[4]	22 018	19 789	12 068	11 709	55	59	9 951	8 080	69	58
OECD[5]	80 324	79 473	49 398	49 126	61	62	30 926	30 347	23	23

1. Data for the period 1985-92 refer to the Czech part of the former Czechoslovakia.
2. Including eastern and western Germany for the whole period 1985-97.
3. The 1995-97 average refer to 1995.
4. EU-15 averages, excluding Luxembourg.
5. OECD averages, excluding Luxembourg.
Source: OECD (2000).

Annex Table 2. **Composition of nitrogen inputs and outputs (uptake) in national soil surface nitrogen balances: 1985-87 to 1995-97**

	Nitrogen inputs from:						Nitrogen outputs (uptake) from:			
	Inorganic fertiliser		Net livestock manure		Other nitrogen inputs[6]		Harvested crops		Pasture	
	Share of total inputs (%)						Share of total outputs (%)			
	1985-87	1995-97	1985-87	1995-97	1985-87	1995-97	1985-87	1995-97	1985-87	1995-97
Australia	4	9	26	24	70	67	11	15	89	85
Austria	39	35	32	34	29	31	36	38	51	50
Belgium	43	38	45	50	12	12	30	35	60	53
Canada	38	41	28	28	34	31	69	72	24	23
Czech Republic[1]	50	44	21	21	29	35	42	51	12	14
Denmark	54	49	32	37	14	14	61	64	21	19
Finland	65	67	26	24	9	9	49	55	10	8
France	53	54	27	26	20	20	51	58	40	33
Germany[2]	53	51	28	27	19	22	35	49	41	38
Greece	54	53	33	35	12	13	49	51	49	47
Hungary	62	45	21	23	17	32	78	84	6	4
Iceland[3]	34	33	35	34	31	33	0	0	60	62
Ireland	44	47	46	45	10	8	9	9	90	91
Italy	45	46	27	28	28	27	63	65	21	20
Japan	46	41	36	39	18	20	66	62	31	36
Korea	66	60	26	35	8	5	94	95	6	5
Mexico	24	19	49	52	26	30	26	26	60	58
Netherlands	45	40	44	49	10	11	17	20	76	72
New Zealand	1	4	38	35	61	61	1	1	99	99
Norway	52	51	42	42	6	7	19	20	25	32
Poland	50	46	27	27	22	27	42	53	34	36
Portugal	37	37	53	54	10	10	51	46	49	54
Spain	49	44	30	35	21	21	56	54	28	31
Sweden	56	53	27	29	17	18	51	44	13	15
Switzerland	25	22	47	46	27	32	15	19	24	25
Turkey	37	41	44	39	19	19	40	39	57	59
United Kingdom	51	47	27	28	23	25	35	35	65	64
United States	34	36	28	29	38	35	48	52	36	35
EU-15[4]	50	49	30	31	19	20	44	49	43	40
OECD[5]	35	35	31	31	34	34	40	43	48	47

1. Data for the period 1985-92 refer to the Czech part of the former Czechoslovakia.
2. Including eastern and western Germany for the whole period 1985-97.
3. The 1995-97 average refer to 1995.
4. EU-15 averages, excluding Luxembourg.
5. OECD averages, excluding Luxembourg.
6. Includes mainly biological nitrogen fixation, nitrogen recycled from organic matter, nitrogen contained in seeds and planting materials, and atmospheric deposition of nitrogen which is mostly independent from agricultural activities.
Source: OECD (2000).

135

BIBLIOGRAPHY

Abrahams, N.A. and J.S. Shortle (1997),
  Uncertainty and the Regulation of Nitrate Pollution from Agriculture, Paper presented to the American Agricultural Economics Association Annual Meeting, August, 1997, Toronto, Canada.

ADEME [French Agency for the Environment and Energy Management] (1999),
  Situation du recyclage agricole des boues d'epuration urbaines en Europe, (only in French "Agricultural Recycling of Urban Sewage Waste in Europe"), October, Angers, France. Available at: *www.ademe.fr/htdocs/publications/cataloguedeseditions/catalpha.htm.*

Agricultural Council of Australia and New Zealand (1993),
  Sustainable Agriculture: Tracking the Indicators for Australia and New Zealand, Standing Committee on Agriculture and Resource Management (SCARM), CSIRO Publications, Victoria, Australia.

Allanson, P., A. Moxey and B. White (1993),
  "Measuring Agricultural Non-Point Pollution for River Catchment Planning", *Journal of Environmental Management*, Vol. 38, pp. 219-232.

Antle, J.M., S.M. Capalbo and S. Mooney (1999),
  Optimal Spatial Scale for Evaluating Economic and Environmental Tradeoffs, Paper presented to the American Agricultural Economics Association Annual Meeting, August 8-11, 1999, Nashville, Tennessee. Available at: *www.agecon.lib.umn.edu/aaea99/sp99an02.pdf.*

Bindraban, P.S., J.J. Stoorvogel, D.M. Jansen, J. Vlaming and J.J.R. Groot (1998),
  Land Quality Indicators for Sustainable Land Management: Yield Gap and Soil Nutrient Balance, paper presented to the 16th Congress of Soil Science, Montpellier France, 22 August, Satellite Symposium – Indicators of Land Quality and Sustainable Land Management, Sponsored by the World Bank.

Bomans, E., L. Vanongeval, H. Vandendriessche and M. Geypens (1996),
  Development of an Indicator for Agricultural Nutrient Balances for the OECD, Report No: 96/AC/010, prepared by the Soil Service of Belgium, for the Ministry of the Flemish Community; Environment and Infrastructure Department; Environment, Nature, Land and Water Management Administration; Brussels, Belgium.

Bonnieux, F. and P. Rainelli (1997),
  "Agricultural Use of Sewage Sludge and Municipal Waste and the Environment", Chapter 10, pp. 157-173, in E. Romstad, J.W. Simonsen and A. Vatn (eds.) (1997), *Controlling Mineral Emissions in European Agriculture: Economics, Policies and the Environment*, CAB International, Wallingford, United Kingdom.

Brouwer, F.M. and W. Kleinhanss (eds.) (1997),
  The Implementation of Nitrate Policies in Europe: Processes of Change in Environmental Policy and Agriculture, Landwirtschaft und Umwelt, Bd. 14, Wissenschaftsverlag Vauk Kiel KG, Kiel, Germany.

Brouwer, F.M., F.E. Godeschalk, P.J.G.J. Hellegers and H.J. Kelholt (1994),
  Mineral Balances of the European Union at Farm Level, Agricultural Economics Research Institute, The Hague, The Netherlands.

Brouwer, F.M., P. Hellegers, M. Hoogeveen and H. Luesink (1999),
  Managing Nitrogen Pollution from Intensive Livestock Production in the EU, Agricultural Economics Research Institute (LEI), The Hague.

Cameron, M. and C. Trenouth (1999),
  Resource Management Act Practice and Performance – Are desired environmental outcomes being achieved at least cost? A case study of dairy effluent management, Ministry for the Environment, Wellington, New Zealand.

Cavigelli, M.A., S.R. Deming, L.K. Probyn and R.R. Harwood (eds.) (1998),
  Michigan Field Crop Ecology: Managing biological processes for productivity and environmental quality, Michigan State University Extension Bulletin E-2646, United States.

Chambers, P. (ed.) (2000),
  Nutrients and their Impact on the Canadian Environment, Environment Canada, Ottawa, Canada.

Commonwealth of Australia (1995),
Sustaining the Agricultural Resource Base, 12th Meeting of the Prime Minister's Science and Engineering Council, Office of the Chief Scientist, Department of the Prime Minister and Cabinet, Canberra, Australia.

Commonwealth of Australia (1998),
Sustainable Agriculture – Assessing Australia's Recent Performance, A Report to the Standing Committee on Agriculture and Resource Management (SCARM) of the National Collaborative Project on Indicators for Sustainable Agriculture, SCARM Technical Report No. 70, CSIRO Publishing, Victoria, Australia.

Cook, H. and C. Norman (1996),
"Targeting Agri-environmental Policy: Analysis relating to the use of Geographical Information Systems", Land Use Policy, Vol. 13, No. 3, pp. 217-228.

Drake, L. (1997),
"Policy Implications of Conflict and Consistency Between Nitrogen Leaching and Other Environmental Impacts of Swedish Agriculture", Chapter 15, pp. 249-260, in E. Romstad, J.W. Simonsen and A. Batn (eds.), Controlling Mineral Emissions in European Agriculture: Economics, Policies and the Environment, CAB International, Wallingford, United Kingdom.

Eckert, H., G. Breitschuh and D. Sauerbeck (1999),
"Criteria for an Environmentally Compatible Agriculture (KUL) – An Approach to Assessing the Ecological State of Farm Enterprises", Agribiological Research, Vol. 52, No. 1, pp. 57-76.

EEA [European Environment Agency] (1995),
Europe's Environment: The Dobris Assessment, Office for Official Publications of the European Communities, Luxembourg. Available at: www.themes.eea.eu.int/ [> all available reports].

EEA (2000),
Monitoring Progress Towards Integration – A contribution to the "Global Assessment" of the fifth Environmental Action Programme of the EU, 1992-1999, and to the Helsinki process on integration, Office for Official Publications of the European Communities, Luxembourg.

Environmental Protection Agency (1999a),
Water Quality in Ireland 1995-1997, Wexford, Ireland.

Environmental Protection Agency (1999b),
Environment in Focus – A Discussion Document on Key National Environmental Indicators, Wexford, Ireland. Available at: www.epa.ie/pubs/default.htm.

European Commission (1999),
"Agriculture and Acidification", Chapter 15, in European Commission, Agriculture, Environment, Rural Development: Facts and Figures – A Challenge for Agriculture, Office for Official Publications of the European Communities, Luxembourg. Available at: www.europa.eu.int/comm/dg06/envir/report/en/index.htm.

EUROSTAT [Statistical Office of the European Communities] (1996),
The Distribution of Nitrogen Inputs to Agriculture, Statistical Document, Luxembourg.

EUROSTAT (1999),
Towards Environmental Pressure Indicators for the EU, Environment and Energy Paper Theme 8, Luxembourg. The background documentation is available at: www.e-m-a-i-l.nu/tepi/ and www.esl.jrc.it/envind/.

Follett, R.F. (1995),
Fate and Transport of Nutrients: Nitrogen, Resource Conservation Act (RCA) III, Working Paper No. 7, September, US Department of Agriculture, Washington, DC., United States.

Galloway, J.N. (1998),
"The Global Nitrogen Cycle: Changes and Consequences", pp. 15-24, in K.W. van der Hoek, J.W. Erisman and S. Smeulders (eds.), Proceedings of the First International Nitrogen Conference, 23-27 March 1998, Noordwijkerhout, The Netherlands, Elsevier Press, Amsterdam.

Ghosh, B.C. and R. Bhat (1998),
"Environmental Hazards of Nitrogen Loading in Wetland Rice Fields", pp. 123-132, in K.W. van der Hoek, J.W. Erisman and S. Smeulders (eds.), Proceedings of the First International Nitrogen Conference, 23-27 March 1998, Noordwijkerhout, The Netherlands, Elsevier Press, Amsterdam.

Hamblin, A. (1998),
Environmental Indicators for National State of the Environment Reporting – The Land, Australia: State of the Environment (Environmental Indicator Reports), Department of the Environment, Canberra, Australia. Available at: www.environment.gov.au/soe/ [Environmental Indicators > Land under "Environmental Indicator Reports"].

Hooper, S., A. Heaney and S. Gordon (2000),
"Phosphorus nutrition in Australian agriculture", Australian Commodities, Vol. 7, No. 2, pp. 341-347.

International Fertiliser Industry Association (1998),
Mineral Fertiliser Use and the Environment, International Fertiliser Industry Association and the United Nations Environment Programme, Paris, France.

Lankoski, J. (1996),
Controlling Agricultural Nonpoint Source Pollution: The Case of Mineral Balances, United Nations Conference on Trade and Development, Discussion Papers No. 116, June, Geneva, Switzerland.

Ledgard, S.F., P.H. Williams, F.D. Broom, B.S. Thorrold, D.M. Wheeler and V.J. Willis (1999),
"OVERSEER™ – A nutrient budgeting model for pastoral farming: wheat, potatoes, apples and kiwifruit", pp. 143-152, in L.D. Currie, M. J. Hedley, D. J. Horne and P. Lognathan (eds.), *Best soil management practices for production*, Occasional report No. 12, FLRC, Massey University, Palmerston North, New Zealand.

Lekkerkerk, L.J.A., G.J. Heij and M.J.M. Hootsmans (eds.) (1995),
Dutch Priority Programme on Acidification. Ammonia: The Facts, Report No. 300-06, Informatie en Kennis Centrum Landbouw, The Hague, The Netherlands.

Lord, E. (1999),
"A Modelling Framework for Evaluating Nitrate Losses at National and Catchment Scales", pp. 48-56, in MAFF [Ministry of Agriculture, Fisheries and Food], *Tackling Nitrate from Agriculture – Strategy from Science*, London, United Kingdom.

MacDonald, K.B. (2000),
"Residual Nitrogen", Chapter 16, in T. McRae, C.A.S. Smith and L.J. Gregorich (eds.), *Environmental Sustainability of Canadian Agriculture: Report of the Agri-Environmental Indicator Project*, Agriculture and Agri-Food Canada (AAFC), Ottawa, Ontario, Canada. Available at: *www.agr.ca/policy/environment/publications/list.html*.

MAFF [Ministry of Agriculture, Fisheries and Food] (2000),
Towards Sustainable Agriculture – A Pilot Set of Indicators, London, United Kingdom. Available at: *www.maff.gov.uk/* [Farming > Sustainable Agriculture].

Meudt, M. (1999),
"Implementation of Environmental Indicators in Policy Information Systems in Germany", Chapter 15, pp. 229-245, in F. Brouwer and B. Crabtree (eds.), *Environmental Indicators and Agricultural Policy*, CAB International, Wallingford, United Kingdom.

Ministry for the Environment (1997),
Environmental Performance Indicators: Proposals for Air, Freshwater and Land, Ministry for the Environment, Wellington, New Zealand.

OECD (1998a),
The Environmental Effects of Reforming Agricultural Policies, Paris, France.

OECD (1998b),
Environmental Performance Reviews: Korea, Paris, France.

OECD (2001),
OECD *National Soil Surface Nitrogen Balances: Preliminary Estimates 1985-1997*, Paris, France. Available at: *www.oecd.org/agr/env/indicators.htm*.

Oppenshaw, S. (1984),
The Modifiable Areal Unit Problem, Concepts And Techniques, in Modern Geography 38, Norwich, Geo Books, United Kingdom.

OSPARCOM [Oslo and Paris Conventions for the Prevention of Marine Pollution Commission] (1994),
OSPARCOM *Guidelines for Calculating Mineral Balances*, Working Group on Nutrients, NUT 94/8/1-E, Berne, Switzerland. Details on the OSPARCOM are available at: *www.ospar.org/eng/html/welcome.html*.

Pirttijarvi, R., S. Rekolainen and J. Gronroos (1999),
"Nutrient Balances and the Implementation of Agricultural Policy Measures in Finland", Chapter 13, pp. 193-209, in F. Brouwer and B. Crabtree (eds.), *Environmental Indicators and Agricultural Policy*, CAB International, Wallingford, United Kingdom.

Reinhard, S. (1999),
Econometric analysis of economic and environmental efficiency of Dutch dairy farms, Wageningen Agricultural University, Wageningen, The Netherlands. Available at: *www2.lei.dlo.nl/LEI-home.html*.

Romstad, E, J.W. Simonsen and A. Vatn (eds.) (1997a),
Controlling Mineral Emissions in European Agriculture: Economics, Policies and the Environment, CAB International, Wallingford, United Kingdom.

Romstad, E., A. Vatn, L. Bakken and P. Botterweg (1997b),
"Economics-Ecology Modelling: the Case of Nitrogen", pp. 225-249, in E. Romstad, J.W. Simonsen and A. Vatn

(eds.), *Controlling Mineral Emissions in European Agriculture: Economics, Policies and the Environment*, CAB International, Wallingford, United Kingdom.

Sapek, A. (ed.) (1999*a*),
Nitrogen Cycle and Balance in Polish Agriculture, Conference Proceedings, Poland Agriculture and Water Quality Protection, Institute for Land Reclamation and Grassland Farming, Falenty IMUZ Publisher, Warsaw, Poland.

Sapek, A. (1999*b*),
"Phosphorus cycle in Polish Agriculture", pp. 8-18, in A. Sapek (ed.), *Phosphorus in Agriculture and Water Quality Protection*, Conference Proceedings, Institute for Land Reclamation and Grassland Farming, Falenty IMUZ Publisher, Warsaw, Poland.

Schleef, K.H. and W. Kleinhanb (1994),
Mineral Balances in Agriculture in the EU, Institute of Farm Economics, Federal Agricultural Research Centre, Braunschweig, Germany.

Shaffer, M.J. (1995),
Fate and Transport of Nitrogen – What Models Can and Cannot Do, Resource Conservation Act (RCA) III, Working Paper No. 11, September, US Department of Agriculture, Washington, DC., United States.

Sharpley, A. (1995),
Fate and Transport of Nutrients – Phosphorus, Resource Conservation Act (RCA) III, Working Paper No. 8, October, US Department of Agriculture, Washington, D.C, United States.

Sharpley, A. (ed.) (2000),
"Practical and Innovative Measures for the Control of Agricultural Phosphorus Losses to Water", *Journal of Environmental Quality*, Vol. 29, No. 1.

Simonsen, J.W. (ed.) (1996),
Inventory on Mineral Pollution from Agriculture, EU concerted action "Policy measures to control environmental impacts from agriculture"(AIR3CT93-1164), Norwegian Agricultural Research Institute, Oslo, Norway.

Slak, M.F., L. Commagnac and S. Lucas (1998),
"Feasibility of National Nitrogen Balances", pp. 235-240, in K.W. van der Hoek, J.W. Erisman and S. Smeulders (eds.), *Proceedings of the First International Nitrogen Conference*, 23-27 March 1998, Noordwijkerhout, The Netherlands, Elsevier Press, Amsterdam.

Statistics Finland (1999),
Finland's Natural Resources and the Environment 1999, Ministry of the Environment, Helsinki, Finland.

UK Department of the Environment (1996),
Indicators of Sustainable Development for the United Kingdom, London, United Kingdom. Available at: *www.environment.detr.gov.uk/* [> Indicators of Sustainable Development for the UK].

United States Senate Committee on Agriculture, Nutrition and Forestry (1997),
Animal Waste Pollution in America: An Emerging National Problem – Environmental Risks of Livestock and Poultry Production, Report compiled by the Minority Staff of the US Senate Committee on Agriculture, Nutrition and Forestry for Senator Tom Harkin, Washington, DC., United States. Available at: *www.senate.gov/~agriculture/animalw.htm*.

USDA [United States Department of Agriculture] (1994),
Agricultural Resources and Environmental Indicators, Agricultural Handbook No. 705, Natural Resources and Environment Division, Economic Research Service, Washington, DC., United States. Available at: *www.ers.usda.gov/* [Briefing Rooms > Agricultural Resources and Environmental Indicators].

USDA (1997),
Agricultural Resources and Environmental Indicators, 1996-97, Agricultural Handbook No. 712, Natural Resources and Environment Division, Economic Research Service, Washington, D.C, United States. Available at: *www.ers.usda.gov/* [Briefing Rooms > Agricultural Resources and Environmental Indicators].

van der Hoek, K.W., J.W. Erisman and S. Smeulders (eds.) (1998),
Proceedings of the First International Nitrogen Conference, 23-27 March 1998, Noordwijkerhout, The Netherlands, Elsevier Press, Amsterdam.

van Eerdt, M.M. and P.K.N. Fong (1998),
"The Monitoring of Nitrogen Surpluses from Agriculture", pp. 227-233, in K.W. van der Hoek, J.W. Erisman and S. Smeulders (eds.), *Proceedings of the First International Nitrogen Conference*, 23-27 March 1998, Noordwijkerhout, The Netherlands, Elsevier Press, Amsterdam.

World Bank (1997),
Expanding the Measure of Wealth – Indicators of Environmentally Sustainable Development, Environmentally Sustainable Development Studies and Monographs Series, No. 17, Washington, DC., United States.

Chapter 2

PESTICIDE USE AND RISKS

HIGHLIGHTS

Context

Agricultural pesticides contribute to agricultural productivity but also pose potential risks to human health and the environment. The risks vary greatly depending on pesticide's inherent toxicity (or hazard) and exposure. Exposure to a pesticide depends on the way it is applied and its mobility and persistence in the environment.

Pesticide use by farmers depends on a multitude of factors, such as climatic conditions, the composition and variety of crops, pest and disease pressures, farm incomes, pesticide cost/crop price ratios, pesticide policies and management practices. Pesticide indicators are potentially a useful tool to help policy makers monitor and evaluate policies and also provide information concerning human and environmental pesticide risks.

All OECD countries have a regulatory system that assesses pesticides prior to their release for sale, to ensure they do not pose unacceptable risks to the environment and public above nationally agreed thresholds. A number of countries have also set targets to reduce the total quantity of agricultural pesticides used over a given time period. In addition, policies to reduce risk, and other measures like pesticide taxes, are being used in some countries, to reduce the environmental and health impacts of pesticide use.

Indicators and recent trends

OECD is developing two kinds of indicators. One shows pesticide use trends over time based on sales and/or use data in terms of active ingredients. The other indicator tracks trends in pesticide risks by combining information on pesticide hazard and exposure with pesticide use data and information on the conditions that might affect risks. Pesticide use indicators are simpler, but because the policies of OECD member countries aim ultimately to reduce risks, it is important to develop the more complex but highly policy relevant indicators of risk trends.

Overall the trend in pesticide use over the last decade has remained constant or declined in most OECD countries, although for a few countries use has increased. The reduction can be explained partly by changing crop prices, greater efficiency of pesticide use as a result of improvements in pest management practices and technology, and government policies aimed at both improving pest management practices, and in some cases targeting a reduction in pesticide use.

There is evidence to suggest an increasing efficiency in the use of pesticides for some OECD countries, with the volume of crop production over the past 10-12 years increasing more rapidly than pesticide use. For a considerable number of countries, however, annual changes in pesticides use appear to be closely correlated with fluctuations in annual crop production trends.

The close correlation between trends in pesticide use and risks estimated by a few OECD countries, over a period of 10 or more years suggest that pesticide risks to human health and the environment can be lowered by reducing the use of particular chemicals. Caution is required, however, in linking trends in pesticide use with changes in risks. This is because a change in pesticide use is not always equivalent to a change in risks, especially with the development of more targeted pesticides, and because different pesticides pose different types and levels of risks.

Preliminary results of OECD work on pesticide risk indicators for the aquatic environment show that different indicator methods can produce different pesticide risk trends, even when using the same data on pesticide risks and use.

1. Background

Policy context

Pesticides are widely used by the agricultural sector in OECD countries to help maintain and improve farm productivity, as well as food product quality. The benefits of pesticide use can be measured in terms of the value of farm output that would be lost if pesticides were not used. In addition, it is argued that intensive agriculture, through the use of chemical fertilisers and pesticides, prevents the loss of wildlife habitat that would occur if additional land was used to produce food with less intensive agricultural production systems (Avery, 1995).

While pesticide use is sometimes subsidised (Turkey[1]) and in other cases taxed (*e.g.* Denmark, Norway, Sweden), farmers usually pay the market price, although they do not always pay the "full" or "social" cost of production. This is because the market price of pesticides does not fully reflect the external costs resulting from their impact on the environment and human health (Pearce and Tinch, 1998). Thus, policy makers need to address a range of human health and environmental issues associated with the external costs of pesticide use, including:

- the exposure of farm workers and the public in the vicinity of where pesticides are applied;
- consumer exposure to pesticide residues in food;
- potential human health risks that are not well understood, for example, hormonal effects;
- contamination of ground and surface water used for drinking by both humans and livestock; and,
- environmental impacts on terrestrial and aquatic habitats, such as risks to non-targeted organisms and wildlife.

Pesticide indicators can provide a useful tool for the evaluation of domestic policies and international obligations related to pesticide use in agriculture. Such indicators can also convey a general idea about trends in pesticide use and risks, and the impact of pesticides on human health and the environment.

A key aspect of pesticide policies in OECD countries, is the regulatory system that assesses pesticides before they can be approved for sale and use. The registration process is to ensure pesticides do not pose unacceptable human health and environmental risks above nationally agreed thresholds. Moreover, most OECD countries have legal standards with respect to maximum permissible residue levels both for individual pesticides and for total pesticide substances in food and drinking water.[2] Even so, uncertainties remain concerning pesticides risks, for example, the so-called "cocktail effect", that is the risk associated with combinations of pesticide residues in food and water.

A number of OECD countries, such as Denmark, Norway and Sweden, have introduced taxes to discourage pesticide use or, like Italy, are in the process of considering such a tax (Rayment *et al.*, 1998, pp. 32-36).[3] In addition, many countries have measures to encourage improvements in pest management by farmers (see Farm Management chapter). Also some countries, for example Denmark, the Netherlands and Sweden, have set targets to reduce the total quantity of agricultural pesticides used over a given time period.[4] Many of the targets that were originally set in terms of tonnes of active ingredients are now being revised to focus on the reduction in pesticide risks.

Under the European Union's Fifth Environment Action Programme the aim is to achieve a significant reduction in pesticide use per unit of agricultural land. Thus, European countries participating in the North Sea Treaty (1983), have commitments to reduce emissions of certain pesticides. Among other things, the Treaty has called for countries to ban or restrict 18 pesticides and reduce by 50 per cent emissions of 36 other pesticides near marine waters. A number of OECD countries bordering the Baltic sea, have also made commitments to reduce emissions of pesticides under the Baltic Sea Treaty (1974).

Canada and the United States have projects to prevent pesticide contamination of the Great Lakes. Under the North American Free Trade Agreement Technical Working Group on Pesticides, there is a commitment to work together towards a single North American market for pesticides, while maintaining current high levels of protection of public health and the environment, and supporting the principles of sustainable pest management.

Internationally, the FAO/WHO CODEX Commission has established maximum residue limits on pesticide residues in fruit and vegetables (Gebbie, 1998). Furthermore, it was agreed under the Montreal Protocol on Substances that Deplete the Ozone Layer (1987), that methyl bromide (mainly used as a soil fumigant by agriculture), should be phased out by 2005, with possible exemption for critical agricultural uses (Figure 9; and Oberthur, 1997; EEA, 1998, pp. 67-69; and UNEP, 1999).

Environmental context

The quantity of pesticide applied by farmers depends on the level of pest and disease pressure, climatic conditions, the type of crop and its resistance to pests and disease, the efficiency of pest management practices, and the influence of economic and policy factors. Moreover, the amount of pesticides that leach into soil and water or evaporate into the air, depends on site specific conditions, such as soil properties and temperature, drainage, type of crop, climate, and application method, time and frequency. The risks posed by different pesticides vary greatly depending on their inherent toxicity (or hazard) and exposure that can occur based on the pesticide's mobility and persistence in the environment and the method and quantity applied.

The *mobility of pesticides* in the environment is mainly determined by the type of pesticide, the rate of pesticide uptake by different crops, topography and soil type, and the climatic conditions where the pesticides are applied. Some of the pesticides applied can evaporate and possibly photodecompose. The fate and mobility of remaining pesticides depends on the organic content of soil, and soil erosion, leaching and run-off rates. The latter are in direct relation to the climatic conditions of a specific drainage basin. Estimates vary widely as to the quantity of pesticides actually applied that reach the target pests, from less than 1 per cent to 75 per cent, with the remainder lost to the environment through soil runoff, erosion, leaching and vaporisation into the atmosphere.

The *persistence of pesticide* residues in the environment and human food chain may vary from a few weeks to 30 years. Despite the ban on DDT in most OECD countries since the mid-1970s, for example, residues of this pesticide compound are still detectable in some aquatic environments, such as in the United States (USGS, 1999, pp. 78). Research also shows that approximately 10 per cent of all herbicides have a persistency in the soil that may adversely affect the yield of crops following those to which the herbicides were first applied (EEA, 1995, pp. 159-60).

Pesticides vary in their *degree of toxicity* depending on the type and concentration of their active ingredients (the chemicals actually controlling or killing the intended pest, weed or disease). When less toxic pesticides are used, environmental damage may decrease despite increases in pesticide use. Moreover, the sensitivity of wildlife to toxic contamination varies both with specific pesticides and with wildlife species. In the United Kingdom, for example, trends in pesticide use show an overall decline in use of products that are acutely toxic to mammals, but an increase in pesticides with high acute toxicity to aquatic organisms (UK Department of the Environment, 1996, p. 138).

The quantification of *human health risks* from exposure to pesticides in foodstuffs is complex, while some uncertainties remain concerning the validity of extrapolating to human health from laboratory tests of pesticide contaminants on animals. In addition, there is the problem of separating out the effects of pesticides from the many other influences on human health, such as the composition of the diet including tobacco and alcohol, age, gender and ethnic background. However, many OECD countries regularly sample and test food products for evidence of pesticide residues, with detection methods improving rapidly.

Similarly the quantification of *risks to terrestrial flora and fauna* from pesticide use is also complex. Pesticides can accumulate in food chains with consequent indirect impacts along the food chain, while they may directly eradicate, remove or reduce food sources for birds and mammals (Rayment *et al.*, 1998, pp. 10-14). In aquatic environments the leaching of pesticides into rivers, lakes and coastal waters is known to cause damage to aquatic biodiversity.

Development of *pest resistance to pesticides* is a global problem, though not a health or environmental concern unless it leads to the use of more hazardous substitute pesticides and/or to increased damage to agricultural crops. In the United States, for example, 183 insect pests are resistant to 1 or more insecticides, and 18 weed species are resistant to herbicides (USDA, 1997, p. 183). The use of genetically modified plants to overcome such problems might be an area of considerable potential leap, although there is a major international research effort underway to examine the environmental and human health effects of genetic engineering (see the Biodiversity chapter).

It is estimated that *methyl bromide* accounts for 5-10 per cent of the global loss of stratospheric ozone, and may be responsible for around 20 per cent of the Antarctic ozone depletion (Mano and Andreae, 1994). Developed countries account for about 80 per cent of methyl bromide use worldwide. The main sources of methyl bromide are vehicle exhaust (from vehicles using leaded petrol), emissions from plankton in the oceans, biomass burning (including grassland and forest fires) and agricultural pesticide use. Methyl bromide is used as a soil fumigant, and it is estimated that this accounts for 90 per cent of total use in the *European Union* (EUROSTAT, 1999, p. 91). According to research by Mano and Andreae (1994), agricultural pesticide use as a source of methyl bromide accounts for 25-60 per cent of total annual global emissions. Grassland and forest fires also provide a major contribution of around 30 per cent to the annual stratospheric bromine budget.[5]

Figure 1 provides a simplified overview of the various linkages between pesticide use and risks and other OECD agri-environmental indicators. Pesticide use is influenced by the whole farm management practices adopted by farmers, for example use of organic farming systems will lower pesticide use (see Figure 3 in the Farm Management chapter). Also the use of specific pest management practices, such as integrated pest management will also affect the use and associated risks from pesticide use (see Figure 5 in the Farm Management chapter).[6] At present OECD pesticide indicator work has concentrated on the indirect change in total sales of pesticides, and on pesticide risks to the aquatic environment (discussed in the following section of this chapter), although work is planned to develop risk indicators to cover human health and terrestrial environmental risks.

The risks to the environment from agricultural pesticide use, are examined in other chapters of this Report, including the chapters concerning soil quality, water quality and biodiversity, although the issue of air quality is not covered, except for a brief discussion in this chapter on the links between methyl bromide emissions and ozone depletion. Those aspects related to pesticide use and human health risks are discussed indirectly in the chapter on water quality, but other aspects related to human health, such as pesticide residues in food, are only examined briefly in this chapter.[7]

2. Indicators

The OECD is developing two types of indicators, one focusing on pesticide use, the other on pesticide risks. Pesticide use indicators are simpler and more straightforward, because they deal with just one type of information rather than combining different types. However, because OECD country policies aim ultimately to reduce risks and not merely pesticide use, it is important to develop the more complex risk indicators that could help measure the effectiveness of these policies.

Pesticide use indicator

Definition

The indicator of pesticide use shows trends over time based on pesticide sales and/or use data.

Method of calculation

The *indicator of pesticide use* is measured in tonnes of active ingredients. The three-year average covering 1985-87 is used in this Chapter as the base year, to reduce the impact of extreme values and also to reflect changes since the agricultural policy reform commitments outlined in the 1987 OECD meeting of Agriculture Ministers (see the Background chapter). The pesticide use indicator is calculated as:

$$\frac{\text{(Quantity of pesticides used in year t)}}{\text{(Average quantity of pesticides used in 1985-87)}} \times 100$$

Figure 1. **Linkages between pesticide use, risk indicators and other agri-environmental indicators**

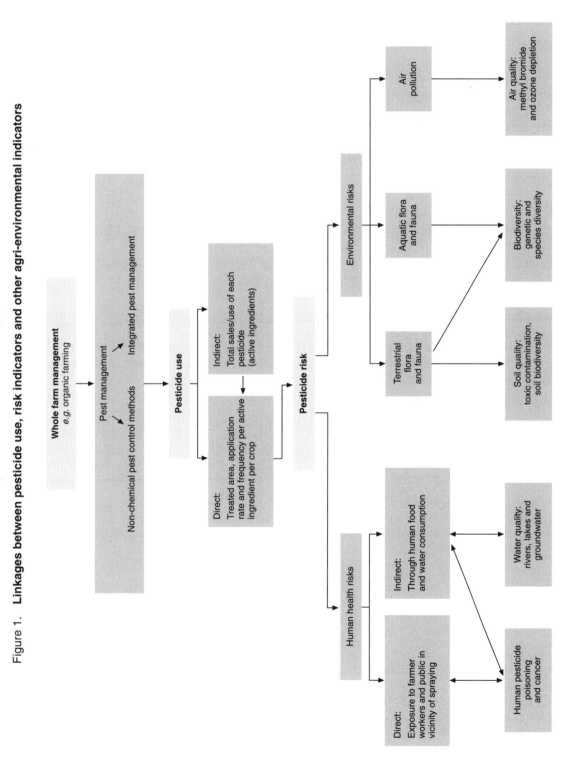

Source: OECD Secretariat.

The indicators of pesticide use track trends over time in the overall quantity of pesticide used. Although the term "pesticide use" is used here, only a few countries have data on actual use and the term generally refers to data on pesticide sales, which is often used as a proxy for pesticide use. For most countries total pesticide use data (and the data used in this Chapter) includes 4 main sub-categories: herbicides (defoliants and desiccants); insecticides (acaricides, molluscicides, nematocides and mineral oils); fungicides (bactericides and seed treatments) and other pesticides (fumigants, rodenticides, anti-coagulants, growth regulators and animal repellents).

National indicators of pesticide use serve various purposes, such as to evaluate trends in pesticide use over time as a crude proxy for potential reduction in risks, and to reveal possible improvements in pesticide use efficiency if crop production is increasing more rapidly than use. They can also determine if lower than recommended rates of pesticide use are effective, and help evaluate whether the use of integrated pest management and other specific farm management practices and policy actions reduce pesticide use.

Recent trends

Several key points emerge from the recent trends in *pesticide use data* shown in Figure 2. Overall the trend in pesticide use over the last decade has remained constant or declined for most OECD countries, although pesticide use increased for a number of countries. For those countries where pesticide use has increased this has, in general, been in response to an expansion in crop production, as illustrated by the examples of B*elgium*, *Greece*, I*reland* and K*orea* (Figure 3).

A significant reduction in pesticide use has occurred in the C*zech Republic*, H*ungary* and P*oland*, which to a large extent can be explained by their transition to a market economy since the early 1990s (Figure 2). The sharp reduction in pesticide use in these countries has been mainly due to the collapse in agricultural support levels, the elimination of subsidies for pesticides, and increasing debt levels in the farm sector limiting farmers' ability to purchase such inputs (OECD, 1998).

Significant reductions in pesticide use, by 30 per cent or more over the past 10 years, are also observed in countries that have set targets to reduce the use of pesticides. Examples include D*enmark*, F*inland*, the N*etherlands*, N*orway* and S*weden*. The reduction has also been linked to the increasing area of crops under organic farming and subject to integrated pest management and other pesticide reduction practices, for example, in I*taly*, S*pain* and S*witzerland* (see Figure 5 in the Pest Management section of the Farm Management chapter).[8]

The expansion in the area under organic farming is also acting to reduce pesticide use in some countries, for example, in A*ustria*, F*inland*, G*ermany*, I*taly*, S*weden* and S*witzerland* (see Figure 3 in the Farm Management chapter). Decreasing pesticide use in the U*nited Kingdom* (Figure 2) has been due, in particular, to the introduction of new herbicides with lower doses (MAFF, 2000).

In J*apan* the reduction in pesticide use has closely reflected the declining trend in crop production, in particular, the decrease in rice production, Japan's major crop (Figures 2 and 3). In N*ew Zealand* pesticide use rose steadily from 1985 reaching a peak in 1996. According to a recent study, however, usage declined by about 10 per cent in 1998 largely reflecting the drop in crop production during that year (Holland and Rahman, 1999).

From the early 1980s up to the 1990s pesticide use decreased in the U*nited States*, as commodity prices fell and large areas of agricultural land were taken out of production under government programmes (Annex Table 1). Since 1990 US pesticide usage has fluctuated with changes in planted area, infestation levels, adoption of new products and other factors, including the increasing adoption of integrated pest management practices by farmers (see the pest management section of the Farm Management chapter; and, Fernandez-Cornejo and Jans, 1999; and USDA, 1997, p. 117).

Interpretation and links to other indicators

The definition and coverage of pesticide use data vary across OECD countries, which limits the use of the indicator as a comparative index. Only a few countries have data on actual pesticide use, but

Figure 2. Pesticide use in agriculture: 1985-87[1] to 1995-97[2]

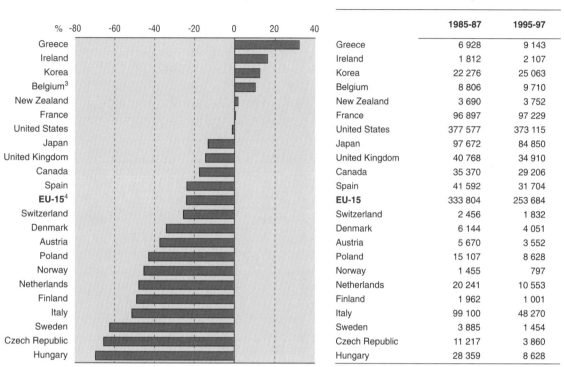

	1985-87	**1995-97**
Greece	6 928	9 143
Ireland	1 812	2 107
Korea	22 276	25 063
Belgium	8 806	9 710
New Zealand	3 690	3 752
France	96 897	97 229
United States	377 577	373 115
Japan	97 672	84 850
United Kingdom	40 768	34 910
Canada	35 370	29 206
Spain	41 592	31 704
EU-15	333 804	253 684
Switzerland	2 456	1 832
Denmark	6 144	4 051
Austria	5 670	3 552
Poland	15 107	8 628
Norway	1 455	797
Netherlands	20 241	10 553
Finland	1 962	1 001
Italy	99 100	48 270
Sweden	3 885	1 454
Czech Republic	11 217	3 860
Hungary	28 359	8 628

1. Data for 1985-87 average cover: 1986-87 average for Greece, Korea, and Spain; 1985 for New Zealand; 1985-86 average for Austria; 1987 for Italy; 1988 for Ireland and Switzerland; and 1989 for the Czech Republic.
2. Data for 1995-97 average cover: 1994-95 average for Hungary; 1994-96 average for Switzerland; 1995-96 average for Italy; 1991-93 average for the United States; 1994 for Canada; and 1997 for New Zealand.
3. Including Luxembourg.
4. Excluding Germany and Portugal.
5. The following countries are not included in the figure: Australia, Germany, Iceland and Mexico (time series are not available); Portugal (data are only available from 1991); and Turkey (data are only available from 1993).
Notes: See sources below and Annex Table 1 for detailed notes on coverage. Some caution is required in comparing trends across countries because of differences in data definitions and coverage.
Sources: OECD *Environmental Data Compendium,* 1999; EUROSTAT (1998); Holland and Rahman (1999).

nearly all OECD countries report data on pesticide sales, which can be used as a proxy for pesticide use, although ideally it should be supported by representative samples of the use data. For some countries, series are either incomplete, especially over recent years, or do not exist.[9] The OECD, in cooperation with EUROSTAT, is beginning a process to help improve the collection of pesticide use data, see for example OECD (1999). A further difficulty is to identify pesticide use specific to agriculture, net of uses for forestry, gardens, golf courses, etc., and the quantity of pesticides used for specific crops and pasture, although some limited data are available on the latter.

Studies in a few OECD countries (see below), suggest that, at least over the short term, there is in some cases, a correlation between trends in pesticide use and environmental risks, *i.e.* as use declines, risks also decrease. However, some caution is required in making this link for a number of reasons examined in the following paragraphs.

A change in pesticide use may not be equivalent to a change in the associated risks because of the continually changing pesticide market and the great variance in risks posed by different

Figure 3. **Pesticide use[1] and crop production:[2] 1985 to 1998**
Index 1989-91 = 100

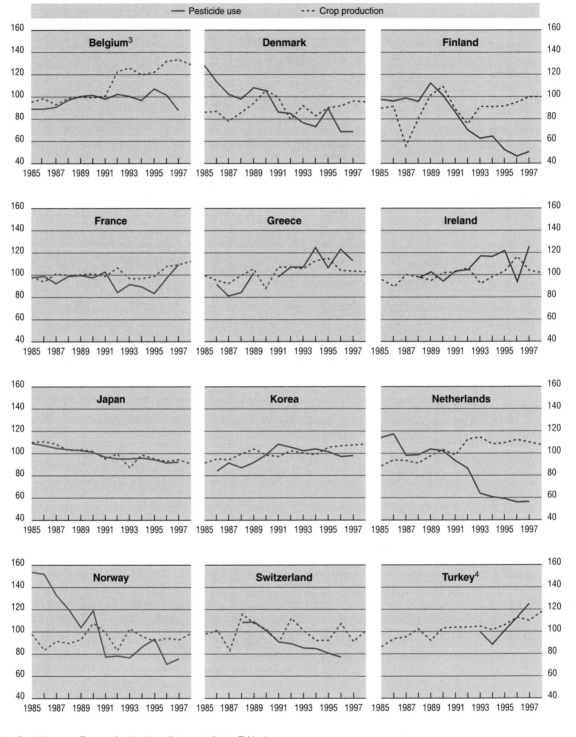

1. Pesticide use – Tonnes of active ingredients, see Annex Table 1.
2. Crop production – FAO Volume Index of Crop Production.
3. Including Luxembourg.
4. Pesticide use: 1993 = 100.

Source: OECD Environmental Data Compendium, 1999.

products. Changes in the herbicide market seen in the 1980s provide a good illustration. During this period, new herbicide products came onto the market that were much more biologically active than their predecessors and were therefore used in much smaller quantities. Pesticide use indicators for this period would show a substantial reduction in herbicide use. By contrast, risk indicators might show no change, or perhaps even an increase, in the environmental and human health risks associated with herbicide use. In addition, the greater use by farmers of pesticides which carry a lower risk to humans and the environment because they are more narrowly targeted, or degrade more rapidly, might also not reveal any change in overall pesticide use trends, and possibly even an increase.

There are an enormous number of pesticide products available for farmers to use. For example, over 700 pesticide products (active ingredients) are marketed in the *European Union*, each of which poses unique environmental and health risks. With respect to risks to water quality, however, a recent *French* study found that, while more than a hundred products are detected at variable concentrations and frequencies in water, most of the water pollution from pesticides in *France* is caused by about ten products. These are mainly herbicides belonging to the triazine family (IFEN, 1998).

Care is also required when comparing trends in pesticide use across countries, because of differences in climatic conditions and farming systems, which affect the composition and level of usage. Variability of climatic conditions (especially moisture), may markedly alter pesticide use. Warmer conditions generally require higher levels of use than colder conditions to maintain agricultural productivity. In the *United States*, for example, the sweet corn crop is typically treated with insecticides 7-14 times annually in southern, warmer regions of the country, compared with only 2-4 treatments in the northern colder regions. In the southern states over 20 per cent of the rice acreage is treated with fungicides for rice blast disease, which is not a problem in California where no fungicides are used (OECD, 1997). However, not all pesticide use increases with warmer weather, an example is herbicide use.

Changes in cropping and rotation systems, tillage practices, the uptake of integrated pest management practices, the use of precision farming technology, and the expansion of organic farming, can also affect agricultural pesticide use (see the Farm Management chapter). The change in agricultural cropping systems from arable and permanent crops to forage, for example, will usually lead to a significant reduction in pesticide use. It is for this reason that the commonly used indicator showing pesticide use per hectare of total agricultural land can be misleading when compared across countries.

The usefulness of pesticide use indicators can be improved by linking them to pesticide risk indicators and to other indicators, particularly, those covering soil and water quality and farm pest management. For example, there is some evidence that moving from intensive farm practices to integrated pest management (IPM) and organic farming systems may achieve a considerable reduction in pesticide use, while maintaining the economic viability of the system (OECD, 1997). On the other hand, maintaining winter green cover to limit nutrient losses from agricultural land, for example, can require the additional use of pesticides (see the Farm Management chapter).

Pesticide risk indicators

Pesticide risk indicators show trends in risks over time by combining information on pesticide hazard and exposure with information on pesticide use. The OECD has developed three models that can be used to calculate indicators of pesticide risk to aquatic organisms (work on indicators for other risk areas, *i.e.* terrestrial and human health risk, is underway). The three models are designed to produce aggregate risk trends at a national level, however, they can also be used to calculate risk trends for smaller areas. In addition, all three methods can be used to calculate trends for short-term (acute) and long-term (chronic) aquatic risks, and at different levels of aggregation, *i.e.* for one, several or all pesticides; one, several or all crops; and one, several or all aquatic organisms.[10]

A growing number of OECD countries have also developed pesticide hazard or risk indicators. In general, these indicators are intended to help measure progress in meeting the goals of national risk reduction programmes. Four examples are given in the following section, and additional indicators are described in the recent OECD survey of National Pesticide Risk Indicators available at the OECD website *www.oecd.org/ehs/*

Despite the high interest in pesticide risk indicators, and the considerable research on them in recent years, there is no consensus on a single methodology that all countries could use. This is partly because individual governments wish to use indicators for different purposes (*e.g.* depending on the focus of their risk reduction programme), and partly because risk indicator models are difficult to design, where risks are influenced by a multitude of factors that vary within and across countries. The OECD is, therefore, focusing initially on the development and testing of different pesticide risk indicator models rather than on reporting risk trends in different countries.

Definition

Pesticide risk indicators show trends in risk over time by combining information on pesticide toxicity and exposure with information on pesticide use.

Method of calculation

Three methods being developed by OECD are intended to represent the range of approaches that could be used to calculate aquatic risk indicators. In particular, they draw on characteristics of the indicator models developed by Denmark, France, Germany, the Netherlands and Sweden. The indicators share some basic features, including that:

- they use identical data on pesticide toxicity and similar data on other pesticide characteristics such as fate and behaviour in the environment; and,

- they have the same basic structure as follows:

$$\text{Pesticide risk} = \frac{\text{exposure}}{\text{toxicity}} \times \text{area treated}$$

where,

exposure: the level of pesticide estimated to occur in water bodies adjacent to farm fields;

toxicity: the level that would be harmful to aquatic organisms, *e.g.* the level that is lethal to 50% of the organisms exposed; and,

area treated: the number of hectares on which the pesticide was used.

The way the indicators differ is in how they calculate exposure. For this, they use different combinations of the two basic approaches used in other national risk indicator work, namely, scoring and the use of a mechanistic model. The *scoring approach* converts data relevant to exposure into scores that reflect their general contribution to exposure, then combines the scores in ways that give appropriate weight to each variable. The *mechanistic approach* combines the actual data values through a series of mathematical equations that mirror scientific understanding of environmental processes that contribute to exposure.

The three methods, which OECD has being developing on the basis of the scoring and mechanistic approaches, are:

1. ratio of exposure to toxicity (REXTOX): based entirely on the mechanistic approach;

2. additive scoring (ADSCOR): uses a simple scoring system but includes some original (unscored) variables; and,

3. synergistic scoring (SYSCOR): uses a more complex scoring system and some original (unscored) variables.

REXTOX is calculated as follows:

$$REXTOX_{short\ term} = \frac{ADR \times (LOSS/Water\ depth) \times Water\ index \times AFT \times BAT}{short\ term\ toxicity}$$

$$REXTOX_{long\ term} = \frac{ADR \times (LOSS/Water\ depth) \times Water\ index \times AFT \times LTF \times BAT}{long\ term\ toxicity}$$

where,

ADR :   actual dose rate

LOSS :   the amount of pesticide that escapes into water bodies due to spray-drift and run-off, taking account of the crop grown, the pesticide application method, the presence and size of untreated buffer zones, etc.

Water depth : depth of water bodies (*e.g.* rivers, lakes)

Water index : the proportion of the treated area bordered by surface water

AFT :   average frequency of treatments

BAT :   basic area treated

LTF :   long term factor (ratio of concentration of the pesticide concerned over a certain period and the initial concentration, with the default value of 21 days)

short term toxicity: for fish, 50% lethal concentration (LC_{50}) over 96 hours; for Daphnia, 50% effect concentration (EC_{50}) over 48 hours; and for algae, 50% effect concentration (EC_{50}) over 96 hours

long term toxicity: for fish, Daphnia and algae, no observable effect concentration (NOEC) over 21 days

ADSCOR is calculated as follows:

$$ADSCOR_{short\ term} = \frac{(short\ term\ exposure\ score + 1) \times BAT}{short\ term\ toxicity}$$

$$ADSCOR_{long\ term} = \frac{(long\ term\ exposure\ score) \times BAT}{long\ term\ toxicity}$$

where,

short-term exposure score : the sum of five scores for average actual dose rate, frequency of treatments per harvesting season, method of application, spray drift buffer zone, runoff buffer zone, and water index

long-term exposure score : short-term exposure score above + the sum of six scores for half life (DT_{50}) in water, photolysis in water, LogKow, half life (DT_{50}) in soil, Koc, and water index

where,

Photolysis: is chemical decomposition induced by light or other energy.

LogKow: is the standard system used often in the assessment of environmental fate and transport for organic chemicals, and is a measurement of how a chemical is distributed at equilibrium between octanol and water.

Koc: is a measure of a material's tendency to adsorb soil particles, measured as the ratio of the chemical adsorbed per unit weight of organic carbon in the soil or sediment to the concentration of the chemical in solution at equilibrium, with high Koc values indicating a tendency for the material to be adsorbed by soil particles rather than remain dissolved in the soil solution.

|151|

SYSCOR is calculated as follows:[11]

$$\text{SYSCOR}_{\text{short term}} = \frac{\text{exposure score(including area treated factor)}}{\text{short term toxicity}}$$

where,

exposure score: the combination of nine scores for cumulative area treated, actual dose rate, method of application, users' training level, water index, solubility in water, half life (DT_{50}) in water, half life (DT_{50}) in soil, and LogKd

where,

LogKd: is the soil-water adsorption coefficient, calculated by using measurements of pesticide distribution between soil and water.

Simplified formula for the three indicators are being considered. They will be tested and their results compared with those of the three indicators described here. Their formulae are:

- REXTOX = tonnes applied/toxicity/buffer;
- ADSCOR = area treated * buffer/toxicity; and,
- SYSCOR = SCORE (area treated, buffer)/toxicity

Recent trends

Initial testing of the three methods for aquatic risk (REXTOX, ADSCOR and SYSCOR) was completed using pesticide use data on arable crops and orchards in *England and Wales*. The risk trends produced by the three indicators for total pesticide use on arable crops between 1977 and 1996 are shown in Figure 4. The results show that different indicator methods can produce different pesticide risk trends, even when using the same data set.

Figure 4. **Aquatic risk from pesticide use on arable crops: England and Wales, 1977 to 1996**
Index 1977 = 100

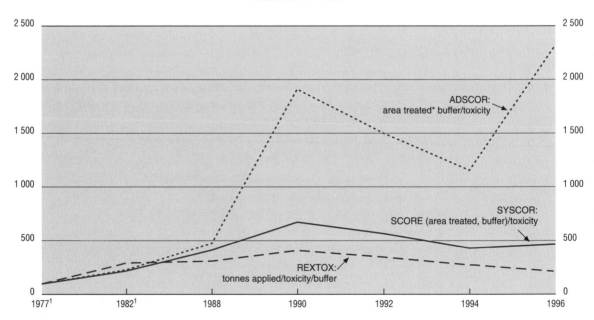

1. Observations only available for 1977 and 1982.
Source: Ministry of Agriculture, Fisheries and Food, United Kingdom.

The relative contribution of single pesticides to the total risk was also analysed in the indicator trial. It was found out that the use of the herbicide Cypermethrin contributed most to the risk trends produced by REXTOX and ADSCOR, and also figured importantly in SYSCOR. The trends diverge after 1988 because of the different ways the indicators deal with pesticide dose rate and untreated buffer zones bordering water bodies, which were required for Cypermethrin in England and Wales starting since 1992.

The next stage of the OECD work on pesticide risk indicators will be a "pilot project" in which OECD countries will try using REXTOX, ADSCOR and SYSCOR with their own national pesticide data. The purpose will be to see how easy the different methods are to use, how the results compare, and how closely the trends they produce correspond to expected risk trends. OECD countries that have developed separate aquatic risk indicator methods will include these in the project as well, to enable comparison of an even broader range of indicator approaches.

Interpretation and links to other indicators

The OECD project has identified the strength and weakness of the three methods for pesticide indicators, which are summarised below.

REXTOX

- Using precise endpoint values rather than scores, REXTOX is the most responsive of the three indicators to changes in input values. It can also be easily adapted to different regional conditions, such as weather, soil, and physical features like slope.

- REXTOX is relatively objective and transparent. By using direct input values and models to calculate pesticide levels in water bodies, which are similar to the ones used for risk assessment, REXTOX minimises reliance on expert judgement to set scores, weight variables, and so forth. This objectivity is only relative, however, because expert judgement was required to establish the indicator and to choose which models to incorporate.

- The precise estimates produced by REXTOX's exposure models rely on various assumptions about exposure processes that may or may not be correct. The indicator results may thus imply a "false precision".

- REXTOX is quite complex. Although scientists and risk assessors may consider it transparent and clear, its formulae may be difficult for others to understand.

ADSCOR

- ADSCOR's basic structure and equation are easy to understand, even by those without technical expertise. ADSCOR is also relatively easy to modify, if a user wants to add new parameters or delete existing ones. Such changes require a consideration of the relative risk contribution of any added parameters, but do not involve complicated mathematical models.

- By expressing risk factors in a qualitative way (low, medium, high), ADSCOR may be easier to grasp than, for example, a precise value for water solubility. In addition, the use of scores makes ADSCOR less demanding on data needs by including ranges rather than exact values for some parameters (*e.g.* $DT_{50} > 60$ days).

- Converting the input values into scores results in a loss of precision and "sensitivity" to minor changes in the values. Scoring indicators can over- or under-estimate such changes depending on where the values fall in relation to the "breakpoints" between the scores. Moreover, assigning scores and weighting the different variables is subjective (based on expert judgement) and dependent upon local conditions that affect pesticide risk.

- ADSCOR and other scoring indicators may require some modification before actual use. The equation to combine the scores will remain constant, but each user will need to review – and in many cases re-establish – scores and their classification categories.

SYSCOR

- As a scoring indicator, SYSCOR shares many of the advantages and disadvantages identified for ADSCOR. However, with its synergistic scoring system, SYSCOR incorporates better than most scoring indicators scientific understanding of the interactions among environmental fate and exposure processes. The disadvantage is that the system is complicated and not fully transparent.

- SYSCOR's complex scoring system makes it difficult to remove or add variables, or to change the number of categories, or the assignment of a variable to a class, if scientific understanding about its importance changes. It is, however, easy to change the classification categories.

National examples of pesticide risk indicators

Denmark

The Danish "Index of Load" was developed to assess progress achieved under the Danish Action Plan that covered the years 1986-96, and might also be used in the new Action Plan that is currently being developed. The index has been used to assess trends in human and environmental impacts of pesticide use. It is a relative measure of load concerning a specific type of toxicity or fate data, and is based on the number of pesticide doses applied per hectare or treatment frequency. The index measures potential rather than actual effects on human health or environment, and is concerned only with direct, acute effects. The index is presented as:[12]

$$\text{Index of load (IL)} = \frac{\sum (\text{kg ai}_{ij} / \text{tox}_i) \times 1000}{\text{hectare}_j}$$

where,

kg ai_{ij} : the quantity of pesticide i sold in year j, measured in tonnes of active ingredients;

tox_i : the lowest toxicity value of pesticide i among a number of toxicity variables (see Table 1); and,

hectare_j : total agricultural land.

The value is multiplied by 1 000 for convenience.

The treatment frequency is defined as the number of pesticide applications per year, provided the recommended standard dose has been used. The recommended standard dose is a measure of the toxicity of a pesticide substance. Thus, the treatment frequency can be regarded as a measure of the quantity weighted by acute toxicity (*i.e.* efficacy) data. The treatment frequency has been a key factor in the Danish Pesticide Action Plan and is being used to track trends with regard to the number of pesticide applications per year on agricultural land under rotation.

A Danish Committee of independent experts has also assessed the overall consequences of a phase-out of pesticides in agriculture, and treatment frequency has been a key factor in the work of the Committee. The Committee has shown that the treatment frequency can be reduced 30-40 per cent over a 5-10 year period without considerable losses to farmers and society. The Committee has stated that the treatment frequency is so far the best indicator available in Denmark, and is going to be a key factor in the second Danish Pesticide Action Plan.

The index for the fate variables, such as degradation time and water solubility, is calculated by multiplying the total quantity of pesticides sold by the fate variables [*i.e.* $\Sigma((quantity\ sold \times fate\ variable)/hectare) \times$ 1 000]. Only arable land in rotation systems is included in the calculation. Set-aside areas are included only if they are used for non-food production purposes, as there are no pesticides used on set-aside land when left uncultivated. The toxicity and environmental fate variables used in the calculations are listed in Table 1. Data on the toxicity and environmental health variables are fairly complete over 15-20 years, especially for mammals, but data are scarce for birds, earthworms, crustaceans, fish and plants.

The index of load is used to describe the trends in different toxicity types and fate measures. Three-year averages are used to reduce the impact of extreme values. Figure 5 shows that the index of load for acute toxicity to mammals has decreased over time primarily because several high risk

Table 1. **Toxicity and environmental fate variables used in the index of pesticide load: Denmark**

Mammals[1]	– Acute oral toxicity (LD_{50}), mg per kg bodyweight.
	– Chronic toxicity, No Observed Adverse Effect Level (*i.e.* statistically non-significant level), mg per kg bodyweight per day.
Birds	– Acute oral, Lethal Dose (LD_{50}), mg per kg bodyweight.
Fish	– 50% Lethal Concentration (LC_{50}), mg per litre water over 96 hours.
Crustaceans	– 50% Effect Concentration (EC_{50}), mg per litre water over 48 hours.
Algae	– 50% Effect Concentration (EC_{50}), mg per litre water over 96 hours.
Soil	– Degradation time (T_{50}) (*i.e.* the length of time it takes for a pesticide to degrade down to half of its initial concentration in soil), days.

1. Applies to mice or rats, depending on which of the two gives the lowest LD_{50} value.
Source: Environmental Protection Agency, Danish Ministry of Environment and Energy.

Figure 5. **Acute pesticide toxicity to mammals:[1] Denmark, 1981-85 to 1994-96**

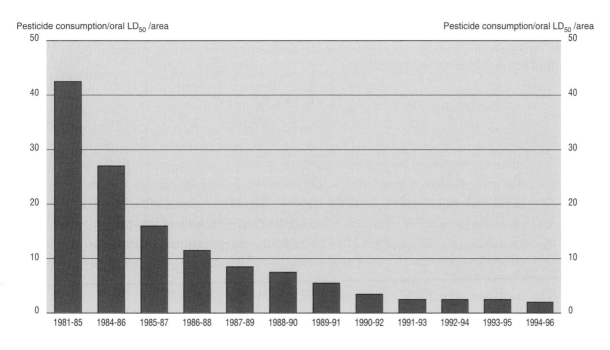

1. Applies to mice or rats, depending on which of the two gives the lowest LD_{50} value.
Source: Environmental Protection Agency, Danish Ministry of Environment and Energy.

pesticides, most notably parathion, are no longer used in Denmark. The same pattern is observed in the trends of chronic toxicity to mammals. Total sales of pesticides classified as possibly having carcinogenic effects declined from the reference period, 1981-85, to the 3-year period 1988-90, after which the sales have returned to the level of the reference period. The evidence on the changes in algal toxicity is inconclusive partly due to data problems.

Germany

The approach of the German pesticide risk indicator is to:

• estimate the usage of each active ingredient for each crop, based on the sales data of the active ingredient, and also taking into account the application method for each crop and other relevant factors;

- estimate the risk of each active ingredient, in terms of four acute, four chronic and six environmental risk categories; and,
- calculate the weighted average risk indicators for each group of active ingredients (*i.e.* herbicide, fungicide and insecticide), in terms of four acute, four chronic and six environmental risk categories.

To calculate the German risk indicator involves three steps. The **first step** involves estimating pesticide usage data per crop (and group of crops) from national sales data, and requires the following information:[13]

- a list of all approved pesticide active ingredients including their authorised application sites, use patterns, and conditions (in Germany this is the "Register of Authorised Plant Protection Products" edited by the Biological Federal Institute for Agriculture and Forestry);
- national-level data on the annual volume sold for each active ingredient;
- national-level data showing the area under cultivation for each major crop; and,
- data on the probability of infestation that requires treatment for each major pest.

Drawing on the above data, the quantity of each active ingredient used for each crop (or group of crops) can be estimated by the formula below. This formula gives the proportion between the quantity of the active ingredient theoretically necessary for all permissible applications to the identified crop and the corresponding quantity for all crops for the registered active ingredient multiplied by the total quantity of active ingredient sold, as follows:

$$Q = SQ \times \sum_{i=1}^{m} (A_i \times R_i \times P_i) / \sum_{i=1}^{n} (A_i \times R_i \times P_i)$$

where,

m = maximum number of permissible applications of the active ingredient to the crop (m < n)

n = maximum number of permissible applications of the active ingredient to all crops

A_i = maximum treated area ($A_i = A_j$ EQUATION m, with A_j = crop area grown) [ha]

R_i = maximum permissible dose rate of the applied active ingredient i [kg/ha]

P_i = probability of application i ($0 < P_i < 1$) (independent of compound, if the same pest requires repeated applications then the sum of the concerning probabilities is equal to the frequency of treatments)

SQ = total quantity of the active ingredient sold per year [kg/yr]

The limitations of the above formula are that it is assumed that:

- the recommended dose is applied, while often farmers use lower dosages;
- the ingredients are used with the same preference for all permissible applications; and,
- the application probabilities are the same over time, although pest infestation varies annually and the application probabilities also vary.

The **second step** is an estimation of risk of each active ingredient, in terms of four acute, four chronic and six environmental risk categories, using the model SYNOPS.[14] The SYNOPS model considers soil, surface water and (optionally) air. On the basis of an exposure calculation for soil and surface water, the acute and chronic toxicological effects on earthworms, algae, *Daphnia*, and fish are estimated for each permissible application of each active ingredient considered. Based on the application probability and the crop area grown, an aggregation of the single results is carried out in such way, that each active ingredient is characterised by a set of six exposure indices and eight biological risk indices.[15]

The **third step** involves calculation of the weighted average risk indicators for each group of active ingredients (*i.e.* herbicide, fungicide and insecticide), in terms of four acute, four chronic and six environmental risk categories. The weighted mean values of 1987, 1994 and 1998, covering herbicides, fungicides and insecticides, provide the change in risk over time with the 1987 data as a baseline (Figure 6). All indicators for herbicides show a decline of risk, while some for fungicides and insecticides have increased.

Figure 6.   **Pesticide risks for herbicides, fungicides and insecticides: Germany, 1987 to 1998**
Index 1987 = 100

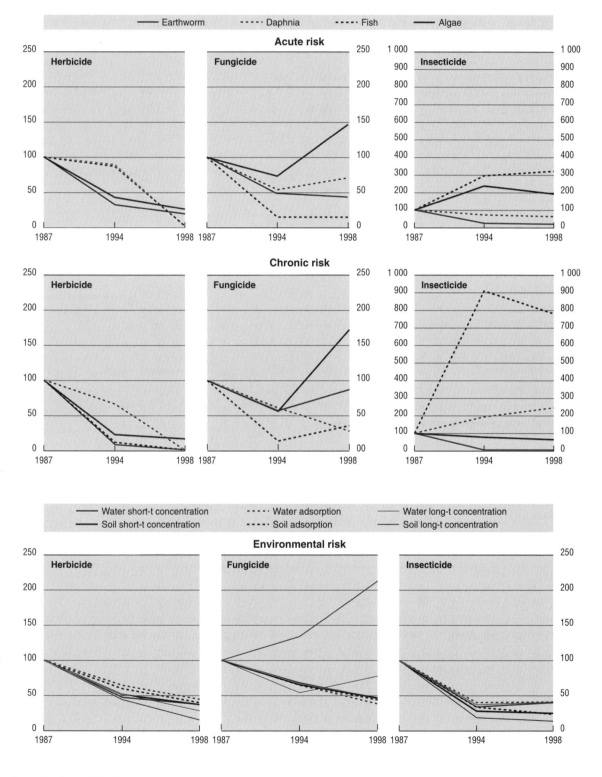

Note: See Annex Table 2.
Source: Gutsche and Rossberg (2000).

Sweden

The National Chemical Inspectorate has developed pesticide risk indicators to measure the progress of the national risk reduction programme. The indicators will also be used as tools in setting goals for the next stage of the programme. The indicators give semi-quantitative estimates of the risk reduction achieved, and they are based on hazard assessment combined with quantities applied. They are considered as temporary indicators as they will be gradually modified and improved.

Two types of indicators are used, one related to human health and the other to the fate and impact on ecosystems. The 200 active substances of nationally approved pesticides were ranked by their hazard classifications, determined from the warning labels on the products. The risk criteria and index scores used to calculate the environmental and human health risk indices are shown in Table 2. The environmental index is mainly based on product labelling and classification data, but also on information on soil degradability, mobility and bio-accumulation properties. In the human health risk index, active ingredients of products with warning labels related to cancer and reprotoxicology, receive automatically the maximum score irrespective of risk category.

Table 2. **Risk criteria and index scores of the pesticide risk indicator: Sweden**

Environmental index score		Human health index score	
Risk criteria	Score	Risk category	Score
Toxic to honeybees	0-2	T+ Very toxic	10
Very toxic	2	T Toxic	7
Toxic	1	C Corrosive	5
Not toxic	0	Xi Irritant	4
		Xn Harmful	3
Toxic to aquatic organisms	0-2	V Moderately harmful	1
Very toxic	2		
Toxic	1		
Not toxic	0		
Other specific environmental risk criteria (toxic to earthworms, dangerous to the ozone layer, etc.)	0-2		
Very toxic	2		
Toxic	1		
Not toxic	0		
Soil degradability	0-2		
Mobility	0-2		
Bioaccumulation	0-2		
Total	0-12	Total	1-10

Source: Swedish National Chemical Inspectorate.

Combining the index score with quantities sold over time for each active ingredient, semi-quantitative estimates expressed as human health or environmental risk indicators can be used to track risk trends:

Human health risk indicator = Σ_i(tonnes_ai$_i$ × h_tox$_i$);

Environmental risk indicator = Σ_i(tonnes_ai$_i$ × e_tox$_i$);

Where,

tonnes_ai$_i$: tonnes of active ingredient of pesticide i sold;

h_tox$_i$: the human health index score for pesticide i; and,

e_tox$_i$: the environmental index score for pesticide i.

For the human health index there is one index score from 1-10 (see the right hand column in Table 2). For each active substance the relevant score is multiplied by the amount sold. The results for

Figure 7. **Comparison of the environmental and health risk indicators with the quantity of pesticides sold: Sweden, 1986 to 1996**

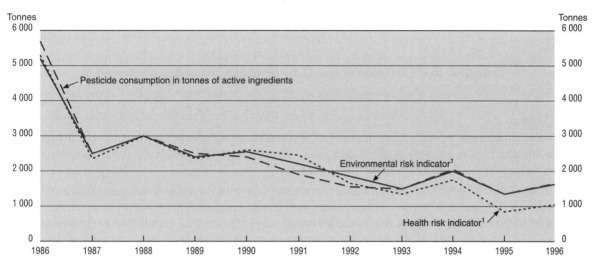

1. For convenience, the scale of the risk indicators has been adjusted to match the scale of pesticide sales measured in tonnes of active ingredients.
Source: Swedish National Chemical Inspectorate.

all active substances sold in Sweden during one year are summed to a human health risk indicator. For the environmental index there are 6 different scores as shown in Table 2, with a highest total score of 12 for an active substance. For each active substance the sum of the scores is multiplied by the amount sold. The results for all active substances sold in Sweden during one year are summed to an environmental risk indicator.

Figure 7 shows the trends in the risk indicators and quantities sold during the period 1986-1996. For convenience, the scale of the risk indicators has been adjusted to match the scale of pesticide use measured in tonnes of active ingredients. The trend of the environmental risk indicator follows the reductions in pesticide use. Even if the use of some environmentally hazardous pesticides has decreased in recent years due to regulatory actions, the use of other environmentally hazardous pesticides, such as cereal fungicides and persistent herbicides that have high environmental index scores, has increased during the same time. The trend of the human health risk indicator drops slightly below that for pesticide use from 1993 onwards, because some highly hazardous pesticides are no longer used.

United States

The United States Department of Agriculture has developed pesticide risk indicators of human health, that can be used to analyse historical trends at the national level (USDA, 1997, pp. 122-125). The indicators measure the potential human health impact from pesticide use, as they are abstractions from variations in the field. The indicators account for only a limited number of environmental and safety factors, but they are more informative than indicators of pesticide use expressed in kilograms applied or area treated.

The human health risk indicators are defined as:[16]

Chronic Risk Indicator = $[\Sigma_i(a_ib_ip_{it})/\Sigma_i(a_ib_i\, p_{i(base)})]$

Acute Risk Indicator = $[\Sigma_i(a_ic_ip_{it})/\Sigma_i(a_ic_ip_{i(base)})]$

where,

a_i: the soil half-life[17] that is the estimated number of days that a pesticide application remains active in the environment,

b_i: the Reference Dose[18] indicator of long term toxicity to humans of one kilogram of pesticide i;

c_i: the Oral LD$_{50}$[19] indicator of acute toxicity of one kilogram of pesticide i;

p_{it}: the number of kilograms of active ingredient of pesticide i applied in period t; and,

$p_{i(base)}$: the number of kilograms of active ingredient of pesticide i applied in the base period.

The summation is across all pesticides i. The calculated index value for each active ingredient is thus multiplied by the quantity applied and then summed over all ingredients to obtain an aggregate indicator of potential risks to human health.

A comparison of pesticide use measured in tonnes of active ingredient with the chronic and acute potential risk indicators is shown in Figure 8 by use of index numbers. The main conclusions over the period from 1964 to 1992 suggest that while pesticide use increased by nearly two and half times, the acute risk indicator showed only a 10 per cent increase and the chronic risk indicator declined sharply.

Much of the reduction in the potential chronic risk indicator reflects the removal of some highly toxic persistent pesticides, such as organochlorine insecticides, aldrin, DDT, chlordane, and toxaphene. Insecticides continue to account for a substantial part of the risks, even after the ban on highly toxic and persistent organochlorine insecticides and other reductions in use. Insecticides accounted for over 90 per cent of the total potential acute risks and 54 per cent of the total potential chronic risks in 1992.

Despite the slight increase in the acute risk indicator, farmworkers' actual exposure to pesticides may be smaller because of improvements in safety regulations and pesticide application practices.

Figure 8. **Indicators of pesticide use and human health risks: United States, 1964 to 1992[1]**

Index 1964 = 100

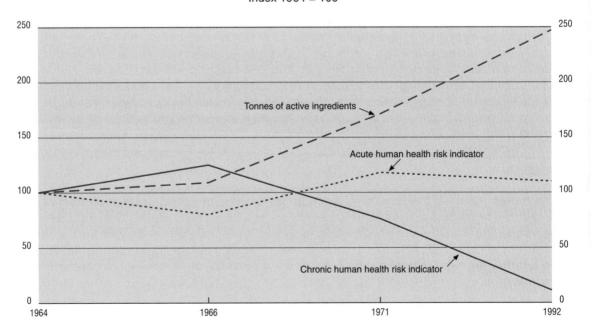

1. Estimates include maize, soybeans, wheat, cotton, sorghum, rice, groundnuts, potatoes, other vegetables, citrus, and apples.
Source: USDA (1997).

Moreover, while total potential risks associated with herbicides and fungicides showed a large increase, these pesticides accounted for under 20 per cent of the total potential chronic risks and 5 per cent of the total potential acute risks in 1992. Also the potential chronic risks from other pesticides – mostly soil fumigants – increased about 75 per cent and accounted for over 30 per cent of the total potential chronic risks in 1992.

A more recent project is underway to develop pesticide risk indicators in the United States, by the US Department of Agriculture and the Environmental Protection Agency (Kellog *et al.*, 1999). In this project, the potential for pesticide loss from farm fields, and subsequently leaching and runoff risk indicators for drinking water, fish, algae and crustaceans, will be estimated from the information regarding pesticide use, soil distribution, irrigation and water quality thresholds.

3. Related information

Cereals, industrial crops, fruit and vegetables account for the major share of agricultural pesticide use in most countries. While pasture and rangeland are the major part of agricultural land use, pesticides on forage account for typically less than 5 per cent of total pesticide usage. In *New Zealand*, however, the use of pesticides on forage areas for weed control is much greater at about 25 per cent of total usage in 1998 (Holland and Rahman, 1999). There is also considerable variation in the quantities of pesticides used per hectare both between various crops and between different countries, although time series and coverage of this data across countries is limited (Brouwer *et al.*, 1994; European Commission, 1999a; EUROSTAT, 1998; OECD, 1997; and USDA, 1997).

There is evidence to suggest an increasing *efficiency in pesticide use*. During the period 1985 to 1997 crop production in certain OECD countries, as measured by the FAO crop production volume index covering all arable and permanent crops, increased more rapidly than pesticide use. Examples include, *Belgium*, *Denmark*, *Finland*, the *Netherlands*, *Norway* and *Switzerland* (Figure 3). This might partly be explained by crop yield improvement, use of low-dose pesticides and pesticide reduction practices. However, for a considerable number of countries, for example *France*, *Greece*, *Ireland*, *Japan*, *Korea* and *Turkey*, changes in pesticides use appear to be correlated closely to fluctuations (an increase or decrease) in annual crop production trends (Figure 3).

Figure 3 should be interpreted with some caution, however. For example, the composition of crops produced, and different pesticide products used, varies over time. Improvements in the efficiency of pesticide use, however, is consistent with the pressure on farmers to reduce costs to improve profitability, and with the increasing adoption of pest management practices and technologies that can lead to significant reductions in pesticide use while maintaining or improving crop yields.

Some indication of the *contribution of pesticides to agricultural productivity* is given by an estimate that in the *United States* an investment of US$1 in pesticides provides a return of about US$4 in terms of crop saved. If the indirect environmental and health costs associated with pesticide use are taken into account, however, this average return falls to about US$1.3 (OECD, 1997). The OECD study notes, however, that these estimates should only be viewed as orders of magnitude of the "true" costs of pesticide use, as the assessment of such costs and benefits is extremely complex.

The *health risks* to those exposed to pesticides during their application, including farm workers, their families and other rural residents living in close proximity to land treated with pesticides, are generally not widely documented across OECD countries. However, in the *United States* it is estimated that there are about 67 000 nonfatal acute poisonings annually, although the extent of chronic health illnesses resulting from pesticide exposure is less well documented (USDA, 1997, pp. 183).[20] In the *United Kingdom* over the period 1991-93 the Health and Safety Executive investigated a total of over 200 suspected public pesticide poisoning incidents, although these are not all related to agricultural use of pesticides, but include other uses, such as forestry (British Agrochemicals Association, 1994, p. 33).[21]

The *levels of pesticide residues in foodstuffs* are, for most OECD countries, below the current maximum permissible levels, although on occasions these limits have been exceeded, especially for fruit and vegetables. Research in the *United States* concludes that the health risks from dietary exposure to pesticide residues in US food products is probably negligible, although some fruit and vegetables exceed negligible risk thresholds (USDA, 1994, pp. 102-105). Also in Japan, the number of cases of excess pesticide residues in food was about 0.03 per cent during 1994-96. Results from the Australian National Pesticide Residue Survey over the period 1987 to 1995 also indicate that Australian agricultural products have low levels of chemical residues. Very few violations of national residue limits have been detected in Australia and the incidence of violations in almost all products has declined over the same period (Commonwealth of Australia, 1998).

In Denmark between 1983-87 the maximum pesticide residue limit values were exceeded in approximately 0.5 per cent of fresh vegetables sampled (WWF, 1992, p. 9). Since this period the total volume of pesticide use in terms of active ingredients has decreased. Similarly in the United Kingdom the maximum residue level of pesticides in food is exceeded in less than 1.5 per cent of samples tested (MAFF, 1998; and MAFF, 2000). Evidence from other European Union countries reveals that in 36 per cent of samples, pesticide residues at or below the minimum residue levels were detected in samples of fruit, vegetables and cereals. In about 3.4 per cent of all samples, residues above the maximum residue limit (both national and EU harmonised limits) were found, mainly in fruit and vegetables (European Commission, 1999b).

An examination of the risks of *drinking water pollution* from pesticides reveals that for surface water pesticide levels in excess of national water standards are not uncommon in OECD countries, although overall contamination is at very low levels (see the Water Quality chapter). This problem is more serious for surface water in the proximity of regions where there is heavy loading of pesticides onto agricultural land and the sensitivity to pesticide leaching in agricultural soils is high. In the case of groundwater, there are few direct and regular measurements of pesticide pollution in OECD countries.

The impact of pesticides on wildlife is poorly reported in most OECD countries (see Biodiversity chapter). Under the Wildlife Incident Investigation Scheme the United Kingdom investigates possible pesticide poisoning incidents amongst wildlife and domestic pets, using an indicator based on the annual number of poisoning incidents for different categories of wildlife. Data for the period 1989 to 1996 reveal no clear trend, with poisoning incidents increasing for domestic pets, variable for exotic species and declining for vertebrates (MAFF, 1998). However, the origin of these poisoning incidents, from agricultural and/or other pesticide users, is not identified in the UK investigation. In Australia the run-off of pesticides from cotton growing areas in excess of surface water quality guidelines, has periodically led to fish mortalities in rivers and coastal waters (Commonwealth of Australia, 1995, p. 26).

Several OECD countries have been successful in limiting the use of *methyl bromide* to the 1991 level as agreed under the Montreal Protocol for the Protection of the Ozone Layer (Figure 9; and UNEP, 1999). In the EU there are large differences in the use of methyl bromide, with its use mainly concentrated in southern EU countries, especially on open field fruit and vegetable production in Italy and Spain. In Austria, Denmark, Finland, Germany, Luxembourg, the Netherlands and Sweden its use is severely restricted or banned (EUROSTAT, 1999, pp. 90-91).

4. Future challenges

A future challenge in developing pesticide use and risk indicators is to improve the collection, coverage and quality of pesticide use/sales data, expressed in terms of the quantity of active ingredients. This work might also include collecting information on pesticide use per crop per hectare. Incomplete data on pesticide use can be a significant obstacle to development of meaningful risk indicators.[22]

The initial focus of the OECD pesticide risk indicators project is on methods for calculating indicators of aquatic risks. Indicators for human and terrestrial risks will follow. A recent OECD survey that identified and described existing pesticide risk indicators developed by OECD countries and work already completed by several countries, will provide a starting point for this work.[23] The basic approach for all risk areas will be to combine information on pesticide hazard and exposure (*i.e.* risks) with information on pesticide use/sales. The project is not seeking to combine the indicators of human

Figure 9. **Methyl bromide use:**[1] **1991 to 1998**

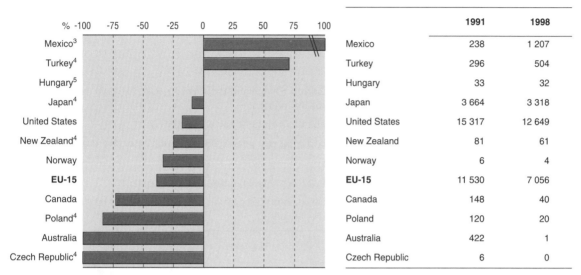

	Change in tonnes of ozone depleting substance equivalents (CFCs)[2]			Tonnes of ozone depletion potential		
					1991	1998
Mexico[3]				Mexico	238	1 207
Turkey[4]				Turkey	296	504
Hungary[5]				Hungary	33	32
Japan[4]				Japan	3 664	3 318
United States				United States	15 317	12 649
New Zealand[4]				New Zealand	81	61
Norway				Norway	6	4
EU-15				**EU-15**	11 530	7 056
Canada				Canada	148	40
Poland[4]				Poland	120	20
Australia				Australia	422	1
Czech Republic[4]				Czech Republic	6	0

1. In Austria, Denmark, Finland, Germany, Luxembourg, the Netherlands, Sweden, and Switzerland methyl bromide use is severely restricted or banned and thus they are not included in this figure.
2. CFCs: chlorofluorocarbons.
3. The percentage equals 407%.
4. Data for 1998 refer to 1997.
5. The percentage equals 0%.
Notes: Methyl bromide is mainly used by agriculture for most countries. The Montreal Protocol for the protection of the ozone layer agreed that for developed countries they should reduce methyl bromide use to 1991 levels by 1995, achieve a 50% reduction by 2001 and phase-out their use by 2005 with the possible exemption for critical agricultural uses.
Source: UNEP (1999).

health and environmental risks into one "general" indicator of pesticide risk trends, as OECD countries consider such an approach scientifically invalid.

As work on pesticide risk indicators develops, however, it will be important to strike the right balance. On the one hand there is a need to develop a simple risk assessment system drawing on readily available data and research, which can be improved over time. On the other hand, developing a more comprehensive system of risk indicators, which may have greater scientific accuracy, can be difficult to manage in terms of its complexity and data requirements, and may not be easily understood by policy makers and other stakeholders. Moreover, pesticide risk indicators need to be related to other agri-environmental indicators rather than used alone, especially those covering farm pest management, soil and water quality, and biodiversity (see Figure 1).

It may also be useful in the future to supplement physical indicators of changes in pesticide use and risks with economic indicators. This might be achieved by exploring the possibility of developing a "cost-benefit" approach that analyses the relationship between the environmental and health costs associated with pesticide use, and the benefits derived from pesticides in terms of improvements in agricultural productivity (Pearce and Tinch, 1998). At present the scale of the costs relative to the benefits of pesticides are uncertain, and it is this relative economic assessment which is needed to better guide policy makers and inform the public.

NOTES

1. Mexico removed its use of pesticide subsidies from 1998, while the Czech Republic, Hungary and Poland also used pesticide subsidies prior to 1990, see the following section.

2. For a review of OECD pesticide policies and the environment see OECD (1997).

3. Italy is in the process of implementing a tax during the year 2000 on about 20 of the most commonly used pesticides in farming, to be levied on producers, distributors and imported products. The revenue from the tax will be used to fund programmes that encourage farming practices that minimise pesticide use (see (International Environment Reporter, Vol. 22, No. 24, November 24, 1999, p. 967).

4. The pesticide reduction programmes of the three countries are summarised as follows (the targets shown here are now under review):

Country	Reduction rate (in terms of active ingredients)	Target year	Base period
Sweden	75%	1997	1981-85
Denmark	50%	1997	1981-85
The Netherlands	40 % (herbicides) 39 % (others)	2000	1984-88

Source: Rayment *et al.* (1998).

5. The UNEP has recently published a report on phasing out ozone depleting methyl bromide, which includes an extensive international database (UNEP, 1999).

6. The OECD also held a Workshop in 1999 in Switzerland on Integrated Pest Management (for further details, see the OECD website at: *www.oecd.org/ehs/* [Pesticide Programme > Pesticide Risk Reduction]).

7. For related studies that have examined the links and related indicators covering pesticide use and risks and other agri-environmental areas, see for example, Commonwealth of Australia (1998); ECNC (2000); European Commission (1999a); MAFF (2000); and USDA (1997).

8. In Germany the use of plant protection products relating to agricultural areas would be reduced by approximately 30 per cent over the period concerned in Figure 2, but data for the former East Germany is not available.

9. In Australia and New Zealand, where pesticide use data time series are incomplete, pesticide use indicators are now being developed, see for example, (Hamblin, 1998, pp. 87-88) for Australia; and Holland and Rahman (1999), for New Zealand.

10. Further information on the OECD's work on pesticide risk indicators is available on the OECD website at: *www.oecd.org/ehs/* [Pesticide Programme > Pesticide Risk Reduction]. For a review of other work on pesticide risk indicators, see, for example, Centre for Agriculture and the Environment (1999); Falconer (1998); and Oskam and Vijftigschild (1999).

11. In the project, SYSCOR was not designed to calculate long-term risk indicator, but could be modified to do so.

12. The Danish index methodology is elaborated in Clausen (1998) and Gyldenkærne (1997).

13. A detailed description of the estimation method can be found in OECD (2000). The estimation method described here was used to track the trend of the environmental risk potential of pesticide usage in Germany in the last ten years. On the basis of annual reports about the domestic sale of active ingredients, the ten most frequently used active ingredients and their application area were estimated.

14. SYNOPS is a German abbreviation of *Synoptische Bewertung des Risiko-Potential von Pflanzenschutzmitteln* ("Synoptic evaluation of potential pesticide risk" in English).

15. See Gutsche and Rosseberg (1997a and 1997b) for a detailed description of the model SYNOPS.

16. For further details of these indicators see Barnard *et al.* (1997).

17. Soil half-life is the length of time it takes for a pesticide to break down to half of its initial concentration. These data are midpoints of the range of soil half-lives reported in research literature, which in turn are based on estimates derived under a variety of soil, moisture, and temperature conditions. Soil half-life data are taken from the US Agricultural Research Service databases.

18. The Reference Dose measure reflects the long-term safety/toxicity of pesticides to humans. It is measured as the no-observable-effect level of a pesticide ingredient multiplied by an uncertainty factor, which adds an additional safety factor in translating animal no-observable-effect levels to human no-observable effect levels. The constructed values represents the "dose" (mg/kg of body weight) which could be consumed daily over a 70-year life span by a person weighing 70 kg without having adverse health effects. An indicator of value 1 is equal to the presence of 1 Reference Dose in the environment for 1 day. The Reference Dose data was taken from the US Environmental Protection Agency (EPA) or World Health Organisation (WHO) in the absence of EPA data, while averages of the active ingredient's chemical family were used in some cases.

19. The Oral LD_{50} measure relates to ingestion of the active ingredient and reflects the pesticide dose level (mg/kg of body weight) which results in 50 per cent mortality of laboratory test animals. An indicator value equal to 1 is the presence of 1 LD_{50} dose in the environment in 1 day. In the absence of Oral LD_{50} data for rats, Oral LD_{50} for a related mammal, usually mice, was used. No effort was made to translate the rat LD_{50} into human terms. The Oral LD_{50} is a severe threshold and such a level of acute exposure is unlikely in reality.

20. A comprehensive research project is underway in the US to examine the impacts of occupational pesticide exposure, see USDA (1997, pp. 183).

21. The WHO estimated in the early 1990s that world-wide 3 million people annually suffer acute, severe, pesticide poisoning, and over 20 000 may die, with agricultural workers in developing countries most at risk, see WWF (1992).

22. OECD in cooperation with EUROSTAT is beginning a process to improve quality and coverage, see OECD (1999).

23. For details of this survey and the future OECD programme of work on pesticide risk indicators, see endnote 10 .

Annex Table I. Total use of agricultural pesticides: 1985 to 1997
Tonnes of active ingredients

	1985	1986	1987	1988	1989	1990	1991	1992	1993	1994	1995	1996	1997
Australia	..	..	..	..	..	..	..	119 654	..	..	..	..	..
Austria	5 270	6 069	..	..	4 615	4 246	4 487	3 897	3 984	3 619	3 402	3 565	3 690
Belgium[1]	8 748	8 748	8 923	9 535	9 885	9 973	9 623	10 060	9 885	9 510	10 536	9 976	8 619
Canada	39 259	32 968	33 883	35 529	..	33 964	..	..	..	29 206	..	..	..
Czech Republic	..	..	..	..	11 217	8 920	6 361	4 817	3 645	3 680	3 783	3 908	3 889
Denmark	6 863	6 085	5 485	5 253	5 795	5 650	4 628	4 566	4 103	3 919	4 809	3 669	3 675
Finland	1 964	1 933	1 988	1 923	2 258	2 037	1 734	1 410	1 260	1 297	1 054	933	1 016
France	98 027	99 697	92 966	99 167	100 433	97 701	103 434	84 709	91 953	89 515	84 006	97 890	109 792
Germany	..	..	..	..	..	..	..	..	..	..	..	..	..
Greece	..	7 346	6 510	6 754	8 151	..	7 860	8 567	8 583	9 973	8 525	9 870	9 034
Hungary	26 342	31 818	26 918	25 341	35 438	25 501	16 129	11 541	10 195	9 560	7 696	..	..
Iceland	..	..	..	..	..	..	..	..	..	..	..	..	..
Ireland	..	..	..	1 812	1 899	1 745	1 915	1 942	2 169	2 160	2 255	1 741	2 325
Italy	99 579	97 550	99 100	100 579	91 070	91 680	58 123	58 848	54 928	46 678	48 490	48 050	..
Japan	..	95 886	95 886	94 096	93 347	92 608	88 014	86 718	87 270	87 598	86 331	83 678	84 541
Korea	..	21 322	23 229	21 967	23 280	25 082	27 476	26 718	25 999	26 282	25 834	24 541	24 814
Luxembourg	..	..	..	..	..	..	253	..	..	..	..	..	..
Mexico	21 002	21 632	18 088	18 172	19 146	18 835	17 206	15 951	36 000	..	..	..	..
Netherlands	..	..	..	..	..	..	..	..	11 761	11 169	10 923	10 338	10 397
New Zealand	3 690	..	..	3 732	..	..	..	..	..	3 757	..	3 752	..
Norway	1 529	1 514	1 323	1 194	1 035	1 184	771	781	765	862	931	706	754
Poland	12 398	14 479	18 444	23 377	20 620	7 548	5 217	6 755	6 791	7 335	6 962	9 420	9 501
Portugal[2]	..	..	..	..	..	..	9 355	6 117	8 984	9 581	11 818	12 457	12 751
Spain	..	39 134	44 050	47 751	46 534	39 562	39 147	31 839	29 408	31 243	27 852	33 236	34 023
Sweden	3 660	5 585	2 409	2 865	2 423	2 344	1 837	1 512	1 464	1 961	1 224	1 528	1 609
Switzerland	..	..	..	2 456	2 464	2 283	2 056	2 022	1 936	1 921	1 827	1 747	..
Turkey	..	..	..	..	..	..	..	..	12 400	11 000	12 500	13 976	15 575
United Kingdom	40 826	40 759	40 719	32 985	32 643	35 858	35 364	31 696	32 400	33 945	33 774	35 523	35 432
United States	390 894	372 280	369 556	383 630	365 924	378 636	370 918	380 564	367 863	..	..	..	..

Notes: See OECD source below for detailed notes on coverage. In many cases "use" data refer to "sales" data.
.. Not available.
1. Including Luxembourg.
2. Sulphur is responsible for about 50% of the total indicated values.
Sources: OECD Environmental Data Compendium, 1999; EUROSTAT (1999); Holland and Rahman (1999).

Annex Table 2. **Pesticide risk trends for herbicides, fungicides and insecticides: Germany, 1987 to 1998**

Index 1987 = 100

	Herbicide			Fungicide			Insecticide		
	1987	1994	1998	1987	1994	1998	1987	1994	1998
Acute biological risk earthworm	100	32	19	100	49	44	100	24	20
Acute biological risk Daphnia	100	89	1	100	54	71	100	72	63
Acute biological risk fish	100	87	2	100	15	15	100	297	323
Acute biological risk algae	100	43	26	100	74	147	100	238	193
Chronic biological risk earthworm	100	8	1	100	57	87	100	5	4
Chronic biological risk Daphnia	100	66	< 0.5	100	61	28	100	193	244
Chronic biological risk fish	100	12	1	100	14	36	100	909	782
Chronic biological risk algae	100	23	17	100	57	172	100	78	64
Short-term concentration in water (mg/m^3)	100	47	37	100	68	46	100	34	40
Adsorption to water sediment (mg/m^3)	100	64	44	100	65	38	100	40	41
Long-term concentration in water (mg*day/m^3)	100	52	28	100	54	78	100	37	41
Short-term concentration in soil (mg/kg)	100	51	37	100	66	47	100	28	25
Adsorption to soil (mg/kg)	100	60	40	100	66	44	100	34	24
Long-term concentration in soil (mg*day/kg)	100	44	15	100	134	213	100	19	14

Source: Gutsche and Rossberg (2000).

BIBLIOGRAPHY

Avery, D.T. (1995),
  Saving the Planet with Pesticides and Plastic, Hudson Institute, Indianapolis, Indiana, United States.

Barnard, C., S. Daberkow, M. Padgitt, M.E. Smith and N.D. Uri (1997),
  "Alternative measures of pesticide use", *The Science of the Total Environment*, No. 203, pp. 229-244.

British Agrochemicals Association (1994),
  Annual Review and Handbook 1994, Peterborough, United Kingdom.

Brouwer, F.M., I.J. Terluin and F.E. Godeschalk (1994),
  Pesticides in the EC, Agricultural Economics Research Institute, The Hague, The Netherlands.

Centre for Agriculture and the Environment (1999),
  Comparing Environmental Risk Indicators for Pesticides, Results of the European Concerted Action on Pesticide Environmental Risk (CAPER) Project, Centre for Agriculture and Environment (CLM) Report No. 426, Utrecht, The Netherlands. A summary is available at: *www.clm.nl/index_uk2.html*.

Clausen, H. (1998),
  Ændringer i bekæmpelsesmidlernes egenskaber fra 1981-1985 frem til 1996 (only in Danish "Changes in the properties of pesticides from 1981-1985 to 1996"), Faglig rapport fra DMU, nr. 223, Miljø- og Energiministeriet, Danmarks Miljøundersøgelser.

Commonwealth of Australia (1995),
  Sustaining the Agricultural Resource Base, 12th Meeting of the Prime Minister's Science and Engineering Council, Office of the Chief Scientist, Department of the Prime Minister and Cabinet, Canberra, Australia.

Commonwealth of Australia (1998),
  Sustainable Agriculture – Assessing Australia's Recent Performance, A Report to the Standing Committee on Agriculture and Resource Management (SCARM) of the National Collaborative Project on Indicators for Sustainable Agriculture, SCARM Technical Report No. 70, CSIRO Publishing, Victoria, Australia.

ECNC [European Centre for Nature Conservation] (2000),
  Agri-environmental Indicators for Sustainable Agriculture in Europe, Final Project Report, Tilburg, The Netherlands. Available at: *www.ecnc.nl/doc/projects/elisa.html*.

EEA [European Environment Agency] (1995),
  Europe's Environment: The Dobris Assessment, Office for Official Publications of the European Communities, Luxembourg. Available at: *www.themes.eea.eu.int/* [> all available reports]

EEA (1998),
  Europe's Environment: The Second Assessment, Office for Official Publications of the European Communities, Luxembourg. Available at: *www.themes.eea.eu.int/* [> all available reports].

European Commission (1999a),
  Agriculture, Environment, Rural Development: Facts and Figures – A Challenge for Agriculture, Office for Official Publications of the European Communities, Luxembourg. Available at: *www.europa.eu.int/comm/dg06/envir/report/en/index.htm*.

European Commission (1999b),
  Monitoring for Pesticide Residues in Products of Plant Origin, in the European Union and Norway – Report 1997, Report of the EU Standing Committee on Plant Health. Available at: *www.europa.eu.int/comm/dg24/* [Food of non-animal origin > Pesticides > Monitoring reports > 1997].

EUROSTAT [Statistical Office of the European Communities] (1998),
  Pesticide Use in the EU, Statistics in Focus Environment, No. 3, Luxembourg.

EUROSTAT (1999),
  Towards Environmental Pressure Indicators for the EU, Environment and Energy Paper Theme 8, Luxembourg. The background documentation is available at: *www.e-m-a-i-l.nu/tepi/* and *www.esl.jrc.it/envind/*

Falconer, C. (1998),
  Classification of Pesticides According to Environmental Impact, Final Report to the UK Royal Society for the Protection of

Birds, RSPB, Centre for Rural Economy, Department of Agricultural Economics and Food Marketing, University of Newcastle-upon-Tyne, United Kingdom.

Fernandez-Cornejo, J. and S. Jans (1999),
Pest Management in US Agriculture, Agricultural Handbook No. 717, Resource Economics Division, Economic Research Service, US Department of Agriculture, Washington DC., United States. Available at: *www.ers.usda.gov/* [Publications > Inputs and Technology > Fertilizer and Pesticides].

Gebbie, D. (1998),
"Chemical Issues in International Trade", pp. 11-19, in P. Rowland and D. Bradford (eds.), *Proceedings of the Australian National Pesticide Risk Reduction Workshop* , Bureau of Rural Sciences, Agriculture, Fisheries and Forestry, Canberra, Australia.

Gutsche, V. and D. Rossberg (1997a),
"SYNOPS 1.1: a model to assess and to compare the environmental risk potential of active ingredients in plant protection products", *Agriculture, Ecosystems and Environment*, Vol. 64, No. 2, pp. 181-188.

Gutsche, V. and D. Rossberg (1997b),
"Die Anwendung des Modells SYNOPS 1.2 zur synoptischen Bewertung des Risikopotentials von Pflanzenschutzmittelwirkstoffgruppen für den Naturhaushalt" (only in German "The use of the SYNOPS 1.2 model for the evaluation of the environmental risk potential of the active ingredients of pesticides"), *Nachrichtenbl, Deut, Pflanzenschutzd*, Vol. 49, No. 11, pp. 273-285.

Gutsche, V. and D. Rossberg (2000),
"Bewertung von Pflanzenschutz – Strategien mittels Riskoindikatoren", (only in German "Evaluation of pesticides – strategies with risk indicators), *Mittelungen Biologishe Bundesanst Land-Forstwirtsch*, Berlin-Dahlem (in print).

Gyldenkærne, S. (1997),
Udvikling i den direkte toksikologiske belastning fra pesticider overfor pattedyr, fugle, bier og vandlevende organismer i perioden 1982/85-1995 (only in Danish "Trends in direct toxicity load from pesticides to mammals, birds, bees and aquatic organisms from 1982/85 to 1995"), Statens Planteavlsforsøg Rapport 11: pp. 63-65, Danmarks.

Hamblin, A. (1998),
Environmental Indicators for National State of the Environment Reporting – The Land, Australia: State of the Environment (Environmental Indicator Reports), Department of the Environment, Canberra, Australia. Available at: *www.environment.gov.au/soe/* [Environmental Indicators > Land under "Environmental Indicator Reports"].

Holland, P and A. Rahman (1999),
Review of Trends in Agricultural Pesticide Use in New Zealand, MAF Policy Technical Paper 99/11, Ministry of Agriculture and Forestry, Wellington, New Zealand. Available at: *www.203.97.170.4/MAFnet/index.htm* [Site A-Z > T > Technical Papers].

IFEN [Institut français de l'environnement] (1998),
Les pesticides dans les eaux (only in French "Pesticides in Water"), Etudes et Travaux n 19, IFEN, Orléans, France. Available at: *www.ifen.fr/pestic/pestic.htm*.

Kellogg, R.L., R. Nehring, A. Grube, S. Plotkin, D.W. Goss and S. Wallace (1999),
Trends in the Potential for Environmental Risk from Pesticide Loss from Farm Fields, poster presentation for the State of North America's Private Land, January, 19-21, Chicago, Illinois, United States.

MAFF [Ministry of Agriculture, Fisheries and Food] (1998),
Developing a Set of Indicators for Sustainable Agriculture in the United Kingdom, Consultation Document, London, United Kingdom.

MAFF (2000),
Towards Sustainable Agriculture – A Pilot Set of Indicators, London, United Kingdom. Available at: *www.maff.gov.uk/* [Farming > Sustainable Agriculture].

Mano, S. and M.O. Andreae (1994),
"Emission of Methyl Bromide from Biomass Burning", *Science*, Vol. 263, pp. 1255-56, 4 March.

Oberthur, S. (1997),
Production and Consumption of Ozone Depleting Substances 1986-1995, Deutsche Gesellschaft fur Technische Zusammenarbeit, Berlin, Germany.

OECD (1997),
Agriculture, Pesticides and the Environment: Policy Options, Paris, France. This document is accompanied by an OECD General Distribution document: *Agriculture, Pesticides and the Environment: Policy Options* – Annexes [OCDE/GD(97)157]. Available at: *www.oecd.org/* [Documentation > 1997 > Reference Components > OCDE > OCDE/GD].

OECD (1998),
The Environmental Effects of Reforming Agricultural Policies, Paris, France.

OECD (1999),
   OECD *Survey on the Collection and Use of Agricultural Pesticide Sales Data: Survey Results*, General Distribution document [ENV/JM/MONO(99)1], Paris, France. Available at: *www.oecd.org/ehs/* [Publication > Pesticides].

OECD (2000),
   Report of the OECD *Pesticide Aquatic Risk Indicators Expert Group*, Paris, France. Available at: *www.oecd.org/ehs/* [Publication > Pesticides].

Oskam, A. and R. Vijftigschild (1999),
   "Towards Environmental Pressure Indicators for Pesticide Impacts", Chapter 11, pp. 157-176, in F. Brouwer and B. Crabtree (eds.), *Environmental Indicators and Agricultural Policy*, CAB International, Wallingford, United Kingdom.

Pearce, D. and R. Tinch (1998),
   "The True Price of Pesticides", Chapter 3, pp. 50-93, in W. Vorley and D. Keeney (eds.) *Bugs in the System – Redesigning the Pesticide Industry for Sustainable Agriculture*, Earthscan Publications Ltd, London, United Kingdom.

Rayment, M., H. Bartram and J. Curtoys (1998),
   Pesticide Taxes – A Discussion Paper, Royal Society for the Protection of Birds, Sandy, United Kingdom.

UK Department of the Environment (1996),
   Indicators of Sustainable Development for the United Kingdom, London, United Kingdom. Available at: *www.environment.detr.gov.uk/* [> Indicators of Sustainable Development for the UK].

UNEP [United Nations Environment Programme] (1999),
   Methyl Bromide Phase-out Strategies: A Global Compilation of Laws and Regulations, Nairobi, Kenya. Available at: *www.uneptie.org/ozonaction.html* [Sector-specific Information > Methyl Bromide > Policy Information].

USDA [United States Department of Agriculture] (1994),
   Agricultural Resources and Environmental Indicators, Agricultural Handbook No. 705, Natural Resources and Environment Division, Economic Research Service, Washington, DC., United States. Available at: *www.ers.usda.gov/* [Briefing Rooms > Agricultural Resources and Environmental Indicators].

USDA (1997),
   Agricultural Resources and Environmental Indicators, 1996-97, Agricultural Handbook No. 712, Natural Resources and Environment Division, Economic Research Service, Washington, DC., United States. Available at: *www.ers.usda.gov/* [Briefing Rooms > Agricultural Resources and Environmental Indicators].

USGS [United States Geological Survey] (1999),
   The Quality of Our Nation's Waters – Nutrients and Pesticides, USGS Circular 1225, Washington, DC., United States. Available at: *www.water.usgs.gov/pubs/circ/circ1225/*.

WWF [World Wildlife Fund] (1992),
   Pesticide Reduction Programmes in Denmark, the Netherlands, and Sweden, International Research Report, November, Gland, Switzerland.

Chapter 3

WATER USE

HIGHLIGHTS

Context

In some regions in OECD countries agriculture is facing increasing competition for surface and groundwater from urban and industrial demands. Also there is a growing recognition to meet environmental needs through allocations of water for the environment and protection of down-stream impacts from agricultural pollution. Even so, for some OECD countries the issue of water use is not a policy concern because they are richly endowed with water resources.

Governments have traditionally invested in the development of irrigation schemes for the purposes of national and regional development. This often involved a substantial subsidy to establish and maintain irrigation systems and the consequent underpricing of water to agriculture. A number of OECD countries are beginning to seek more efficient and effective use of water in agriculture, by moving towards a full-cost recovery system of water pricing, as a means of adequately valuing water as an input to agricultural production.

Indicators and recent trends

OECD is developing three indicators related to agriculture's use of surface and groundwater: first the intensity of water use by agriculture relative to other users in the national economy; second the measurement of the technical (volume) and economic (value) efficiency of water use on irrigated land; and third a water stress indicator to gauge the extent to which diversions or extractions of water from rivers are impacting on aquatic ecosystems.

The share of agriculture in total national water utilisation is high for most OECD countries, with the sector currently accounting for nearly 45 per cent of total OECD water utilisation, and over 60 per cent for nine OECD countries. While utilisation levels are far below available water resources for most countries, in more arid regions the utilisation intensity of water, especially by agriculture, is a much higher share of available resources. In these situations agriculture has to compete with other users for scarce available water resources. Even where competition for water resources between agriculture and other sectors is less pronounced, the growing need to meet recreational and environmental demands for water may require that agriculture improves its efficiency of water use.

Information on the technical or economic efficiency of irrigation water use across OECD countries is extremely limited. Since the early 1980s there has been a continuous upward trend in water use for irrigation in many OECD countries, associated with the increase in the irrigated land area. The expansion in the irrigated area has been mainly encouraged by government investment in irrigation infrastructure and an irrigation water subsidy. The price of water paid by farmers in many OECD countries is substantially below that paid by industrial and household users, even when differences in water quality and the costs of water conveyancing systems between agriculture and other users are taken into account.

There is relatively little information on the extent or trends in water stress caused by diverting surface water from rivers for agricultural use. Also very few OECD countries define and monitor flow rates for rivers subject to diversion of water for agricultural use. In part, this lack of information highlights for many OECD countries that water stress caused by agricultural diversions from rivers is not a concern. Where flow rates are defined and measured, this is to help allocate inter-provincial river flows or transboundary flows.

1. Background

Policy context

A number of OECD governments have traditionally invested in the development of irrigation schemes in order to promote national and regional development. This has often involved a substantial subsidy to establish and maintain agricultural irrigation systems. The appropriateness of continuing these subsidies, which results in the under-valuation of water resources, when demand for water in some regions of OECD countries is exerting increasing pressure on available resources, is open to question.[1] However, for some OECD countries which are richly endowed with water resources, the issue of water use is not a policy concern.

Many OECD countries are beginning to encourage the more efficient and effective use of water in agriculture, by moving towards a regime of water pricing that involves full-cost recovery. This is one means of adequately valuing water as an input to agricultural production. Because of the complex nature of the pressures on available water resources, however, the management and policy response is likely to consist of a range of complementary measures, with different combinations being appropriate for different circumstances.

The range of measures may include pricing and economic reform; ecological sustainability; institutional and structural reform; reform of property rights regimes, trading and market reform; and community involvement and education. In this context, agricultural water use indicators can be useful to policy makers, by helping to reveal the extent to which the pressures on the total available water resource are modified through improved policies, management practices and technologies.

Some OECD countries depend on other countries for a significant share of their water resources (Annex Table 1). Reliance on transboundary sources, rivers for example, can lead to tensions between countries, especially where total availability in the upstream country is less than in the downstream country. Against this background a number of OECD countries in North America and Europe have signed international water sharing agreements. In these circumstances, agricultural water use indicators can be helpful tools for policy makers to monitor their obligations under these agreements.

Environmental context

Water underpins most aspects of human life. It is becoming increasingly clear that the availability of safe water is now a substantial limiting factor regarding the health and welfare of the global population.[2] Although water is a renewable resource, its availability is finite in terms of the amount available per unit of time. The extent of the pressures on total water resources and the consequent impacts on ecological processes vary from region to region reflecting, in many instances, population pressures, availability of water, and technological developments.

In many areas, however, agriculture is facing increasing competition from urban and industrial demands. Also there is a greater recognition of and willingness to meet environmental needs through both formal allocations of water for the environment and also protection from any down-stream impacts of agricultural pollution. In a growing number of regions within OECD countries choices will therefore have to be made about the amount of water that can be allocated for food production as compared to other uses and for environmental purposes.

Irrigation has been used in many countries to extend the level of agricultural production where the natural rainfall pattern is at variance with crop needs and already accounts for 70 per cent of water utilisation in the world. Almost 98 per cent of all global water is salt water, leaving just over 2 per cent as fresh water. Nearly 70 per cent of the fresh water is frozen in icecaps, and most of the remainder is present as soil moisture, or lies in deep underground aquifers as groundwater not accessible for human use. As a result, less than one per cent of the world's fresh water supply is readily accessible for direct human use in surface rivers and lakes, or stored as groundwater (UN, 1997). Most aquifers are replenished slowly, with an average recharge rate that ranges from 0.1-0.3 per cent per year. The main interactions between the hydrologic cycle, water resources and water utilisation are presented in Figure 1.

Figure 1. **The interaction between the hydraulic cycle, water resources and water use**

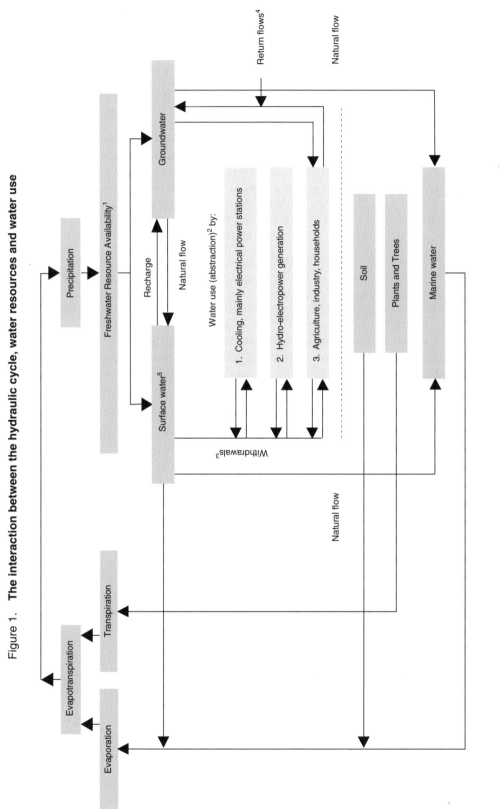

1. Mean annual precipitation + transborder water flows - mean annual evapotranspiration. Evapotranspiration is the addition of evaporation (*i.e.* water loss from mainly surface and marine water, but also soil) and transpiration (*i.e.* water loss from plants and trees). Overexploitation of groundwater resources was not included in the calculation.
2. Water use (abstraction) defined as the amount of water drawn from surface or groundwater and conveyed to place of use.
3. Water withdrawals defined as water use from surface and groundwater resources and conveyed to main users, plus water returned to surface water and used by a downstream user, for example, from irrigation systems.
4. Return flows in the form of water infiltration into soil and drainage.
5. Rivers and lakes.
Source: OECD Secretariat.

Agriculture is capable of affecting the water available for other uses and for the maintenance of natural environmental processes through a variety of pathways. Changes to the hydrologic cycles in water catchment areas resulting from the replacement of forests/natural vegetation by pasture or crops generally increases the net run-off to surface water and reduces replenishment of groundwater reserves. While direct diversion from surface or groundwater sources for irrigation and livestock uses reduces the amount available for other purposes, this can be offset to some extent by leakage from irrigation systems, and less efficient use of precipitation by rain-fed crops. However, this may also lead to the deterioration in water quality through mobilisation of salts, nutrients (*e.g.* nitrogen, phosphates) and pesticides in the soil.

Environmental needs are increasingly being recognised as legitimate demands on total water resources. Diversions by agriculture from surface water, rivers and lakes, can effectively compete directly with the water needs of ecosystems, aquaculture and fisheries. This can compound the effects of agricultural chemical run-off on overall water quality. Natural in-stream processes are important in maintaining suitable water quality levels and flow patterns. There are natural purification and flow control processes that risk being damaged by excessive diversions and elevated nutrient and contaminant levels in run-off waters from agriculture (see the Water Quality, Soil Quality, and Land Conservation chapters).

In areas where utilisation of water by agriculture and other users are particularly high, river flows may decrease and result in lakes shrinking and damage to wetlands. Hydrological records have shown a marked reduction in the annual discharge flows of some of the world's major rivers such as the Murray (*Australia*) and Colorado (*United States*) (Redaud, 1998). When wetlands dry up, either because of low river flows or reduced seepage, the associated wildlife suffers as well as the species depending on wetlands to migrate. However, if properly designed irrigation infrastructures, such as reservoirs, can make a valuable contribution to the conservation of aquatic species and wildlife, such as waterfowl. In addition, under certain water management systems, agriculture can contribute to stabilising water flows in downstream areas (see Land Conservation chapter).

The excessive use of groundwater can have serious effects on the base flow of rivers, especially during dry periods, with potentially harmful effects on aquatic ecosystems. The physical consequences of lowering groundwater levels can be that watercourses and aquatic areas in clay soil catchments dry out in the summer period. In *Hungary*, for example, between the Danube and Tisza rivers, agricultural activity and droughts, particularly in the early 1990s, have led to a lowering of the shallow groundwater table, threatening some natural wetlands (OECD, 2000). Lowering the water table can also lead to direct changes in groundwater quality, in some cases.

In coastal aquifers excessive pumping of groundwater can cause sea water to penetrate into aquifers with previously acceptable water quality, rendering them unfit for human or agricultural uses. Overpumping in some irrigated areas in *Spain* has caused intrusion from saline aquifers, both near the coast and inland (OECD, 1997a).

There are other, less obvious considerations in assessing the impacts of water diversion on the environment. The application of water to land through irrigation substantially in excess of the natural water balance can significantly and adversely affect the condition of the soil through waterlogging, soil structure decline, and rising saline water tables. There is evidence that excessive groundwater pumping can result in land subsidence. Potentially this can adversely affect land drainage patterns, dependent ecosystems, agricultural enterprises, water resource developments and other infrastructure.[3]

2. Indicators

Water use intensity

Definition

The share of agriculture water use in national total water utilisation.

Method of calculation

This indicator captures the share of agriculture water use in national total water utilisation, and requires data on the extent of freshwater utilisation for major uses, for example, agriculture (mainly irrigation and livestock), household drinking water, industry and power generation. The indicator reveals the overall importance of the agricultural sector in total water utilisation, and whether the changing use of water by agriculture relative to other uses, both economic and environmental, is potentially intensifying the pressure on available water resources.

In view of the absence of data on total agricultural water use for a number of countries, the irrigation water use total is used instead as a proxy. For most countries irrigation water represents over 80 per cent of total agricultural water use, with much of the remainder accounted for by the livestock sector (Annex Table 2). For this reason trends in irrigated water use and irrigated area are also examined below as related information to this indicator.

The data on agricultural water use needed to calculate the indicator are generally available in OECD countries, although consistency in data coverage, definitions and estimation methods vary. The term agricultural water use in this Report refers to the utilisation (abstraction) by farming of water from surface water (rivers, lakes) and groundwater reserves, used mainly for irrigation and livestock, but excludes the precipitation falling on agricultural land.

For countries where groundwater utilisation as a share of total water resource availability is significant, the relationship between water movement into groundwater bodies and its extraction, and hence the rate at which watertable levels rise and fall is an important measure of the water balance in a region. Groundwater depth can provide a useful indication of the overall water balance at regional (catchment) level, although measuring it can be costly in most cases.

Recent trends[4]

The share of agriculture in total national water utilisation is high for most OECD countries, with the sector currently accounting for 44 per cent of total OECD water utilisation, and greater than 60 per cent for nine countries (Figure 2). Since the early 1980s the increase in agricultural water use, has been in excess of 10 per cent for a number of countries (Figure 3). To a large extent variations in the level of water use by agriculture reflect changes in irrigated area and livestock numbers. However, for some countries reductions in water subsidies, coupled with lower support levels for agriculture, has resulted in a substantial decrease in farm output and water utilisation by the sector, for example, in the *Czech Republic*, *Hungary* and *Poland* (Figure 3).

In *Canada*, trends in sectoral water use show an increasing share of thermal power and a slight rise in utilisation by agriculture (Figure 3). In the Prairie region of Canada, where supplies are already limited, a high water utilisation rate by agriculture may have negative implications for wildlife populations. It is foreseen that irrigation will be expanded significantly in some regions of Canada.[5]

While there are wide variations between OECD countries in the utilisation intensity of total water resources in most cases the intensity of use is low, although for eight countries the total use of available water resources is greater than 20 per cent (Figure 2). However, while nationally current utilisation levels are far below water resource availability for most countries, in certain arid regions of *Australia*, *Spain* and the *United States*, for example, the utilisation intensity of water, especially by agriculture, is a much higher share of available resources. Moreover, in many cases the costs of transporting water from humid to arid regions of a country may be too costly.

In these more arid regions of OECD countries, there are indications that the agricultural sector is coming under greater competition with other water users for a limited supply of water resources. This is particularly serious in situations where water users are competing over scarce groundwater resources and groundwater extraction rates are in excess of recharge rates. Even where competition for water resources between agriculture and other sectors is less pronounced, the growing demand for various recreational uses of surface water and to preserve wetlands and other aquatic ecosystems, may require that agriculture improves its efficiency of using water (OECD, 1998c).

Figure 2. **National and agricultural water use: mid/late 1990s**

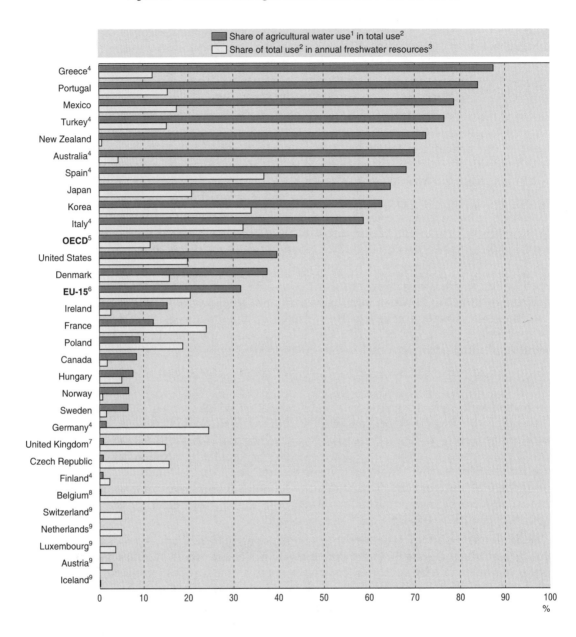

1. Agricultural water use includes water abstracted from surface and groundwater, and return flows (withdrawals) from irrigation for some countries, but excludes precipitation directly onto agricultural land.
2. Total use (abstractions) of water by all users, including public water supply, agriculture, industry, and for power station cooling.
3. Annual freshwater resources include: Mean annual precipitation + transborder water flows – mean annual evapotranspiration (overexploitation of groundwater resources was not included in the calculation).
4. Data for irrigation water use were used as data for agricultural water use are not available.
5. Austria, Iceland, the Netherlands and Switzerland are excluded from the calculation of the share of agricultural water use but included for the calculation of the share of total use.
6. Austria, the Netherlands and Portugal are excluded for the calculation of the share of agricultural water use but included for the calculation of the share of total use.
7. England and Wales only.
8. The share of agricultural water use is less than 1% of total utilisation and includes Luxembourg.
9. Data for agricultural water use are not available, except Luxembourg for which data are included in the share of Belgium.
Note: See Annex Tables 1 and 3.

Sources: OECD *Environmental Data Compendium*, 1999; INAG (1995); Ministry of Agriculture, Fisheries and Food, United Kingdom.

Figure 3. **Total agricultural water use:**[1] **early 1980s to mid/late 1990s**

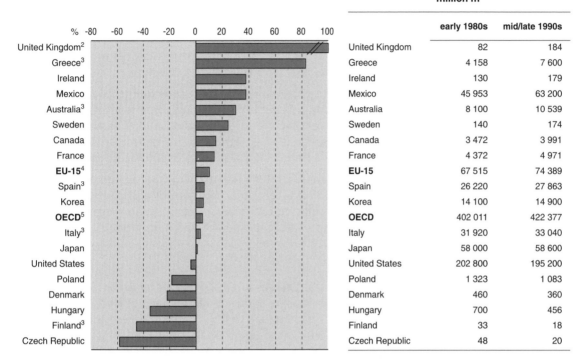

	Agriculture water use million m³	
	early 1980s	**mid/late 1990s**
United Kingdom	82	184
Greece	4 158	7 600
Ireland	130	179
Mexico	45 953	63 200
Australia	8 100	10 539
Sweden	140	174
Canada	3 472	3 991
France	4 372	4 971
EU-15	67 515	74 389
Spain	26 220	27 863
Korea	14 100	14 900
OECD	402 011	422 377
Italy	31 920	33 040
Japan	58 000	58 600
United States	202 800	195 200
Poland	1 323	1 083
Denmark	460	360
Hungary	700	456
Finland	33	18
Czech Republic	48	20

1. Agricultural water use includes water abstracted from surface and groundwater, and return flows (withdrawals) from irrigation for some countries, but excludes precipitation directly onto agricultural land.
2. England and Wales only. Percentage equals 124%.
3. Data for irrigation water use were used as data for agricultural water use are not available.
4. Austria, Belgium, Germany, Luxembourg, the Netherlands and Portugal are excluded.
5. Austria, Belgium, Germany, Iceland, Luxembourg, the Netherlands, New Zealand, Norway, Portugal, Switzerland and Turkey are excluded.
Note: See Annex Table 2.
Source: OECD *Environmental Data Compendium*, 1999.

Interpretation and links to other indicators

Interpretation of the indicator should focus on longer run trends and not the annual variation in the share of agriculture in total utilisation. Annual fluctuations may reflect changes in irrigated area and the composition of agricultural production, however, agriculture's share in total use is also influenced by changes in water used by other sectors in the economy. Annual trends are also distorted by fluctuations in climatic conditions, and these trends should be interpreted in the context of trends in national water use intensity, for all uses. However, in some agricultural systems water utilisation can contribute to the stability of river flows down-stream through returning water to rivers or recharging groundwater (see Land Conservation chapter).

It is not always clear as how estimates of agricultural water use are obtained, for example, if drainage of water from agricultural land is taken into account. It is also uncertain in some cases whether total agricultural water utilisation refers to all uses by the sector or refers only to the use of water for irrigation. But some caution is required in using irrigation water as a proxy measure for total agricultural water use, as for some countries the use of water for irrigation is less than 40 per cent of total agricultural use, for example, *Belgium, Denmark, Hungary* and *Poland* (Annex Table 2).

There are no benchmarks or targets for this indicator given the wide diversity in conditions across regions and countries. However, a downward trend could indicate more efficient farming practices, a greater reliance on imports of food and fibre, and/or increasing water use by other sectors. Work by OECD (1998d) has identified thresholds of utilisation pressure on available water resources, defined as categories of (share of total water use in total available resources): low <10 per cent; moderate 10-20 per cent; medium-high 20-40 per cent; and high >40 per cent.[6] Pimentel *et al.* (1997), also defines pressure on water resources to occur when water availability ranges from 1 000 to 1 700 m³/capita/year. Moreover, in *Europe*, the annual per capita water availability is considered to be extremely low below 1 000 m³, very low between 1 000 m³ and 2 000 m³, and low from 2 000 m³ to 5 000 m³ (EEA, 1995).

In *Japan*, the effectiveness (sustainability) of agricultural water use is defined as the ratio of total water use less non-renewable water use divided by total water use [(T-N)/T], where total water use (T) is agricultural water use, including groundwater, and renewable water use (N) is agricultural use of groundwater, except the amount of water recharge through agricultural land. However, to better assess water use intensity, it is necessary to incorporate renewable water use into the indicator.

There are several links between the indicator related to water use and other agri-environmental issues, in particular those related to irrigation and water management. Water use by agriculture can impair water quality, through salinisation, or eutrophication, while indicators for land conservation focus on measuring the off-farm environmental consequences related to water retention and off-farm sediment flow.

Related information

Over the past 15-20 years there has been an increase in **water use for irrigation** purposes in some countries (Figure 4). This has been associated with the expansion in the area of land irrigated for most of these countries, and as a result the ratio of irrigated land to total arable and permanent crop area has also risen significantly (Annex Table 3). While for most countries irrigated land is used mainly for the production of cereals, fruit and vegetables, for some countries, such as *Australia* and *New Zealand*, the major part of irrigated land is used for fodder and pasture production. The notable exception to these trends, are the *Czech Republic*, *Hungary* and *Poland* where a decrease in support to agriculture has led to significant reductions in farm output and water use as noted above.

The substantial expansion of the irrigated area in *France* has largely been due to policy measures which provided subsidies to farmers installing irrigation equipment, as well as guaranteeing low water prices for agriculture (Figures 4 and 6; OECD, 1999b). The expansion of the irrigated area and water for irrigation in *Greece* over the past 20 years is also the outcome of a commitment by the government to increase both agricultural production and farm incomes in rural areas and subsidise irrigation water (Figures 4 and 6). It is also the result of private initiatives, which currently represent about 60 per cent of the total Greek irrigated area (OECD, 1999b).

Similarly in *Spain*, more than two-thirds of irrigated land use has been publicly developed as a means to promote economic development and agricultural production (Figure 4). About 50 per cent of total rural employment in Spain is directly or indirectly dependent on irrigated agriculture (OECD, 1999b).

The irrigated crop land in the *United States* contributes around 40 per cent of the total value of crops on about 12-15 per cent of the total arable and permanent crop land area (USDA, 1997, pp. 67-82). While the US irrigated area expanded by 5 per cent over the past 20 years, further expansion is likely to be limited by a lack of suitable project sites for irrigation, reduced funding, increased pressure for water resources from other users and public concerns for environmental consequences (Figure 4). About 20 per cent of US irrigated land is supplied by water from the Ogallala aquifer (which is located under the Great Plains region), and there are increasing concerns that overpumping the Ogallala faster than recharge rates, is leading to falling water tables and higher pumping costs as farmers need to bore deeper wells in search of water (Postel, 1999).

Care is required when comparing national data on irrigated land, as it is essential to know the definition given by countries of irrigated area. Irrigated areas are usually defined as those purposely provided with water, including land irrigated by different irrigation technologies (*e.g.* flooding, spray

Figure 4. **Irrigation water use and irrigated area: early 1980s to mid/late 1990s**

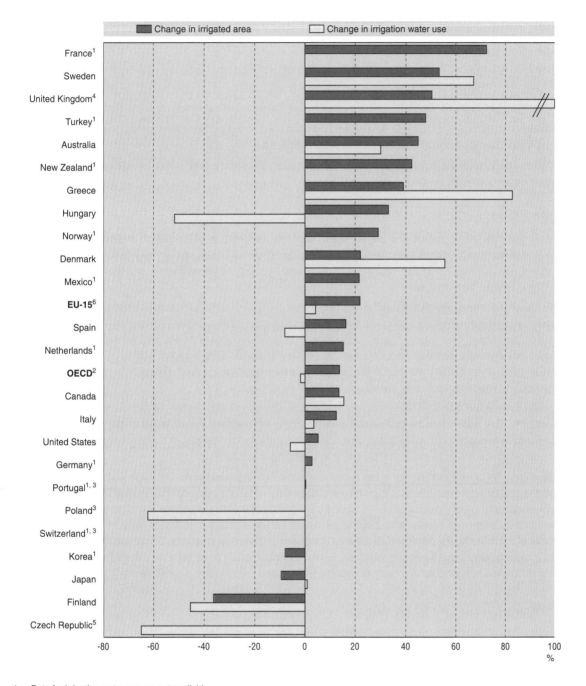

1. Data for irrigation water use are not available.
2. Austria, Belgium, France, Germany, Iceland, Ireland, Korea, Luxembourg, Mexico, the Netherlands, New Zealand, Norway, Portugal, Switzerland and Turkey are excluded for the calculation of change in irrigation water use. Belgium, Czech Republic, Iceland, Ireland and Luxembourg are excluded for the calculation of the change in irrigated area.
3. The change in irrigated area is less than 1%.
4. England and Wales only. Percentage for irrigation water use equals 301%.
5. The change in irrigated area is not available.
6. Austria, Belgium, France, Germany, Ireland, Luxembourg, the Netherlands and Portugal are excluded for the calculation of irrigation water use. Belgium, Ireland and Luxembourg are excluded for the calculation of the change in irrigated area.
Notes: See Annex Tables 2 and 3.
Source: OECD *Environmental Data Compendium*, 1999.

guns, etc.) for crop production or pasture improvement, whether this area is irrigated several times or only once during the year stated. The irrigated area is often estimated as 80 per cent of the irrigable area, which takes into account farmers not wishing or unable to irrigate at any given time (OECD, 1973).

Water use efficiency

Definitions

The indicators of water use efficiency cover irrigated agricultural land, and are defined as:

1. *Water Use Technical Efficiency*: For selected irrigated crops, the mass of agricultural production (tonnes) per unit volume of irrigation water utilised.

2. *Water Use Economic Efficiency*: For all irrigated crops, the monetary value of agricultural production per unit volume of irrigation water utilised.

Method of calculation

Water use efficiency indicators are a measure of the utilisation of irrigation water by crops relative to the water input to the farming system, thus identifying overall leakage, evaporation, and other water loss that are not utilised by crops. This indicator takes account of the different methods of irrigation, as well as water losses from the system.

The indicators require information on the physical mass (and value for the economic efficiency indicator) of agricultural produce over the accounting period, and the volume of water diverted or extracted for irrigation, less storage and transmission losses and return flows, and excluding precipitation. In order to remove the annual fluctuations caused by changes in climatic conditions and commodity prices, interpretation needs to focus on longer-run trends which may reflect changes in irrigation practices, the selection of crops irrigated and trends in crop productivity.

In calculating the economic efficiency indicator, the monetary value of production is defined as being equal to the difference between the gross margin of irrigated production and the gross margin of alternative rain-fed agricultural production. The assessment of the water use in terms of the value of agricultural produce assumes a common base for valuing the produce.

The issues in valuing the produce are more complex, however, as there are likely to be many aspects of government policy and practice that effectively distort any cross-country comparisons. These may be clear and deliberate actions of government for specific purposes, for example price support schemes for either the domestic or export markets, and subsidies or tax relief on farm inputs, or they may be hidden and unintentional, such as water pricing that fails to cover environmental impacts. Some means of correcting for changes in commodity prices will be required to track performance over time as prices for specific produce or commodities will respond to a variety of market factors and potentially distort the indicator.

Recent trends

Information on the technical or economic efficiency of irrigation water use is limited. Trends in the technical and economic efficiency for rice in *Japan* suggest no significant change in water use efficiency over the past ten years (Figure 5).

Average losses in irrigation projects suggest that only about 45 per cent of water diverted or extracted for irrigation actually reaches the crop (FAO, 1994). In some regions and countries, however, much higher efficiencies in the use of irrigation water are obtained. Losses occur at distribution on farm, during field applications, and in irrigation systems.

An indirect measure of the possible improvement in the technical efficiency of using water for irrigation, is shown by comparing the growth rates in water used for irrigation purposes with the expansion in the irrigated area. Where the irrigated area has been expanding more rapidly that the rate of growth in use of water for irrigation this could indicate an improvement in the technical efficiency of the irrigation system, such as in *Australia*, *Italy*, *Spain* and the *United States* (Figure 4).

Figure 5. **Technical and economical efficiency of irrigation water utilisation for rice: Japan, 1985 to 1995**

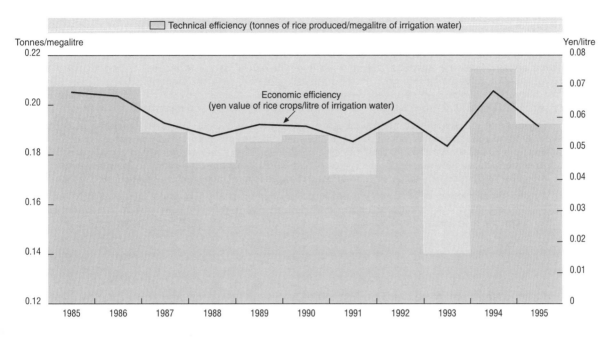

Note: Water utilisation data represent gross water extracted (*i.e.*, including return flows).
Source: OECD Agri-environmental Indicators Questionnaire, 1999.

Interpretation and links to other indicators

The indicator of technical water use efficiency is perhaps more robust than that for economic water use efficiency, responding to fewer external factors. The former is, however, more difficult to interpret where there is more than one commodity involved, while the economic indicator reduces all forms of agricultural production to a common denominator. Moreover, caution is required for interpreting the economic efficiency indicator, as the price for both irrigated and rain-fed agricultural production are influenced by a variety of market factors and government policies.

An indicator of technical water use efficiency is more likely to be useful in comparing and tracking performance of different areas or countries for specific industries. An indicator of economic water use efficiency can be helpful useful in assessing performance over whole countries or regions/catchments/river basins as they are able to integrate all forms of production on a common base (value), especially if some means of correcting for changes in commodity prices were developed.

Water use efficiency could also be estimated by measuring the volume of drainage flows from irrigation regions and the depth of watertables below irrigation regions. However, interpretation of this information can be difficult, for example, groundwater variations under an irrigation area can result from activities outside the irrigation area and aquifer recharge rates depend on geological factors, which differ between areas.

These indicators are strongly linked with various aspects of farm management, in particular irrigation and water management indicators. The link with these indicators is important in revealing the extent to which the application of different forms of irrigation technology affect irrigation water efficiency.

Related information

In the United Kingdom an indicator has been developed showing the volume of irrigation water used against capacity of water storage on farms (see Figure 9 in the Farm Management chapter). The indicator is useful as it shows the sustainable contribution storage can make. Water is collected during the winter

---

Box 1. Water use efficiency in irrigated agriculture in Australia

The cotton industry in Australia has expanded spectacularly in the past 20 years, with a 10-fold increase in production, to become the world's fourth largest exporter. Cotton receives 9 per cent of the water used for irrigation in Australia. At a strategic level the crucial issue is what area of crop to grow with a given supply of water taking into account the probability of rainfall to supplement irrigation, particularly when allocations of water are reduced. Supplies of irrigation water are severely limited, and water use efficiency (WUE) is a vital issue. WUE has two components, engineering and agronomic.

Engineering efficiency: water received at the farm gate that is used in evapo-transpiration. Studies have identified significant differences between areas and between years in irrigation water use efficiency (ranging from 30 per cent in 1989-90 to 85 per cent in 1995-96). These may be related to climatic conditions and to farm practices. Low values occur in years of high rainfall and run-off during the growing season, but the improving WUE since 1975 suggests fundamental changes in farm management practices and technology.

Agronomic efficiency: kg of cotton lint produced per mm evapo-transpiration. Increases in cotton lint yield/mm evapo-transpiration suggest a noteworthy improvement, reflecting changes in plant varieties as well as in farming practices and technology.

(it would otherwise run off to sea and be lost to the water environment) and subsequently used during summer stress periods (which reduces environmental damage through abstraction).

Irrigation water use in the *United Kingdom* has changed from supporting lower value output to higher value output, with the irrigated area of cereal and pasture crops declining and that of field crops, such as potatoes and vegetables, increasing. This trend towards irrigating only higher value output crops is more efficient and profitable as the use of irrigation water provides a higher return on investment than in the past. It is therefore likely to continue. Various forecasts have been made of future irrigation water demand, and, although these are subject to considerable uncertainty due to climate change, reform of the Common Agricultural Policy and market conditions, the consensus is that the level will reach 250 million m^3 by 2021, an increase of 52 per cent on 1995 (MAFF, 2000).

In *Australia*, recent research has revealed some improvement in the efficiency of water use in agriculture (see Hearn, 1998; and Box 1). The need to improve water use efficiency in Australia is an integral part of the country's water reform programme (see below). Australia is also in the process of developing a water use index for agriculture as a tool for assessing the extent of water utilisation at national, regional or large catchment scales (Commonwealth of Australia, 1998).

Water stress

Definition

The proportion of rivers subject to diversion or regulation for irrigation without defined minimum reference flows (MRFs).

Method of calculation

The state of river flows is an important indicator of the extent to which diversions or extractions are impacting on natural environmental processes. However, it is difficult to identify unequivocally these impacts, and a surrogate indicator is used as a more effective means of assessing water stress. The indicator is calculated as the percentage of river lengths that do not have recommended minimum flow rate reference levels, that is, where there are no regulations to ensure the maintenance of downstream flows.

The indicator is based on information on regulatory measures that provide for minimum flow rates in rivers. It assesses the risk of environmental damage through the absence of provisions for meeting environmental needs in those river systems subject to diversion for agricultural use.

Recent trends

There is relatively little evidence on the extent or trends in water stress caused by diverting surface water for agricultural use. Moreover, very few OECD countries define and monitor MRFs for rivers subject to diversion of water for agricultural use. In part, this lack of information highlights for many OECD countries that water stress caused by agricultural diversions from rivers is not a concern. Also in some cases MRFs are not monitored because either the irrigated agricultural area is a very small share of the total arable and permanent crop area (Annex Table 3), or that groundwater figures prominently in total agricultural water utilisation (Annex Table 1).

Where MRFs are defined and measured, this is to help allocate inter-provincial flows (*e.g.* between Provinces in *Canada*) or transboundary flows (*e.g.* between *Canada* and the *United States* under the 1909 Boundary Water Treaty). In other instances MRFs are only relevant to power stations so as to protect aquatic habitats (*e.g. Germany*).

Poland has defined its MRF as 90 per cent of minimal statistical flows using hydrological criteria. *Portugal* uses a range of MRFs depending on the type and dimension of rivers and dams, while *Spain* defines MRFs (using environmental criteria) for every river basin, and *Switzerland* uses MRFs to assure the functioning of aquatic ecosystems and dams. In *Australia*, development of MRFs is being incorporated as part of the country's programme to audit water resources and reform water policies (Box 2).

Box 2. **Incorporating environmental needs into Defined Minimum Reference Flows for Rivers in Australia**

Defined minimum reference flows for rivers in Australia are increasingly being developed with explicit determination of environmental water needs, and a subsequent informed decision to supply all or part of these needs in the light of competing demands for water and their relative merits. The Council of Australian Governments formally agreed, in 1995, to a package of measures, including the recognition of the environment as a legitimate user of water and the need to make provisions for meeting environmental needs in the allocation of water.

There are many drawbacks associated with traditional methods for assessing the environmental flow requirements of rivers through consideration of only a few taxa (such as certain fish species) and issues (such as flushing flows). Dissatisfaction with existing methodologies, including the in-stream flow methodology has stimulated the development of more comprehensive approaches to the formulation of environmental flow guidelines for river systems, sometimes referred to as holistic methodologies – variations on the "natural flows paradigm".

This assumes that the natural flows of a river maintain, in a dynamic manner, all of the in-stream biota, riparian vegetation, floodplain and wetlands systems, and any estuarine and off-shore systems affected by river flows. It is also assumed that, if critical features of a river's natural (unregulated) flow regime can be identified and adequately incorporated into the modified or regulated flow regime, the existing biota should persist and much of the functionality of the riverine ecosystems should be maintained.

Flow recommendations for environmental purposes are usually developed in two different contexts. First, planning for new water development projects, where certain quantities/patterns of river flow are set aside for environmental purposes as part of the design and construction process. Second, planning for reinstatement of environmental flows where the infrastructure has been in place for some time and the river flow is already regulated or modified.

Defined minimum reference flows being developed in Australia explicitly recognise the environment as a legitimate demand on water resources by utilising more sophisticated means of assessing environmental needs and specifying management rules to accommodate these needs.

Source: Information supplied by Australia to the OECD Workshop on Agri-environmental Indicators, York, United Kingdom, 1998.

Interpretation and links to other indicators

A benchmark for this indicator could be the share of all river systems with defined MRFs subject to diversion by agriculture and deemed to be stressed, that is where water is diverted to the detriment of key environmental qualities. However, it may be difficult to define a single MRF level for all rivers, as MRFs may vary depending on factors such as local climatic conditions and seasonal flow patterns in rivers. Even so, for some rivers problems of water stress are not evident. This indicator should not be confused with other less specific, but more commonly used indicators of the intensity of pressure on available water resources.

The water stress indicator does not cover groundwater, and in some regions of OECD countries unsustainable use of groundwater is a major problem and recharge rates may be extremely slow. To ensure that groundwater utilisation does not exceed recharge rates, a sustainable groundwater use index can be calculated as the ratio between groundwater utilisation and the estimated sustainable utilisation rate.

The indicator of water stress is closely linked to indicators of biodiversity and habitat through the impact of water diversions and extractions on surface or groundwater dependent ecosystems. The increased occurrence of algal blooms in major river systems, for example, is in part due to reduced flow rates and farm nutrient run-off into surface water. This has had significant adverse effects on the quality of urban and other domestic water supplies as well as affecting ecosystem functioning.

3. Related information

Water pricing

In many OECD countries, large collective irrigation networks are managed by public bodies and the price of water supplied to farmers rarely reflects its "full cost". Recent OECD reports on water pricing (OECD, 1999*a-d*) reveal that for a number of OECD countries industrial and household water users pay more than 100 times as much per cubic metre of water as agricultural users (Figure 6).

Some caution, however, is required in drawing comparisons between water prices paid by the different users shown in Figure 6, because water supplied to agriculture is usually of lower quality than that used by households. Also, the capital and running cost of water conveyance systems are generally lower for agriculture than for households or industry. Ideally, a comparison of water prices charged to various users should take into account these quality and cost differentials.

Moreover, caution is also required in drawing comparisons of agricultural water pricing systems across OECD countries shown in Figure 6, as this is a complex task (OECD, 1999*b*). A number of generic factors, however, can be identified as contributing to the explanation of some of the observed differences. For countries in which irrigation is relatively important, some of the key explanatory variables include the type of water rights, pricing criteria, the type of charges and the performance and use of alternative economic instruments. To properly assess the economic distortions that may be caused by under-pricing agricultural water it is important to take into account both the negative and positive effects of agriculture water use on the environment. These effects may vary according to different agro-ecosystems, farming systems, climatic conditions and government policies.

Even if these caveats are taken into account in comparing water prices between different users, it is evident that significant differences remain. In particular, it is likely in most cases that the quality of water supplied to industry is of a similar quality to that provided to agriculture. Also, government subsidies for irrigation water and conveyancing systems are widespread amongst OECD countries, as detailed below (Redaud, 1998).

While underpricing of water to agriculture is widespread, a number of OECD countries are beginning to embark on major reforms of the water industry, including moving toward full cost recovery for water supplied to agriculture and other users (OECD, 1998*b*). Australia, for example, has initiated a programme to reform the water industry, the National Water Reform Framework, which provides for full cost recovery by rural water supply authorities by 2001. Where full cost-recovery is not possible, remaining subsidies on water use are to be reported and made transparent. The implementation of the new water

Figure 6. **Comparison of agricultural, industrial, and household water prices:[1] late 1990s**

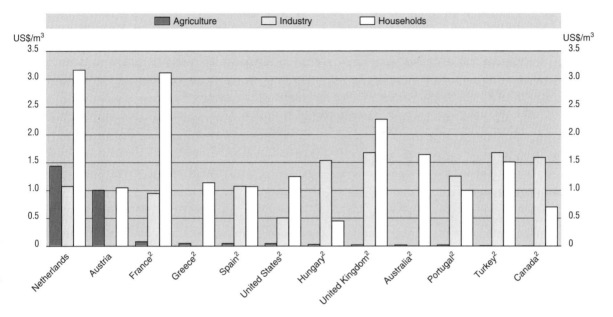

1. For agriculture, industry, and households, prices are the median values for the range of prices for each category.
2. Agricultural water prices are less than 0.1 US$/m3, see Annex Table 4.
Notes: See Annex Table 4. Some caution is required in comparing agricultural water prices with other user prices because water supplied to agriculture is usually of a lower quality than that provided to households and, on occasion, industry; while the capital costs of water conveyance systems are generally lower for agriculture than for household or industry.
Sources: OECD (1999a, 1999b, 1999c, 2000).

pricing system has so far resulted in water charges to farmers increasing by 35-50 per cent Figure 6; and OECD, 1998b, pp. 5-32).

In *Canada*, in keeping with the policy of making farmers pay more of the true cost of water services, changes to water service rates were implemented in the late 1980s. By the time the new rate structure is fully implemented in the year 2000, the price for water will have increased almost 300 per cent with the irrigators paying approximately 60 per cent of the operating and maintenance costs (Figure 6; and OECD, 1998b, pp. 37-51).

Based on data from the National Water Commission, 197 of the 294 water basins in *Mexico* are overexploiting available water resources. Over 80 per cent of the country's water supply is used without charge for agricultural irrigation, and an estimated 50 per cent of this water is likely wasted through inefficiencies in irrigation water management. The government is in the process of developing technical assistance programmes to help improve irrigation management practices.[7]

According to the *United States* Department of Agriculture (USDA, 1997, p. 73), water costs are typically based on access and delivery costs of supplying water to farmers, but generally do not convey signals about water's relative scarcity and the full social cost of its use (Figure 6). As with other OECD countries, there is increasing discussion and actions taking place to reform US water management policies that promote economic efficiency and meet multiple and competing needs (OECD, 1998b, pp. 205-217).

Under the newly adopted (September 2000) *European Union* Water Framework Directive, EU farmers will be required to comply with water pricing policies that meet environmental objectives. Evidence in some EU member States (*e.g. Austria*, the *Netherlands*, see Figure 6) would suggest that farmers are close or already paying the full recovery cost for water, while in some other member States this is not the case (*e.g. France*, *Greece*, *Portugal*, *Spain* and the *United Kingdom*, see Figure 6).

The system adopted for water abstraction in the United Kingdom (England and Wales) is based on a formula linking the type of source (tidal water, supported water – water which is subject to artificial diversion but to meet a specific need – or unsupported water – water which is following its natural flow), the season (summer of winter) and the loss factor (amount of water returned to the environment). This means that the most expensive water would be from a supported source in summer with no return to the water environment. All abstractions come under the same system and water companies which extract, store, treat and distribute drinking water to industry charge a higher rate to customers which includes their capital and running costs. Agriculture water charges for spray irrigation are ten times more expensive for water abstracted during the summer than during the winter.

Prior to 1990, irrigation water in Hungary was provided at a fixed, uniform rate across the country. From 1990, farmers have been required to bear the operational (but not maintenance) cost of water infrastructure, while new water infrastructure investments (e.g. canals, dams) have been subsidised up to 40 per cent (Figure 6 and OECD, 2000).

4. Future challenges

To help improve the analytical capability of the *indicator of water use intensity* it could be further refined to facilitate cross-regional and national comparisons where there are common land and climatic conditions or where there is dependence on a common water resource. The indicator could also be further developed to assess agricultural water utilisation against a measure of the "divertible" or "renewable" water resource, and over-exploitation of groundwater resources.

Further development of the indicator of economic *water use efficiency* could be useful to help examine the efficiency of irrigated agriculture. However, provided the price for irrigation water reflects the full cost of supply, and there are no price distortions favouring one form of production over the other, market-based mechanisms will optimise the allocation of investments between the two forms of agriculture without the need for major policy intervention.

To better understand the effects of *water stress* on environmental needs, it would help to improve the definition of the defined minimum reference flow (MRF) to include: an explicit determination of the water requirements for maintenance of water-dependant ecosystems; a clear allocation of the water provided; and an explicit evaluation of the trade-offs involved. Not all environmental allocations will provide for all of the environment needs, but a decision to supply less than the environmental requirement needs to be transparent. The degree of regulation and/or diversion therefore needs to be specified.

Given the increasing demand on the use of groundwater resources in some countries and regions, defined minimum reference levels for groundwater management might also require specification. These may be specified in terms of either levels (distance from the land surface) or pressure. Further, they may be specified as a single static store of water, or one that is expected to vary with time in a specified manner, possibly to reflect natural movements in level or pressure, or to meet specific requirements of groundwater-dependent ecosystems.

To reveal the potential *economic distortions* in the use of water caused by under-pricing, free access or government intervention in the management of irrigation water, it may be useful to develop related indicators of policy and management response. Indicators might include measurement of the cost recovery of water supply to agriculture and community involvement in water management, and further development of the preliminary work already undertaken in OECD on water pricing (OECD, 1999a-d).

NOTES

1. For a review of OECD country policies related to agriculture, water and the environment, see OECD (1998*a*; 1998*b*; 1999*a*; 1999*b*).

2. It is estimated that world annual water utilisation by agriculture increased from about 0.5 million km^3 in 1900 to around 2.5 million km^3 in 1995 due to the increasing reliance on irrigation to expand food production (UN, 1997). For a recent overview of world water resources see Gleick (2000).

3. Land subsidence caused by excessive pumping of groundwater reserves has been recorded in *Japan*, *Mexico* and the *United States* (UN, 1997).

4. Only a few OECD country highlights are included in this section, for a more detailed description of country trends in agricultural water use, and related issues of water policies and pricing see the following reports: OECD (1999*a*; 1998*a*; 1998*b*; and 1997*a* for *Spain*).

5. For an extensive review of water use in Canadian agriculture see Coote and Gregorich (2000).

6. These water pressure categories are similar to those used elsewhere, for example, in Mediterranean countries, it is generally agreed that indices of intensity of water use equal to or greater than 25 per cent are signs of local and circumstantial tensions (Blue Plan Regional Activity Centre, 1997), above 50 per cent, they point to more frequent and more regional pressure, and towards 100 per cent, and especially if above, the indices indicate generalised structural water shortages.

7. The information on Mexican agricultural water use is drawn from *International Environment Reporter*, 1999, Vol. 22, No. 2, pp. 881-82, Bureau of National Affairs Incorporated, Washington, DC., United States.

Annex Table 1. **National water resources and utilisation: early 1980s to mid/late 1990s**

	Annual freshwater resources[1]		Share of transborder water in annual freshwater resources	Utilisation intensity: Share of total use[2] in annual freshwater resources		Share of groundwater in total use	
				%		%	
	Billion m^3		%	Early 1980s	Mid/late 1990s	Early 1980s	Mid/late 1990s
Australia	352		0	3	4	21	..
Austria	84		35	3	3	52	61
Belgium	17		25	..	42	..	10
Canada	2 792		2	1	2	2	2
Czech Republic	16		5	23	16	22	24
Denmark	6		0	20	16	96	99
Finland	110		3	3	2	5	10
France	170		6	18	24	18	15
Germany	178		40	..	24	..	18
Greece	72		17	7	12	31	41
Hungary	120		95	4	5	26	15
Iceland	170		0	0.1	0.1	95	97
Ireland	46		7	2	3	12	19
Italy	175		4	32	32	21	28
Japan	435		0	20	21	14	15
Korea	70		0	25	34	..	11
Luxembourg	2		45	4	3	..	51
Mexico	462		10	12	17	30	36
Netherlands	91		88	10	5	11	23
New Zealand	327		0	0.4	1	..	40
Norway	393		3	0.5	1	..	..
Poland	63		13	23	19	16	16
Portugal	72		48	..	15	..	..
Spain	111		0	36	37	13	14
Sweden	178		4	2	2	14	23
Switzerland	53		25	5	5	36	35
Turkey	234		3	7	15	27	17
United Kingdom	147		2	14	15	12	11
United States	2 478		1	21	20	22	22
EU-15	1 192		22	15	20	22	12
OECD	9 157		6	10	12	21	19

Note: See source below for country specific notes.

.. Not available.

1. Annual freshwater resources include: Mean annual precipitation + transborder water flows – mean annual evapotranspiration. Evapotranspiration is the addition of evaporation (*i.e.* water loss from mainly surface and marine water, but also soil) and transpiration (water loss from plants and trees). Overexploitation of groundwater resources was not included in the calculation.

2. Total use (abstractions) of water by all users, including public water supply, agriculture, industry, and for power station cooling.

Sources: OECD Environmental Data Compendium, 1999; INAG (1995).

Annex Table 2. **Agricultural water abstractions and irrigation water withdrawals: early 1980s to mid/late 1990s**

	Agriculture water use[1] (abstractions)		Irrigation water use (withdrawals)		Share of irrigation water use in agriculture water use	
	Million m^3		Million m^3		%	
	Early 1980s	Mid/late 1990s	Early 1980s	Mid/late 1990s	Early 1980s	Mid/late 1990s
Australia	..	..	8 100	10 539	..	..
Austria	..	..	..	..	..	..
Belgium[2]	..	10	..	0	..	0
Canada	3 472	3 991	2 765	3 193	80	80
Czech Republic	48	20	40	14	83	70
Denmark	460	360	90	140	20	39
Finland	..	..	33	18	..	..
France	4 372	4 971	..	..	..	..
Germany	..	..	..	616	..	..
Greece	..	..	4 158	7 600	..	..
Hungary	700	456	336	162	48	36
Iceland	..	..	..	..	..	..
Ireland	130	179	..	..	..	..
Italy	..	..	31 920	33 040	..	..
Japan	58 000	58 600	57 600	58 100	99	99
Korea	14 100	14 900	..	..	..	..
Luxembourg	..	..	..	..	..	..
Mexico	45 953	63 200	..	61 900	..	98
Netherlands	..	..	..	..	..	..
New Zealand	..	1 450	..	1 100	..	76
Norway	..	170	..	145	..	85
Poland	1 323	1 083	291	110	22	10
Portugal	..	..	..	9 383	..	..
Spain	..	..	26 220	27 863	..	..
Sweden[3]	140	174	64	107	46	61
Switzerland	..	..	..	..	..	..
Turkey	..	..	..	27 204	..	..
United Kingdom[4]	82	184	55	164	67	89
United States	202 800	195 200	200 100	188 500	99	97
EU-15[5]	67 515	74 389	n.c.	n.c.	n.c.	n.c.
OECD[5]	402 011	422 377	n.c.	n.c.	n.c.	n.c.

Note: See source below for country specific notes.
.. Not available.
n.c. Not calculated.
1. Agricultural water utilisation includes water abstracted from surface and groundwater, and return flows (withdrawals) from irrigation for some countries, but excludes precipitation directly onto agricultural land.
2. Including Luxembourg.
3. Data for irrigation water are estimates, not actual data, based on the quantity of irrigation water and the irrigated area that would be necessary in a dry year.
4. England and Wales only. Data for irrigation water use refer to spray irrigation.
5. Data for irrigation water use were used as data for agricultural water use are not available.
Sources: OECD Environmental Data Compendium, 1999; INAG (1995).

189

Annex Table 3. **Intensity of agriculture water use and change in the irrigated area: early 1980s to mid/late 1990s**

	Share of agriculture water use[1] in total use		Share of irrigation water use in total use		Share of irrigated area in cultivated area[2]	Change in irrigated area
	%		%		%	%
	Early 1980s	Mid/late 1990s	Early 1980s	Mid/late 1990s	1994-96	1980-82 to 1994-96
Australia	..	..	74	70	5	45
Austria	..	..	..	..	0.3	..
Belgium[3]	..	0.1	..	0	..	..
Canada	9	8	7	7	2	14
Czech Republic	1	1	1	1	1	..
Denmark	38	37	7	15	20	22
Finland	..	..	1	1	2	−36
France	14	12	..	..	8	72
Germany	..	..	..	1	4	3
Greece	..	..	83	87	34	39
Hungary	15	8	7	3	4	33
Iceland	..	..	..	..	..	..
Ireland	12	15	..	..	..	..
Italy	..	..	57	59	25	13
Japan	66	65	65	64	63	−9
Korea	81	63	..	..	61	−8
Luxembourg	..	..	..	..	..	..
Mexico	82	79	..	77	22	22
Netherlands	..	..	..	..	61	15
New Zealand	..	73	..	55	9	42
Norway	..	7	..	6	10	29
Poland	9	9	2	1	1	0
Portugal	..	..	..	84	22	0.3
Spain	..	..	66	68	18	16
Sweden[4]	3	6	2	4	4	53
Switzerland	..	..	..	..	6	0
Turkey	..	..	..	77	15	48
United Kingdom[5]	0	1	0.3	1	2	50
United States	39	40	39	38	12	5
EU-15[6]	n.c.	32	n.c.	n.c.	15	22
OECD[7]	n.c.	44	n.c.	n.c.	12	14

Note: See source below for country specific notes.

.. Not available.

n.c. Not calculated.

1. Agricultural water use includes water abstracted from surface and groundwater, and return flows (withdrawals) from irrigation for some countries, but excludes precipitation directly onto agricultural land.
2. Cultivated area refer to arable and permanent crop area.
3. Including Luxembourg.
4. Data for irrigation water are estimates, not actual data, based on the quantity of irrigation water and the irrigated area that would be necessary in a dry year.
5. England and Wales only. Data for irrigation water use refer to spray irrigation.
6. Austria and the Netherlands are excluded from the calculation of the share of agriculture water use in total use. Irrigation water use data were used as a proxy for Finland, Germany, Greece, Italy, Portugal and Spain.
7. Austria, Iceland, the Netherlands and Switzerland are excluded from the calculation of the share of agriculture water use in total use. Irrigation water use data were used as a proxy for Australia, Finland, Germany, Greece, Italy, Portugal, Spain and Turkey.

Sources: OECD Environmental Data Compendium, 1999; INAG (1995); Ministry of Agriculture, Fisheries and Food, United Kingdom.

Annex Table 4. **Comparison of agricultural, industrial, and household water prices: late 1990s**

| | Water prices | | |
| | Agriculture | Industry | Households |
	US$/m^3		
Australia	0.0195	..	1.64
Austria[1]	0.23-1.78	..	1.05
Canada[2]	0.0017-0.002	0.19-2.99	0.7
France[3]	0.0046-0.158	0.9-1.0	3.11
Greece	0.021-0.082	..	1.14
Hungary[4]	0.002-0.056	0.25-2.82	0.25-0.65
Netherlands[5]	1.44	0.54-1.61	3.16
Portugal[6]	0.010-0.025	0.41-2.1	0.98-1.02
Spain[7]	0.027-0.07	1.06-1.09	1.07
Turkey[8]	0.005	1.61-1.74	1.51
United Kingdom[9]	0.013-0.028	0.55-2.8	1.44-3.11
United States[10]	0.0159-0.0759	0.03-0.98	1.25

Note: For further details on agricultural water prices, see OECD (1999*b*, p. 43), for industrial water prices, see OECD (1999*c*) and for household water prices, see OECD (1999*d*, p. 38). All the currencies have been converted to US dollars, using exchange rates shown in The Economist (first issue of March 1998), unless the source provides the figure directly in dollar terms, in which case the figure has been transposed to this table as it appears in the source. Some figures might have originated from surface pricing, but were then converted into volumetric ones, using the estimated consumed volumes.

.. Not available.
1. Water used for livestock activities is obtained from municipal systems and priced at household rates (see OECD, 1999*b*, p. 19).
2. Industry: these rates apply to commercial establishments only. While this may include small industries, the rates do not apply for major industrial operations.
3. Agriculture: data refer to the regions: Adour-Garonne and C.d.Côteaux de Gascogne. Industry: the values refer to 1990-93 and exclude taxes, pollution and abstraction fees.
4. Agriculture: the values refer to 1998 water abstraction charges. Households and Industry: the values refer to 1998 maximum and minimum user charges for public water supply.
5. Farmers are required to pay the full supply costs and, where appropriate, the full drainage costs as well (see OECD, 1999*b*, p. 27).
6. Agriculture: data refer to the region: Sorria. The values were based on the estimated water volumes, the value per m^3, and the extra crop taxes for maize and tomatoes.
7. Agriculture: data refer to the region: Andalucia and Castille. Industry: the values refer to 1992-94.
8. Data for agricultural price provided by the Turkish State Institute of Statistics. Industry: data refer to the cities: Ankara and Istanbul.
9. Agriculture: data refer to England and Wales. Industry: average prices for large users incorporate a reduction of 15%, to reflect the impact of the "large user" tariffs.
10. Agriculture: data refer to the region: Sacramento River + Tehama.
Sources: OECD (1999*a*, 1999*b*, 1999*c*, 1999*d*, 2000).

BIBLIOGRAPHY

Blue Plan Regional Activity Centre (1997),
   Water in the Mediterranean Region, Situations, Perspectives and Strategies for Sustainable Water Resources Management, prepared for the Euro-Mediterranean Conference on Local Water Management held in Marseilles on 25-26 November 1996, Sophia-Antipolis, France.

Commonwealth of Australia (1998),
   Sustainable Agriculture – Assessing Australia's Recent Performance, A Report to the Standing Committee on Agriculture and Resource Management (SCARM) of the National Collaborative Project on Indicators for Sustainable Agriculture, SCARM Technical Report No. 70, CSIRO].Publishing, Victoria, Australia.

Coote, D.R. and L.J. Gregorich (eds.) (2000),
   The Health of our Water – Toward sustainable agriculture in Canada, Agriculture and Agri-Food Canada (AAFC), Ottawa, Canada. Available at: *www.agr.ca/* [English > Site Index > Environment and Resource Management].

EEA [European Environment Agency] (1995),
   Europe's Environment: The Dobris Assessment, Office for Official Publications of the European Communities, Luxembourg. Available at: *www.themes.eea.eu.int/* [> all available reports].

FAO [United Nations Food and Agriculture Organisation] (1994),
   Water for Life, World Food Day, Rome, Italy.

Gleick, P.H. (2000),
   "The Changing Water Paradigm: A look at twenty-first century water resources development", *Water International*, Vol. 25, No. 1, pp. 127-138. Available at: *www.iwra.siu.edu/win/* [> Archives of Contents].

Hearn, A.B. (1998),
   Summer Rains on Vertisol Plains: a Review of Cotton Irrigation Research in Australia, paper given to "Water is Gold" Conference, National Conference and Exhibition Centre, Irrigation Association, Brisbane, Australia.

INAG [Instituto Nacional da Água] (1995),
   Water Resources in Mainland Portugal and its Use (only in Portuguese), Lisbon, Portugal.

MAFF [Ministry of Agriculture, Fisheries and Food] (2000),
   Towards Sustainable Agriculture – A Pilot Set of Indicators, London, United Kingdom. Available at: *www.maff.gov.uk/* [Farming > Sustainable Agriculture].

OECD (1973),
   Guide to the Economic Evaluation of Irrigation Projects, Paris, France.

OECD (1997*a*),
   Environmental Performance Reviews: Spain, Paris, France.

OECD (1997*b*),
   Water Subsidies and the Environment, General Distribution document [OCDE/GD(97)220], Paris, France. Available at: *www.oecd.org/* [Documentation > 1997 > Reference Components > OCDE > OCDE/GD].

OECD (1998*a*),
   The Sustainable Management of Water in Agriculture: Issues and Policies – The Athens Workshop, Paris, France.

OECD (1998*b*),
   OECD *Workshop on the Sustainable Management of Water in Agriculture: Issues and Policies – The Athens Workshop: Case Studies*, General Distribution document [COM/AGR/CA/ENV/EPOC(98)87], Paris, France. Available at: *www.oecd.org/* [Documentation > 1998 > Reference Components > COM].

OECD (1998*c*),
   Water Management: Performance and Challenges in OECD Countries, Paris, France.

OECD (1998*d*),
   Towards Sustainable Development: Environmental Indicators, Paris, France.

OECD (1999*a*),
   The Price of Water – Trends in OECD Countries, Paris, France.

OECD (1999*b*),

Agricultural Water Pricing in OECD Countries, General Distribution document [ENV/EPOC/GEEI(98)11/FINAL], Paris, France. Available at: *www.oecd.org/* [Documentation > 1998 > Reference Components > ENV > ENV/EPOC/GEEI].

OECD (1999*c*),

Industrial Water Pricing in OECD Countries, General Distribution document [ENV/EPOC/GEEI(98)10/FINAL], Paris, France. Available at: *www.oecd.org/* [Documentation > 1998 > Reference Components > ENV > ENV/EPOC/GEEI].

OECD (1999*d*),

Household Water Pricing in OECD Countries, General Distribution document [ENV/EPOC/GEEI(98)12/FINAL], Paris, France. Available at: *www.oecd.org/* [Documentation > 1998 > Reference Components > ENV > ENV/EPOC/GEEI].

OECD (2000),

Environmental Performance Reviews: Hungary, Paris, France.

Pimentel, D., J. Houwer, E. Preiss, O. White, H. Fang, L. Mesnick, T. Barsky, S. Tariche, J. Schreck and S. Alpert (1997),

"Water Resources: Agriculture, the Environment, and Society – An Assessment of the Status of Water Resources", BioScience, Vol. 47, No. 2, pp. 97-106.

Postel, S. (1999),

"When the World's Wells Run Dry", pp. 30-38, World Watch Magazine, September/October, Worldwatch Institute, Washington, DC., United States. Available at: *www.worldwatch.org/mag/1999/99-5.html*.

Redaud, J. L. (1998),

"Indicators to Measure the Impact of Agriculture on Water Use: Pricing and Cost of Water Services", pp. 81-109, in OECD, The Sustainable Management of Water in Agriculture: Issues and Policies – The Athens Workshop, Paris, France.

UN [United Nations] (1997),

Comprehensive Assessment of the Freshwater Resources of the World, Department for Policy Coordination and Sustainable Development, New York, United States.

USDA [United States Department of Agriculture] (1997),

Agricultural Resources and Environmental Indicators, 1996-97, Agricultural Handbook No. 712, Natural Resources and Environment Division, Economic Research Service, Washington, DC., United States. Available at: *www.ers.usda.gov/* [Briefing Rooms > Agricultural Resources and Environmental Indicators].

Part IV

ENVIRONMENTAL IMPACTS OF AGRICULTURE

Chapter 1

SOIL QUALITY

HIGHLIGHTS

Context

Enhancing soil quality is essential for maintaining agricultural productivity. It can be degraded through three processes: *i)* physical (*e.g.* erosion, compaction); *ii)* chemical (*e.g.* acidification, salinisation); and *iii)* biological degradation (*e.g.* declines in organic matter). These degradation processes are linked to changes in farm management practices, climate and technology. There can be lags between the incidence of degradation, the initial recognition of a problem by farmers and the development of conservation strategies.

Some aspects of soil degradation are only slowly reversible (*e.g.* declines in organic matter) or are irreversible (*e.g.* erosion). Essentially farmers need to balance three key aspects of soil quality: sustaining soil fertility, conserving environmental quality, and protecting plant, animal and human health. Given the importance of maintaining soil quality to ensure agricultural productivity, expenditure on soil conservation, both from private and government sources, is frequently a substantial share of total agri-environmental expenditure. Government policies dealing with soil quality improvement commonly provide a range of approaches, including investment and loans to promote conservation practices, and advice on soil management.

Indicators and recent trends

There are two OECD indicators that address on-farm soil quality: *i)* risk of water erosion and *ii)* risk of wind erosion. These are estimates of the share of agricultural land affected at different risk intervals from low/tolerable to high/severe categories. Water and wind erosion indicators are considered to be of highest priority, as other soil degradation processes, such as soil compaction and salinisation are, in general, only of concern in specific regions of OECD countries. Wind erosion is more prevalent in farming regions with major expanses of cultivated open prairies and rangeland.

While the area of agricultural land at high/severe risk to water and wind erosion is not extensive, for certain OECD countries more than 10 per cent of agricultural land fall within this risk class. Trends in water erosion over the past ten years, for a limited number of OECD countries appear to show a reduction from high/moderate classes into tolerable/low classes of water erosion. The reduction in both water and wind erosion largely reflects a combination of the adoption of conservation or no tillage, less intensive crop production and the removal of marginal land from production.

While, in some OECD countries, certain regions are affected to a significant extent by other forms of soil degradation, such as acidification, salinisation, soil compaction and toxic contamination, there is evidence that these problems are beginning to improve in some cases. These improvements are being achieved as a result of government schemes that provide encouragement and advice to farmers to adopt soil conservation practices, such as crop residue management, conservation and land retirement.

There are few estimates of the value of agricultural production foregone as a result of soil degradation, but those available indicate that it might be in excess of 5 per cent of the total annual value of agricultural production in some countries.

1. Background

Policy context

The limitations on the availability of soil resources to provide safe, nutritious food for an expanding world population is a critical issue when considering global food security. High quality soils are rare and at risk of degradation and loss through, for example, urbanisation. There is a need to know which soils are where, their condition, and the results of policy measures to restore or maintain soil quality. Although sustaining soil quality is recognised as an important issue by all countries, the extent and trends in soil degradation processes have yet to be determined for many countries.

The soil quality issue is significant to policy makers because some aspects of soil degradation are only slowly reversible (declining organic matter) or irreversible (erosion), although the relative importance of each issue varies between countries. Essentially agricultural policy makers need to balance three key aspects of soil quality: sustaining soil fertility, conserving environmental quality, and protecting plant, animal and human health.[1] Hence, soil quality indicators are needed by policy makers to:[2]

- monitor the long term effects of farm management practices on soil quality;
- assess the economic impact of alternative management practices designed to improve soil quality, such as cover crops and minimum tillage practices;
- examine the effectiveness of policies designed to address the agricultural soil quality issue;
- improve policy analysis of soil quality issues by including not only environmental values but also taking into account economic and social factors.

Government policies dealing with soil quality commonly provide a range of approaches including subsidies and farm management advisory schemes that promote conservation practices that minimise the risks of soil degradation and enhance production and environmental safety.

At an international level there are no formal agreements or conventions that relate directly to the soil quality issue, although there are various international initiatives to co-ordinate current research in the area, such as the International Soil Reference and Information Centre, and the World Bank Land Quality Indicator initiative.[3] The UN Convention to Combat Desertification, for which most OECD countries are party, places an obligation on countries to prepare national action programmes, including aspects related to soil quality.[4] A more recent international development of relevance to soil quality indicators, is the on-going examination of the soil organic carbon issue within the context of the UN Framework Convention on Climate Change (see the Greenhouse Gas chapter).

Environmental context

The formation of soil is slow, averaging 100-400 years for a centimetre of topsoil to develop. This process occurs through the interaction over time of climate, topography, organisms (including soil micro-organisms, plants, animals, and man) and mineral parent material. Thus, the soil resource is essentially non-renewable in human life spans (Doran, 1996), although nitrogen applications, for example, can provide short-term improvements in soil quality, but not over the long term (Kim *et al.*, 1998).

Agricultural soils can "tolerate" a certain amount of erosion without adversely impacting on long-term productivity because new soil is constantly being formed to replace losses. The tolerable limit varies between different soil depths, types and agro-climatic conditions, but typically ranges from 1 tonne/hectare/year on shallow sandy soils to 5 tonnes/hectare/year on deeper well-developed soils. However, with a very slow rate of soil formation, any soil loss of more than 1 tonne per annum can be considered to cause irreversible damage within a time span of 50-100 years (EEA, 1998, pp. 189).

The concept of soil quality encompasses two distinct, but related parts (Goebel *et al.*, 1997):

- **Inherent quality**, which results from the innate properties of soils, as determined by the factors that lead to soil formation, such as climate, topography, biota, and parent material, including trace elements. The inherent quality of soil is often used to compare one soil against another, and to assess their suitability for different uses, for example, a loamy soil with higher water holding capacity compared with a sandy soil.

- **Dynamic quality**, which results from the changing health or condition of soil properties influenced by agricultural use and farm management practices. Some land use and management practices can have negative impacts on soil quality, such as acidification from excessive nitrogen fertiliser application, while others have positive effects, for example, increasing soil cover (see the Farm Management chapter).

These dynamic qualities interact with the effects of other changes, such as the weather and technology, over which individual farmers have little or no control. As part of this dynamic process, the forms of degradation may also change so that there can be lags between the incidence of degradation, the initial recognition of a problem by farmers and the development of conservation strategies (Industry Commission, 1996). There is also the issue, in this context, of the loss of highly fertile agricultural land to the process of urban and industrial expansion (see the Contextual Indicators chapter).

Soil quality can be degraded through three processes: physical, chemical and biological degradation. The linkages between these processes and the related agri-environmental indicators covered in this Report are outlined in Figure 1.[5] It should be emphasised that many of the elements shown in Figure 1 are closely linked and will be affected by similar phenomena. For example, the overall extent of water and wind erosion partly depends on the intensity of rainfall and the magnitude of the slope of agricultural land, as well as the chemical and biological condition of the soil.

Physical degradation, mainly covers the processes of wind, water and tillage erosion, soil compaction and waterlogging. The on-farm results of these processes include lower land productivity, which partly depends on soil structure, tilth and water-holding capacity. Soil compaction may be increased by use of heavier agricultural machinery. The off-farm effects of soil erosion, can impair air

Figure 1. **Linkages between soil quality and other agri-environmental indicators**

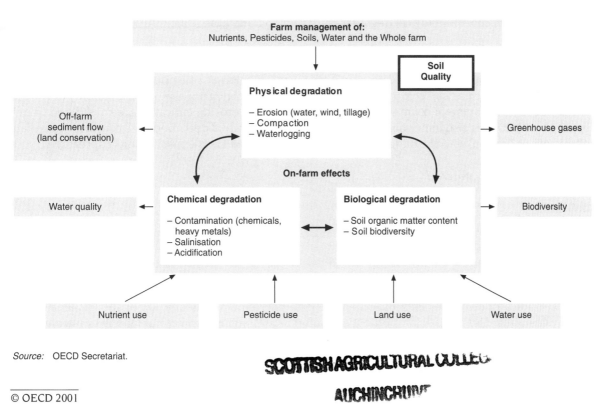

and water quality causing damage to aquatic habitats and human health (see the Land Conservation chapter). Some estimates suggest more than 60 per cent of the soil erosion loss from agricultural land is delivered into aquatic environments (Castro and Reckendorf, 1995, p. 39). Wind eroded sediments can have a serious effect on air quality and dust clouds can limit visibility creating dangerous driving conditions (McRae *et al.*, 2000).

Soil erosion also reduces the capacity for soil to fix carbon dioxide and act as a greenhouse gas sink. Different tillage, cover crop and crop residue practices can alter soil carbon levels. Recent research in the United States suggests that limiting soil erosion is a more effective way to increase carbon sequestration in agricultural soils than removing land from agricultural production (Mitchell *et al.*, 1996), although this may not apply to all soils across OECD countries. The issue of soil acting as either a source or sink of carbon is an area now being intensively researched (see Jaenicke, 1998, pp. 11-13; and the Farm Management and Greenhouse Gas chapters).

Chemical degradation, consists of the loss of soil nutrients and organic matter, and accumulation of heavy metals and other toxic compounds, leading to loss of fertility, salinisation in arid and semi-arid climates, acidification, and toxic contamination. Soil contamination from heavy metals and other toxic elements can also originate from non-agricultural sources, for example, the mining industry and the close proximity of major road transport networks. One of the main forms of chemical deterioration is salinisation. Moderate to severe salinity on agricultural land can reduce the annual yields of most cereal and oilseed crops by about 50 per cent (McRae *et al.*, 2000). There is also some positive correlation between increasing soil salinisation and the expansion of the area under irrigation, and in some regions this trend is leading to irreversible damage and loss of land to agricultural production.

Biological degradation, includes declines in organic matter content and the amount of carbon from biomass. It also includes reduced activity and diversity of soil biota (Cavigelli *et al.*, 1998). Soil biota are responsible for many of the key processes and functions of soil including the decomposition of plant and animal residues, transformation and storage of nutrients, infiltration of water and exchange of gases, formation and stabilisation of soil structure, and the synthesis of humic compounds (Dick, 1997).

Of the three degradation processes of soil quality identified here, the biological component is the most difficult to quantify (Kennedy and Smith, 1995). Biological degradation is considered by some as the most serious form of soil degradation because it affects the organic matter significantly and the soil fertility. Currently little is known about how agricultural activities change a soil's biological properties, and the potential cost of biological degradation to the food and fibre system (USDA, 1997).

2. Indicators

Among the various soil degradation processes, soil erosion is a key policy issue for many OECD countries. Issues such as soil compaction, salinisation and waterlogging are, in general, only of concern in specific regions of certain countries. Hence, water and wind erosion indicators are considered to be a priority by OECD. It is also important to emphasis that the indicators described here consider the on-farm effects of soil erosion, with the off-farm impacts examined in the Land Conservation chapter.

Risk of soil erosion by water

Definition

The agricultural area subject to water erosion, that is the area for which there is a risk of degradation by water erosion above a certain reference level.

Method of calculation

This indicator combines information on the inherent vulnerability of a soil or specific area (based on physiographic and climatic properties) and information on how agricultural land is being managed. The most widely accepted method of estimating water induced soil erosion is the so-called Universal Soil Loss Equation (USLE), used extensively in many countries, although the USLE is usually adapted for local conditions (see Annex Table 1).[6] The index of water erosion risk is calculated by the USLE and tolerable soil loss rate as:

$$E_{water} = R*K*LS*C*P / T$$

Where

E_{water} = water erosion risk index

R = rainfall and runoff erosivity, accounting for frequency, duration and intensity of rainfall events

K = soil erodibility, *e.g.* soil texture, drainage conditions

LS = slope length and steepness factor

C = crop management factor, *e.g.* cropping patterns

P = conservation management factor, *e.g.* tillage practices

T = tolerable soil loss rate

The R, K and LS factors in the equation represent the climate, soil and topography conditions at the site being measured, for which statistical series are often available. C and P estimate the degree to which the use and management of the soil reduces erosion, and are the most difficult aspects of the USLE to quantify. Where C and P factors are not available, the value shows the level of potential risk of water erosion based on the soil type, and on geo-physical and climatic conditions. While at this stage C and P factors can be set to one if not available, these factors might be obtained by drawing on the development of soil management indicators (see the Farm Management chapter).

Recent trends[7]

The extent of water erosion across OECD countries reveals that only a relatively small number of countries are experiencing widespread problems of high and severe water erosion. For some countries, such as *Italy, Portugal* and *Spain*, more than 10 per cent of agricultural land is in this class (see Figure 2). Trends in water erosion over the past ten years, for a limited number of OECD countries, show a reduction from higher/moderate classes into tolerable or low classes of water erosion (see Figure 2). The reduction in water erosion largely reflects a combination of the adoption of conservation/no tillage, less intensive crop production and the removal of marginal land from production in some areas.

North America

The decreasing risk of water erosion in *Canada* between 1981-1996 reflects the combined effects of reduced tillage, less intensive crop production, a decline in summerfallow, and the removal of marginal land from production (Table 1, Figures 2 and 3). The declining risk of tillage erosion has been linked to the adoption by farmers of conservation tillage and no-till practices, made possible by the advent of direct seeding equipment and the use of chemicals to control weeds. Less intensive production, the reduced area under summerfallow and the removal of marginal land from production also contributed to the decrease in tillage erosion risk.

It is estimated that agricultural activities are responsible for around 60 per cent of total soil erosion in the *United States*. The remaining 40 per cent results from natural events, mainly fire, flooding and drought, and also from activities such as forestry, construction, and off-road vehicle use. Erosive forces, water and wind, are calculated to have removed nearly 2.8 billion tonnes of soil from agricultural land in 1982. This figure declined to 1.9 billion tonnes by 1992 (see Figures 2 to 5).

Much of this improvement has been due to the increased use of soil conservation practices by farmers such as crop residue management, contour tillage and land retirement. In 1995 about 35 per cent of cultivated cropland was under conservation tillage, an increase of 37 per cent from 1989. Moreover, the Conservation Reserve Program (CRP) provided incentives to plant trees and grasses and develop windbreaks on environmentally sensitive land (see also the discussion on changes in US soil management practices in the Farm Management chapter).

Table 1. **Share of agricultural land area affected by different soil quality issues:[1] Canada, 1981 to 1996**

Area assessed million ha[5]	Water erosion[2]		Wind erosion[3]		Tillage erosion		Soil salinisation[3]		Soil compaction[4]	
	40		34		40		34		4	
Level of risk[6]	Average[7]	Range[8]	Average[7]	Range[8]	Average[7]	Range[8]	Average[7]	Range[8]	Area affected	Range[8]
	%		%		%		%		%	
Tolerable/Low										
1996	92	72-95	77	. .	68	54-94	56	42-76	11	4-18
1981	88	66-93	63	. .	58	43-92	56	50-75	13	4-22
Change	+4	n.a.	+14	. .	+10	n.a.	0	n.a.	−2	n.a.
Moderate				. .						
1996	5	3-12	17	. .	31	6-46	33	20-42	. .	. .
1981	7	2-22	22	. .	39	8-52	30	21-39	. .	. .
Change	−2	n.a.	−5	. .	−7	n.a.	+3	n.a.	. .	. .
High/Severe										
1996	2	0-11	6	. .	0	0-10	11	4-21	9	1-16
1981	5	0-12	15	. .	4	0-11	14	4-22	6	1-9
Change	−3	n.a.	−9	. .	−4	n.a.	−3	n.a.	+3	n.a.

. . Not available.
n.a. Not applicable.
1. For a description of how each soil quality category was calculated, see Annex Table 1 and source below.
2. See Annex Table 2.
3. Data only relate to Prairie Provinces (i.e. Alberta, Saskatchewan, and Manitoba), i.e. 46% of Canadian agricultural land area, although the Provinces of Newfoundland and Labrador were not included in the calculations.
4. Data cover Ontario and the Maritime Provinces (New Brunswick, Nova Scotia and Prince Edward Island) i.e. 5% of Canadian agricultural land. Data under the High/Severe category cover soils susceptible to compaction under cropping systems that cause compaction. Data under the Tolerable/Low category, highly compacted soils under cropping systems that reduce soil compaction are reported.
5. The spatial coverage measured by each soil quality indicator varies, see total area assessed by each respective soil quality category, and Annex Table 1.
6. The level of risk uses different units for each soil quality category, for example, for water erosion tonnes of soil loss per hectare, and for salinisation areas at risk to salinity.
7. Average percentages may not add to 100% due to rounding areas.
8. The range of risk for each respective soil quality category is measured at the level of Provinces, i.e. Canada has 10 Provinces, although of varying surface area, e.g. Sasketchewan, 19 million ha, and Nova Scotia, 0.13 million ha.
Source: Adapted from McRae et al. (2000).

The average annual soil erosion on CRP land between 1982 to 1992 declined from 46 tonnes/hectare to under 4 tonnes/hectare. Results from 1992 and 1998 indicate a continuation of the downward trend in soil erosion.[8] However, about one-third of total agricultural land continues to be subject to erosion rates which could impair the long-term productivity of the soil. In addition, the off-farm damage from soil erosion has been estimated at US$2-8 billion annually (USDA, 1997, pp. 46; see also the off-farm sediment flow indicator in the Land Conservation chapter).

Between 15-40 per cent of agricultural land in Mexico is either totally or severely eroded (Abler, 1996, p. 18). Soil erosion has been linked with off-farm costs in terms of losses of capacity in dams and reservoirs and reductions in the productivity of aquatic ecosystems.

Australia, New Zealand, Japan and Korea

Water erosion in Australia remains a problem as evidenced by sheet and rill based movement of soils on poorly vegetated regions, occurring at up to 100 times the soil formation rate on sloping ground (Campbell, 2000). The problem is particularly severe in the sloping sheep grazing lands of southern Australia, while flatter areas are little affected.

In New Zealand soil erosion has been recognised as a serious problem since the 1930s, with an estimated 10 per cent of the total land area classed as severely eroded (Figure 2; and OECD, 1996, pp. 136-37). There

Figure 2. **Share of agricultural land area affected by water erosion
by area assessed: 1990s[1]**

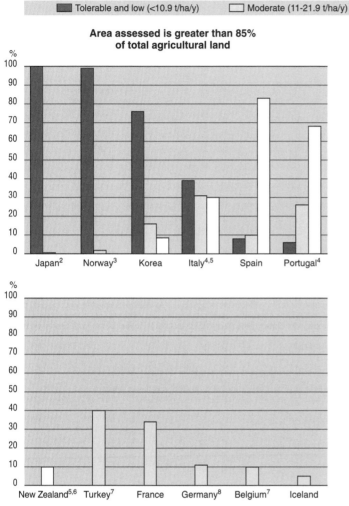

■ Tolerable and low (<10.9 t/ha/y)   □ Moderate (11-21.9 t/ha/y)   □ High and severe (>22 t/ha/y)

**Area assessed is greater than 85%
of total agricultural land**

	% of agricultural area assessed	Period assessed
Japan	100	1987
Norway	100	1997
Korea	97	1985-97
Italy	100	early 1990s
Spain	87	1980
Portugal	100	early 1990s
New Zealand	100	mid/late 1970s
Turkey	100	early 1990s
France	100	mid-1990s
Germany	100	1996
Belgium	100	mid-1990s
Iceland	100	late 1990s

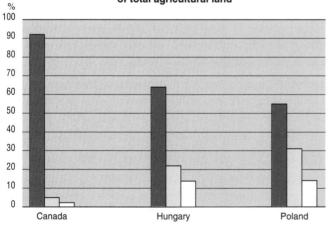

**Area assessed is between 45% and 70%
of total agricultural land**

	% of agricultural area assessed	Period assessed
Canada	54	1996
Hungary	69	1995-1998
Poland	48	1998

Figure 2. **Share of agricultural land area affected by water erosion by area assessed: 1990s[1]** *(cont.)*

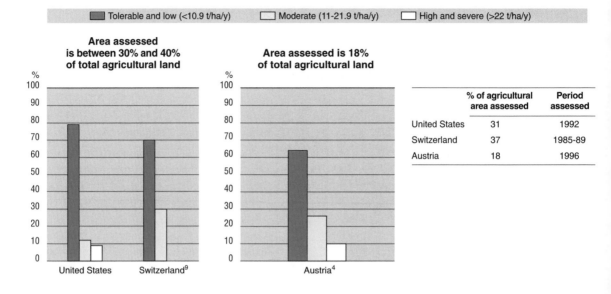

	% of agricultural area assessed	Period assessed
United States	31	1992
Switzerland	37	1985-89
Austria	18	1996

1. Some caution is required when making comparisons between graphs due to differences in agricultural land areas assessed, and the time period covered. It should be noted that the classification of different soil erosion categories used in this figure is not necessarily that used by countries (see Annex Table 2) as categories were changed to aid comparison. Data for the Netherlands are not included as the area assessed is only 1% of total agricultural land.
2. Tolerable and low: 99.7%, Moderate: 0.3 %, High and severe: 0.01%
3. Tolerable and low: 99%, Moderate: 1 %, High and severe: 0%
4. Values in figure apply to potential risk.
5. Water and wind erosion combined.
6. Data exist only for high and severe erosion and relate to surface erosion, mass movement erosion, and fluvial erosion.
7. Values exist only for areas "susceptible" to erosion.
8. Data represent East Germany.
9. High and severe: 0%
Note: See Annex Tables 1 and 2.
Source: See Annex Table 1.

are no quantitative data on the relative rates of natural and induced erosion, but it is clear that erosion caused by human activities is superimposed upon high but variable rates of natural erosion. Erosion of hill slopes is causing long term productivity losses, with pasture production on the affected sites reduced by as much as 20 per cent. At least 26 per cent of the total land area is at risk from soil slippage and 39 per cent is affected by water and wind erosion (Ministry for the Environment, 1997, pp. 105-111). It is believed that with the reform of agricultural policies in New Zealand, sheep and cattle numbers have declined in the marginal hill areas leading to reduced rates of soil erosion on marginal land. Longer term evidence will be required before this can be substantiated (OECD, 1996, pp. 136-37).

In both *Japan* and *Korea* the share of agricultural land subject to high/severe water erosion is not significant (Figure 2). Of some concern for the future prospects for limiting water erosion in Korea, is the reduction in the number of days over the year that the soil is covered with vegetation (see Figure 6 in the Farm Management chapter).

Europe

For *Austria*, the expansion of the area under organic farming is seen as a positive development to limit erosion (see Figure 3 in the Farm Management chapter). It is estimated that 380 000 hectares of cultivated land bear a potential risk of soil erosion, where soil loss may exceed 1-10 tonnes/ha depending on soil type (Figure 2). Under the Austrian Agri-Environmental Programme a series of

Figure 3. **Agricultural land area affected by water erosion:**[1,2] **early 1980s to late 1990s**

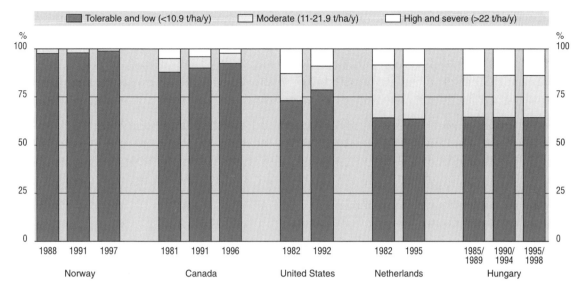

1. For details of methodology and risk class categories for water erosion, see Annex Tables 1 and 2; and on the share of agricultural land area covered, see Annex Table 1.
2. Some caution is required in interpreting this figure due to differences in the share of agricultural land assessed for erosion, which were: Norway: 100%, Canada: 54%, United States: 31%, Netherlands: 1% and Hungary: 68-70%.
Sources: OECD Agri-Environmental Indicators Questionnaire, 1999; Canada: Adapted from McRae *et al.* (2000); United States: USDA (1996).

measures have been implemented to address soil conservation issues, including conservation of grass acreage and landscape elements, mulching in wine and fruit orchards over 10 months, and obligatory partial catch-crop growing combined with improved crop rotations.[9] In 1995, the programme resulted in 245 000 hectares of arable land where catch crops are grown, and another 100 000 hectares of set-aside, which effectively reduces soil erosion.

For *Belgium* water erosion in the high/severe risk categories is limited to a very small share of the total agricultural land area (Figure 2). However, a study by Bomans *et al.* (1996) suggests that in *Belgium* water erosion is seen as a growing problem because of an increase in the average field size and the absence of measures to combat soil erosion.

Quantitative model assessments of water erosion in *Finland* show that values are low, typically less than 2 tonnes per hectare per year (Puustinen, 1999).[10] Estimates for *France* reveal that in the mid-1990s about 17 per cent of total agricultural land was affected by water erosion (Figure 2; and IFEN, 1997, p. 27). Soil erosion affects most of the main cereal growing areas and other major agricultural crop production regions. This compares with the 1950s when it was estimated that 8 per cent of the total agricultural land area in France was affected by erosion.

In *East Germany* water erosion is causing considerable damage to soil fertility and ecological functioning (Figure 2; and Frielinghaus and Bork, 2000), but the German Soil Protection Act (1999) is beginning to address the problem, as described below in the following section. Water erosion in *Poland* also appears to be at levels which merit concern (Figure 2). Trends in water erosion in *Hungary* over the period 1985 to 1998 suggest a slight improvement in the share of agricultural land area affected by high and severe erosion, but a problem still remains for about 10 per cent of agricultural land (Figures 2 and 3).

Soil erosion, water and wind, resulting from the loss of vegetation cover in *Iceland*, is considered to be one of the country's main environmental problems, with recent estimates suggesting that about 5 per cent of the total land area is affected by water erosion (Figure 2). An OECD study reveals that

205

about 20 per cent of the area affected by water and wind erosion is permanent meadows and pasture, with over-grazing identified as one of the principal causes. (OECD, 1993a, pp. 45-48).

Erosion data for Italy covers the total land area, and combines water and wind erosion. Estimates for the early 1990s show that about 60 per cent of the country suffered from a high/severe potential risk of erosion (Figure 2; and Italian Ministry of Environment, 1993). Over the past ten years, the number of days in a year when the soil is covered with vegetation has decreased in Italy (see Figure 6 in the Farm Management chapter). This may exacerbate the problem, although the area under organic farming has increased (see Figure 3 in the Farm Management chapter).

In the Netherlands water erosion is only of concern on less than one per cent of the agricultural land area, and over the past ten years the area affected by moderate to high/severe water erosion has declined (Figure 3). Local government expenditure on cleaning roads and water basins of eroded soil, also declined from 4.0 to 2.6 million guilders (US$1.2 to 1.6 million) between 1985 to 1995. Data for Norway also reveals that only a negligible share of agricultural land is affected by moderate water erosion, with a considerable reduction in the land area in this risk category (no land is classed as highly/severely eroded, see Figures 2 and 3).

Erosion is a major concern in Portugal with 85 per cent of the total land area at moderate to high "real" risk of erosion and 94 per cent at "potential" risk (Figure 2; and OECD, 1993b, pp. 49-64). The problem of soil degradation is aggravated by a combination of unfavourable natural conditions including the high proportion of steeply sloping land, heavy rainfall in autumn and winter when land cover is reduced, a thin topsoil layer, and the semi-arid climate in the south of the country. Loss of soil productivity in the eroded areas is a major problem, as is sedimentary deposition downstream, with erosion triggering potentially irreversible degradation and desertification. The aggravation of erosion has been attributed, depending on the region, to cereal growing in unsuitable soil, overgrazing and deforestation, especially in mountainous areas, and also an increase in forest fires.

In the past soil conservation policy has not been closely integrated with agricultural policy in Portugal, but recent developments have aimed to strengthen soil conservation programmes (OECD, 1993b). These include: reforestation programmes and schemes to control forest fires; specific agriculture programmes including encouragement to replace arable crops by permanent crops and pasture; information and training campaigns to improve soil tillage practices; and the development of irrigation in order to permit more intensive agriculture and reduce the total area cultivated.

The factors in Spain that most influence vulnerability to erosion are steep slopes, drought followed by intense rainfall, lack of topsoil and sparse vegetation cover (OECD, 1997, p. 102). A major part of the land affected by erosion is non-irrigated grassland, the so-called maquis or garrigue, and to a lesser extent areas of permanent crops such as vines, almonds and olives. An estimate for 1980 revealed that in total 81 per cent of the agricultural land area was considered as severely eroded (Figure 2). The cost of the direct impact of erosion (including the loss of agricultural production, impairment of reservoirs and damage due to flooding) is estimated at 280 million ECU (US$332 million) per year, with the cost of soil rehabilitation estimated at about 3 000 million ECU (US$3558 million) over a period of 15 to 20 years (EEA, 1995, p. 155).

In Switzerland, a report estimated that about 40 per cent of agricultural land was affected by water erosion, with 30 per cent of this area considered to have water erosion in excess of 6 tonnes per hectare per year (OFEFP, 1994, p. 150; and Figure 2). This has caused not only a loss of agricultural productivity but impaired aquatic environments. Recent improvements in soil cover and other soil conservation practices might be expected to reduce problems of water erosion (see Figure 7 in the Farm Management chapter).

Intensification of agriculture in Turkey is considered to have aggravated soil erosion problems, with 40 per cent of total agricultural land affected by moderate to severe water and wind erosion in the early 1990s (Figures 2 and 4; and OECD, 1992, pp. 30-31).

Interpretation and links to other indicators

When examining the current condition and trends in soil quality across OECD countries, shown in Figures 2 and 3, it is important to take into account variations in methodological approaches, and spatial and temporal coverage (Annex Table 1). While most national calculations of water erosion are derived from using the USLE methodology, the use of the model varies between countries. Moreover, the classification of soil erosion rates into low and tolerable, moderate, high and severe categories also varies, depending on site specific soil, climatic and geophysical conditions.

A positive trend in the indicator highlights the decline in areas of agricultural land under high/ severe erosion categories with a shift to low/tolerable categories. The low/tolerable category of water erosion will differ according to soil conditions, climate, etc., but usually ranges from about 1 to 5 tonnes/ hectare/year, as discussed previously. These limits are also used as thresholds, that is, higher rates imply non-sustainable soil use practices. However, the USLE only accounts for sheet and not gully erosion; and does not indicate the destination of the eroded material, either on or off-farm.

The water erosion indicator is associated with the wind erosion indicator and also with measures of productivity such as crop yields per hectare, water quality, and off-farm sediment flows examined under the Land Conservation chapter. Farm management practices are obviously linked to estimates of soil erosion, together with more general indicators of land use and land cover, and are also important in global carbon dynamics, being linked to greenhouse gas indicators (Figure 1).

Risk of soil erosion by wind

Definition

The agricultural area subject to wind erosion, that is the area for which there is a risk of degradation by wind erosion above a certain reference level.

Method of calculation

The index of wind erosion risk is calculated with the following equation:[11]

$$E_{wind} = KC(V^2 - \rho W^2)^{1.5} (1 - R)$$

where E_{wind} = index of wind erosion risk

   K = surface roughness and aggregation factor, *i.e.* size of soil particles

   C = factor for soil resistance to movement by wind

   V = drag velocity, *i.e.* wind speed at the soil surface

   ρ = variable related to the soil moisture content when erosion begins

   W = surface soil moisture content

   R = erosion reduction factor, *e.g.* crop type, crop residues, cultivation systems

As with the water erosion risk indicator, this indicator combines information on the inherent vulnerability of a soil or specific area to wind erosion (based on geophysical and climatic properties), and information on how agricultural land is being managed. The R factor can be set to zero if not available, although it might be obtained by drawing on the development of farm management indicators for soils. Where the R factor is not available, the value shows the level of potential risk of wind erosion based on the soil type and on geophysical and climatic conditions. Losses from wind erosion will vary with soil type, and usually wind damage is estimated annually. Susceptibility to wind erosion may be easier to estimate than actual loss of agricultural productivity.

Recent trends

For those countries with major areas of cultivated open prairies (such as in Australia, Canada, the United States, and parts of Central Europe), wind erosion is a more significant issue than in areas where this type of farming system is not as prevalent, for example in Korea, Japan, and most of Western Europe (see Figure 4).

Trends in wind erosion in the *United States* have shown a gradual improvement over the past 10 to 20 years, mainly due to the adoption of conservation tillage practices, the planting of windbreaks, less intensive crop production and the removal of marginal land from production (Figures 4 and 5). The reduction in tillage across the prairies in *Canada* has resulted in a 20-25 per cent decline in the risk from wind erosion, although changes in the types of crop cultivated and the frequency of summerfallow have also contributed to this trend (Table 1 and Figures 4 and 5).

Half to two-thirds of cropping land in *Australia* is at risk in any one season from wind erosion, particularly where cropping practices do not include stubble retention and minimum tillage (Figure 4). Wind erosion is being measured in Australia by using a Dust Storm Index, which shows that while wind erosion is still a significant problem in many regions, there has been a noticeable reduction over the period 1965 to 1996, particularly as a result of rangeland reclamation and adoption of conservation tillage (Commonwealth of Australia, 1998).[12]

For most European countries wind erosion appears to be a relatively minor issue relative to other threats to soil quality. In *Hungary* and *Poland*, however, moderate to high risk of wind erosion affects in excess of 20 per cent of the total agricultural land area (Figure 4). *Iceland* also reports that 50 per cent of

Figure 4. **Share of agricultural land area affected by moderate to high wind erosion:[1] 1990s**

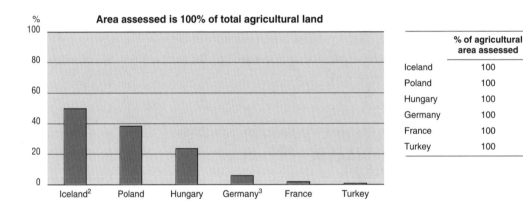

	% of agricultural area assessed	Period assessed
Iceland	100	late 1990s
Poland	100	1995-98
Hungary	100	1995-98
Germany	100	1996
France	100	mid-1990s
Turkey	100	early 1990s

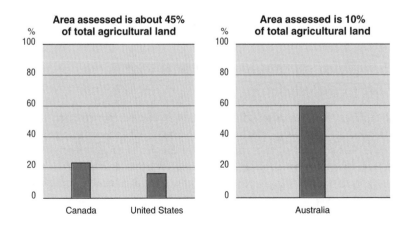

	% of agricultural area assessed	Period assessed
Canada	46	1996
United States	44	1992
Australia	10	early 1990s

1. For methodology, see Annex Table 1.
2. Covers total national land area.
3. Data represent East Germany.

Sources: OECD Agri-Environmental Indicators Questionnaire, 1999; Australia: Commonwealth of Australia (1995); Canada: Adapted from McRae *et al.* (2000); France: IFEN (1997); United States: USDA (1996).

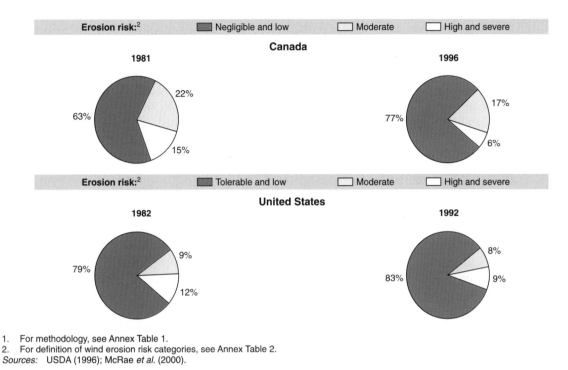

Figure 5.   **Area of agricultural land affected by wind erosion: Canada and United States,[1]**
early 1980s to mid-1990s

1.   For methodology, see Annex Table 1.
2.   For definition of wind erosion risk categories, see Annex Table 2.
Sources: USDA (1996); McRae *et al.* (2000).

the total land area is vulnerable to wind erosion (Figure 4). Even so, for most other OECD European countries wind erosion is considered insignificant, for example in *France* and *East Germany* it affects only 2 per cent and 6 per cent of the agricultural land area, respectively (IFEN, 1997, p. 27; and Figure 4).

Interpretation and links to other indicators

As in the case of the water erosion indicator, caution is necessary in interpreting trends of wind erosion because methodologies, spatial and temporal coverage vary across countries. For example, *Canada* has only assessed wind erosion on cultivated land in arid and semi-arid regions of the country.

The magnitude of wind erosion is related to the area affected and the rate at which the land is eroding. A positive trend in the indicator, as with water erosion, reflects a reduction in the agricultural area affected by high/severe wind erosion and an increase in low/tolerable risk categories. This indicator should be treated as a unitless relative index, but can be expressed as a quantitative estimate of soil loss through wind erosion in terms of $kg/m^2/hour$. Water quality indicators are associated with wind erosion, as are farm management and conservation practices such as windbreaks, conservation tillage, minimising fallow periods and the removal of land from cultivation. Wind-based soil erosion is also important in global carbon dynamics, linking to greenhouse gas indicators (Figure 1).

3.   Related information

Overview of soil quality trends

While there are a large number of "threats" that impair soil quality, the research literature suggests that in *Europe* the main influences come from the use of farm chemicals, water and wind erosion and acidification (EEA, 1995 and 1998). Available evidence suggests that these are also the dominant forms of soil degradation in other OECD countries outside Europe. In *North America, Australia and New Zealand,* however, problems of water and wind erosion rank higher than in Europe, salinisation and soil compaction are also significant, while chemical pollution of soil is considerably lower. In *Korea*, the incidence of wind erosion is negligible, while water erosion and chemical soil pollution is more pronounced.

Although the extent of soil degradation affects a significant share of the total agricultural area in OECD countries, improvements in soil quality are being achieved through the greater adoption of soil conservation practices by farmers, such as increasing the number of days in a year when the soil is covered with vegetation (see Figure 6 in the Farm Management chapter). Much of this improvement has been due to measures that provide incentives to plant trees and grasses and develop windbreaks on environmentally sensitive land, and also schemes that provide encouragement and advice to farmers to adopt soil conservation practices, such as crop residue management, conservation and contour tillage and land retirement.

Soil degradation is considered an important issue to the agricultural industry in *Canada* over the long term (Table 1). Recent preliminary research on national trends in soil quality in Canada, indicate that it will continue to deteriorate in areas of intensive cropping and on marginal land where soil conservation practices are not used, although there are important differences at a regional level (McRae *et al.*, 2000; and Acton and Gregorich, 1995).

Overall soil quality in *Canada* has improved during the period 1981-1996, particularly with respect to water, wind and tillage erosion, soil salinisation and compaction (Figure 1). Nevertheless, almost 5 million hectares (or 7 per cent of the total agricultural area) of marginal prairie land continues to be cultivated with a high risk of soil degradation. At the same time, the adoption of soil conservation practices has increased significantly since 1981, and as a result some agricultural soils are improving in quality and becoming less susceptible to erosion (see Table 7 in the Farm Management chapter).

While damage to the quality of agricultural soils in the *United States* remains a major environmental problem there have been significant gains in reducing threats to the productive capacity of agricultural land, particularly over the past decade (Figures 2 to 5). The amount of land still requiring conservation treatment to maintain productivity fell by nearly a quarter between 1982 to 1992. This was in part because of land retirement, but also because of the adoption of soil conserving crop management practices such as conservation tillage (see Table 8 in the Farm Management chapter; and Council on Environmental Quality, 1997; USDA, 1995, 1996, and 1997).

The degradation of the land resource base in *Australia* is considered to be substantial (Commonwealth of Australia, 1995; and Industry Commission, 1996). Up to a third of the total area of rangeland shows acute symptoms of degradation, including bare ground and salt scalds. A government report noted that current attempts to deal with the scale and impact of land degradation problems in Australia are insufficient (Commonwealth of Australia, 1995, p. 31). However, the newly introduced government's National Strategy for Ecologically Sustainable Development and the associated Natural Heritage Trust have now been implemented to tackle issues such as soil degradation, including developing relevant indicators (Hamblin, 1998).[13]

It has been estimated that the production equivalent of land degradation in *Australia* (the estimated decline from the value of production obtainable from current land uses had there been no degradation) is between 5-6 per cent of the value of agricultural production or around A$1.1 to 1.5 billion (US$0.8-1.1 billion in 1994-95 values) annually (Industry Commission, 1996). At the same time A$198 million (US$154 million) of public expenditure in 1991-92 was used for soil conservation and land management activities, and private environmental spending by the agriculture sector amounted to A$285 million (US$222 million) (see the Farm Management chapter).

A recent survey of soil quality conditions and trends in *East Germany* reveals that soil degradation has occurred over a long period, particularly due to inappropriate soil and land conservation practices in the past (Frielinghaus and Bork, 2000). While soil compaction is the major problem affecting soil quality in the region, water and wind erosion are also causing considerable damage. Due to low stocking densities, however, concerns related to chemical degradation are less significant. The German Soil

Protection Act of 1999 provides the framework to help maintain and enhance soil quality through soil conservation measures, such as encouraging erosion prevention and minimum tillage practices.

Indicators being developed in the *United Kingdom* of concentrations of organic matter, acidity, nutrients and heavy metals in soil reveal varying trends for arable and grassland soils. In general, however, they suggest that during the past 20 years no marked deterioration in the quality of agricultural soils has occurred (UK Department of the Environment, 1996, pp. 142-46).

Acidification and sodification of soils

Large areas of *Australian* agricultural land are composed of naturally acidic and sodic soils, that is soils that have developed chemical imbalances related to their pH (low pH acidic/ high pH alkaline soils) and sodium status (sodic soils). But current farming practices and systems are increasing the extent of acidic/sodic soils, leading to a fall in crop yields and increased risk of soil degradation (Commonwealth of Australia, 1998). The problem of sodic soils is also closely related to the issue of the salinisation of soil, discussed below.

Little attention is being paid to the acidic/sodic problem in *Australia*, which can be ameliorated by applying lime or dolomite to lower acidity and gypsum to combat sodicity. A total of 182 million hectares of sodic and acidic agricultural land would benefit from such treatment (nearly 40 per cent of the total agricultural land area), but at present only 0.005 per cent of this land is being treated, and the total tonnage of lime and gypsum over the period 1990-96 has increased only marginally. Problems of acidity and sodicity provide significant constraints to improving productivity on more than two-thirds of Australia's improved agricultural land (Commonwealth of Australia, 1998).

Soil acidification affects around 38 per cent of total agricultural land in *Hungary*, although the problem has been declining since the early 1980s (Hungarian Ministry of Agriculture, 1994). In the *United Kingdom*, the acidity of grassland soils has increased, although it has declined for arable soils (UK Department of the Environment, 1996).

Salinisation of soils

The risk of soil salinisation in *Canada* decreased over the 1981-1996 period, with the adoption of conservation tillage and the reduction of summerfallow contributing to this development (Table 1). In the *United States*, some 5 per cent of the cropland and pasture is currently affected by soil salinity problems and, at least in the short term, these saline soils cannot be used for agricultural production. In the state of Montana, about 2 per cent of the total cropland has been taken out of production because of salinisation, and recent surveys indicate that affected areas are growing at the rate of 10 per cent annually (USDA, 1997).

The incidence of soil salinisation is increasing on dry and irrigated land, particularly in the Murray-Darling Basin and south-western part of *Australia*, with some districts in these areas subject to irreversible damage (Commonwealth of Australia, 1995). It was estimated that in 1996 2.5 million hectares of agricultural land in Australia were affected by dryland salinity, and projected that over 12 million hectares will potentially be affected, which would be more than 2 per cent of the current total agricultural land area (Ridley and Joffre, 2000). Salinisation of soil is also a problem in *Turkey* associated with poor irrigation management practices in some regions (OECD, 1992, pp. 30-31).

Soil compaction

The *Canadian* indicator of soil compaction risk reveals that there was an increase in the proportion being cropped in ways that cause compaction, with respect to agricultural land with soils susceptible to compaction (Table 1). While only a small part of the country has been assessed for evidence of soil compaction, the total extent of the problem in Canada is suspected to be fairly widespread. Soil compaction is also a problem is some areas of the *United States*. In Minnesota, Wisconsin, Iowa, Illinois, Indiana and Ohio, the value of the yield losses from soil compaction could be high as US$100 million annually for these states combined (USDA, 1997, pp. 47).

211

Figure 6. **Organic matter content of agricultural topsoils: United Kingdom,[1] 1979-81 and 1995**

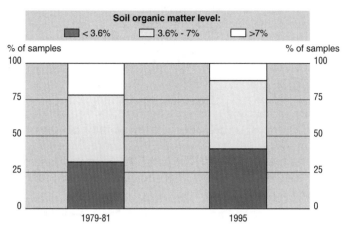

1. Data cover England and Wales.
Source: MAFF (2000).

Soil compaction is also reported as a problem for certain European countries. It is estimated for *Hungary* that 28 per cent of the total agricultural land area is affected by soil compaction (Hungarian Ministry of Agriculture, 1994). Also in *East Germany* soil compaction is the major process damaging soil quality, with 28 per cent of agricultural land in that region of Germany affected. The German Soil Protection Act (1999), mentioned previously, provides the framework to help overcome this type of problem.

Soil fertility

Soil organic matter plays a key role in maintaining soil fertility and is mainly derived from crop residues in the soil, organic manure and microbial biomass in the soil. Soil fertility estimates in *Australia* show one-third of cereal cropping land is seriously deficient in nitrogen, with no yield gain for forty years (Commonwealth of Australia, 1995). Over the period 1979-1995 soil organic matter content levels have generally decreased in the *United Kingdom* by an average of 0.5 per cent per annum (Figure 6). Soils in the UK under long-term arable cropping have generally been stable or only lose organic matter very slowly, with larger reductions on grasslands ploughed up for arable use.

Chemical and heavy metal pollution of soils

The pollution of soil from chemical farm inputs and heavy metals are not considered a serious threat to soil quality in *Australia*, although abandoned sheep and cattle dips with very high and toxic arsenic levels are a problem in the eastern and southern grazing areas (Commonwealth of Australia, 1995). In *Korea* the accumulation of phosphorus in soil from the overuse of phosphorus fertiliser has been reported (Korean Ministry of Agriculture and Forestry, 1999, unpublished). In crop growing areas (excluding rice) of Korea the phosphorus excess is 51 per cent above that required for the optimal level of crop growth (see the Nutrient Use chapter).

Data collected on the accumulation of heavy metals in agricultural topsoil's of the *United Kingdom*, reveal different trends over the past 15 years (Figure 7). The decrease in concentration of some metals is thought to be related to the increasing depth of cultivation which has diluted the metal load. The UK report found the problem of heavy metal pollution of soils to be very localised, and while the source of pollution includes usage of livestock manure, chemical fertilisers and sewage sludge by agriculture,

Figure 7. **Accumulation of heavy metals in agricultural topsoils: United Kingdom,[1] 1980 and 1995**

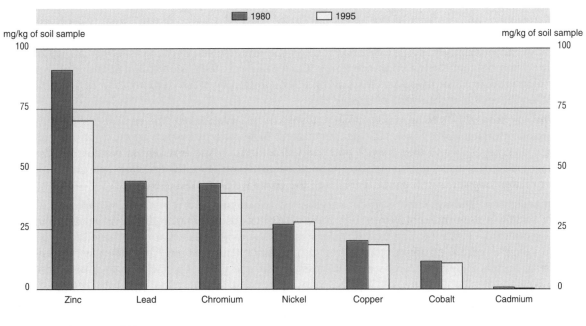

1. Data cover England and Wales.
Source: MAFF (2000).

other sources include parent material (underlying geology), mine wastes and atmospheric deposition (MAFF, 2000). For phosphorous and potassium the share of UK agricultural land on which concentrations are below the threshold to impair crop growth has declined or remained stable (UK Department of the Environment 1996).

4. Future challenges

To determine the extent to which *soil erosion* is affecting the sustainability of agriculture, it would be useful to clarify the meaning of what is the "sustainable" use of soil resources by agriculture. This might be achieved by more clearly establishing the definition of "low and tolerable" loss through soil erosion. Also, to provide a more complete coverage of the soil erosion issue, indicators of wind and water erosion could be complemented by a tillage erosion indicator, as already being developed by some countries (*e.g.* Canada, see Table 1). Tillage has a positive effect on soil quality, by the development of a thick homogenous soil layer through the mixture of the top soil layer with lower layers. At the same time, tillage, exposing subsoil to wind and water, may cause serious erosion problems, in particular, when the soils are highly erodible (Lobb and Lindstrom, 1999).

Currently little is known about how agricultural activities change a soil's biological properties, and the potential cost to the food and fibre system of damage to soil biodiversity. This knowledge gap could be overcome through the development of *soil biodiversity indicators* (SBI). An advantage of using SBIs for assessing soil quality is that they can reflect the combined effects of many factors, that would otherwise be too difficult, costly or time consuming to measure. Until recently there have been few attempts to use SBIs to evaluate soil quality and a clear relationship between soil organisms and agricultural soil quality has not yet been established. Many biological properties of soil are sensitive to changes in environmental conditions (*e.g.* temperature, moisture, organic matter inputs) that occur on relatively short time scales (days to months).

213|

SBIs that are being developed include microbial indicators of soil quality, covering such aspects as microbial form, function and diversity, and measurement of biomass quantity and activity.[14] Faunal indicators of soil quality are also being considered, which involve measuring the role of earthworms as a catalyst of the reaction that produces soil organic matter out of plant residues. As such, earthworm populations are an indicator of the rate of accumulation of organic matter, and, therefore, of soil quality.[15] The widespread use of SBIs for assessing soil quality will depend upon establishing justifiable optimum values, setting criteria for when and under what conditions the indicators should be measured and defining their confidence limits (Cameron *et al.*, 1998). Monitoring SBIs during periods of soil contamination, degradation and restoration will be important when defining their critical thresholds and determining acceptable rates of change.

The soil biodiversity issue is also closely related to *soil organic matter* (the term soil organic carbon is often used interchangeably with soil organic matter). Soils with adequate amounts of organic matter have good aggregation and tilth, permit water and air infiltration, are resistant to erosion, and help provide favourable biological habitats. Conversion of pasture land to cultivated cropland reduces the soil organic matter to lower maintenance levels (see the *United Kingdom* example above).

In assessing the impacts of soil conservation programmes and in measuring carbon credits for energy trading in the context of current international discussion on climate change, it would be useful to develop indicators related to soil organic matter (see Greenhouse Gas chapter). These indicators could help reveal the extent of organic matter in soils under existing conditions which is related to the resistance of soils to degradation by erosion, compaction, and excessive use without supplements.

In order to locate agricultural areas having an imbalance between soil capability and actual land use, an indicator of *inherent soil quality* could be developed. This would help to determine the land area where current land use exceeds the assessed capability. The indicator involves developing a map of inherent soil quality. By comparing this "capability" map with one of land use, it would be possible to identify areas of imbalance, and thus to focus the attention of policy makers on areas that were at risk from soil degradation.

This indicator should be regarded as a composite indicator, which covers various processes relevant to each country, including the stock and fluxes of soil organic carbon in agricultural soils, aggregate stability, water holding capacity, biological activity, bulk density, pH, aeration and water infiltration rate (Jaenicke, 1998; and USDA, 1997, pp. 47). Researchers and policy makers could use the indicator in setting research priorities, to document changes in the soil resource base, and to predict how soil quality changes affect water and air quality, as well as food safety.

In providing *economic valuations of soil quality* that are firmly based on the current activities and decisions of farmers, there is a need to improve the information on land degradation and the environment, and develop links between that information, agricultural activities and farm management practices.[16] Moreover in establishing valuations of the benefits of higher farm productivity through improving soil quality, it is may also be important to consider the external effects of soil degradation on other farmers and the community generally. In addition, consideration should be given to alternative land uses, and the time horizon over which costs and benefits should be evaluated. While economic assessment of soil quality is complex, it can capture the physical dimension of soil quality by assigning economic values (USDA, 1994, p. 25).

Economic analysis could provide estimates of the on-and off-farm costs of soil degradation and the costs of maintaining soil quality (USDA, 1997). An economic valuation may cover the on-farm costs, such as those associated with declines in soil fertility. Valuation of the off-farm costs of erosion, might include those linked to sediment loading of rivers, lakes and reservoirs which can impair aquatic habitats, degrade recreational resources, and damage water conveyance systems (see also the off-farm sediment flow indicator in the Land Conservation chapter).

NOTES

1. The issue of soil degradation, agricultural output and profitability is examined by Gretton and Salma (1997).

2. These aspects are discussed by the Ministry for the Environment (1997, pp. 99-127); USDA (1994); and USDA (1997).

3. Information on the International Soil Reference and Information Centre (ISRIC) can be found on the ISRIC website at: *www.isric.nl/*; and concerning the World Bank Land Quality Indicators, which is a joint FAO, UNEP and UNDP initiative, see: *www-esd.worldbank.org/lqi/*

4. For information on the UN Desertification Convention see the website: *www.unccd.de/*.

5. The text here draws, in particular, from Acton and Gregorich (1995); Cameron *et al.* (1996); and USDA (1994 and 1997). Also for an examination of soil degradation in arid areas, see Rubio and Bochet (1998). Frielinghaus *et al.* (1999), discuss the links between soil quality and soil/land management indicators.

6. The USLE was first developed in the *United States*, see Wischmeyer and Smith (1978), also FAO (1996) provides a survey of land quality indicators and related databases.

7. The reader should note that in this section, from the literature reviewed, it has not always been possible to separate discussion of water erosion trends from more general trends in soil erosion encompassing water, wind, and tillage erosion.

8. According to data provided by the US, in its response to the OECD Agri-environmental indicator questionnaire, the area affected by water erosion and with an Erodibility Index of <8t/ha/year (EI, reflects erosion potential relative to vulnerability to productivity loss, see USDA, 1997, pp. 46), declined from 1992 to 1998 by 8 per cent, while the area with an EI of >8t/ha/year also declined by 14 per cent.

9. Details of the Austrian Agri-environmental Programme are provided in Box 1 of the Farm Management chapter.

10. For further details on the issue of soil quality in *Finland* see also, Rekolainen and Leek (1996); and Valpasvuo-Jaatinen *et al.* (1997).

11. This index, like the water erosion equation, draws on work first developed in the United States, see the website of the US Department of Agriculture Wind Erosion Research Unit at: *www.weru.ksu.edu/*.

12. Details of the *Australian* Dust Storm Index are described in Commonwealth of Australia (1998, pp. 123-125).

13. For further details on the monitoring programmes under the Australian National Strategy for Ecologically Sustainable Development see the website at: *www.environment.gov.au/* [Environment in Government > National Strategy for Ecologically Sustainable Development]. Concerning the Natural Heritage Trust see the website at: *www.affa.gov.au/* [Environment > Natural Heritage Trust].

14. In *Australia* the biological condition of the soil is also considered to cover elements such as, feral animal and pest invasions, woody shrub infestations and clearance of native vegetation (Industry Commission, 1996).

15. For two recent contributions to the development of soil biodiversity indicators see Schouten *et al.* (1997); and Schouten *et al.* (1999).

16. The need to develop a broader economic assessment of the soil quality issue has been examined in a study by the Industry Commission (1996).

Annex Table 1. **Summary of the methodologies, spatial and temporal coverage being used to measure different aspects of soil quality**

	Source	Aspect of soil quality measured	Methodology	Spatial coverage — Land categories assessed	Spatial coverage — % of total agricultural land area assessed	Temporal coverage — Period	Temporal coverage — Number of observations over time series
Australia	Commonwealth of Australia (1995)	Wind	Unknown	Arable crops	10	Early 1990s	1
Austria	OECD	Water[1]	Soil erosion model which covers rainfall, heavy rain, thunderstorms and relief mapping	Four arable crops[2]	18	1996	1
Belgium	Bomans et al. (1996)	Water	Universal Soil Loss Equation (USLE)	All agricultural land	100	Mid-1990s	1
Canada	Adapted from McRae et al. (2000)	Water	Modified USLE equation	Arable crops and summer fallow[3]	54	1981-96	3
		Wind	Model based on rainfall, windspeed, cropping systems and tillage practices	Arable crops and summer fallow[4]	46	1981-96	3
		Tillage	Model based on tillage system and soil landscape and surface form	Arable crops and summer fallow	54	1981-96	3
		Salinisation	Model based on state of salinity, topography, soil drainage, climate and land use	Arable crops and summer fallow[4]	46	1981-96	3
		Compaction	Model based on soil properties, such as organic carbon, bulk density	Arable crops and summer fallow[5]	5	1981-96	3
		Soil Organic Carbon	Computer simulation model (CENTURY) of soil-plant-climate interactions	All agricultural land	Total losses 23%	1910-1980	..
Finland	OECD	Water	USLE	All agricultural land	100	Mid-1990s	..
France	IFEN (1997)	Water	Unknown	All agricultural land	100	Mid-1990s	1
		Wind	Unknown	All agricultural land	100	Mid-1990s	1
Germany[6]	OECD	Water	USLE	All agricultural land	100	1996	1
		Wind	USLE	All agricultural land	100	1996	1
Hungary[7]	OECD	Water	USLE, using sample field survey	All agricultural land	68-70	1985-98	3
		Wind	USLE, using sample field survey	All agricultural land	100	1995-98	1
Iceland	OECD	Water	Field Survey	All agricultural land	100	Late 1990s	1
		Wind	Field Survey	All agricultural land	100	Late 1990s	1
Italy	Italian Ministry of Environment (1993)	Water and Wind	Coordinated Information on the Environment (CORINE)	All land, excluding urban areas, lakes, rock outcrops, and glaciers	100	Early 1990s	1
Japan[8]	OECD	Water	Modified USLE	Total land	100	1987	1
		Depth of plough layer	Depth of plough layer sample points	Paddy; arable crops; orchards; meadows	100	1981-1991	3

Annex Table 1. **Summary of the methodologies, spatial and temporal coverage being used to measure different aspects of soil quality** (*cont.*)

	Source	Aspect of soil quality measured	Methodology	Spatial coverage — Land categories assessed	Spatial coverage — % of total agricultural land area assessed	Temporal coverage — Period	Temporal coverage — Number of observations over time series
Korea	OECD	Water[9]	USLE	All agricultural land; crop; pasture	97	1985-97	1
Mexico	Abler (1996)	Water and Wind	USLE	All agricultural land	100	Early 1990s	1
Netherlands	OECD	Water	USLE	Areas soils with < 20% clay and > 30% silt, on slopes < 0.5% which are temporarily uncovered by vegetation	1	1982-1995	2
		Wind	USLE	Area of sugarbeets and flowerbulbs on soils with < 6% clay and > 20% silt	..	1975-1996	2
New Zealand	OECD (1996)	Surface erosion, mass movement erosion, fluvial erosion	Not specified	All land	100	1974-1979	..
Norway	OECD	Water[9]	USLE	All agricultural land; crop; pasture	100	1988-97	3
Poland	OECD	Water	Three tiered model based on landform, level of afforestation, and type of soil	All agricultural land	48	1995-1998	1
		Wind	Field Survey	All agricultural land	48	1998	1
Portugal	OECD	Water[9]	Risk of degradation above a certain reference level	Total land	100	Early 1990s	1
Spain	OECD	Water[10]	Modified USLE (*i.e.* landscape and rainfall) over a map of land use	All agricultural land; crop; pasture	87	1980	1
Sweden	OECD	Soil erosion estimates are not calculated as soil erosion is not deemed a problem in Sweden					
Switzerland	OECD	Water[9]	USLE, modified by depth of soil	Arable and permanent crop land	37	1985-1989	..

Annex Table 1. **Summary of the methodologies, spatial and temporal coverage being used to measure different aspects of soil quality** (*cont.*)

	Source	Aspect of soil quality measured	Methodology	Spatial coverage		Temporal coverage	
				Land categories assessed	% of total agricultural land area assessed	Period	Number of observations over time series
Turkey	OECD	Water	Risk of degradation above a certain reference level	All agricultural land	100	Early 1990s	1
	OECD	Wind	Risk of degradation above a certain reference level	All agricultural land	100	Early 1990s	1
United Kingdom[11]	OECD	Water[10]	USLE not used, and erosion risk categories only for England and Wales	All agricultural land; crop; pasture	51	1995-98	1
United States	USDA (1996)	Water	USLE and tolerable soil loss	Cultivated crop land	31	1982-92	2
	USDA (1996)	Wind	WEQ, $E = g$ (I, K, C, L, V), where E = estimated average annual soil loss due to wind erosion in tons per acre per year; I = soil erodibility factor; K = the roughness factor, reflects the presence of ridges which, if at right angles to the wind, reduces wind erosion by reducing surface velocity and trapping particles; C = climatic factor, accounts for the influence of wind velocity and surface soil moisture; L = the unsheltered travel distance along the prevailing wind. Erosion direction for the field/area to be evaluated; and V = vegetative cover. The function $g(.)$ is nonlinear.	All agricultural land; crop; pasture	44	1982-92	2

. Not available.
1. Wind erosion is negligible in Austria because of small field size and planting of windbreaks.
2. Crops included: maize, potatoes, sugar beet, spring cereals.
3. Erosion is minimal for meadows and pasture, due to permanent ground cover, so not included.
4. Wind erosion and soil salinisation only calculated for arable land at greatest risk: Alberta, Manitoba and Saskatchewan.
5. Soil compaction only calculated for areas most at risk: Ontario, New Brunswick, Nova Scotia and Prince Edward Island.
6. Data represent East Germany.
7. Crop yield losses were measured in areas vulnerable to erosion in the 1960s and 1970s.
8. Depth of plough layer (in centimetres) is used as a soil erosion indicator combining the interaction of farm management with soil erosion.
9. Wind erosion is negligible and not measured.
10. Wind erosion not measured.
11. Soil erosion indicator being developed.
Source: OECD Agri-Environmental Indicators Questionaire, 1999. For other sources, see bibliography.

Annex Table 2.   **Total agricultural land area affected by water erosion: early 1980s to late 1990s**

	% of total agricultural area assessed	OECD Categories t/ha/year	National erosion risk t/ha/year	Year		
				Area affected in '000 hectares (or % of area affected)		
Australia	. .	. .	. .	. .	. .	. .
Austria[1]	18					1996
		Tolerable erosion < 6	0.09-2.5	. .	. .	159
		Low erosion 6-10.9	2.6-5	. .	. .	102
		Moderate erosion 11-21.9	5.1-10	. .	. .	140
		High erosion 22-32.9	10.1-20	. .	. .	159
		Severe erosion > 33	20.1-33.3	. .	. .	64
Belgium	100			Mid-1990s		
		Tolerable erosion < 6				
		Low erosion 6-10.9				
		Moderate erosion 11-21.9	Susceptible	. .	150	. .
		High erosion 22-32.9				
		Severe erosion > 33				
Canada	54			1981		1996
		Tolerable erosion < 6				
		Low erosion 6-10.9	Tolerable/Low	88%	. .	92%
		Moderate erosion 11-21.9	Moderate	7%	. .	5%
		High erosion 22-32.9	High/Severe	5%	. .	2%
		Severe erosion > 33				
Czech Republic	. .	. .		. .	. .	. .
Denmark	. .	. .		. .	. .	. .
Finland	Water erosion is not deemed a problem in Finland			. .	. .	. .
France	100			Mid-1990s		
		Tolerable erosion < 6				
		Low erosion 6-10.9				
		Moderate erosion 11-21.9	Not specified;	. .	17%	. .
		High erosion 22-32.9	assumed moderate			
		Severe erosion > 33				
Germany[2]	100					1996
		Tolerable erosion < 6				
		Low erosion 6-10.9				
		Moderate erosion 11-21.9	Not specified;	. .	. .	11%
		High erosion 22-32.9	assumed moderate			
		Severe erosion > 33				
Greece	. .	. .		. .	. .	. .
Hungary	68-70			1985-1989	1990-1994	1995-1998
		Tolerable erosion < 6		2 010	1 830	1 850
		Low erosion 6-10.9		990	900	910
		Moderate erosion 11-21.9		1 020	930	940
		High erosion 22-32.9		640	580	590
		Severe erosion > 33		. .	. .	. .
Iceland	100					Late 1990s
		Tolerable erosion < 6				
		Low erosion 6-10.9				
		Moderate erosion 11-21.9	Not specified;			5%
		High erosion 22-32.9	assumed moderate			
		Severe erosion > 33				

219|

Annex Table 2.   **Total agricultural land area affected by water erosion: early 1980s to late 1990s** (*cont.*)

	% of total agricultural area assessed	OECD Categories t/ha/year	National erosion risk t/ha/year	Year		
				Area affected in '000 hectares (or % of area affected)		
Ireland	..	..		..	..	..
Italy[3, 4]	100	Potential risk:		Early 1990s		
		Tolerable erosion < 6				
		Low erosion 6-10.9	Low risk	..	39%	..
		Moderate erosion 11-21.9	Moderate risk	..	31%	..
		High erosion 22-32.9	High risk	..	30%	..
		Severe erosion > 33				
		Real risk:		Early 1990s		
		Tolerable erosion < 6				
		Low erosion 6-10.9	Low risk	..	55%	..
		Moderate erosion 11-21.9	Moderate risk	..	34%	..
		High erosion 22-32.9	High risk	..	11%	..
		Severe erosion > 33				
Japan[4]	100			1987		
		Tolerable erosion < 6	Very small	6 691	..	..
		Low erosion 6-10.9	Small	160	..	..
		Moderate erosion 11-21.9	Moderate	18	..	..
		High erosion 22-32.9	High	1	..	..
		Severe erosion > 33	Very high	0	..	..
Korea	97			1985-1997		
		Tolerable erosion < 6		..	1 385	..
		Low erosion 6-10.9		..	260	..
		Moderate erosion 11-21.9		..	340	..
		High erosion 22-32.9		..	176	..
		Severe erosion > 33		..	7	..
Luxembourg	..	..		..	..	..
Mexico	100			Early 1990s		
		Tolerable erosion < 6		..	..	..
		Low erosion 6-10.9		..	..	..
		Moderate erosion 11-21.9		..	..	..
		High erosion 22-32.9		..	..	..
		Severe erosion > 33	Severely or totally eroded	..	15-40%	..
Netherlands[5]	1			1982		1995
		Tolerable erosion < 6	< 4	9.3	..	5.1
		Low erosion 6-10.9	5-9	6.1	..	3.3
		Moderate erosion 11-21.9	10-14	4.7	..	2.5
		High erosion 22-32.9	15-19	2.0	..	1.2
		Severe erosion > 33	> 20	2.0	..	1.1
New Zealand[4]	100			Mid/late 1970s		
		Tolerable erosion < 6		..	..	..
		Low erosion 6-10.9		..	..	..
		Moderate erosion 11-21.9		..	..	..
		High erosion 22-32.9		..	..	..
		Severe erosion > 33	Severely eroded	10%	..	

Annex Table 2.   **Total agricultural land area affected by water erosion: early 1980s to late 1990s** (*cont.*)

	% of total agricultural area assessed	OECD Categories t/ha/year	National erosion risk t/ha/year	Year		
				Area affected in '000 hectares (or % of area affected)		
Norway	100	Categories adjusted by Norway:		1988	1991	1997
		Tolerable erosion < 6		868	877	985
		Low erosion 6-10.9		71	62	40
		Moderate erosion 11-21.9		24	21	13
		High erosion 22-32.9		0	0	0
		Severe erosion > 33		0	0	0
		Norwegian categories:		1988	1991	1997
		Low < 0.5		621	649	745
		Moderate 0.5-2		245	225	229
		High 2-8		73	66	52
		Severe > 8		24	21	13
Poland	48					1995-1998
		Tolerable erosion < 6	< 6	..	..	4 878
		Low erosion 6-10.9				
		Moderate erosion 11-21.9	6 – 20	..	..	2 752
		High erosion 22-32.9				
		Severe erosion > 33	> 20	..	..	1 250
Portugal[4]	100	Potential risk:		Early 1990s		
		Tolerable erosion < 6	Low	..	6%	..
		Low erosion 6-10.9				
		Moderate erosion 11-21.9	Moderate	..	26%	..
		High erosion 22-32.9	High	..	68%	..
		Severe erosion > 33				
		Real risk:				
		Tolerable erosion < 6	Low	..	15%	..
		Low erosion 6-10.9				
		Moderate erosion 11-21.9	Moderate	..	55%	..
		High erosion 22-32.9	High	..	30%	..
		Severe erosion > 33				
Spain	87			1980		
		Tolerable erosion < 6		1 113	..	..
		Low erosion 6-10.9		1 012	..	..
		Moderate erosion 11-21.9		2 627	..	..
		High erosion 22-32.9		2 002	..	..
		Severe erosion > 33		20 410	..	..
Sweden	Water erosion is not deemed a problem in Sweden					
Switzerland[6]	37			1985-1989		
		Tolerable erosion < 6	< 6	70%	..	..
		Low erosion 6-10.9				
		Moderate erosion 11-21.9	> 6	30%	..	..
		High erosion 22-32.9				
		Severe erosion > 33				
Turkey	100			Early 1990s		
		Tolerable erosion < 6		..	..	..
		Low erosion 6-10.9		..	..	..
		Moderate erosion 11-21.9	Moderate and high	..	15 859	..
		High erosion 22-32.9		..	..	..
		Severe erosion > 33		..	..	..

221

Annex Table 2. **Total agricultural land area affected by water erosion: early 1980s to late 1990s** (*cont.*)

	% of total agricultural area assessed	OECD Categories t/ha/year	National erosion risk t/ha/year	Year		
				Area affected in '000 hectares (or % of area affected)		
United Kingdom[7]	51					1995-1998
		Tolerable erosion < 6	Very small	..	..	7 500
		Low erosion 6-10.9	Small	..	..	250
		Moderate erosion 11-21.9	Moderate	..	..	650
		High erosion 22-32.9	High	..	..	350
		Severe erosion > 33	Very high	..	..	50
Unites States[8]	31			1982	1992	
		Tolerable erosion < 6		..	..	..
		Low erosion 6-10.9	< T	73%	79%	..
		Moderate erosion 11-21.9	T-2T	14%	12%	..
		High erosion 22-32.9	> 2T	13%	9%	..
		Severe erosion > 33		..	..	..

.. Not available.
1. Potential risks.
2. Data represent East Germany.
3. Water and wind erosion combined.
4. Applies to all land.
5. Values refer to area soils with < 20% clay and > 30% silt, on slopes > 0.5% which are temporarily uncovered by vegetation (vegetables, potatoes, wheat, sugarbeets, maize, flowerbeds).
6. Values refer to arable and permanent crop land affected by water erosion.
7. For England and Wales only; excluding rough grazing.
8. Risk categories are defined as follows:
   Tolerable and low: < T
   Moderate: T – 2T
   High and severe: > 2T
   T = level of erosion believed tolerable on different soils to maintain productivity.
Source: See Annex Table 1.

BIBLIOGRAPHY

Abler, D.G. (1996),
The Environmental Impacts of Agro-environmental Policies: An International Comparison, Report, prepared for the Natural Resources and Environment Division, Economic Research Service, US Department of Agriculture, March, Washington, DC., United States.

Acton, D.F. and L.J. Gregorich (eds.) (1995),
The Health of our soils – Toward Sustainable Agriculture in Canada, Agriculture and Agri-Food Canada, Ottawa, Canada. Available at: *www.agr.ca/* [English > Research and Technology > Scientists > Achievements and Highlights].

Bomans, E., L. Vanongeval, H. Vandendriessche and M. Geypens (1996),
Development of an Agricultural Soil Quality Indicator, Ministry of The Flemish Community, Environment and Infrastructure Department, Environment, Nature, Land and Water Management Administration, Brussels, Belgium.

Cameron, K.C., M.H. Beare, R.G. McLaren and H. Di (1998),
Selecting physical, chemical, and biological indicators of soil quality for degraded or polluted soils, Symposium at the 16th World Congress of Soil Science Montpellier, August 1998.

Cameron, K.C., I.S. Comforth, R.G. McLaren, M.H. Beare, L.R. Basher, A.K. Metherell and L.E. Kerr (1996),
Soil Quality Indicators for Sustainable Agriculture in New Zealand: Proceedings of a Workshop, Lincoln Soil Quality Research Centre, Lincoln University, New Zealand.

Campbell, A. (2000),
"A Future Australian Landscape Without Sheep", in A. Hamblin (ed.), *Visions of Future Landscapes*, Proceedings of the Australian Academy of Science Fenner Conference on the Environment 2-5 May 1999, Canberra, Bureau of Rural Sciences, Canberra, Australia (in press). Details on the Conference are available at: *www.brs.gov.au/* [Resources > Publications > Conference Proceedings].

Castro, J. and F. Reckendorf (1995),
Effects of Sediment on the Aquatic Environment, Resource Conservation Act (RCA) III, Working Paper No. 6, Natural Resources Conservation Service, US Department of Agriculture, Washington, DC., United States.

Cavigelli, M.A., S.R. Deming, L.K. Probyn and R.R. Harwood (eds.) (1998),
Michigan Field Crop Ecology: Managing biological processes for productivity and environmental quality, Michigan State University Extension Bulletin E-2646, United States.

Commonwealth of Australia (1995),
Sustaining the Agricultural Resource Base, 12th Meeting of the Prime Minister's Science and Engineering Council, Office of the Chief Scientist, Department of the Prime Minister and Cabinet, Canberra, Australia.

Commonwealth of Australia (1998),
Sustainable Agriculture – Assessing Australia's Recent Performance, A Report to the Standing Committee on Agriculture and Resource Management (SCARM) of the National Collaborative Project on Indicators for Sustainable Agriculture, SCARM Technical Report No. 70, CSIRO Publishing, Victoria, Australia.

Council on Environmental Quality (1997),
Environmental Quality 1994-95 Report, 25th Report of the United States Council on Environmental Quality, Washington, DC., United States. Available at: *www.whitehouse.gov/*CEQ/ [News and Information > Publications].

Dick, R.P. (1997),
"Soil enzyme activities as integrative indicators of soil health", pp. 121-156, in C. Pankhurst and V.V.S.R. Gupta (eds.), *Biological Indicators of Soil Health*, CAB International, New York, United States.

Doran, J. (1996),
"The International Situation and Criteria for Indicators", Chapter 7, pp. 20-39, in K.C. Cameron, I.S. Comforth, R.G. McLaren, M.H. Beare, L.R. Basher, A.K. Metherell and L.E. Kerr, *Soil Quality Indicators for Sustainable Agriculture in New Zealand: Proceedings of a Workshop*, Lincoln Soil Quality Research Centre, Lincoln University, New Zealand.

EEA [European Environment Agency] (1995),
  Europe's Environment: The Dobris Assessment, Office for Official Publications of the European Communities, Luxembourg. Available at: *http://themes.eea.eu.int/* [> all available reports].

EEA (1998),
  Europe's Environment: The Second Assessment, Office for Official Publications of the European Communities, Luxembourg. Available at: *http://themes.eea.eu.int/* [> all available reports].

FAO [United Nations Food and Agriculture Organisation] (1996),
  Land Quality Indicators and Their Use in Sustainable Agriculture and Rural Development, FAO Land Water Bulletin No. 5, Rome, Italy. Available at: *www.fao.org/docrep/W4745E/W4745E00.htm*.

Frielinghaus, M., H. Petelkau, D. Deumlich, R. Funk, L. Muller and B. Winnige (1999),
  Soil indicator system to minimise the risk of soil degradation in Northeastern Germany. Proceedings of the 10th International Soil Conservation Conference – "Sustaining the Global Farm", West Lafayette, Indiana, United States.

Frielinghaus, M and H.R. Bork (2000),
  "Soil and Water Conservation in the Former East Germany", Chapter 22, pp. 343-362 in T.L. Napier, S.M. Hapier and J. Tvrdon (eds.), *Soil and Water Conservation Policies and Programs – Successes and Failures*, Soil and Water Conservation Society, CRC Press, London, United Kingdom.

Goebel, J.J., M.J. Mausbach and D.L. Karlen (1997),
  Using the National Resources Inventory as a framework to assess soil erosion, soil conservation and soil quality, paper presented to the 23rd Study Group on Food and Agricultural Statistics in Europe, UNECE/FAO/EUROSTAT/OECD, 2-3 July, Geneva, Switzerland.

Gretton, P. and U. Salma (1997),
  "Land degradation: links to agricultural output and profitability", *The Australian Journal of Agricultural and Resource Economics*, Vol. 41, No. 2, pp. 209-225.

Hamblin, A. (1998),
  Environmental Indicators for National State of the Environment Reporting – The Land, Australia: State of the Environment (Environmental Indicator Reports), Department of the Environment, Canberra, Australia. Available at: *www.environment.gov.au/soe/* [Environmental Indicators > Land under "Environmental Indicator Reports"].

Hungarian Ministry of Agriculture (1994),
  Soil Conservation in Hungary, Department of Agro-environmental Management in the Ministry of Agriculture, Budapest, Hungary.

IFEN [Institut français de l'environnement] (1997),
  Agriculture et environnement : les indicateurs (only in French, "Agriculture and the Environment: Indicators"), edition 1997-1998, Orléans, France. Available at: *www.ifen.fr/* [> Publications].

Industry Commission (1996),
  Land Degradation and the Australian Agricultural Industry, Staff Information Paper, Australian Government Publishing Service, Canberra, Australia.

Italian Ministry of Environment (1993),
  Report on the State of the Environment in Italy, Istituto Poligrafico e Zecca dello Stato, Rome, Italy.

Jaenicke, E.C. (1998),
  From the Ground Up: Exploring Soil Quality's Contribution to Environmental Health, Policy Studies Report No. 10, Henry A. Wallace Institute for Alternative Agriculture, Greenbelt, Maryland, United States.

Kennedy, A.C. and K.L. Smith (1995),
  "Soil microbial diversity and the sustainability of agricultural soils", *Plant and Soil*, No. 170, pp. 75-86.

Kim, K., B.L. Barham and I. Coxhead (1998),
  The Evolution of Agricultural Soil Quality: A Methodology for measurement and some land market implications, paper presented at the American Agricultural Economics Association Annual Meeting, Salt Lake City, Utah, United States. Available at: *http://agecon.lib.umn.edu/aaea98/spkimk01.pdf*.

Lobb, D.A. and M.J. Lindstrom (1999),
  Tillage Translocation and Tillage Erosion, Manitoba Soil Science Meetings, Poster Presentation, Winnipeg, Manitoba, Canada, February 2-3.

MAFF [Ministry of Agriculture, Fisheries and Food] (2000),
  Towards Sustainable Agriculture – A Pilot Set of Indicators, London, United Kingdom. Available at: *www.maff.gov.uk/* [Farming > Sustainable Agriculture].

McRae, T., C.A.S. Smith and L.J. Gregorich (eds.) (2000),
  Environmental Sustainability of Canadian Agriculture: Report of the Agri-Environmental Indicator Project, Agriculture and Agri-Food Canada (AAFC), Ottawa, Ontario, Canada. Available at: *www.agr.ca/policy/environment/publications/list.html*.

Ministry for the Environment (1997),
   Environmental Performance Indicators: Proposals for Air, Freshwater and Land, Wellington, New Zealand.

Mitchell, P.D., P.G. Lakshminarayan, T. Otake and B.A. Babcock (1996),
   The Impact of Soil Conservation Policies on Carbon Sequestration in Agricultural Soils of the Central United States, Working Paper 96-WP 170, Center for Agriculture and Rural Development (CARD), Iowa State University, Ames, Iowa, United States.

OECD (1992),
   Environmental Policies in Turkey, Paris, France.

OECD (1993*a*),
   Environmental Performance Reviews: Iceland, Paris, France.

OECD (1993*b*),
   Environmental Performance Reviews: Portugal, Paris, France.

OECD (1996),
   Environmental Performance Reviews: New Zealand, Paris, France.

OECD (1997),
   Environmental Performance Reviews: Spain, Paris, France.

OFEFP [Office fédéral de l'environnement, des forêts et du paysage] (1994),
   The State of the Environment in Switzerland, Report on the Environment 1993, Berne, Switzerland.

Puustinen, M. (1999),
   Viljelymenetelmien vaikutus pintaeroosioon ja ravinteiden huuhtoutumiseen (Effect of soil tillage on surface erosion and nutrient transport: in Finnish with English abstract), Suomen ympäristö 285, Suomen ympäristökeskus (The Finnish Environment 285, Finnish Environment Institute), Helsinki, Finland.

Rekolainen, S. and R. Leek (eds.) (1996),
   Regionalisation of erosion and nitrate losses from agricultural land in Nordic countries, Nordic Council of Ministers, Stockholm, Sweden.

Ridley, A.M. and R. Joffre (2000),
   "The Iberian dehesa: Unrealistic parkland or practical solution?", in A. Hamblin (ed.), *Visions of Future Landscapes*, Proceedings of the Australian Academy of Science Fenner Conference on the Environment 2-5 May 1999, Canberra, Bureau of Rural Sciences, Canberra, Australia (in press). Available at: *www.brs.gov.au/* [Resources > Publications > Conference Proceedings].

Rubio, J.L. and E. Bochet (1998),
   "Desertification indicators as diagnosis criteria for desertification risk assessment in Europe", *Journal of Arid Environments*, Vol. 39, pp. 113-120.

Schouten, A.J., L. Brussaard, P.C. de Ruiter, H. Siepel and N.M. van Straalen (1997),
   Een indicatorsysteem voor life support functies van de bodem in reatie tot biodiversiteit (An indicator system for the life support functions of the soil in relation to biodiversity: in Dutch with English Summary), RIVM Report 712910005, the Netherlands Institute of Public Health and the Environment (RIVM), Bilthoven, The Netherlands.

Schouten, A.J., A.M. Breure, J. Bloem, W. Didden, P.C. de Ruiter and H. Siepel (1999),
   Life support functies van de bodem: operationalisering t.b.v. het biodiversiteitsbeleid (Life support functions of the soil: Operationalisation for biodiversity policy: in Dutch with English Summary), RIVM Report 607601003, the Netherlands Institute of Public Health and the Environment (RIVM), Bilthoven, The Netherlands.

UK Department of the Environment (1996),
   Indicators of Sustainable Development for the United Kingdom, London, United Kingdom. Available at: *www.environment.detr.gov.uk/* [> Indicators of Sustainable Development for the UK].

USDA [United States Department of Agriculture] (1994),
   Agricultural Resources and Environmental Indicators, Agricultural Handbook No. 705, Natural Resources and Environment Division, Economic Research Service, Washington, DC., United States. Available at: *www.ers.usda.gov/* [Briefing Rooms > Agricultural Resources and Environmental Indicators].

USDA (1995),
   National Resources Inventory, A Summary of Natural Resource Trends in the US Between 1982 and 1992, Natural Resources Conservation Service, Washington, DC., United States.

USDA (1996),
   America's Private Land – A Geography of Hope, Natural Resources Conservation Service, Washington, DC., United States. Available at: *www.nrcs.usda.gov/* [> Geography of Hope under "Features"].

USDA (1997),
   Agricultural Resources and Environmental Indicators, 1996-97, Agricultural Handbook No. 712, Natural Resources and Environment Division, Economic Research Service, Washington, DC., United States. Available at: *www.ers.usda.gov/* [Briefing Rooms > Agricultural Resources and Environmental Indicators].

Valpasvuo-Jaatinen, P., S. Rekolainen and H. Latostenmaa (1997),
   "Finnish Agriculture and its Sustainability: Environmental Impacts", *Ambio*, Vol. 26, No. 7, pp. 448-455.

Wischmeyer, W.H. and D.D. Smith (1978),
   Predicting rainfall erosion losses – A guide to conservation planning, Agricultural Handbook No. 537, US Department of Agriculture, Washington, DC., United States.

Chapter 2

WATER QUALITY

HIGHLIGHTS

Context

The key areas of concern regarding agriculture and water quality are related to nitrate pollution in surface and groundwater; phosphorus levels in surface water; contamination with pesticides; and the harmful effects of soil sediments and mineral salts. An excessive level of agricultural pollutants in water is a human health concern since it impairs drinking water quality, while excessive concentrations of pollutants cause ecological problems including eutrophication.

Indicators and recent trends

Two approaches are being developed by OECD with respect to measuring the impacts of agriculture on water quality. These are "risk" and "state" indicators with emphasis on nitrate and phosphorus. Risk indicators estimate the potential contamination of water originating from agricultural activities. State indicators measure the actual trends in concentrations of pollutants in water against a threshold level, in areas vulnerable to pollution from agriculture. Risk indicators are being used in a number of countries, partly because monitoring the state of water quality can be costly and difficult, especially in terms of distinguishing between the contribution of agriculture and that of other sources of water quality impairment, such as from industry.

Those OECD countries which are establishing risk indicators have helped to provide an indirect measure of the impacts of nitrate and phosphorus losses from agriculture to water. The indicators have been useful in revealing the overall national trends in risk on nutrient contamination, and differences at a regional level, drawing on a range of existing data to develop the indicator, including nutrient balances.

While agriculture is not the only sector which burdens aquatic environments with pollutants, in the case of nitrogen and phosphates it is a major contributor in most OECD countries. Recent estimates indicate that, in a considerable number of countries, agriculture accounts for more than 40 per cent of all sources of nitrogen emissions and over 30 per cent of phosphorus emissions into surface water. Although the trend in nutrient surplus from agriculture is declining in most OECD countries, the growing contribution of agriculture to the overall level of nutrient contamination of water largely reflects the trend towards the reduction in point sources of nutrient pollution, such as pollution from industry.

The extent of groundwater pollution from agricultural nutrients is less well documented than is the case for surface and marine waters, largely because of the cost involved in sampling groundwater. Moreover, correlating nutrient contamination levels in groundwater with changes in farming practices and production systems is difficult, because it can take many years for nutrients to leach through overlying soils into aquifers.

An indication of the overall OECD situation and trends for other agricultural pollutants of water, such as pesticides and soil sediment, is less clear. Extrapolating from trends in soil erosion losses and changes in pesticide use, however, would suggest that in many countries impairment of water quality from these agricultural pollutants is probably declining, but there remain serious pollution problems in some regions and countries. Concerning pesticides, while their use has decreased in many OECD countries since the mid-1980s, the long time lag between their use and detection in groundwater means that, as with nitrates, the situation could deteriorate before it starts to improve.

227

1. Background

Policy context

While in most OECD countries a considerable effort has been undertaken to diminish emissions of pollutants from agriculture into surface, ground and marine waters, the level of pollutants in many areas is deemed to be too high, especially in regions with intensive agricultural activities. Agriculture is not the only sector that burdens aquatic environments with pollutants, but for many OECD countries it is a major contributor. Moreover, options for controlling agricultural pollution of water are more limited than for other environmental discharges because fewer opportunities for abatement exist due to the diffuse nature of the discharge.[1]

The principal sources of water pollution from agriculture include nutrients (mainly livestock waste and inorganic fertiliser), pesticides and soil sediments. Problems of acidification, salinisation, biological and heavy metal contaminants associated with agriculture are also important, for some countries and in certain sub -national regions.

Water quality protection is a key component in both agricultural and environmental policies for most OECD countries, with a range of different instruments used to reduce agriculture's pollution of water, including regulations, subsidies, and farm management advice.[2] A common goal for many countries is to set targets and/or thresholds for the reduction in the total quantity of contaminants discharged into water over a given period of time. Two sets of targets/thresholds levels usually exist, one for human health associated with drinking water (and by association the quality of water for livestock) and the other for the protection of the environment (including aquatic life in all its forms and life stages).

At the international level there are a number of agreements which concern the prevention, control and reduction of transboundary impacts of water pollution from agricultural and other sources, notably the 1992 Helsinki Convention on the Protection and Use of Transboundary Watercourses and International Lakes.[3] Other agreements to which OECD countries are committed to improve water quality include, for example, the Oslo and Paris Conventions for the Prevention of Marine Pollution (OSPAR Convention), which agreed to aim for a 50 per cent reduction of nitrogen and phosphorus emissions into the marine environment of the Baltic and North Seas between 1985 and 1995; the International Joint Commission Agreement on Great Lakes Water Quality in North America; and the *European Union*'s Water Framework Directive.[4]

Environmental context

In most OECD countries, agriculture is the major land use activity and the influence of the sector on water quality is, therefore, significant. The effects of pollutant discharges can be direct, as a toxin to humans and aquatic biota when exceeding critical concentrations or indirect, by leading to increased phytoplankton. The key environmental issues related to excessive quantities of these pollutants in water and the main agricultural activities that are the source of these pollutants are shown in Table 1.

Pollutant emissions from agricultural activities into water cannot be avoided totally, but the rates of loss can be influenced by the type of farm management practices used by farmers (Black, 1995). For some pollution agents, such as nitrates, phosphorus, and soil sediments, there are naturally occurring background concentrations of these agents in surface and groundwater, depending on local geological conditions, biological activity in soil and streambed sediment, and the chemical properties of the atmosphere (USGS, 1999, p. 34). In general, agricultural water contamination is concentrated in certain regions and types of farm enterprises, such as those with a high livestock density, or a high share of crops subject to intensive application rates of fertiliser and plant protection products, including most open field fruit and vegetable production.[5]

There are various pathways for **nutrients** to contaminate water from agriculture (Figure 1). Nitrogen can percolate into the groundwater or be washed out directly into surface waters by run-off. Phosphorus

Table 1. **Sources of water pollution from agricultural activities**

Pollutant	Key water quality issue related to pollutant	Main agricultural activities that are the source of the pollutant
– Nutrients (mainly nitrates and phosphates)	– Eutrophication and impairment of drinking water (blue-baby syndrome due to excess nitrates and stomach cancer)	– Agricultural production (run-off of excess nitrates and phosphates from fertilisers and animal manure into water)
– Toxic contaminants (largely heavy metals, pesticides)	– Harmful to aquatic life and impairs drinking water (contamination of water)	– Spreading sewage sludge on agricultural land (heavy metals) and plant protection (pesticides)
– Soil sediments	– Harmful to aquatic life and water transport systems (turbidity of water)	– Inappropriate soil conservation practices (wind and water soil erosion)
– Organic matter	– Harmful to aquatic life (deoxygenation of water)	– Spreading manure on livestock farms
– Acid substances	– Harmful to aquatic life (acidification of water)	– Livestock production (ammonia volatilisation)
– Biological contaminants	– Impairs drinking water (pathogenic bacteria and viruses)	– Faecal discharge from livestock into water
– Mineral salts	– Impairs drinking water, the use of water for irrigation, and aquatic life (salinisation of water)	– Inappropriate land use (clearing of perennial vegetation and irrigation practices)

Source: OECD Secretariat.

is generally not a problem for groundwater, but does pollute surface waters.[6] In some cases, *Finland*, for example, nitrate levels have increased in streams from virtually undisturbed forest catchments during the last 20 to 25 years, due to atmospheric deposition and nitrogen saturation (PFRA, 1997).

Agriculture can accelerate the run-off of nutrients into water, particularly from the overuse of inorganic fertilisers and inappropriate manure management practices. In lakes, reservoirs, slowly flowing rivers and coastal areas, nutrients stimulate the growth of phytoplankton and other aquatic plants and, in turn, that of organisms higher up the aquatic food chain (the process of eutrophication).

Figure 1. **Nutrients in water: a schematic diagram of pathways from agricultural use**

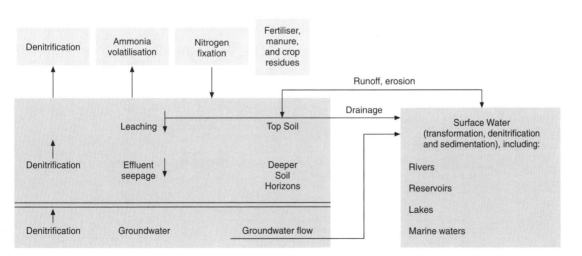

Source: OECD Secretariat.

Depending on the acidity and temperature of the water, ammonium may be converted to ammonia, which is poisonous to fish, or to nitrate which contributes to eutrophication and affects human health.[7]

The decomposition of phytoplankton can also reduce the oxygen concentration in water, leading to a reduction of aquatic life. Low oxygen levels may also enhance the release of phosphorus from sediments, thereby further enhancing phytoplankton production. Excessive phytoplankton affects both the use of water (taste and odour problems) and the aesthetic quality of water. An excessive level of nitrates in water is also a human health concern since it impairs drinking water quality and can cause methemoglobinemia or "blue-baby" syndrome, and stomach cancer in adults.[8]

Organic compounds found in *agricultural pesticides* usually take a long time to break down in water, and are conveyed into water from the atmosphere or by water and sediment erosion. These substances can percolate into groundwater after application, or affect surface waters by drift (see Figure 2). Pesticide behaviour in water (absorption, by plants and soil particles, chemical or biological degradation, bioaccumulation) is largely unknown, and once these substances reach groundwater little is understood about the ability of aquifers to cleanse themselves or how long such processes might take.[9]

While the key issue of pesticide run-off into water relates to human health, there is also concern related to the impacts on aquatic environments, and in some cases livestock (*e.g.* nitrate contamination of dairy cow milk). Recent studies suggest that some pesticides can disrupt endocrine systems and affect reproduction by interfering with natural hormones. However, the long term effects of low level exposure to pesticide compounds, punctuated with seasonal pulses of higher concentrates, is not yet well understood either as a threat to human health or the environment (USGS, 1999).

The emission of *soil sediments* may result in river pollution, as topsoil is often very rich in nitrates, phosphorus, organic matter and trace elements (*e.g.* zinc, lead). Some estimates suggest more than 60 per cent of the soil erosion loss from agricultural land is delivered into aquatic environments (Castro and Reckendorf, 1995, p. 39). Accelerated soil erosion is also responsible for the loss of water quality from turbidity. This reduces the amount of sunlight and dissolved oxygen available to aquatic plants and can lead to the reduction of fish and shellfish populations. In addition, off-farm sediment flows can damage aquatic environments by impairing water storage capacity in rivers, lakes and reservoirs increasing flooding and damaging water systems for fishing, recreation and transport (see the off-farm sediment flow indicator in the Land Conservation chapter).

Additional sources of water pollutants include the run-off of *heavy metals* from agricultural land, which may originate from the use of sewage sludge, manure, chemical fertilisers, and pesticides. Aquatic biota are usually harmed by much lower concentrations of heavy metals than would endanger drinking water quality. Cadmium is highly toxic in water, particularly associated with phosphate fertiliser use and copper can also be found in water in the form of compounds from pesticide use.

Figure 2. **Pesticides in water: a schematic diagram of pathways from agricultural use**

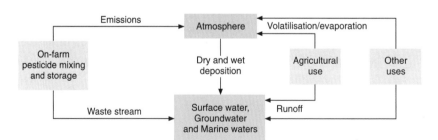

Source: OECD Secretariat.

Inland surface water polluted by *biological contaminants* from man and livestock may transport a variety of pathogenic bacteria and viruses. Many dry parts of rivers have become saline because of high concentrations of dissolved *salts* such as fluoride, sodium and chloride. This impairs the use of water for human and livestock consumption as well as water use for irrigation and even by industry. Increased salinity in irrigation water can affect soil salinity, which in turn negatively influences soil quality.

2. Indicators

Water quality indicators may include both "risk" and "state" indicators. Risk indicators estimate the potential contamination of water originating from agricultural activities. When comparing indicators across regions or countries, the point of comparison should not be the level of emissions but rather the risk of exceeding common threshold values. This is because one level of emissions (or a certain type of agricultural practice) may lead to significantly different concentrations in water bodies depending on the location. State indicators measure the actual trends in concentrations of pollutants in water against some threshold value.[10]

Water quality risk indicator

Definition

The potential concentration of nitrate (or phosphorus) in the water flowing from a given agricultural area, both percolating water and surface run-off.

Method of calculation

The indicator, in the case of nitrate, is estimated as:

$$PNC \ (mg/l) = PNP \ (mg/ha) \ / \ EW \ (l/ha)$$

where:

PNC = potential nitrate concentration (mg/l)

PNP = potential nitrate present: (mg/ha) (for a given area, "excess nitrate" multiplied by the ratio of "excess water" to "soil water holding capacity plus excess water")

EW = excess water (l/ha) (precipitation less evapotranspiration by crop type).

In order to identify the areas at risk, the *potential nitrate concentration* is estimated for each sub-national region defined as having broadly uniform soil types and climatic conditions. The calculation of the potential nitrate concentration draws on the soil surface nitrogen balance for agriculture at the sub-national level. The methodology to calculate the soil surface nitrogen balance is discussed in the Nutrient Use chapter.

Excess water can be estimated from long-term (*e.g.* 30 years) average precipitation and evapo-transpiration data or using annual data. This choice clearly depends on the aim of the comparison. Long-term average values are useful in order to reveal time trends in the contamination risk caused by changes in agricultural production, whereas annual values are relevant if the aim is to compare the "actual" contamination risk from year to year (Figure 3).

The *soil water holding capacity* is estimated according to the predominant soil types for each sub-national region. For example, the capacity of sand or sandy loam soils to hold available water is variable (Box 1). If the excess water (precipitation minus evapotranspiration and excluding annual variation in precipitation) is less than the soil water holding capacity most of the time, the soil is not saturated and the risk of excess nitrogen into surface/groundwater is at a minimum. But where the soil is saturated and plant growth is reduced, high concentrations of nutrients can occur in leached water.

Recent trends

Amongst the countries that are developing risk indicators of water quality associated with agriculture, *Canada* has established two indicators to address the risk of water contamination by nitrogen

---

Box 1. The Canadian Indicator of the Risk of Water Contamination by Nitrogen from Agriculture

The Canadian indicator is based on estimates of the potential concentration of nitrate-nitrogen in water leaving farmland (MacDonald, 2000). The level of risk associated with various concentrations is based on the *Canadian Water Quality Guidelines* safe limit for drinking water of 10 mg/l of nitrate-nitrogen (or 44 NO_3 mg/l, Annex Table 1). The performance objective for the agricultural industry is to ensure that the quality of water moving off agricultural land to groundwater and surface water is not seriously impaired by agricultural activity.

The potential concentration of nitrogen in water leaving farmland was determined by dividing the amount of nitrogen by the amount of water available to dilute this nitrogen (called excess water). The quantity of nitrogen that is potentially available to move off farmland, called residual nitrogen, was calculated in a similar way to a soil surface nutrient balance. Values for residual nitrogen are directly related to crop production and provide a reasonable estimate of nitrogen loading under average land uses. They include the input of nitrogen from animal manure, but the results were averaged over areas that were usually too large to show the impacts of localised areas of intensive livestock production, where manure nitrogen values may be much higher.

The amount of water that is potentially available to move off farmland was calculated by devising a moisture budget based on 30-year averages for precipitation (moisture input) and potential evapotranspiration (moisture output). The difference between these two values was used as the estimate of water surplus or water deficit. Only mapping areas with a water surplus were used to calculate the indicator, located in the agricultural regions of British Columbia, Ontario, Quebec, and the Atlantic Provinces.

Share of farmland for which the estimated risk of nitrogen water pollution changed: Canada, 1981 to 1996

Ecozone	Farmland area[1]	Share of farmland for which the nitrogen content of water changed		
	Million hectares	Content decreased by at least 1 mg N/l	No change −1 to +1 mg N/l	Content increased by at least 1 mg N/l
British Columbia	0.1	31	12	57
Ontario	4.2	2	30	68
Quebec	1.9	1	22	77
Atlantic Provinces	0.4	2	36	62

mg N/l: milligrams of nitrogen per litre.
1. Farmland area is the sum of all 1996 *Census of Agriculture* land classes except All Other Land. Value for British Columbia is for the south coastal region only.
Source: McRae *et al.* (2000).

The capacity of the soil to hold available water was also an important factor in the water budget. This capacity was estimated at 100 mm for sand or sandy loam, 150 mm for loam, 200 mm for clay loam, and 250 mm for clay. If the available moisture (precipitation − potential evapotranspiration) is less than the available water holding capacity, the soil profile is not saturated and movement of nitrogen into groundwater is unlikely. The opposite is also true.

The risk of water contamination by nitrogen was expressed in three risk classes: low (0-6 mg/l), which is below the drinking water guideline; intermediate (6.1-14 mg/l), showing areas where nitrogen levels in water may approach or exceed the drinking water guideline; high (14.1 mg/l or greater), showing areas where exceeding the drinking water guideline is likely. To show trends in the indicator, changes (increases or decreases) by more than 1 mg/l were used, representing 10 per cent of the drinking water standard.

---

and phosphorus from agriculture. With the emergence in Canada of water quality as a high-priority environmental issue for agriculture, these indicators are designed to address several policy needs. These include, the clarification of agriculture's potential to impact on water quality, the targeting of remedial policies and programmes, and the development of predictive models and systems to assess impacts (see Box 1 for details on the methodology related to the risk of water contamination by nitrogen).

The results from both the nitrogen and phosphorus risk indicators of water contamination reveal that about 90 per cent of *Canada*'s agricultural land is generally not at risk of causing water contamination from nitrogen and phosphorus run-off (McRae *et al.*, 2000). However, the indicator does not capture nutrient contamination in semi-arid regions associated with major storms and run-off events, intensive livestock operations or irrigation. For the remaining 10 per cent of agricultural land area at risk to contamination by nitrogen in 1996, 47 per cent was in the low risk category, that is below the Canadian drinking water guideline of 10mg/l, and 13 per cent in the high risk class >14mg/l.

Between 1981 and 1996 the estimated nitrogen content of water in *Canada* increased by at least 1mg/l on 70 per cent of the land at risk, mainly due to a shift in cropping patterns towards crops requiring higher levels of nitrogen, such as soybeans and maize, and also an increase in stocking densities of livestock, resulting in greater quantities of manure nitrogen to be managed. Similar trends in the risk of water contamination by phosphorus pollution from agriculture were also evident between 1981 to 1996.[11]

A similar approach to that of Canada and OECD is being developed in *Denmark*, with an indicator of the Potential Nitrate Concentration (PNC) in the percolating water leaving the rootzone to surface and groundwater. The PNC is calculated by dividing the nitrogen surplus at field level (calculated from a soil surface nitrogen balance) by the net precipitation (the amount of water leaving the rootzone). The PNC thus shows what the nitrate concentration would be in the water leaving the rootzone, if the total nitrogen surplus were lost only as nitrate leaching (NO_3).

As the *Danish* calculation excludes transport processes (horizontal or vertical water flow), the indicator does not reflect whether nitrate is lost to surface or groundwater recipients. Nor is the nitrate removal (*e.g.* denitrification) during transport reflected. This underlines that the PNC cannot be compared directly to drinking water threshold values. Nevertheless, the PNC holds a number of positive attributes as a risk indicator, since it is easy to calculate based on the already available nitrogen balances, is comparable among countries, and time series can be calculated quite easily in order to identify time trends. The PNC can be updated annually, and if data are available the indicator can be calculated for different geographical scales depending on the environmentally relevant level of analysis (*e.g.* national, regional level, eco-district, catchment level).

The *Danish* indicator shows a downward trend in mg of nitrate per litre of water leaving the rootzone over the period 1985-1997 (Figure 3). This trend corresponds to the reduction in the absolute nitrogen surplus for Denmark by about 26 per cent over the same period (see the Nutrient Use chapter).

The *United Kingdom* has also recently used a risk modelling approach to provide an indirect indicator of the impacts of nitrate and phosphorus losses to water (MAFF, 2000). The indicator is based on the results of ongoing work to model nitrate and phosphorus losses at catchment and national level. Catchments, in particular Nitrate Vulnerable Zones (NVZs), have been selected to provide a range of land-use and hydrological situations, compared with non-NVZ catchments with similar land uses (Figure 4).

Interpretation and links to other indicators

Risk indicators can provide an early warning of potential problems (Harker, 1998). A growing number of countries are developing risk indicators to estimate the potential agricultural impact on water quality, mainly because monitoring the "state" of water quality is expensive and it is usually difficult to distinguish the contribution of agriculture compared with other sectors. Furthermore, indicators of the risk of water contamination can facilitate the identification of vulnerable areas and the interpretation of the main causes.

This is important, since there are relatively few attempts to evaluate the economic costs of the impairment of water quality from agricultural activities, or the economic benefits from altering farm management practices to alleviate potentially negative water quality impacts from agriculture. In addition, the effects of measures implemented to prevent or control water pollution cannot be

Figure 3. **Potential nitrate concentration in water flowing from agricultural land: Denmark, 1985 to 1997**

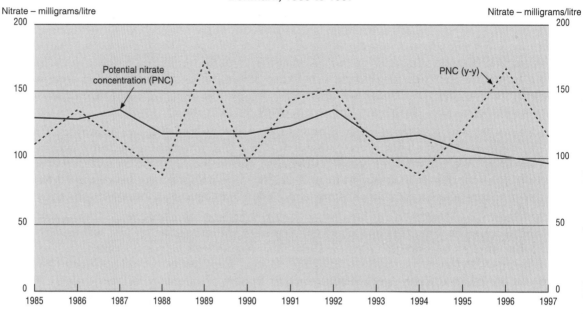

Notes: Calculated precipitations minus actual evaporation is used as an estimate of net precipitation. PNC is based on a thirty-year average of net precipitation (1961-90); and PNC (y-y) is based on year-to-year figures of net precipitation.
Source: Schou and Kyllingsbaek (1999).

Figure 4. **Nitrate and phosphorus losses from agriculture: United Kingdom, mid-1990s**

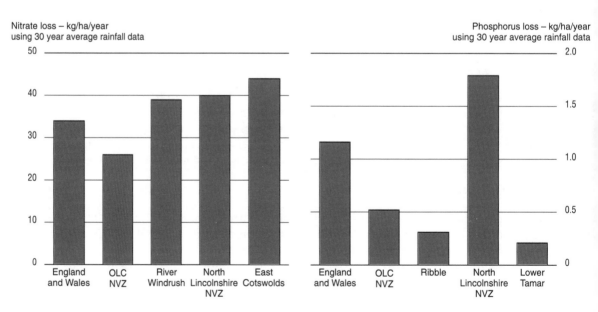

OLC: Rivers Ouse, Leam, Cherwell; NVZ: Nitrate Vulnerable Zone.
Notes: Left figure shows national average for England and Wales, two surface water catchments (OLC and River Windrush), and two groundwater catchments (North Lincolnshire and East Cotswolds). Right figure shows national average for England and Wales, two predominantly arable catchments (OLC and North Lincolnshire), and with two predominantly grassland catchments (Ribble and Lower Tamar).
Source: MAFF (2000).

predicted with accuracy because there is often no linear relationship between the driving forces (farming activities) and the state of water quality. An additional problem is the time lag between emissions by agriculture and the impact on groundwater quality, which might be long (see the example of the United Kingdom in the following section).

Those areas with potential nitrogen concentrations above respective national threshold values, for example 50 mg/litre, in surface water (Annex Table 1), reveal the potential risk to water quality contamination from agriculture. Trends in areas at risk will mainly highlight changes in nitrogen surplus in each area, and to a lesser extent changes in agricultural area.

A key limitation to this indicator is the implicit assumption that nitrate leaching is the major form of nitrogen emission to the environment and that retention within the soil and watercourse systems is not significant. Experience in the United Kingdom, for example, has shown that at low to moderate nitrogen surplus values, there is a poor relationship with nitrate concentration, and that land use and management has a strong influence on the relationship between surplus and nitrate loss. This emphasises the need for the indicator to be clear as to the meaning of "excess nitrate" in the context of varying agricultural land use patterns and management systems.

As the calculation does not take into account the transport processes (horizontal or vertical water flow) the indicator does not reflect whether nitrate is lost to surface or groundwater. Nor is nitrate removal (e.g. denitrification) during transport reflected. This underlines the point that the indicator can not be compared directly to threshold values such as nitrate in drinking water.

This approach, however, holds a number of positive attributes as a risk indicator. It is easy to calculate based on the already available soil surface nitrogen balances for OECD countries (where these are calculated at the sub-national level), it is comparable among countries, and time series can be calculated quite easily in order to identify time-trends. The indicator can also be calculated for different geographical scales depending on the environmentally relevant level of analysis (e.g. regional level, eco-district level, catchment level), drawing on geographic information systems linked with physically based models.

This indicator draws on information provided through the soil surface nitrogen balance and could be extended to phosphorus where phosphorus balances are available. As the indicator is developed, information from the nutrient management and land conservation (water retaining capacity indicator) could also be drawn on.

Water quality state indicator

Definition

Nitrate (or phosphorus) concentration in water in vulnerable agricultural areas: the proportion of surface water and groundwater above a national threshold value of nitrate concentration (NO_3 mg/l) or phosphorus (P_{total} mg/l).

Method of calculation

The indicator, in the case of nitrate, is derived by taking sample concentrations of nitrate (mg/l) for groundwater and flow-weighted mean concentrations (mean concentrations per year) of nitrate (mg/l) for surface waters, in areas vulnerable to contamination from agriculture. The indicator reveals the share of the number of measurement points in vulnerable agriculture areas that are above national drinking (and/or environmental) water threshold values, as directly measured by national authorities (Annex Table 1).

It is necessary to establish the policy relevant criteria to determine what constitutes a vulnerable agricultural area. Under the European Union's Nitrate Directive (91/676), nitrate vulnerable zones (NVZs) are defined as all known areas of land that drain into waters where a) the nitrate concentrations exceed, or are expected to exceed, 50 mg/litre (the EU drinking water standard) or b) where there is evidence of nitrate limited eutrophication (MAFF, 1994).[12] Most OECD countries outside of the EU do not define or designate areas as "vulnerable" zones, although Norway and Switzerland utilise a similar definition to the EU in their legislation concerning water quality.[13] In the *United States*, the National Water Quality Assessment Program collects water samples from targeted land uses, including agricultural land, defined as watersheds with more than 70 per cent cropland and pasture (see USGS, 1999, pp. 30-31).

Recent trends

General

While agriculture is not the only sector that burdens aquatic environments with pollutants, for most OECD countries it is a major contributor in the case of nitrogen and phosphates. Recent estimates indicate agriculture accounts for more than 40 per cent of all sources of nitrogen emissions and over 30 per cent of phosphorus emissions into surface water for a considerable number of OECD countries (Figure 5). While the trend in nutrient surplus from agriculture is declining for most OECD countries (see Nutrient Use chapter), the growing contribution of agriculture in the overall level of nutrient contamination of water largely reflects the trend towards the significant reduction in point sources of nutrient pollution (*e.g.* from industry, sewage, etc.).

Although agriculture may be the major source of nutrient pollution of water, the share of measuring points in vulnerable agricultural areas above national nitrate/phosphorus threshold values is low, for those few OECD countries where this information is available (Annex Table 1). However, there are some exceptions, including *Austria, Japan, Korea*, the *Netherlands*, and *Portugal* for nitrates in groundwater, and the *Netherlands* for nitrates in surface water.

The extent of *groundwater pollution* from agricultural nutrients is less well documented than for surface and marine waters, largely because of the cost involved in sampling groundwater. Moreover, correlating nutrient contamination levels in groundwater with changes in farming practices and production systems is difficult, because it can take many years for nutrients to leach through overlying soils into aquifers. In

Figure 5. **Share of agriculture in total emissions of nitrogen and phosphorus into surface water: mid-1990s**

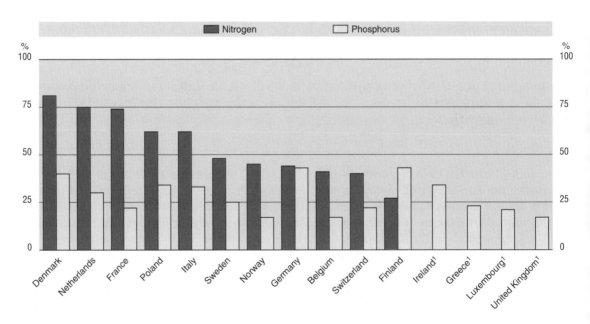

1. Data for nitrogen emissions are not available.
Note: See Annex Table 2.
Source: See Annex Table 2.

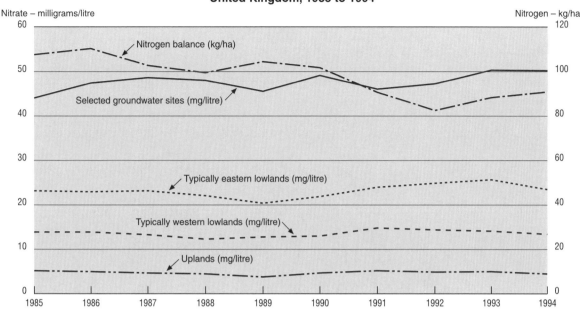

Figure 6. **Nitrogen balance and nitrates in rivers and groundwater: United Kingdom, 1985 to 1994**

Sources: United Kingdom Department of the Environment, (1996). For nitrogen balance data, see Nutrient Use chapter in this Report.

the *United Kingdom*, for example, where nitrate concentration in groundwater appears to be rising, the UK nitrogen balance surplus has declined (Figure 6; and the Nutrient Use chapter). In the late 1990s 7 per cent of measuring points in vulnerable agricultural areas in the UK had nitrate levels in groundwater above the national threshold value, compared with less that 3 per cent of measuring points for surface water (Annex Table 1).

United States, Australia, New Zealand and Korea

The *United States* regularly reports on the state of the country's water quality, following the enactment of the US Clean Water Act in 1972, and also identifies the role of different sources of water quality impairment, including agriculture, municipal point sources, urban run-off and storm sewers. Recent assessments indicate that nearly two-thirds of water bodies meet designated water quality standards. For the remaining one-third of sampled water bodies which fall below these standards, agriculture is the major source of impairment in rivers and lakes, but is less important in estuaries.[14]

Trends in the share of agriculture as a source of impairment to surface water quality in the *United States* since 1988 (in percentage of area impaired) show an increase for estuaries, a smaller rise for rivers, and a decrease for lakes (Figure 7). Leading stressors causing water quality impairment in lakes, rivers and estuaries (in terms of percentage of area affected by a particular stressor) are nutrients, bacteria (except in lakes), siltation (except in estuaries) and oxygen depleting substances. Non-point agricultural sources are responsible for almost all siltation and for more than 80 per cent of both nitrogen and phosphorus reaching surface water.

To reduce loadings of water pollutants from agriculture the United States has introduced a substantial programme of measures that cover technical and financial assistance and research, directed at agricultural non-point source pollution. Research in the US has indicated, however, that links between improved farm management practices and observed changes in water quality usually involve long time lags. For example, it

237

Figure 7. **Share of agriculture in the impairment of surface and marine water quality:
United States, 1988 to 1996**

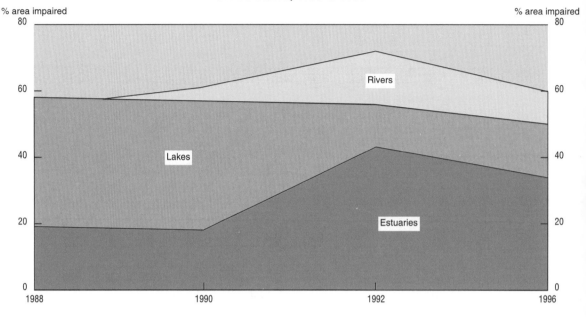

Note: Figure shows agriculture's contribution to water pollution, from sources (*e.g.* soil sediment, nitrogen, phosphorus, pesticides, etc.) for the
one-third of the nation's water bodies assessed to be below designated water quality standards.
Sources: USDA (1996a, 1996b, 1997).

may take many years to see aquatic habitats restored (*i.e.* increased fish stocks and aquatic plants, etc.),
after farm practices to manage chemicals have been improved.

From a national perspective, nitrate contamination of surface and groundwater from agriculture in
the United States has improved since the introduction of the Clean Water Act. This has been associated
with, in particular, improvements in farming practices that have helped reduce the run-off of nutrients
into surface and groundwater (see the chapter on Farm Management).

Nitrate pollution of major aquifers, large rivers and smaller streams in the *United States*, does not
pose a human health risk, according to a national survey completed in 1997 (USGS, 1999). However,
there are some concerns for aquifers used for rural domestic water supply, where nitrate concentrations
are in excess of national drinking water standards for certain aquifers in these areas. Moreover, the
presence of elevated nitrate levels in shallow groundwater in rural areas, raises concerns to potential
future risks for consumption of water from deeper wells in these rural aquifers.

Groundwater nitrate data from across the *United States* suggests that nitrate concentration in groundwater
increases with higher nitrogen inputs and better drained soils (Nolan and Ruddy, 1996). Median nitrate
concentration and the percentage of wells from which water exceeds the drinking-water standard for
nitrate are lowest in poorly drained soils with low nitrogen input and highest in well-drained soils with
high nitrogen input.

Concerning the impact of elevated nutrient levels on aquatic life in the *United States*, the US
Geological Survey (USGS, 1999) survey notes that eutrophic conditions were observed in some rivers
across the nation, but that at present it is premature to attempt a national summary of eutrophication
because of limited methodologies to determine the effects of eutrophication. Even so, nitrate run-off
into coastal waters is stimulating algal growth and affecting marine ecosystems.

Excessive nutrient concentrations have been linked to hypoxic zones in US coastal areas, that is to
say a concentrated area of algal blooms that consume oxygen when they decompose, such as in the Gulf
of Mexico (USGS, 1999). This has lead to the death and displacement of fish in the Gulf, and some

57 per cent of the shellfish growing area within the Gulf has been closed because of human health risks (OECD, 1996c). High nutrient levels are also believed to be one cause for the growth of *Pfiesteria piscicda*, a toxin that is potentially harmful to humans, fish, and other organisms. Outbreaks of this toxin are thought to have been linked to agricultural nutrient run-off in coastal waters along the North Carolina coast and in Chesapeake Bay, leading to fish kills involving millions of fish (UNEP, 1999, pp. 150-152).[15]

In the Murray-Darling Basin region of *Australia*, which accounts for over 40 per cent of the nation's agricultural production, eutrophication of surface water bodies is becoming increasingly common (Commonwealth of Australia, 1995, p. 61). *New Zealand* also reports problems of eutrophication of some lakes and rivers from nutrient run-off and certain cases of nitrate pollution of groundwater (OECD, 1996a; 1998b, pp. 139-151; and New Zealand MAF, 1993, p. 10). A small number of lowland lakes have become eutrophic, with ecosystem collapses. Groundwater is commonly of the highest quality, but some shallow aquifers show slight nitrate contamination from dairy farming.

In *Korea* nitrate levels in water bodies are high in urban and agricultural areas. The concentration of total nitrogen and phosphorus has increased significantly in many Korean rivers in the 1990s, and eutrophication is a problem in lakes, with around half of the major lakes and reservoirs affected. These developments correspond to the major increase in the Korean nitrogen surplus (see the Nutrient Use chapter). "Red tides" of decomposing algae have occurred every summer since the early 1990s in many locations of the shallow Korean coastal waters (OECD, 1998c).

Europe

Less than 2 per cent of measuring points in the vulnerable agricultural areas of *Austria* are above the threshold value for nitrate and phosphorus in surface water. The situation for agricultural pollution from nitrate in groundwater is more serious, with 17 per cent of measuring points in vulnerable agricultural area above national threshold values (Annex Table 1). The total surface area in Austria subject to ground water quality monitoring, including non-coherent groundwater bodies aquifers, amounts to approximately 3.4 million hectares (40 per cent of the total land area).

A national network of sampling sites monitoring water quality in rivers has also been established in Austria. The installation of the sampling site network for groundwater and rivers was completed in 1996 and currently comprises of 1782 groundwater sampling sites, 237 springs and 244 river sampling sites. In the future, the observation programme will be enlarged to include lakes, which will complete the water quality monitoring network coverage in Austria in accordance with the EU Water Framework Directive, which obliges EU member States to monitor groundwater as well as surface water quality in a comprehensive way.

In *Denmark*, which has an extremely high dependence on groundwater for its water supplies (see Water Use chapter), only 3 per cent of nitrate samples from aquifers exceeded the 50 mg/l standard, with 10 per cent above the 25 mg/l guiding limit during the early 1990s (Frederiksen and Schou, 1996). Denmark now has all farms operating under a nutrient management plan, which might be expected to help alleviate water pollution problems from nutrients (Figure 5; and Figure 4 in the Farm Management chapter).

The nitrate and phosphorus run-off into surface water in *Finland* is considered excessive in areas with large-scale livestock enterprises. Agriculture in Finland provides a major share of nitrate and phosphorus loadings of rivers and lakes, and recently has introduced a range of measures to help in reducing this problem, although it is too early to assess the effects of these measures on water quality (Figure 5; and OECD, 2000, pp. 27-30).

There has been a trend towards deterioration in many small rivers, polluted by nitrates and phosphorus from agriculture in *France*, with over 70 per cent of the nitrate loading of surface waters from agricultural sources, and over 20 per cent for phosphorus (Figure 5). A third of the country has been classified as vulnerable to river eutrophication (OECD, 1997a). The situation of water pollution from nutrients is most acute in Brittany, where animal stocking densities per hectare are high and fertilisers are used for the region's vegetable production (Bonnieux and Rainelli, 1996). A recent report by the

French Ministry of Regional Planning and the Environment (2000) suggests that it may cost about FF10 billion (US$ 1.5 billion) to reduce nitrate pollution from intensive livestock operations.

Agriculture is a major source of both nitrate and phosphorus pollution of surface water in *Germany* (Figure 5). About 4 per cent of drinking water samples had a nitrate concentration above 50 mg/l in 1989, declining to 2 per cent in the mid-1990s. In the new Länder, nitrate contamination is also evident in certain regions (OECD, 1993a).

A survey in *Ireland* has identified agriculture as the main cause of slight and moderate pollution of rivers and lakes from nutrient loadings of nitrates and phosphates, especially from large scale livestock operations (Lucey *et al.*, 1999). Agriculture accounts for about a third of total phosphorus emissions into surface water (Figure 5).

Agriculture in the *Netherlands* contributes to 75 per cent of nitrate discharges into water bodies (Figure 5). Diffuse phosphorus loadings from agriculture are not likely to decrease before 2000, while eutrophication of surface and coastal waters remains a major problem (OECD, 1995). In the late 1990s nitrate and phosphorus concentrations were estimated to exceed "acceptable" limits at over 60 per cent of all measuring locations in the national grid, and over 25 per cent for nitrates in groundwater (Annex Table 1).

The rise in concentrated discharges of nutrients from the residential sector in *Norway*, and higher fertiliser use in agriculture have led to increased eutrophication of water (Figure 5). It is estimated that more than a third of the population lives close to a eutrophic waterway (OECD, 1993b). None of the groundwater in vulnerable agricultural areas, however, exceeded the 50 mg/l threshold in the late 1990s (Annex Table 1). Nitrate pollution of the North Sea coastal area from Norwegian agriculture declined by 19 per cent over the period 1985-95, while phosphorus discharges showed a larger reduction of 26 per cent.[16] These developments reflect, in part, that a significant number of Norwegian farms are now using nutrient management plans (see Figure 4, Farm Management chapter).

While data are limited on the extent of nutrient pollution of water in *Poland*, it is reported that about 50 per cent of farm wells have nitrate levels in excess of Polish drinking water standards (Sapek, 1999). The main source of this pollution is considered to be leakage from livestock manure storage facilities, with agriculture the major source of nutrient pollution in surface waters (Figure 8).

In some areas of intensive livestock production in *Spain* the nitrate content in groundwater exceeds 100 mg/l (double the EU Nitrate Directive level of 50 mg/l), with agriculture as an important cause of groundwater pollution for many acquifers across the country (Iglesias and Sumpsi, 1996). However, other non-agricultural sources of nitrate pollution are also significant.

About one in six lakes in *Sweden*, have such high phosphorus concentrations (25µg/l or more) that they can be described as eutrophic (OECD, 1996b). In agricultural areas elevated nitrate concentrations have been recorded in places, accounting for nearly a half of total nitrate and a quarter of phosphorus emissions into surface water (Figure 5). In *Switzerland*, the share of nitrates in surface water and groundwater derived from agriculture is around 40 per cent, with a share of 20 per cent for phosphorus in surface water (Figure 5).

Interpretation and links to other indicators

In developing state indicators, one of the issues to consider is whether the data should be collected on a nation-wide basis or monitoring should be confined to areas vulnerable to water pollution from agriculture. Vulnerable areas could be defined using criteria such as livestock densities, proportion of crops requiring high nutrient applications, presence of sandy soils and steep slopes, and the intensity of irrigation. The vulnerable area approach to developing "state" indicators of water quality in agriculture has the advantage over a national monitoring approach because for some countries it is too costly to establish a nation-wide representative monitoring network. Even so, in some countries regular nation-wide monitoring of surface and groundwater quality is well established.[17]

A key difficulty in collecting representative data on the national state of water quality, is that while there is complete and regular monitoring of certain catchment areas or for particular pollution problems, for other catchments or problems monitoring is incomplete. There is also the scarcity of systematic, consistent and long-term monitoring programmes; and differences in measuring methods by various agencies. With a national approach, it is also very difficult to differentiate the effects of different polluters (*e.g.* agriculture, industry, households, traffic), since actual losses of nutrients from agricultural activities cannot be measured directly. Thus, the agricultural contribution can, usually only be estimated by reference to the predominant land use in a particular area. In a growing number of countries, there is an increasing interest in watershed-based management approaches, by using watersheds as a basis for developing indicators and implementing water resource protection and restoration activities.

Estimates of the impairment of water quality by agriculture need to be interpreted with caution as it is not always clear how these data were obtained and if they include cross-border pollution, where relevant, and discharges by the agri-food industry.[18] To interpret trends in "state" water quality indicators, also requires the definition of some threshold value and minimum level of sample frequency. Many OECD countries have established threshold values for nitrates, but fewer countries for phosphates, as summarised in Annex Table 1. Binding limits or threshold values do differ across OECD countries, and also vary by the purpose of water use, either for drinking or environmental uses.

It should be remembered that being in a "natural" state does not necessarily mean that water is ideal for human purposes (*e.g.* the high level of naturally occurring humus in some lakes or of salts in groundwater). The natural composition of water also varies according to natural climatic and geochemical conditions. In cool temperate climates, soils have less salts and more organic components. There are also areas with naturally occurring high iron (*Denmark*), fluoride (*Germany*), arsenic and strontium levels (in some mountainous countries).

The state water quality indicators are related to other agri-environmental areas, notably nutrient use and farm management indicators, and also the water retention aspect (in helping to stabilise water flows) of the land conservation indicators. These indicators, at a disaggregated sub-national level, signal where high nutrient inputs into water may occur and where changes in farm management practices and/or water retaining capacity can help reduce nutrient water pollution problems.

3. Related information

General

Improvements in water quality not only bring benefits to human and environmental health, they also provide aesthetic qualities and generate employment and economic growth. In the *United States*, for example, anglers spend roughly US$24 billion on their sport and generate US$69 billion for the country's economy. Lake Erie on the Canadian border supports a US$600 million per year fishing industry, and crops grown on irrigated land are valued at nearly US$70 billion a year, about 40 per cent of the total value of all crops marketed in the United States (EPA, 1998, p. 2). Equally, the benefit to water quality from erosion control on US cropland alone could total over US$4 billion annually (USDA, 1997, pp. 93-94).

An indication of the overall OECD situation and trends for agricultural pollutants of water, other than nitrogen and phosphorus, such as pesticides, soil sediment, is more difficult. Extrapolating from trends in soil erosion losses and changes in pesticide use, described in other chapters, would suggest that in many countries impairment of water quality from these agricultural pollutants is probably declining, but there remain serious pollution problems from these contaminants in some regions and countries.[19]

Agricultural pesticides contamination of water

General

Direct measurements of pesticides in surface or groundwater are not widely available across OECD countries, mainly because of the high costs of chemical analysis. Furthermore, many pesticides are not

241

found in water bodies simply because they are not searched for, although when they are looked for they are frequently detected (EEA, 1998, pp. 187-191). While the use of pesticides has fallen in many OECD countries since the mid-1980s (see Figure 1 in the Pesticide Use and Risks chapter), the long time lag between use and their detection in groundwater means that, as with nitrates, the situation could deteriorate before it starts to improve.

A further complicating factor is isolating the source of pesticides found in water. In the *United Kingdom*, for example, it was found, through sampling selected rivers and groundwater, that the most commonly detected pesticides are used for non-agricultural purposes, such as atrazine applied to road and railway verges where run-off can occur easily (UK Department of the Environment, 1996, pp. 104-05). Even so, a recent study in the *United States* detected a significant relationship between the occurrence of pesticides in groundwater and the presence of agricultural land in close proximity (CEC, 1999, pp. 241-245).

United States, New Zealand and Japan

According to a recent survey of pesticide pollution of water in the *United States*, in agricultural areas more than 80 per cent of sampled rivers and fish, contained one, or more often, several pesticides (Figure 8). Pesticides found in rivers were primarily those that are currently used, whereas in fish and riverbed sediment, organochlorine insecticides, such as DDT (now prohibited), which were used decades ago, were detected. Moreover, pesticides currently in use in the United States are more soluble and breakdown more rapidly in the natural environment, than the insecticides used in the past. The US survey also revealed that nearly 60 per cent of wells (shallow groundwater) sampled in agricultural areas contained one or more pesticides (Figure 8). It also apparent that pesticide pollution of water in non-agricultural areas, is also important, with around 20-30 per cent of total pesticide use in the US accounted for by non-agricultural uses, in particular, urban gardens and golf courses.

Figure 8. **Pesticide occurence in fish, streams and groundwater: United States, mid-1990s**

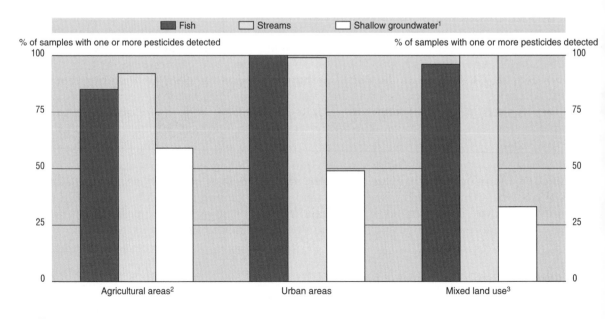

1. Shallow groundwater, mainly wells less than 30 meters deep.
2. Water with more than 70% cropland and pasture.
3. Areas mainly downstream from major metropolitan areas.
Source: USGS (1999).

An estimate for the early 1990s showed that direct annual losses from fish kills due to pesticides in the US are less than US$1 million, though the authors consider this could be an underestimate (Ribaudo *et al.*, 1999, p. 13). Moreover, the same study also reveals that the additional costs needed for treatment facilities to meet current US regulations for pesticides in water (and other specific chemicals) would be about US$400 million, with about another US$100 million required over the next 20 years.

In *New Zealand* concentrations of pesticides in surface water are reported to be much lower than maximum acceptable limits set for drinking water in the country, although some incidences of groundwater pollution from pesticides have been recorded (OECD, 1996a). A survey in *Japan* of surface water quality carried out from 1983 to 1994 has showed that agricultural pesticide concentration rarely exceeded the authorised standard (OECD, 1994).

Europe

The results of pesticide sampling in groundwater across a number of *European Union* countries, found a considerable number of sites with pesticide concentrations >0.1µg/l (microgram per litre), which is the maximum admissible concentration of pesticides specified in the EU Drinking Water Directive 80/778/EEC (EEA, 1998, pp. 187-191).[20] In the OECD countries of Central Europe (*i.e. Czech Republic, Hungary* and *Poland*), it is very likely that the potential pollution of water bodies from pesticide and nutrient run-off from agricultural land has diminished considerably, especially due to the sharp reduction in the use of farm chemicals and livestock numbers over the 1990s (FAO, 1999; Scheierling, 1995; and also see the Nutrient Use, and Pesticide Use and Risks chapters).

A recent study of pesticides in water in *France* concludes that, despite problems of the quality and quantity of monitoring data, pesticides are present in excessive quantities in the water environment (IFEN, 1998). Surface waters are most affected, with pesticides detected in all rivers, but even in the downstream reaches of large rivers where extensive dilution of potential pesticide pollution can occur, only 3 per cent of monitoring points showed no pesticides were present. Groundwater is better protected with 52 per cent of all monitoring points considered to be unaffected.

For *French* drinking water supplies, however, pesticides are detected in around a quarter of the cases where drinking water does not conform with national drink water standards, although there was some improvement from 1993 to 1995. Insufficient information is currently available to assess the health risks of pesticide contamination and its impact on the environment. A report on the Brittany region in France, which accounts for 6 per cent of the country's total agricultural land area and 4 per cent of total pesticide consumption, reveals that two-thirds of the region's drinking water sources are at risk from pesticide contamination (OECD, 1997a).

In 1986, widespread herbicide pollution was discovered in drinking water in large areas of Northern and Central *Italy*, known as the "atrazine emergency", from herbicide used on maize and sorghum (Cori, 1997). Following the ban on atrazine, other herbicides have been found in drinking water. Out of the 50 pesticide compounds being monitored in the *Netherlands*, more than two-thirds have been detected in groundwater at concentrations exceeding the drinking water quality standard of 0.1 µg/l (OECD, 1995).

About 20 years ago, tests in *Sweden* showed very high concentrations of toxic substances in fish, birds and mammal species, such as pesticides and cadmium, but levels of some substances have since fallen and many species are showing signs of recovery (OECD, 1996b). Tests for pesticides in *Switzerland* carried out so far show that groundwater contamination mainly involves atrazine, which may result from its long-term and widespread use as a herbicide for maize, as its use on railway embankments has been banned since 1990 (OFEFP-OFAG, 1998).

In the *United Kingdom* the concentrations of commonly used agricultural pesticides are generally low in rivers, and even lower in groundwater, and well within the standards set under the EU Drinking Water Directive (UK Department of the Environment, 1996, pp. 104-105). While pesticide pollution into water bodies may be within EU drinking water standards, for the UK to comply with the EU standards it cost the water industry in 1992 around £800 million (US$1 280 million) in investment and about £80 million (US$128 million) per year in running costs (Falconer, 1997).

243

Soil sediment loadings of water

To assess the risk of soil sediment loadings to surface water, in the United States, the Department of Agriculture tracks the rate of sediment erosion from agricultural cropland through the National Resources Inventory (NRI), which is conducted every 5 years. The amount of sediment eroded from cropland decreased from about 2 million tonnes in 1977 to around 1 million tonnes in 1992 (Ribaudo *et al.*, 1999; USDA, 1997). In view of the improvements in limiting losses from water and wind erosion in the United States, it would seem likely that this source of water pollution maybe declining in the US (see Figures 2 to 5 in the Soil Quality chapter). Moreover, the improvements in US soil management practices are also helping to ameliorate soil erosion (see the Farm Management chapter).

The reduction of off-farm sediment flows into water bodies, is also reported in a few other countries (see the Off-farm Sediment Flow indicator in the Land Conservation chapter). Moreover, given the reduction in soil erosion, both water and wind, in a number of OECD countries it is also likely that this source of water pollution has also decreased (see the Soil Quality chapter).

Salinisation of water

The salinisation of water is a problem commonly associated with the return flows of water from irrigated cropland, and hence, is an issue mainly confined to areas under irrigation. In the United States surveys made in the late 1980s report an increasing level of dissolved solids (mainly ions of calcium, magnesium, sodium, potassium, bicarbonate, sulphate and chloride) in water catchments with significant irrigation water utilisation (Ribaudo *et al.*, 1999). In the Colorado River damage to agriculture from river salinity in the period 1976-85 has been estimated at US$113-122 million (Ribaudo *et al.*, 1999).

Salinity of rivers, due mainly to excessive irrigation and clearance of perennial vegetation, is increasing in many parts of Australia, particularly in arable regions.[21] While saline water is a natural feature of some Australian water bodies, the negative impact of recent land management practices on the hydrological balance and subsequent in-stream water quality is a matter of grave concern (Commonwealth of Australia, 1998). Moreover, because of the time lag between any changes in land use and occurrence of salinity, it appears likely that stream salinity will continue to rise in Australia over the next few decades. However, the development of water quality monitoring programmes and improvements in land management practices should help to improve the salinity problem in the future.

Other sources of agricultural contaminants in water

Agriculture is in general not a prominent source of water pollution from *heavy metals*. This is because for many OECD countries the heavy metal content of fertilisers is limited by regulations, and pesticides based on compounds such as arsenic and mercury are prohibited. The increasing use of sewage sludge and municipal waste on agricultural land in some countries, however, could potentially be a source of heavy metal pollution unless the waste material is treated.[22]

There is increasing concern related to the release of *pathogens from animal waste* into water, that could pose a serious threat to human health, for example, the remains of hormones and antibiotics from livestock operations. Outbreaks of *cryptosporidia*, a parasite found in the faeces of some animals that causes gastrointestinal illness, was implicated in gastro-enteritis outbreaks in Milwaukee, United States, for example. This outbreak led to 400 000 cases of illness and 100 deaths in 1993, and cost in excess of US$54 million (USDA, 1997, p. 91). Another parasite, *giardia*, commonly found in beef herds, has been estimated as a health cost in the United States of US$1.2 to 1.5 billion annually (Ribaudo *et al.*, 1999).

4. Future challenges

Developmental work on the indicator of the *risk of water contamination from nutrients* (nitrogen and phosphorus) would be useful to determine the effects of practices such as conservation tillage and winter cover crops, and to improve the water balance calculations by taking into consideration additional soil characteristics and the moisture uptake characteristics of different crops and crop rotations.

In addition, water-partitioning considerations such as surface run-off, tile flow, travel time and groundwater recharge would help to improve the sensitivity of these indicators

While an indicator of the *risk of water contamination by pesticides* could be developed in a similar way to that for nitrogen/phosphorus, interpreting the risk of water contamination by pesticides is currently hampered, in many countries, by the absence of spatially disaggregated pesticide use data. The future development of this indicator may benefit from on-going work in the OECD on agricultural pesticide risk indicators (see the Pesticide Use and Risks chapter).

As a more effective way of establishing *state water quality indicators*, information provided by countries on state monitoring of water quality (sampling frequency, sampling depth, station type, representativeness of the station) could be improved in the future. This might be achieved by drawing on internationally established standards through the International Standard Organisation (ISO) and the World Health Organisation (WHO) Drinking Water Guidelines.

Developing indicators that more firmly establish the magnitude of the *economic costs and benefits related to agricultural water pollution and control* would help improve policy decision making. Some countries have now begun to undertake an economic evaluation of the effects of agriculture on water quality. Recently, for example, *Australia* initiated the A$32 million (US$25 million) National Land and Water Resources Audit, to provide better information to underpin policy development and programme delivery in the natural resource area, including water use and quality (Fairweather and Napier, 1998, p. 4).

Relatively few studies, however, have been made of the national costs of water pollution and the benefits of water pollution control, and even fewer, if any, take a comprehensive view by including the costs and benefits to all water users.[23] It is evident from the few studies that do exist that the monetary benefits of improving water quality could be substantial. At the same time, the costs borne by water treatment companies and water users to reduce the level of agricultural and other pollutants in drinking water are significant.

NOTES

1. Agriculture is the major cause of diffuse, or non-point water pollution. Non-point discharges are difficult to monitor because they occur over wide areas and vary from day to day depending on weather conditions and the frequency and timing of application of potential pollutants, such as fertilisers and pesticides.

2. For a recent review of OECD policies related to agriculture and water quality see OECD (1998a; and 1998b).

3. For details of the Helsinki Convention and its status see the UNECE website: *www.unece.org/env/water_h.htm*.

4. Concerning background to the OSPAR Convention see the website at: www.ospar.org/; for the North America International Joint Commission see their website at: *www.ijc.org/boards/greatw.html*; and the EU Water Framework Directive can be found at the EU website: *http://europa.eu.int/water/index_en.html*.

5. For a review of agriculture's impact on water quality, see Zilberman (1998).

6. For an examination of the technical aspects of agricultural phosphorous losses to water see Sharpley (2000).

7. The deposition of ammonia volatilised from agriculture, mainly from livestock manure, may in some cases be a major cause of acidification. Acidification can severely lower fish stocks, as many fish species are unable to tolerate pH levels below 5.5. When the pH level falls below 3, iron and heavy metals, such as zinc, lead and aluminium, may dissolve in water and become toxic to animals, plants and humans.

8. The incidence of "blue-baby" syndrome in OECD countries is extremely low and often associated with exposure to non-agricultural sources of nitrates. The US Department of Health (see Morbidity and Mortality Weekly Report, March 1997) reported that during 1985-90 only 18 cases were reported. However, recent evidence in the US has suggested that nitrate contaminated drinking wells (greater than 4 mg/nitrate/litre) are associated with an elevated risk of stomach cancer (non-Hodgkins' lymphoma), see Cancer Web Report, April 20, 1999 at: *http://infoventures.com/cancer/canlit/etil195a.html*.

9. In the Pesticide Use and Risks chapter it is noted that the persistence of pesticide residues in the environment and human food chain may vary from a few weeks to 30 years. Despite the ban on DDT in most OECD countries since the mid-1970s, for example, residues of this pesticide compound are still detectable in some human foodstuffs and also aquatic environments, see for example, USGS (1999).

10. For a review of risk and state indicators related to agriculture's impact on water quality, see Harker (1998).

11. For a detailed examination of the impact of agriculture on water quality in *Canada*, see Coote and Gregorich (2000).

12. The experience of implementing the Nitrate Directive in the *United Kingdom* is examined by Parsisson (1996).

13. Information on vulnerable zones was taken from the responses to the OECD Agri-environmental Indicator Questionnaire, 1999. Erwin and Tesoriero (1997), have also developed a modelling approach to define vulnerable areas in the context of the pollution of groundwater from nitrates in the *United States*.

14. The discussion here on *United States* water quality and the role of agriculture draws on EPA (1998); Ribaudo *et al.* (1999); USDA (1996a; 1996b, pp. 40-48; and 1997, pp. 83-96); and USGS (1999).

15. For an economic assessment of the losses in fisheries from algal blooms, for a number of OECD countries, see McGinn (1999).

16. These data are drawn from the *Norwegian* Institute for Water Research (1998); but also see Annex Table 2; and OECD (1999, pp. 31-32).

17. In *Austria*, for example, there is a national network to monitor anthropogenic impacts on surface and groundwater, while the *United States* also has an extensive monitoring network, see USGS (1999).

18. For a discussion of the interpretation of agricultural water quality indicators, see Harker *et al.* (1998).

19. The development of state indicators are, in part, already being undertaken by the OECD showing water quality of selected rivers and lakes, measured in terms of annual mean concentrations of dissolved oxygen (DO), biochemical oxygen demand (BOD), nitrates, phosphorus, ammonium, lead, cadmium, chromium and copper (OECD, 1997b). However, as the measurement locations are at the mouths or downstream frontiers of rivers, there is no distinction between different sources of pollutants, such as agriculture.

20. Goodchild (1998), provides a description of the EU Drinking Water Directive, and Rayment (1998), p. 9, provides a critical examination of the Directive with respect to pesticides.

21. The clearing of vegetation and excessive irrigation can result in rising water tables and an increased movement of saline groundwater into surface water, as described in the Commonwealth of Australia (1998, pp. 61-62).

22. Trends in the accumulation of heavy metals in agricultural topsoils of the United Kingdom are examined in the Soil Quality chapter, see Figure 7. Remains of medicaments in sewage sludge applied to farmland are also a concern in some cases.

23. For a review of estimates in the *United States* of the monetary costs from water pollution and the benefits of water pollution control, see Ribaudo *et al.* (1999). The *French* Ministry of Regional Planning and the Environment (2000) has also recently made an estimate of the cost of agricultural water pollution.

Annex Table 1. **Drinking water threshold values and trends in surface and groundwater quality in agricultural vulnerable areas**

	Drinking water threshold values			% of measurement points in agriculture vulnerable areas above drinking water threshold values					
	Surface water		Groundwater	Surface water				Groundwater	
	Nitrate NO$_3$ mg/l	Phosphorus P total mg/l	Nitrate NO$_3$ mg/l	Nitrate NO$_3$ mg/l		Phosphorus P mg/l		Nitrate NO$_3$ mg/l	
				Early 1990s	Late 1990s	Early 1990s	Late 1990s	Early 1990s	Late 1990s
Austria[1]	50	0.2	50	0	0	4	1	17	17
Canada	44	0.03[2]	44	..	..	..	..	..	..
Denmark	50	..	50	..	..	..	..	3[3]	..
Finland	25	0.1	25	..	..	..	..	..	..
France	50	50	..	..	..	..	..	..	..
Germany[4]	50	..	50	..	2	..	..	..	..
Japan[5]	44	..	44	..	..	..	..	13	..
Italy[6]	1.3-50	0.07-0.3	50	0 (83)	0 (82)	2 (10)	2 (7)	12	1
Korea[7]	..	..	20	..	..	..	..	14	24
Netherlands[8]	50	0.15	50	73	71	71	62	25	26
Norway	..	..	50	..	..	..	..	0	0
Poland[9]	< 6-> 60	< 0.1-< 0.4	..	..	..	..	..	..	..
Portugal	50	..	50	..	0	..	..	..	60
Spain	50	..	50	..	..	..	..	..	..
Sweden	44	0.025-0.1	44	..	..	..	..	..	..
Switzerland	25	..	25	..	..	..	..	..	..
United Kingdom[10]	50	..	50	3	3	..	..	..	7
United States	44	..	..	..	..	..	..	..	..
EU-15	50	..	50	..	..	..	..	..	..

Note: The following countries have not established national threshold values for nitrate: Iceland and Norway; for phosphorus: Iceland, Spain and the United Kingdom.

.. Not available.
1. The reference value for phosphorus refers to orthophosphorus.
2. Data are for Quebec.
3. 10% of samples were above the 25 mg/l guiding limit.
4. In 1995, 10% of the measurement points of the shallow groundwater layer had a nitrate concentration above 50 mg/l.
5. Data for early 1990s refer to the 1986-88 period. Percentage for nitrate in groundwater refers to agricultural use only.
6. Data apply only to the Veneto Region of Italy, with four levels of nitrate concentration in surface water ranging from 1.3 mg/l ("high quality") to 50 mg/l ("poor quality"); and 3 levels for phosphorus in surface water ranging from 0.07 mg/l ("high quality") to 0.30 mg/l ("sufficient quality"). Figures in brackets are for areas above the 1.3-6.6 mg/l of nitrate in surface water and 0.07-0.15 for phosphorous.
7. Percentage for early 1990s refers to mid-1990s.
8. The threshold values for nitrate and phosphorous are summer averages in lakes. Data for early 1990s refer to the average 1989-91. Data for late 1990s refer to the average beween 1994 and 1996.
9. Different classes of thresholds are defined.
10. Percentages for nitrate in groundwater for early 1990s and late 1990s refer respectively to the years 1996 and 1997.
Sources: OECD Agri-environmental Indicators Questionnaire, 1999; Canada: McRae et al. (2000); Denmark: Frederiksen and Schou (1996); United States: USDA (1997).

Annex Table 2. **Share of agriculture in total emissions of nitrogen and phosphorus into surface and marine water: mid-1990s**

	Surface		Marine	
	Nitrogen	Phosphorus	Nitrogen	Phosphorus
	% of total		% of total	
Belgium	41	17	..	..
Denmark	81	40	64	11
Finland	27	43	..	..
France	74	22	..	..
Germany	44	43	..	..
Greece	..	23	..	..
Ireland	..	34	..	..
Italy	62	33	..	..
Luxembourg	..	21	..	..
Netherlands	75	30	..	..
Norway	45	17	45	23
Poland	62	34	..	..
Sweden	48	25	42	21
Switzerland	40	22	..	..
United Kingdom	..	17	..	..

.. Not available.

Sources: See bibliography for full reference.

Belgium: van Gijseghen and van Holder (1996, p. 122).

Denmark: Christensen *et al.* (1994, pp. 67-69); EEA (1998, p. 201).

France: OECD (1997*a*, p. 59); IFEN (1997, p. 9).

Finland: Statistics Finland (1999, p. 19).

Germany: EEA (1998, p. 201); Werner (1997).

Greece, Ireland, Luxembourg and United Kingdom: Various sources: EEA (1998); OECD (1998*b*); Romstad *et al.* (1997); Simonsen (1996).

Italy and Poland: EEA (1996).

Netherlands: Ministry of Agriculture, Nature Management and Fisheries (1995, p. 8).

Norway: OECD (1993*a*, p. 53); Johnsen (1993, p. 400).

Sweden: Ministry of Agriculture (2000, unpublished).

Switzerland: Swiss Agency for the Environment, Forests and Landscape (2000, unpublished).

BIBLIOGRAPHY

Black, P.E. (1995),
"The critical role of "unused' resources", *Water Resources Bulletin*, Vol. 31, No. 4, pp. 589-592, American Water Resources Association.

Bonnieux, F. and P. Rainelli (1996),
"Mineral emissions from agriculture: the French case", pp. 101-118, in J.W. Simonsen (ed.), *Inventory on Mineral Pollution from Agriculture*, EU concerted action "Policy measures to control environmental impacts from agriculture"(AIR3CT93-1164), Norwegian Agricultural Research Institute, Oslo, Norway.

Castro, J. and F. Reckendorf (1995),
Effects of Sediment on the Aquatic Environment, Resource Conservation Act (RCA) III, Working Paper No. 6, Natural Resources Conservation Service, US Department of Agriculture, Washington, DC., United States.

CEC [Commission for Environmental Cooperation] (1999),
"Feedlot Production of Cattle in the United States and Canada: Some Environmental Implications of the North American Free Trade Agreement", Issue Study 2, pp. 183-259, in CEC, *Assessing Environmental Effects of the North American Free Trade Agreement (NAFTA): An Analytic Framework (Phase II) and Issue Studies*, Montreal, Canada. Available at: *www.cec.org/* [English > Publications and Information Resources > CEC Publications > Environment, Economy and Trade].

Christensen, N., H. Paaby and J. Holten-Andersen (1994),
Environment and Society – A Review of Environmental Development in Denmark, National Environmental Research Institute, Technical Report No. 108, Ministry of the Environment, Roskilde, Denmark.

Commonwealth of Australia (1995),
Sustaining the Agricultural Resource Base, 12th Meeting of the Prime Minister's Science and Engineering Council, Office of the Chief Scientist, Department of the Prime Minister and Cabinet, Canberra, Australia.

Commonwealth of Australia (1998),
Sustainable Agriculture – Assessing Australia's Recent Performance, A Report to the Standing Committee on Agriculture and Resource Management (SCARM) of the National Collaborative Project on Indicators for Sustainable Agriculture, SCARM Technical Report No. 70, CSIRO Publishing, Victoria, Australia.

Coote, D.R. and L.J. Gregorich (eds.) (2000),
The Health of our water – Toward sustainable agriculture in Canada, Agriculture and Agri-Food Canada (AAFC), Ottawa, Canada. Available at: *www.agr.ca/* [English > Site Index > Environment and Resource Management].

Cori, L. (1997),
"Policy Case Study of Italy", Annex 4, in OECD, *Agricultural Policy, Pesticide Policy and the Environment: Annexes*, General Distribution document [OCDE/GD(97)157], Paris France. Available at: *www.oecd.org/* [Documentation > 1997 > Reference Components > OCDE > OCDE/GD].

EEA [European Environment Agency] (1996),
Water Quality of Large Rivers, European Topic Centre on Inland Waters, Topic Report 4, Copenhagen, Denmark.

EEA (1998),
Europe's Environment: The Second Assessment, Office for Official Publications of the European Communities, Luxembourg. Available at: *http://themes.eea.eu.int/* [> all available reports].

EPA [Environmental Protection Agency] (1998),
Clean Water Action Plan: Restoring and Protecting America's Water, Washington, D.C, United States. Available at: *www.cleanwater.gov/*.

Erwin, M.L. and A.J. Tesoriero (1997),
Predicting Ground-Water Vulnerability to Nitrate in the Puget Sound Basin , Fact Sheet FS-061-97, US Geological Survey, Washington, DC. Available at: *wwwdwatcm.wr.usgs.gov/fs.061-97/index.html*.

Fairweather, P. and G. Napier (1998),
Environmental Indicators for National State of the Environment Reporting – Inland Waters, Australia: State of the Environment (Environmental Indicators Reports), Department of the Environment, Canberra, Australia.

Falconer, K.E. (1997),
"Policy case Study of the United Kingdom", Annex 7, in OECD, *Agricultural Policy, Pesticide Policy and the Environment: Annexes*, OECD General Distribution document [OCDE/GD(97)157], Paris France. Available at: *www.oecd.org/* [Documentation > 1997 > Reference Components > OCDE > OCDE/GD].

FAO [United Nations Food and Agriculture Organisation] (1999),
Central and Eastern European Sustainable Agriculture Network, First Workshop Proceedings, REU Technical Series 61, FAO Subregional Office for Central and Eastern Europe, Rome, Italy. Available at: *www.fao.org/regional/europe/public-e.htm*.

Frederiksen, B.S. and J.S. Schou (1996),
"Mineral emissions from agriculture: Denmark", pp. 181-198, in J.W. Simonsen (ed.), *Inventory on Mineral Pollution from Agriculture*, EU concerted action "Policy measures to control environmental impacts from agriculture"(AIR3CT93-1164), Norwegian Agricultural Research Institute, Oslo, Norway.

French Ministry of Regional Planning and the Environment (2000),
Rapport d'Évaluation sur la Gestion et le bilan du Programme de Maîtrise des Pollutions d'Origine Agricole (only in French "An Evaluation of the Agricultural Pollution Control Programme"), Report No. 99-M-018-01, Paris, France. Available at: *www.environnement.gouv.fr/actua/com2000/mars/10-pmpoa.htm*.

Goodchild, R.G. (1998),
"EU Policies for the Reduction of Nitrogen in Water: The Example of the Nitrates Directive", pp. 737-740, in K.W. van der Hoek, J.W. Erisman and S. Smeulders (eds.), *Proceedings of the First International Nitrogen Conference*, 23-27 March 1998, Noordwijkerhout, The Netherlands, Elsevier Press, Amsterdam, The Netherlands.

Harker, B. (1998),
"The Impact of Agriculture on Water Quality: Indicators and Policy Measures", pp. 151-172, in OECD, *The Sustainable Management of Water in Agriculture: Issues and Policies – The Athens Workshop*, Paris, France.

Harker, D.B., B.D. Hill and H.H. McDuffie (1998),
The Risk Agriculture Poses to Water Quality – Factors Affecting Our Interpretation of Findings, paper presented at the 1st International Conference on Children's Health and Environment, Amsterdam, The Netherlands, August 11-13.

IFEN [Institut français de l'environnement] (1997),
Agriculture et environnement: les indicateurs (only in French, "Agriculture and the Environment: Indicators"), édition 1997-1998, Orléans, France. Available at: *www.ifen.fr/* [> Publications].

IFEN (1998),
Les pesticides dans les eaux (only in French "Pesticides in Water"), Études et Travaux n 19, Orléans, France. Available at: *www.ifen.fr/pestic/pestic.htm*.

Iglesias, E. and J.M. Sumpsi (1996),
"Mineral Emissions from Agriculture: Spain", pp. 33-48, in J.W. Simonsen (ed.), *Inventory on Mineral Pollution from Agriculture*, EU concerted action "Policy measures to control environmental impacts from agriculture"(AIR3CT93-1164), Norwegian Agricultural Research Institute, Oslo, Norway.

Johnsen, F.H. (1993),
"Economic analysis of measures to control phosphorus run-off from non-point agricultural sources", *European Review of Agricultural Economics*, Vol. 20, No. 4, pp. 399-418.

Lucey, J., J.J. Bowman, K.J. Clabby, P. Cunningham, M. Lehane, M. MacCarthaigh, M.L. McGarrigic and P.F. Toner (1999),
Water Quality in Ireland 1995-1997, Environmental Protection Agency, Wexford, Ireland.

MacDonald, K.B. (2000),
"Risk of Water Contamination by Nitrogen", Chapter 12, in T. McRae, C.A.S. Smith and L.J. Gregorich (eds.), *Environmental Sustainability of Canadian Agriculture: Report of the Agri-Environmental Indicator Project*, Agriculture and Agri-Food Canada (AAFC), Ottawa, Ontario, Canada. Available at: *www.agr.ca/policy/environment/publications/list.html*.

MAFF [Ministry of Agriculture, Fisheries and Food] (1994),
Consultation Document – *Designation of Vulnerable Zones in England and Wales Under the EC Nitrate Directive* (91/676), London, United Kingdom.

MAFF (2000),
Towards Sustainable Agriculture – A Pilot Set of Indicators, London, United Kingdom. Available at: *www.maff.gov.uk/* [Farming > Sustainable Agriculture].

McGinn, A.P. (1999),
"Harmful Algae Blooming Worldwide", pp. 126-127, in L.R. Brown, M. Renner and B. Halweil, *Vital Signs 1999: The Environmental Trends that are Shaping Our Future*, Worldwatch Institute, Washington, DC., United States.

McRae, T., C.A.S. Smith and L.J. Gregorich (eds.) (2000),
Environmental Sustainability of Canadian Agriculture: Report of the Agri-Environmental Indicator Project, Agriculture and Agri-Food Canada (AAFC), Ottawa, Ontario, Canada. Available at: *www.agr.ca/policy/environment/publications/list.html*.

Ministry of Agriculture, Nature Management and Fisheries (1995),
Policy Document on Manure and Ammonia, The Hague, The Netherlands.

New Zealand MAF [Ministry of Agriculture and Fisheries] (1993),
  Sustainable Agriculture , MAF Policy Position Paper 1, Wellington, New Zealand.

Nolan, B.T. and B.C. Ruddy (1996),
  Nitrate in the Ground Waters of the United States – Assessing the Risk, Fact Sheet FS-092-96, US Geological Service, Washington, DC., United States. Available at: *wwwrvares.er.usgs.gov/nawqa/*FS-092-96.*html*.

Norwegian Institute for Water Research (1998),
  Auditing the agricultural sector, 1998: Effects of pollution measures, Oslo, Norway.

OECD (1993*a*),
  Environmental Performance Reviews: Germany, Paris, France.

OECD (1993*b*),
  Environmental Performance Reviews: Norway, Paris, France.

OECD (1994),
  Environmental Performance Reviews: Japan, Paris, France.

OECD (1995),
  Environmental Performance Reviews: The Netherlands, Paris, France.

OECD (1996*a*),
  Environmental Performance Reviews: New Zealand, Paris, France.

OECD (1996*b*),
  Environmental Performance Reviews: Sweden, Paris, France

OECD (1996*c*),
  Environmental Performance Reviews: United States, Paris, France.

OECD (1997*a*),
  Environmental Performance Reviews: France, Paris, France.

OECD (1997*b*),
  OECD *Environmental Data: Compendium* 1997, Paris, France.

OECD (1998*a*),
  The Sustainable Management of Water in Agriculture: Issues and Policies – The Athens Workshop, Paris, France.

OECD (1998*b*),
  OECD *Workshop on the Sustainable Management of Water in Agriculture: Issues and Policies – The Athens Workshop: Case Studies*, General Distribution document [COM/AGR/CA/ENV/EPOC(98)87], Paris, France. Available at: *www.oecd.org/* [Documentation > 1998 > Reference Components > COM].

OECD (1998*c*),
  Environmental Performance Reviews: Korea, Paris, France.

OECD (1999),
  Sustainable Economic Growth: Natural Resources and the Environment in Norway, Economics Department Working Papers No. 218, General Distribution document [ECO/WKP(99)10], Paris France. Available at: *www.oecd.org/* [Documentation > 1999 > Reference Components > ECO].

OECD (2000),
  Enhancing Environmentally Sustainable Growth in Finland, Economics Department Working Papers No. 229, General Distribution document [ECO/WKP(2000)2], Paris, France. Available at: *www.oecd.org/* [Documentation > 2000 > Reference Components > ECO].

OFEFP-OFAG [Office fédéral de l'environnement, des forêts et du paysage – Office fédéral de l'agriculture] (1998),
  Strategie pour réeduire les emissions d'azote, (only in French "Strategy to reduce emissions of nitrates"), Schriftenreihe Umwelt Nr 273, Berne, Switzerland.

Parsisson, D. (1996),
  "United Kingdom Country Report on Mineral Emissions from Agriculture", pp. 145-164, in J.W. Simonsen (ed.), *Inventory on Mineral Pollution from Agriculture*, EU concerted action "Policy measures to control environmental impacts from agriculture"(AIR3CT93-1164), Norwegian Agricultural Research Institute, Oslo, Norway.

PFRA [Prairie Farm Rehabilitation Administration] (1997),
  Nonpoint Agricultural Effects on Water Quality: A Review of Documented Evidence and Expert Opinion, Sustainable Development Service, Agriculture and Agri-Food Canada, Regina, Canada.

Rayment, M., H. Bartram and J. Curtoys (1998),
  Pesticide Taxes – A Discussion Paper, Royal Society for the Protection of Birds, Sandy, United Kingdom.

Ribaudo, M.O., R.D. Horan and M.E. Smith (1999),
  Economics of Water Quality Protection From Nonpoint Sources – Theory and Practice, Resource Economics Division, Economic Research Service, Agricultural Economic Report No. 782, US Department of Agriculture, Washington DC., United States. Available at: *www.econ.ag.gov/epubs/pdf/aer782/*.

Romstad, E., J.W. Simonsen and A. Vatn (eds.) (1997),
   Controlling Mineral Emissions in European Agriculture: Economics, Policies and the Environment, CAB International, Wallingford, United Kingdom.

Sapek, A. (1999),
   "Nitrogen balance and cycling in Polish agriculture", pp. 7-24, in A. Sapek (ed.), *Nitrogen Cycle and Balance in Polish Agriculture*, Conference Proceedings, Poland Agriculture and Water Quality Protection, Institute for Land Reclamation and Grassland Farming, Falenty IMUZ Publisher, Warsaw, Poland.

Scheierling, S.M. (1995),
   Overcoming Agricultural Pollution of Water: The Challenge of Integrating Agricultural and Environmental Policies in the European Union, World Bank Technical Paper No. 269, World Bank, Washington DC., United States.

Schou, J.S. and A. Kyllingsbæk (1999),
   An Indicator of Water Contamination Risk with Nitrogen in Agriculture, Danish Institute of Agricultural and Fisheries Economics and Danish Institute of Agricultural Science, Personal communication with the OECD Secretariat.

Sharpley, A. (ed.) (2000),
   "Practical and Innovative Measures for the Control of Agricultural Phosphorus Losses to Water", *Journal of Environmental Quality*, Vol. 29, No. 1.

Simonsen, J.W. (ed.) (1996),
   Inventory on Mineral Pollution from Agriculture, EU concerted action "Policy measures to control environmental impacts from agriculture"(AIR3CT93-1164), Norwegian Agricultural Research Institute, Oslo, Norway.

Statistics Finland (1999),
   Finland's Natural Resources and the Environment 1999, Ministry of the Environment, Helsinki, Finland.

UK Department of the Environment (1996),
   Indicators of Sustainable Development for the United Kingdom, London, United Kingdom. Available at: *www.environment.detr.gov.uk/* [> Indicators of Sustainable Development for the UK].

UNEP [United Nations Environment Programme] (1999),
   Global Environment Outlook 2000, Nairobi, Kenya. Available at: *www.grid.unep.ch/geo2000/english/index.htm.*

USDA [United States Department of Agriculture] (1996a),
   Water Quality, Natural Resources Conservation Service, Resource Conservation Act (RCA) Issue Brief 9, Washington, DC., United States.

USDA (1996b),
   America's Private Land – A Geography of Hope, Natural Resources Conservation Service, Washington, DC., United States. Available at: *www.nrcs.usda.gov/* [> Geography of Hope under "Features"].

USDA (1997),
   Agricultural Resources and Environmental Indicators, 1996-97, Agricultural Handbook No. 712, Natural Resources and Environment Division, Economic Research Service, Washington, DC., United States. Available at: *www.ers.usda.gov/* [Briefing Rooms > Agricultural Resources and Environmental Indicators].

USGS [United States Geological Survey] (1999),
   The Quality of Our Nation's Waters – Nutrients and Pesticides, USGS Circular 1225, Washington, DC., United States. Available at: *http://water.usgs.gov/pubs/circ/circ1225/.*

van Gijseghem, D. and L. van Holder (1996),
   "Mineral Emissions from Agriculture", pp. 119-130, in J.W. Simonsen (ed.), *Inventory on Mineral Pollution from Agriculture*, EU concerted action "Policy measures to control environmental impacts from agriculture" (AIR3CT93-1164), Norwegian Agricultural Research Institute, Oslo, Norway.

Werner, W. (1997),
   "Implementation and Efficiency of Counter-measures against Diffuse Nitrogen and Phosphorus Input Groundwater and Surface Waters from Agriculture", pp. 73-88, in E. Romstad, J.W. Simonsen and A. Vatn (eds.), *Controlling Mineral Emissions in European Agriculture: Economics, Policies and the Environment*, CAB International, Wallingford, United Kingdom.

Zilberman, D. (1998),
   "The Impact of Agriculture on Water Quality", pp. 133-149, in OECD, *The Sustainable Management of Water in Agriculture: Issues and Policies – The Athens Workshop*, Paris, France.

Chapter 3

LAND CONSERVATION

HIGHLIGHTS

Context

The availability of land and water resources is basic to all agricultural activity. Agriculture is often the major user of both of these resources, which can affect the flow of surface water and the loss of soil sediment from agricultural land. Appropriate land use, combined with environmentally sound soil and water management practices can help to reduce the peak flow of surface water and loss of soil sediment.

Damage caused by off-farm sediment flows is important in many OECD countries, but especially in regions where there are alternate periods of drought, which limits soil vegetation cover, followed by heavy rainfall. For countries with steep and rapid rivers and experiencing heavy rainfall, a high priority is placed on flood and landslide prevention, the consequences of which can be costly to the economy.

Indicators and recent trends

An important consideration for policy makers is to take into account the risks that are increased or mitigated by certain land use and management practices in agriculture. The measurement of such risks, can contribute to better decision-making to promote or moderate changes in land use, and appropriate management practices. Two indicators are being developed by OECD to address land conservation issues, first, the water retaining capacity of agriculture, and second, the off-farm soil sediment flow from agriculture.

The *water retaining capacity indicator* measures the quantity of water that can be retained in the short term in agricultural soil, as well as on agricultural land, and by agricultural irrigation or drainage facilities. This indicator shows how much water a given area of land can hold taking into account differences in land use, soil types, management practices and other relevant factors. A decrease in water retaining capacity implies a greater potential risk of flooding.

The indicator of the water retaining capacity of agricultural land mainly reflects differences in land use, which vary in their capacity to retain water. There is at present a lack of information on soil types and management practices, which would help to improve the sensitivity of the indicator. On the basis of this more limited appraisal of agricultural water retaining capacity, however, most OECD countries have experienced a decrease, and only a few an increase, in water retaining capacity over the last decade.

The *off-farm sediment flow indicator* measures the quantity of soil erosion sediments delivered to off-farm areas as a result of agricultural soil erosion. The focus of this indicator is on the mitigation of soil erosion through land use and management practices, rather than just the measurement of soil erosion itself. It is not possible to show the trend of this indicator across OECD countries as the approach needs to be harmonised and data deficiencies overcome.

Some estimates, however, of the annual monetary cost of the damage to rivers, lakes and reservoirs incurred through soil sediment removal off-farm and damage to the recreational, transport and environmental functions associated with many water courses, suggest these costs are high. Evidence from related indicators on soil management and soil erosion would suggest that the rate of soil sediment flows from agricultural land to off-farm areas, especially water courses, might be decreasing for some countries.

1. Background

Policy context

The availability of land and water resources is basic to all agricultural activity. Agriculture uses both these resources, which can affect the flow of surface water and the loss of soil sediment from agricultural land. The flow of surface water can cause flooding and landslides, and can aggravate groundwater resources. Water flow and loss of soil sediment can affect rivers and lakes, wildlife habitats and built-up urban areas.

Appropriate land use and land cover, combined with environmentally sound land, soil and water management practices can help to reduce the peak flows of surface water and loss of soil sediment. The main issues for governments and farmers include reducing the off-farm effects by enhancing and maintaining environmentally sustainable land use, cropping patterns and farm management practices.

The off-farm environmental effects related to agricultural land use can be significant. Rates of soil sediment flows, incidence of flooding and landslides, and aggravation of groundwater recharge rates, often incur substantial costs, such as harm to infrastructure (*e.g.* roads and buildings) and even the loss of life.

Damage caused by off-farm sediment flows is an important issue in many OECD countries, as is the fall in the productivity of farmland (the latter is the subject of the Soil Quality chapter). Such damage is especially pronounced in regions where there are alternate periods of drought, which limits soil vegetation cover, followed by heavy rainfall. For countries with steep and rapid rivers and experiencing heavy rainfall, a high priority is placed on flood and landslide prevention, the consequences of which are difficult to reverse. It is apparent, therefore, that the importance of these effects varies among countries depending on their geo-physical and climatic conditions.

An important consideration for policy makers is to take into account the risks that are increased or mitigated by certain land use and management practices in agriculture. The measurement of such risks can contribute to better decision-making to promote or moderate changes in land use, and appropriate management practices.

Environmental context

Water and soil sediments flows from agricultural land may cause serious environmental problems to off-farm areas downstream, the extent of which depends on geographic and climatic conditions and management practices. Rainfall is often absorbed by the soil, but it can also flow, together with loose soil sediments, over the soil surface, eventually reaching lower, downstream areas. A large quantity of rainfall within a short period may result in flooding or landslides in downstream areas, but water can be retained for longer periods on agricultural land depending on natural and artificial features (*e.g.* ponds, dykes, etc), land use patterns and farm management practices (Figure 1).

The process of water and soil sediment flows is affected by various factors such as the amount and intensity of rainfall, land slope, soil type, in particular texture and water retaining capacity, soil cover including crops and natural vegetation, and other natural and artificial features of the land. Certain farming practices may also control the rate of water and soil sediment flows. These include tillage or no tillage, and terracing.[1] For example, well-ploughed land may have a substantial capacity for water retention but, at the same time, produce a significant quantity of soil sediments.

In semi-arid regions, typical of many areas of *southern European* countries, the effect of alternate periods of drought and heavy rainfall is also a common cause of soil erosion. The lack of water in certain months does not allow vegetation to fully cover the soil nor create a tight rooting network, which makes the soil more vulnerable to erosion when heavy, and sometimes torrential, precipitation occurs.

Soil sediment flows from agricultural land may lead to problems of water quality, raising the cost of water treatment for municipal and industrial water uses and affecting the aquatic biosphere, which may

Figure 1. **Water flow and discharge from agricultural land**

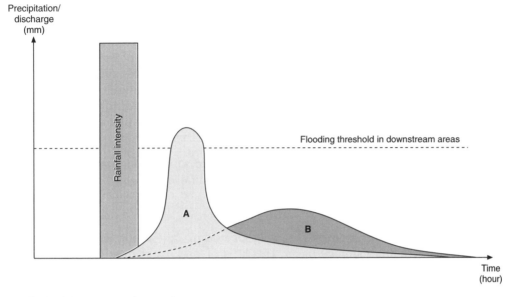

A: Agricultural land with low water retention capacity.
B: Agricultural land with high water retention capacity.
Source: Adapted from Norberg (1999).

lead to damage in commercial and recreational fisheries. The sediments also raise the floor of riverbeds and reservoirs, increasing the risk of flooding, and reducing the useful life of reservoirs (Clark *et al.*, 1985; Feather and Hellerstein, 1997; Ribaudo, 1986). Another possible influence of changes in land conservation practices and land use patterns relates to groundwater resources. Since the path to the groundwater is usually not well known, activities in upstream areas may have important implications for the recharge of these resources.

The environmental effects of water retention control, off-farm sediment flow control, landslide prevention and groundwater recharge can be described as follows:

- *Water retention control*: appropriately managed agricultural land can retain a large quantity of water. This stabilises water flow from agricultural land and mitigates flood damage in downstream off-farm areas. Water can also be stored above the soil surface in the case of agricultural land that is used as a temporary flood storage basin, and above the normal flooding level in paddy fields. Agricultural irrigation and drainage facilities can also conserve water above the normal level. As a result of this water retaining capacity, peak water flow to downstream areas is reduced and the risk of flooding reduced.

- *Soil sediment flow control*: off-farm soil sediment flow can be either exacerbated or reduced as a result of agricultural activity. Together with the soil which absorbs a large quantity of water as stated above, levees and planted crops delay the velocity of water flow on the soil surface, thus reducing sediment flow to off-farm areas. Off-farm sediment flow can also be reduced by appropriate land management, such as terracing, contour tillage, and the planting of hedgerows on sloping land.

- *Landslide prevention*: through the regulation of water and soil sediment flow described above, landslides in hill and mountain areas can be prevented and, as a result, environmental as well as economic and human damage in downstream off-farm areas can be avoided, or mitigated.

- *Groundwater recharge*: groundwater is recharged as a result of the absorption of rainfall or irrigation water by agricultural land, reducing the run-off on the soil surface. A part of the water retained in the soil is also released slowly to rivers contributing to the stabilisation of river flow level.

The importance of these functions differs across countries because of the variation in the potential risk level of adverse weather conditions. For example, deaths from flooding during the last decade were 700 in Japan and 1 000 in Korea, 1 000 over the last 50 years in Italy, compared to 20 in Canada and 1 in Norway over the past decade.[2]

In Japan, annual precipitation is extremely high (1 400 to 1 800 mm) and a long chain of mountains ranging from 2 000 to over 3 000 metres high, is situated along the middle of the country. Most rivers run from mountainous areas to the plains with very steep gradients. Under such conditions, terraced agriculture, which has considerable water retaining capacity, plays a significant role in regulating water flow especially that arising from heavy rain. This contributes to the protection of down-stream areas, including urban areas, from flood damage. It also reduces the velocity of water flow and the volume of soil sediments flow, to off-farm areas, as well as assisting the recharging of groundwater resources.

When such terraced land is left uncultivated, the levees disappear and water-retaining capacity is reduced substantially. The land will gradually change into natural forest, which can possess a high level of water retaining capacity, but this process can take between 50 and 100 years, during which time the risk of disasters is high.

In the United States, the Sacramento river basin located in California integrates agricultural land along with the river into a flood storage basin. This kind of land use is possible in the area because floods often occur during the winter season when crops are not planted, and there is no urban development in the area concerned (Naka and Fujii, 1998).

Flood storage basins in Germany have been established in order to reduce the effects of the flooding from the River Rhine. Some of these basins are used for agriculture, partly converted from intensive to extensive activity for flood control. A trial scheme has been introduced to compensate farmers for the reduction in crop output caused by flooding, which occurs every two to three years (Hayase and Masumoto, 1998).

Greece has a dry climate, with a large share of agricultural land located in steeply sloping areas, where terracing is practised in order to reduce soil erosion. Sheep grazing is also controlled through the terracing. If such sloping areas are not appropriately managed, the terracing collapses, leading to uncontrolled grazing and the disappearance of crop production. In the long run, the land would become severely degraded, and soil erosion and landslides would be exacerbated (Sumelius, 1997; Tikof, 1997).

The cost to society in Italy of sediment deposits from agricultural land is perceived to be high, particularly in terms of stream degradation and disturbance to wildlife habitat, as well as through the direct costs of deposit dredging and water storage loss associated with reservoirs. Floods along the Po River in November 1951 and the Arno River in November 1966 were estimated to have cost more than US$13 million, with thousands of people left homeless.[3]

2. Indicators

Water retaining capacity

Definition

The quantity of water that can be retained in the short term, *in* agricultural soil, as well as *on* agricultural land where applicable (*e.g.* flood storage basins) and *by* agricultural irrigation or drainage facilities.

Method of calculation

The Water Retaining Capacity indicator (WRC) is expressed as:

$$W = Ws + Wo + Wf$$

Table 1. **Water retaining capacity per area by land use type**

Arable land	Permanent crops (e.g. orchards, groves, etc.)	Grassland (permanent meadows and pasture)	Forest and other wooded land	Other land use types	
Tonnes/hectare					
374[1] (Japan)	1 060 (Japan)	220 (Japan)	1 500 (Netherlands)	Bare hillside:	150 (Japan)
1 250 (Netherlands)	1 500 (Netherlands)	700 (Netherlands)	1 750 (Japan)	Uncultivated	
1 550-2 150[2] (Spain)	2 100 (Spain)	1 500 (Spain)	2 220 (Spain)	agricultural land:	150 (Japan)
2 073[3] (Korea)					1 145 (Italy)
2 083[3] (Japan)				Gardens, national	
3 450 (Poland)				parks, scrubland: 1 145 (Italy)	
				Wetlands:	3 000 (Spain)

1. Other than paddy rice fields.
2. 1 550 tonnes/ha for non-irrigated land and 2 150 tonnes/ha for irrigated land.
3. Paddy rice fields.
Source: OECD Agri-environmental Indicators Questionnaire, 1999.

where:

W   = total WRC

Ws = WRC in agricultural soil

Wo = WRC on agricultural land

Wf = WRC by agricultural irrigation or drainage facilities

The quantity of water that can be retained *in* agricultural soil (covering cropland, grassland, and orchards) (Ws) is calculated as (the rationale behind this simplified formula is described in Box 1):

$$Ws = \Sigma \ (Ai \ Pi \ Fi1 \ Fi2 \ ......)$$

where:

Ws = WRC in agricultural soil (tonnes)

Ai   = area of land use i (ha)

Pi   = WRC per area for land use i (tonnes/ha)

Fi1, Fi2, ... = adjustment factors for different soil conditions, management practices, etc.

i   = type of land use (cropland, grassland, orchard, etc.).

The WRC *on* agricultural land (Wo) can be calculated by the same method as the one for Ws described above, taking into account the potential depth of excessive water. WRC *by* agricultural irrigation or drainage facilities (Wf) are calculated separately.

Data are required with respect to land area (ha) for each agricultural land use (crop field, pasture, orchard, etc.), and WRC per area (tonnes/ha) for each agricultural land use. Several OECD countries have reported estimates of WRCs per area for certain types of land use (Table 1). The diversity shown reflects the variation in climatic and geo-physical conditions among Member countries.

Recent trends

The WRCs were calculated to show the trends of a range of OECD countries, based on FAO land use data and the WRCs per area for certain types of land use reported to the OECD (Figure 2).

The results of the calculations indicate only broad trends in WRC, partly because the national coefficients of WRC per area by land use type are not available across all countries. Nevertheless, some key points emerge from the results shown in Figure 2.

- During a 10 year-period from 1985/87 to 1995/97, the WRC of agriculture has declined in most countries, implying an increase in the potential risk of flooding. A minor change in the WRC is

259

Box 1. Incorporation of policy relevant parameters

In order to improve the policy relevance of the WRC indicator, it needs to incorporate a range of policy relevant parameters. These include land cover, agricultural practices (cropping patterns, type of tillage, maintenance of hedgerows, etc.) and soil type. Although inherent soil type is not policy relevant, the proportion of land of specific soil types that is actually cultivated is affected by policies, for example, through the withdrawal of cultivation from highly erodible soils.

One approach might be to attempt to disaggregate the WRC according to different conditions such as farming practices and soil types. This can be expressed as:

$$W = \Sigma\,(Aijk\ldots \times Pijk\ldots)$$

where:

    W   = total WRC (tonnes)

    Aijk = area of land use i, tillage type j, soil type k, etc.

    Pijk = WRC per area (tonnes/ha) for land use i, tillage type j, soil type k, etc.

    i   = land use (cropland, grassland, orchards, etc.)

However, this method could require a large number of WRC coefficients for different conditions and make the calculation impractical. Thus the following simplified method is proposed:

$$W = \Sigma\,(Ai \times Pi \times Fi1 \times Fi2 \times \ldots\ldots)$$

where:

    W   = total WRC (tonnes)

    Ai = area of land use i

    Pi = WRC per area (tonnes/ha) for land use i

    Fij = adjustment factor j for land use i (*e.g.* tillage type, soil type, etc.)

    i   = land use (c: cropland, p: paddy field, g: grassland, o: orchards)

    Fij is obtained as Fji = Fi(Fk × Rk)

where:

    Fk = adjustment factor for condition k

    Rk = presence ratio of condition k. Σ Rk = 1

For example, an adjustment factor on tillage type for cropland (FCT) is expressed as:

$$FCT = 1.0 \times 0.5 + 0.7 \times 0.3 + 0.5 \times 0.2 = 0.81$$

where the adjustment factor and presence ratios are:

    for conventional tillage   1.0 and 0.5 (50%)

    for minimum tillage   0.7 and 0.3 (30%)

    for no tillage   0.5 and 0.2 (20%)

An adjustment factor on soil type for cropland (FCS) is expressed as:

$$FCS = 1.0 \times 0.8 + 1.5 \times 0.2 = 1.1$$

where the adjustment factor and presence ratios are:

    for the predominant soil type 1.0 and 0.8 (80%)

    for the minor soil type   1.5 and 0.2 (20%)

By this method, different factors are treated separately so that difficulties are minimised. Although the interaction between factors are ignored, this method still reflects the effects of different conditions that are relevant to policy and policy changes. It should be noted, however, that other ways to simplify the methodology could be developed according to the relative importance and data availability concerning land use, tillage type and soil type.

Source: Ministry of Agriculture, Forestry and Fisheries, Japan.

Figure 2. **Water retaining capacity of agriculture: 1985-87 to 1995-97**

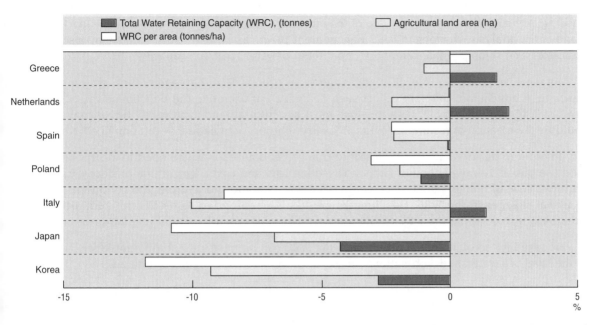

Note: Where the WRC coefficients (WRC per unit area) for certain land use type are not available or specified, those estimated by Japan are used. WRC of agricultural facilities are not included.
Sources: FAO Database, 1999; OECD Agri-Environmental Indicators Questionnaire, 1999; OECD Secretariat.

observed in *Greece* and the *Netherlands*, where the increase in the average WRC per area offsets the decrease in the agricultural land area.

• In *Italy*, where the WRC of agriculture declined, the increase of average WRC per area to some extent offset this decrease. On the other hand, both the quantity of agricultural land and the average WRC per area declined in *Japan* and *Korea*, resulting in a substantial decrease of the WRC.

Several OECD countries reported the WRCs of agricultural facilities such as irrigation dams and canals (Table 2). These were not included in the calculations shown in Figure 2 because time-series data are not available at this stage.

Table 2. **Water retaining capacity of agricultural facilities: 1990s**

	Italy	Japan	Korea	Portugal	Spain	Switzerland	United Kingdom
	Million tonnes						
Irrigation dams	6 187	2 710	12 321	7 367	. .	700	. .
Ponds and reservoirs	300	4 767	2 967	. .	. .	300	. .
Irrigation/drainage canals	. .	75	170	. .	. .	. .	. .
Others	. .	13 814	465	. .	. .	. .	64 840
Total	6 487	21 366	15 923	. .	53 806	. .	. .

. . Not available.
Source: OECD Agri-environmental Indicators Questionnaire, 1999.

Interpretation and links to other indicators

A decrease in WRC implies that there is a smaller contribution by agriculture to reducing the risk of flooding. Although the trends over time of the indicator values mainly reflect changes in land use at this stage of the analysis, changes in land management practices or land use systems may also affect the indicator trend through enhancement or impairment of water retention capacity.

As there are considerable differences between countries in their agricultural systems, setting a baseline or benchmark can help reflect such diversity. For example, the benchmark can be set at the level of WRC provided by the use to which most agricultural land is currently being converted. This could be the creation of residential areas in some countries, or of natural vegetation in others.

In order to better relate this indicator to changes in policies, it would need to incorporate not only land use but also a range of other factors. These include land cover, agricultural practices (*e.g.* cropping patterns, type of tillage, maintenance of hedgerows), climatic and hydrological conditions, as well as seasonal changes in the WRC. Benchmarks would also be needed to be determined, although one possibility is to compare the WRC of different land uses, for example natural vegetation and urban use.

To take into account spatial differences, the WRC can be measured at different levels, for example at the level of a watershed, sub-national region or country, and the results compared.

The WRC indicator draws on land use data and coefficients of WRC by land use. To make the WRC indicators more relevant for agricultural policies, other parameters affecting soil and land management would need to be included. These WRC indicators may also have implications for water use indicators, since reduced peak water flow as expressed by the WRC may increase the availability of water in total precipitation.

Related information

Adjustment factors, which reflect different soil conditions and management practices, should be incorporated in the WRC in order to improve the relevance of the indicator to agricultural policy and policy changes. For certain soil types, Japan and Norway reported adjustment factors pertinent to their situation (Table 3). Switzerland has also identified retention capacity for pore space, soil depth and topography as being adjustment factors meriting further consideration. Further research work would be required to obtain data for these factors.

Table 3. **Examples of adjustment factors indicator for the water retaining capacity**

Soil type	Adjustment factors
Japan	
– Volcanic ash soil (Andosol)	1
– Brown forest soil (moderate)	1.25
– Brown forest soil (fine)	0.68
Norway	
– Silt	1.6

Note: Other suggested adjustment factors include topography (external water influence, infiltration) and soil depth.
Source: OECD Agri-environmental Indicators Questionnaire, 1999.

It is not easy to provide a clear association between changes in the WRC and the incidence of flooding, because flooding does not occur with enough frequency to easily facilitate statistical analysis. The limited available evidence does imply, however, that a fall in the WRC may lead to an increase in the potential risk of serious flood damage (Box 2).

Box 2. Agricultural land use and river flooding – Japan

The water balance has been analysed in the basin of Koshigaya City in Japan, which is located 25 km north of Tokyo. The city centre of Koshigaya is surrounded by paddy fields but in recent years residential development has rapidly advanced and the paddy field area has consequently declined.

During the period when the paddy area was greater than 2000 hectares, less than 1000 houses had been flooded below the floor level. ("floor level" here refers to around 50-60 cm above the ground level, at which floors of Japanese houses are constructed.) More recently, the paddy field area has declined to less than 2000 hectares, and more than 3000 houses have been flooded below the floor level and more than 1000 houses above the floor level, demonstrating that a decline in the paddy field area has contributed to increased flood damage.

Area of paddy fields and frequency of flooding (Koshigaya, Japan)

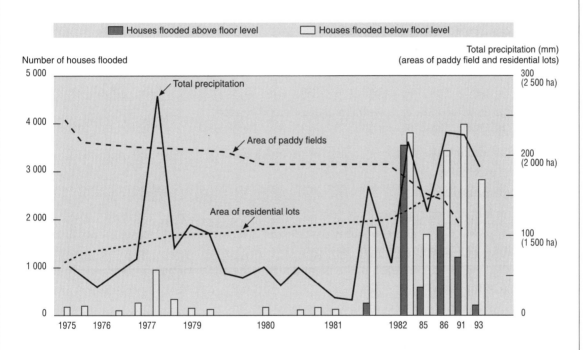

Research undertaken in various cities and towns in Japan, suggests that the water retaining capacity of agricultural lands has been significantly reduced between 1980 and 1990 (Seino, 1997). Because of the increased flood damage caused by the reduction in the paddy field area following rapid residential development, several cities and towns in Japan, including Koshigaya, pay subsidies to farmers to maintain paddy fields and their water retaining capacity.

The Tone River has a catchment area of 1.7 million hectares, the largest in Japan, and has major population centres in the river basin. The water retaining capacity of agricultural land in the Tone basin (603 million tonnes, of which paddy fields contribute 522 million tonnes) is estimated to be equal to the total water retention capacity of flood control dams and flood storage basins along the river (respectively 256 million tonnes and 200 million tonnes) (Ohnishi, 1997).

The River Management Authorities of the Tone River estimate the potential level of flood flow. These estimates have increased at each revision since the late 19th Century, largely because the calculation takes account of the reduction in agricultural land and agricultural water management facilities that occur as a result of land use changes in the basin (Suga, 1995).

Off-farm sediment flow

Definitions

Two approaches have been taken to develop the off-farm sediment flow (OFSF) indicator:

1. OFSF risk indicator: the estimated risk of the quantity of soil erosion sediments transferred from farm to off-farm areas and water bodies.

2. OFSF state indicator: the actual (or state) quantity of soil erosion sediments transferred from farm to off-farm areas and water bodies.

Method of calculation

The **OFSF *risk indicator*** measures the risk or potential changes in off-farm sediment flow based on land use history, type of cultivation, soil morphology, soil erodibility, climatic changes and other relevant factors. The merit of this approach lies in its relative ease in obtaining relevant data and in simulating hypothetical or planned situations, although it does not measure the net quantity of off-farm sediment flows (*i.e.* the eroded quantity minus the quantity deposited across different farms). This can be calculated in two ways as described below.

The *first* method of calculating the off-farm sediment flow (OFSF) is:

$$OFSF = f\ (T,C,S,K,R,L)$$

Where:

T = time duration after agricultural management is ceased

C = type of cultivation

S = soil morphology

K = soil erodibility

R = climatic zoning

L = livestock grazing capacity

Instead of providing the actual quantity of sediment flow, the method focuses on obtaining an index of risk associated with off-farm sediment flow by:

- analysing and describing each of the parameters in the OFSF formula with respect to their spatial distribution;

- ranking each parameter according to its importance; and,

- drawing on the knowledge of field experts, regarding the parameters.

A *second* alternative method of calculating the indicator is to use a simplified Universal Soil Loss Equation (USLE) in order to evaluate the erodibility of soil using available geographical and meteorological data. The purpose of this method is to identify the soil loss prevented by particular land use or management practices. The modified USLE is presented as follows (Ishihara, 1990):

$$E_0 = E_1{}^*E_2{}^*E_3{}^*(E_4+E_5)/2{}^*100\ (1)$$

where:

E_0 = value of soil erodibility,

E_1 = rainfall coefficient,

E_2 = slope coefficient,

E_3 = land use coefficient,

E_4 = soil coefficient, and

E_5 = soil texture coefficient.

In this equation, the value of E_1 is available from rainfall intensity data, while geographical information systems (GIS) can provide the values of E_2 to E_5.

Soil loss (tonnes/ha/year) is then calculated using the following equation:

$$E = k*E_0 \quad (2)$$

where:

E = soil loss (tonnes/ha/year), and

k = conversion coefficient.[4]

A benchmark level of soil loss can be calculated using equations (1) and (2) above with certain assumptions regarding vegetation cover. The soil loss prevented by a specific activity (or its prevention function) is calculated as the difference between soil loss from the land concerned and the benchmark level.

$$E_p = E_b - E_m$$

where:

E_p = prevented soil loss,

E_b = soil loss at the benchmark level, and

E_m = soil loss under certain activity.

By aggregating data at national level, the total benefit of the soil erosion prevention function of agricultural activities in a certain country can be estimated.

The **OFSF *state indicator*** directly measures the quantity of soil sediments in surface water, such as river, lakes and reservoirs. Compared with the risk approach, this approach more directly measures the actual sediment flow to downstream areas. It allows estimation of damage in monetary terms, although it requires on-site data collection.

The OFSF state indicator can be measured by monitoring the suspended sediment (concentration) at selected river gauging stations of a representative group of watersheds. The OFSF can also be measured by monitoring the sediment deposited in reservoirs that collect water of representative watersheds at selected time intervals. In some countries, advanced technology with Global Positioning System (GPS) is used to monitor the sediment accumulation in reservoirs (Box 3).[5] The soil sediment quantity can be obtained from the resultant measurement taking into account the total volume of river flow or accumulation period and the watershed area.

Recent trends

In *Italy*, the risk of off-farm sediment flows from agricultural land as well as total national sediment flows for all land have declined over the past decade (Figure 3). Time series data, however, is not available on off-farm sediment flows for other OECD countries.

An attempt was made to map how the current land use contributes to the prevention of soil erosion in *Japan*, using nation-wide data from the Digital National Land Information on a 1 km^2-mesh basis (Kato *et al.*, 1997). Under a hypothetical alternative situation, where all farming activity is ceased, annual soil loss would increase to 54.2 tonnes/ha from the current 9.6 tonnes/ha. Prevented soil loss from current agricultural land is therefore estimated to be 44.6 tonnes/ha.[6]

Some OECD countries have *ad hoc* data related to OFSF sedimentation in rivers and lakes (Table 4). In other cases regional data is available but it is difficult to aggregate this to derive national data.

Interpretation and links to other indicators

Currently, there is insufficient information available regarding off-farm soil sediment flows to analyse the implications of soil loss control. Another difficulty concerns distinguishing the source, agricultural or non-agricultural origin, of sediment in rivers and lakes. In the future work could focus on obtaining relevant data, particularly regarding sediment production and the cost of the associated damage. Detailed analysis of specific examples of damage costs could be useful for this purpose, and linking this indicator with those pertaining to soil and water quality.

Box 3. **Reservoir Sediment Survey**

There are two basic methods used to locate and determine the surface area of sediment deposits. They are the contour and range methods and in some situations they can be combined. The choice of method depends upon the amount and distribution of sediment as indicated by reconnaissance, the availability of previous base maps, and the degree of accuracy desired.

The contour method uses essentially topographic mapping procedures and is suitable for aerial surveys, while the range method consists of "profiling" ac.ross selected range lines. Sonic sounders and differential Global Positioning System (GPS) (see A in diagram) are used to survey submerged portions of ranges (see B in diagram). Sub-bottom profilers, that use two different sonic frequencies at the same time, can be used to measure the thickness of the sedimentary pack. Standard land surveying techniques are used to profile the portions of ranges above waterlines.

How close the ranges are spaced varies with the degree of accuracy required in volume estimates. Ranges also should be located across the mouths of all principal arms of the reservoir and the range network extended up the tributaries in a manner similar to that on the main stem.

Schematic drawn off sediment survey in reservoir

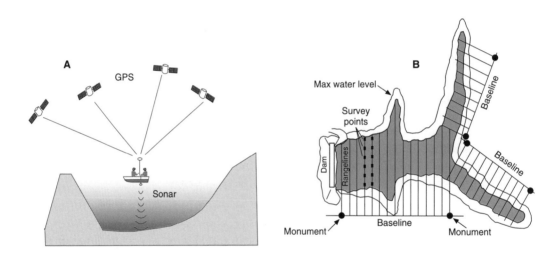

It is advisable to establish a measured baseline along one side of the reservoir running generally parallel to the main valley. A few permanent survey points are set at the position where the baseline intersects the range end. This facilitates the future re-profiling of range lines. Survey points can be interpolated with the use of commercial software programmes, which also calculate the volume of sediments.

Source: Ministry for Agricultural Policies, Italy.

Off-soil sediment flows are directly related to water quality indicators, subsequently influencing biodiversity and wildlife habitats. Water use indicators, which mainly address water use by agriculture, are affected by both treatment costs and the useful life of reservoirs. Off-farm sediment flows can be controlled by appropriate farming practices, some of which are included in farm management indicators.

Figure 3. **Share of agriculture in total sediment flows: Italy, 1985 to 1995**

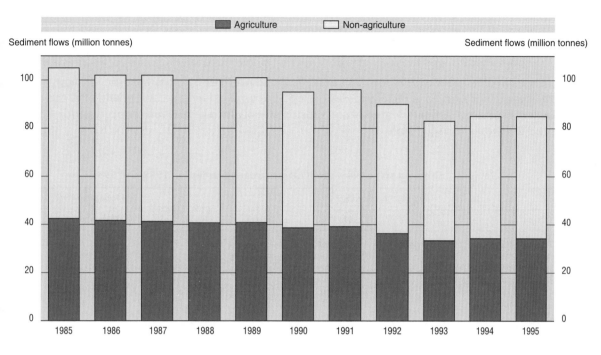

Source: OECD Agri-Environmental Indicators Questionnaire, 1999.

Table 4. **Environmental impacts of off-farm sediment flows**

Sediment production	
Hungary	2-3% of eroded soil particles enter surface water bodies.
Japan	The estimated amount of off-farm sediment flow in 1987 was 9.6 million tonnes.
Mexico	Annual sediment production is 365 million tonnes, 69% of which goes into lakes and 31% is deposited in the water infrastructure.
Netherlands	Annual sediment production is 150 thousand tonnes.
Storage loss in reservoirs	
Italy	Annual storage loss due to sediments is 54 million tonnes for large dams (capacity of one million tonnes or above) and 5 million tonnes for small dams (capacity of less than one million tonnes).
Spain	Annual reservoir sedimentation amounts to 0.16% of the capacity of reservoirs (ranging from a minimum of 0.07% to a maximum of 0.25%).
Norway, Poland	Few problems with soil sediments filling up water bodies while long term effects may cause problems.
Other impacts	
United Kingdom	Agriculturally derived fine sediment is recognised as a major threat to river fish, although shoreline sediment in lakes and rivers enables aquatic faunal and vegetable life to flourish.

Sources: OECD Agri-Environmental Indicators Questionnaire, 1999; United Kingdom Environment Agency (1998).

Related information

Sediments that accumulate in rivers, lakes and reservoirs engender costs incurred through their removal, or lead to permanent damage to the resource. The estimation of annual sediment damage is between US$2 billion and US$8 billion in the *United States*, where silting is perceived as one of the serious pollution problems in rivers and lakes (USDA, 1997), although suspended sediment concentration is marginally decreasing (Smith *et al.*, 1993).[7]

Translation of the physical quantity of soil sediment into monetary measurement would allow the OFSF indicator to be better incorporated into more general policy analysis. Relevant data to take these measurements include the cost per unit of sediment removal, the number of people, households and establishments affected, and the foregone benefits that would have arisen from specific activities.

Changes in land use may enhance soil erosion and consequently off-farm sediment flow, and that the rate at which soil erosion is increased depends on the type of land use before and after the change. In Japan, it is estimated that the degree of soil erosion sharply increases when terraced paddy fields are converted to other land uses (Table 5).

Table 5. **Effect on soil erosion from land use changes: Japan, 1989 and 1995**

Change in land use		Annual erosion
1989	1995	Tonnes/ha/year
From: Terraced paddy and cropland field	To: Uncultivated land	92.7
Pasture land	Uncultivated land	43.2
Terraced paddy field	White oak groves	19.0
Terraced paddy field	Pasture land	11.9
Cropland field	Pasture land	11.4
Uncultivated land	Uncultivated land	10.1
Cropland field	Cropland field	8.3
Pasture land	Pasture land	7.2
Terraced paddy field	Terraced paddy field	2.8

Source: Ministry of Agriculture, Forestry and Fisheries, Japan.

3.   Future challenges

While the importance of land conservation indicators varies across OECD countries depending on their geo-physical and climatic conditions, further elaboration of these indicators could be useful to improve definitions, standardise coefficients and data, and improve methods of calculation. Further conceptual work might be needed on landslide prevention and groundwater recharge associated with agriculture in order to address these concerns in a number of countries. Concerning landslide prevention, one possibility as a basis for future consideration is to develop a landslide prevention index.[8]

Although the present focus is mainly on the development of physical indicators of land conservation, an estimation of the associated economic costs and benefits would allow for a more complete economic assessment of land conservation, and could provide a significant basis for policy evaluation and design.

NOTES

1. See Potter (1991) for examples where soil conservation practices significantly affected hydrology.
2. OECD Agri-Environmental Indicators Questionnaire, 1999. See OECD (1997) for the statistics on natural disasters.
3. See Baldock *et al.* (1995) for examples in *southern Europe*, and the Swiss Federal Office of Agriculture (1997) in *Switzerland*.
4. The coefficient was estimated as 2.5 in the case of Japan.
5. See Baldassarre *et al.* (1993) for an actual application.
6. See Jager (1994) and Schaub and Prasuhn (1996) for further examples of soil erosion mapping.
7. In The *Netherlands*, annual costs for removing sediments have been reduced over ten years from 4 million guilders (or US$1.9 million) in 1985 to 2.6 million guilders (or US$1.2 million) in 1995. *Japan* also recently reported that it spent one hundred million yen (or US$830 000) to remove 19 000 tonnes of sediment.
8. For example, *Japan* has proposed an integrated index for landslide prevention, using a rating system with various elements involved, instead of seeking an actual quantity of landslide. In this proposal, the index for the landslide prevention function is expressed as: CP = SWiCPi, where: CP = integrated evaluation value of landslide prevention function, Wi = weight of factor i, and CPi = rating value of element i.

BIBLIOGRAPHY

Baldassarre, G., B. Radina, P. Bazzoffi and S. Pellegrini (1993),
"Evaluation of erosion in the Cmastra basin (Southern Appennines, Italy)", in A. Anagnostopoulos (ed.), *Proceedings of an International Symposium on Geotechnical Engineering of Hard Soil – Soft Rocks*, Athens, Greece, 20-23 September 1993.

Baldock, D., G. Beaufoy and J. Clark (1995),
The Nature of Farming, Low Intensity Farming Systems in Nine European Countries, Institute for European Environmental Policy, London, United Kingdom.

Clark, E.H., J.A. Haverkamp and W. Chapman (1985),
Eroding Soils: The Off-Farm Impacts, The Conservation Foundation, Washington, DC., United States.

Feather, P. and D. Hellerstein (1997),
"Calibrating Benefit Function Transfer to Assess the Conservation Reserve Program", *American Journal of Agricultural Economics*, Vol. 79, pp. 151-162.

Hayase, Y. and T. Masumoto (1998),
Overseas Investigation Report 1998 of the Project "Trade and the Environment", Agriculture, Forestry and Fisheries Research Council, Ministry of Agriculture, Forestry and Fisheries (MAFF), Tokyo, Japan.

Ishihara, A. (1990),
"Evaluation of soil erosion prevention function", *Project Research Report*, No. 242, pp. 65-67, Agriculture, Forestry and Fisheries Research Council, Ministry of Agriculture, Forestry and Fisheries (MAFF), Tokyo, Japan.

Jager, A. (1994),
"Modeling regional soil erosion susceptibility using the universal soil loss equation and GIS", pp. 167-177, in R.J. Rickson (ed.), *Conserving Soil Resources: European Perspectives*, Cambridge, United Kingdom.

Kato, Y., M. Yokohari and R.D. Brown (1997),
"Integration and visualization of the ecological value of rural landscapes in maintaining the physical environment of Japan", *Landscape and Urban Planning*, Vol. 39, No. 1, pp. 69-82.

Naka, T. and H. Fujii (1998),
"Water management and flood control in Sacrament river basin in USA", *Journal of Japanese Society of Irrigation Drainage and Reclamation Engineering*, Vol. 66, pp. 171-176.

Norberg, J. (1999),
"Linking nature's services to ecosystems: some general ecological concepts", *Ecological Economics*, Vol. 29, No. 2 pp. 183-202.

OECD (1997),
OECD *Environmental Data: Compendium 1997*, Paris, France.

Ohnishi, R. (1997),
"Water conservation function of agricultural land and future farm management", pp. 55-61, in *Agriculture, Rural Communities and the Environment*, Yokendo Publisher, Tokyo, Japan.

Potter, K.W. (1991),
"Hydrological Impacts of Changing Land Management Practices in a Moderate-Sized Agricultural Catchment" *Water Resource Research*, Vol. 27, No. 5, pp. 845-855.

Ribaudo, M. (1986),
Reducing Soil Erosion: Offsite Benefits, Agricultural Economic Report No. 561, US Department of Agriculture Economic Research Service, Washington, DC., United States.

Schaub, D.M. and V. Prasuhn (1996),
"A soil erosion map of Switzerland as a planning tool for sustainable land use", in *Towards sustainable land use*, Proceedings of 9th International Soil Conservation Organisation (ISCO), 26-30 August 1996, Bonn, Germany, pp. 34

Seino, H. (1997),
Located characteristic of local government which take a measure to prevent flood, NIAES Symposium Report No. 17, National Institute of Agro-Environmental Sciences, pp. 39-46, Tsukuba, Japan.

Smith, R.A., R.B. Alexander and K.J. Lanfear (1993),
"Stream water quality in the conterminous United States – Status and trends of selected indicators during the 1980's", in United States Geological Survey (USGS), *National Water Summary* 1990-91: *Hydrologic Events and Stream Water Quality*, Water-Supply Paper 2400, Washington, DC., United States.

Suga, K. (1995),
Flood of Tone river, Sankaido Publisher, Tokyo, Japan.

Sumelius, J. (1997),
Concerns Related to Possibly Effects of Trade Liberalisation on Landscape and Biodiversity in the Nordic Countries, Paper presented at the NJF-seminar on Agriculture, Trade and the Environment, Greve, Denmark, 22-24 May.

Swiss Federal Office of Agriculture (1997),
"Switzerland: Government Policy to Stimulate Environmental Benefits", pp. 159-167, in OECD, *Helsinki Seminar on Environmental Benefits from Agriculture, Country Case Studies*, OECD General Distribution document [OCDE/GD(97)110], Paris, France. Available at: *www.oecd.org/* [Documentation > 1997 > Reference Components > OCDE > OCDE/GD].

Tikof, M. (1997),
"Greece: Policy Measures and Practices, and Environmental Benefits from Agriculture", pp. 95-112, in OECD, *Helsinki Seminar on Environmental Benefits from Agriculture, Country Case Studies*, OECD General Distribution document [OCDE/GD(97)110], Paris, France. Available at: *www.oecd.org/* [Documentation > 1997 > Reference Components > OCDE > OCDE/GD].

United Kingdom Environment Agency (1998),
Sedimentation and Salmonids in England and Wales, Research and Development Technical Report P194, Bristol, United Kingdom.

USDA [United States Department of Agriculture] (1997),
Agricultural Resources and Environmental Indicators, 1996-97, Agricultural Handbook No. 712, Natural Resources and Environment Division, Economic Research Service, Washington, DC., United States. Available at: *www.ers.usda.gov/* [Briefing Rooms > Agricultural Resources and Environmental Indicators].

271

Chapter 4

GREENHOUSE GASES

HIGHLIGHTS

Context

It is now widely believed that the increased atmospheric concentration of greenhouse gases (GHGs) is contributing to the process of climate change and global warming. Most OECD countries, under the 1994 United Nations Framework Convention on Climate Change, committed themselves to stabilise emissions of GHGs at 1990 levels by 2000, and further agreed to implement the 1997 Kyoto Protocol, which specified the levels of emissions for the target period 2008 to 2012.

It is not only the contribution of agriculture in the climate change process, but also the impact of climate change on agriculture that is of concern to farmers and policy makers. Monitoring the role of agriculture as a source and sink for GHGs is of importance to policy makers, in view of the need for countries to assess domestic strategies, and to meet international obligations to reduce GHG emissions. Data on the specific contribution of agriculture as both a source and sink of GHG in relation to climate change, relative to other sectors in the economy, can help to develop appropriate policies.

Indicators and recent trends

The greenhouse gas indicator measures the gross agricultural emissions of three gases: carbon dioxide (CO_2), methane (CH_4) and nitrous oxide (N_2O), expressed in CO_2 equivalents. The share of agriculture in OECD total national gross GHG emissions in CO_2 equivalents is below 10 per cent, although for methane and nitrous oxide agriculture contributes a major share in the emission of these gases, about 40 and 60 per cent, respectively. For a few OECD countries the contribution to national total GHG emissions is above 20 per cent, which is largely a reflection of the greater importance of the agricultural sector in the economies of these countries.

Livestock farming and the use of inorganic fertilisers are key sources of methane and nitrous oxide gases. The trend in agricultural emissions of GHGs has declined since the early 1990s for most OECD countries. This is mainly explained by a reduction in cattle numbers and the use of fertilisers. For a few countries GHG emissions have been rising, because of an overall expansion in crop and livestock production.

The work to date on agricultural GHG indicators focuses on emissions, because as yet there are no systematic estimates of agriculture's role as a sink for GHGs across OECD countries. Agriculture's capacity as a GHG sink is enhanced by improvements in management practices, such as tillage practices, crop cover and residue management.

The development of a comprehensive net GHG balance indicator would address both GHG emissions and removals. A number of OECD countries have begun to measure soil carbon fluxes and agriculture's capacity to act as a GHG sink. Research in *Canada*, for example, shows that net CO_2 emissions from agricultural soils in Canada have been considerably reduced by converting from conventional tillage to no-till systems, increasing cover cropping and improving crop residue management practices. A study in *France* calculated net CO_2 emissions from changes in agricultural land use. Overall the French research showed emissions exceeded removals, with an increase in CO_2 by converting grassland to other uses and clearing forests, while agricultural land left uncultivated acted as a CO_2 sink.

273|

1. Background

Policy context

The atmospheric concentrations of greenhouse gases (GHGs) have grown significantly since the 18th century, and it is now widely believed that the increased concentration of GHGs is contributing to the process of climate change and global warming.[1] In the absence of mitigation policies or significant technological advances that reduce emissions and enhance sinks, concentrations of GHGs are expected to grow throughout the 21st century (IPCC, 1996a). Models project an increase in global mean surface temperature relative to 1990 of about 1 to 3.5 °C by 2100. Even in the lowest case, the average rate of warming would probably be greater than any seen over the last 10 000 years with considerable natural variability in the annual to decadal changes.

Against this background, most OECD countries under the 1994 United Nations Framework Convention on Climate Change (UNFCCC), committed themselves to stabilise emissions of GHG at 1990 levels by 2000.[2] Following this 1994 Agreement, the third Conference of the Parties to the Convention (COP3), held in Kyoto in December 1997, adopted the Kyoto Protocol, in which most OECD countries committed themselves to reduce or limit their GHG emissions.[3] Specific commitments were made in terms of the total GHG emission levels in CO_2 equivalent for the target period 2008 to 2012 compared to the base period, which is 1990 levels in most cases (Table 1).[4]

The COP3 identified the future potential to reduce the emissions of GHG, such as the role of agricultural soil as a sink, as an issue for consideration at the later COPs. A recent report of the Intergovernmental Panel on Climate Change (IPCC, 2000a) has examined different approaches and estimated net change in carbon stocks through improved management practices and changes in land-use.

While the emission levels of GHGs from agriculture are largely affected by the type and scale of agricultural production (e.g. type and number of livestock, area of fertilised cropland, etc.), farm management practices also affect emission levels. In fact, some countries report in their National Communications under the UNFCCC programme that further emission reductions are possible through improved farm and manure management practices (UNFCCC, 1998). In this context many OECD countries are currently undertaking research and implementing measures to help in reducing agricultural emissions of GHGs, and fostering practices that enhance agriculture's role as a GHG sink.[5]

Monitoring the role of agriculture as a source and sink for GHGs is now of considerable policy relevance, in view of both the need for countries to assess domestic strategies, and also to meet international obligations to reduce GHG emissions. Furthermore, agricultural policy makers need to take into account not only the contribution of agriculture to the process of climate change, but also the impact of climate change on agriculture. Thus, it is necessary to identify the specific role of agriculture as both a source and sink of GHG in relation to climate change, relative to other sectors in the economy.[6]

Table 1. **National commitments for greenhouse gas emissions under the Kyoto Protocol to 2008-12**

	Commitment level in 2008-12 in carbon dioxide equivalent (relative to the base period 1990)[1]
Iceland	+10%
Australia	+8%
Norway	+1%
New Zealand	+/–0%
Canada, Hungary, Japan, Poland	–6%
United States	–7%
Czech Republic, Switzerland, European Union	–8%

1. For Hungary and Poland, the base periods are 1985-87 average and 1988, respectively.
Source: Annex B of Kyoto Protocol to the United Nations Framework Convention on Climate Change.

Environmental context

The process of climate change through increased GHG concentrations is thought to lead to a rise in average global temperature, changes in the frequency and distribution of precipitation, and variations in the pattern and occurrence of droughts and floods (Parry and Swaminathan, 1992). As a result, climate change could pose a serious challenge for agriculture, although recent studies indicate there is more adaptation potential in the sector to warming than was found in earlier studies (USDA, 1997).[7] The major impacts for agriculture of global warming and higher CO_2 concentrations are thought to lead to changes in the area cultivated,[8] plant growth, crop yields,[9] crop types and varieties, and farm management practices, such as the use of irrigation water.

GHGs are transported and/or transformed in various pathways from agriculture into the environment (Figure 1).[10] The main agricultural activities which lead to emissions of GHGs include: livestock production, crop production and the use of fertilisers, fossil fuel combustion, biomass burning and wetland rice cultivation (Figure 4). The magnitude of emissions from these activities may depend on management practices. Use of biomass for energy and production of biofuel can contribute to the substitution of fossil fuel combustion (IEA, 1998). While, at this stage, the contribution to energy needs from biofuels is limited, this could change on account of a number of countries adopting policies to promote biofuel production.

Livestock, especially large ruminants (beef and dairy cattle) produce CH_4 emissions as a by-product of the normal digestive process by rumen bacteria. Other livestock also produce some emissions.[11] CH_4 and N_2O are also produced from manure storage, especially when manure is stored in large quantities. Emission levels of CH_4 and N_2O produced from livestock may vary according to feeding practices, manure management and the conditions under which manure is stored (Sneath et al., 1997a; and 1997b).

Figure 1. **Pathways of sources and sinks of greenhouse gases associated with agriculture**

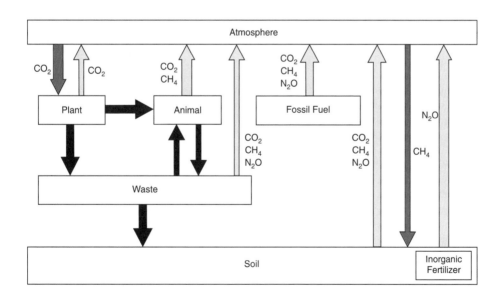

CO_2: Carbon dioxide, N_2O: Nitrous oxide, CH_4: Methane

⇒ emission → removal → transformation of organic matter into carbon (C) and nitrogen (N).

Note: The width of arrows increases with the general importance of each flow, although actual flows of gas will depend on site-specific conditions.
Source: Adapted from Desjardines and Riznek (2000).

Crop production through the use of agricultural soils is a major source of N_2O emissions mainly originating from inorganic and organic fertiliser application, while crop residues, biological nitrogen fixation and soil tillage also contribute to these emissions. The CO_2 emissions from cultivated soils are affected by management practices, for example, plough-based soil tillage increases emissions while returning crop residues to the soil, which enhances soil carbon capacity, tends to reduce emissions (Lal *et al.*, 1995a).

Cultivation of organic soil such as peat is also a source of CO_2, while reducing CH_4 emissions. Agricultural soils have a substantial capacity to break down CH_4 into radiatively less active CO_2, although this potential of cultivated land is smaller than that of forests and natural grassland, and is reduced when intensively cultivated (Phipps and Hall, 1994).

Changes in land use can affect the exchange of carbon between the soil carbon and atmospheric CO_2.[12] If "native land" is converted to agricultural use, large losses of soil carbon can be expected. Similarly, if native land is subjected to high-intensity burning, soil organic carbon is also lost (Johnson, 1995). In contrast, the conversion of agricultural land to forest and/or uncultivated land ("wilderness") may provide greater potential for carbon absorption.[13]

Photosynthetic fixation by agricultural crops acts to remove CO_2 from the atmosphere. The contribution of this process to global CO_2 removal is usually regarded as negligible, as the carbon contained in food and feed crops are soon released into the atmosphere by human and animal respiration. However, the increase of biomass both above and under the ground through enhanced photosynthetic fixation on improved pasture and/or by the "fertiliser effect" is sometimes considered as a sink of CO_2.

Agricultural fossil fuel combustion, from the operation of farm vehicles and to a lesser extent greenhouse heating and grain drying, are the main sources of CO_2 emissions from farming.[14] CH_4 and, to a smaller degree, N_2O are also emitted through fossil fuel consumption in agriculture, although the contribution to the emission of these gases is smaller than from soils, livestock production and rice cultivation.

Agricultural biomass burning, such as the burning of crop residues in fields, is a source of CH_4 and N_2O, although its contribution is limited compared to other major sources. Grassland burning is also a source of these gases, although this is less common for most OECD countries. CO_2 emissions from burning crop residues and grassland are generally not accounted for since it is assumed that an equivalent amount of CO_2 is removed by regrowing grassland vegetation or crops in the following year. The appropriate use of biomass burning for energy purposes can contribute to a reduction in CO_2 emissions through less fossil fuel combustion.

Use of *non-wood biofuel* (*e.g.* ethanol made from maize) results in a reduction in CO_2 emissions when substituted for fossil fuels, although the costs are at present high (OECD, 1994). Burning biofuel from non-wood energy crops is not regarded as a source of anthropogenic CO_2 emission for the same reason as for biomass burning mentioned above.

Wetland rice cultivation is another agricultural source of CH_4 produced in the soil of flooded rice fields during the anaerobic decomposition of organic material. The amount of CH_4 released depends on the water management practices during the growing season, soil characteristics such as soil temperature and type, application of inorganic and organic fertilisers, and other cultivation practices.[15]

2. Indicator

Gross agricultural greenhouse gas emissions

Definition

Gross total agricultural emissions of carbon dioxide (CO_2), methane (CH_4) and nitrous oxide (NO_2), expressed in CO_2 equivalents.

Method of calculation[16]

Emissions and removals of CH_4 and N_2O are converted to CO_2 equivalents, in terms of weights, using Global Warming Potentials (GWPs).[17] The total CO_2 equivalent (measured in metric tonnes) of the three agricultural GHGs is calculated as:

$$E_{CO_2eq} = 1 \times E_{CO_2} + 21 \times E_{CH_4} + 310 \times E_{N_2O}$$

where:

E_{CO_2eq} total gross agricultural emissions in CO_2 equivalent;

E_{CO_2} total gross agricultural emission of carbon dioxide (CO_2);

E_{CH_4} total gross agricultural emission of methane (CH_4);

E_{N_2O} total gross agricultural emission of nitrous oxide (N_2O);

1, 21 and 310 are GWPs over 100 years for CO_2, CH_4 and N_2O, respectively (see endnote 17).

The UNFCCC Inventories provide data on agricultural emissions of GHGs. Major agricultural sources of CH_4 and N_2O, such as enteric fermentation, livestock waste, agricultural soil and rice production, are covered by the agricultural module of the Inventories. CO_2 from fossil fuel combustion is also included in the energy module of the Inventories. However, agricultural sources of CO_2 emissions are limited to on-farm fossil fuel combustion, and aggregated with emissions from forestry and fisheries.[18] It should be noted that the data used for the indicator includes CO_2 emissions from forestry and fisheries, which could be excluded in further refinement of the indicator.

CO_2 emissions from agricultural soils are reported by a limited number of countries and, therefore, excluded from the indicator calculation. CO_2 emissions from upstream and downstream sectors such as fertiliser and pesticide production, electricity use, transportation and processing are also not included because data are not available, and because the OECD focus of the GHG indicator is at present on primary agriculture.

A three-year average of the emission level for the period of 1990-92 is taken as the benchmark for this indicator, taking into consideration that:

- most OECD countries have agreed under the Kyoto Protocol to reduce anthropogenic GHG emissions for the target period using 1990 as the benchmark;

- the revised IPCC Guidelines (IPCC, 1997) recommend using a 3-year average for agricultural emissions; and

- the UNFCCC National Inventories cover the period from 1990.

Recent trends

The OECD gross emissions of agricultural GHGs contributed about 8 per cent of total OECD national GHG emissions for the 1995-97 period, an increase of 1.4 per cent from the reference period of 1990-92 (Figure 2). However, trends in agricultural emissions vary considerably among countries.

- Agriculture represents a small share in total GHG emissions for most OECD countries, but the share is 20 per cent or above for *Australia, Denmark, Ireland* and *New Zealand* although the total GHG emissions for these countries are relatively small compared with some other OECD countries.

- Agricultural emissions for the *Czech Republic, Hungary* and *Poland* have declined substantially, following the transition of these countries to a market economy. This was, in particular, related to the large reduction in cattle numbers and inorganic fertiliser use in these countries (see the Nutrient Use chapter).

- Many OECD countries have shown a reduction in GHG emissions during the period of 1990-92 to 1995-97, although the reductions are smaller than 10 per cent in most cases. For *Austria, Belgium,*

Figure 2. **Gross emissions of greenhouse gases from agriculture: 1990-92 to 1995-97**

Change in gross emissions of greenhouse gases from agriculture	Percentage share of agriculture in total GHG emissions

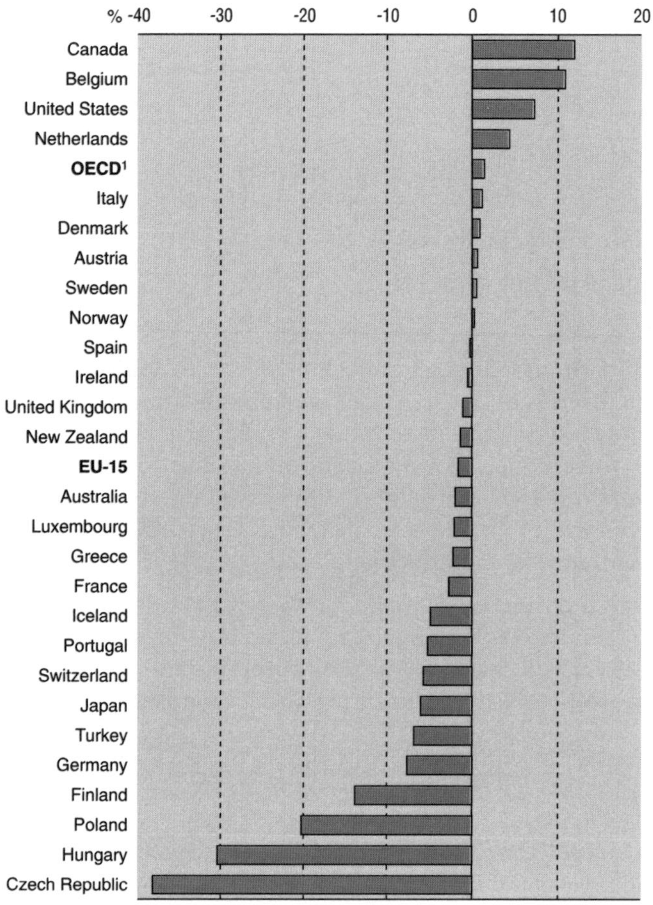

	1995-97
Canada	9.8
Belgium	10.0
United States	7.4
Netherlands	12.2
OECD	8.4
Italy	9.6
Denmark	21.7
Austria	7.0
Sweden	13.7
Norway	9.9
Spain	13.5
Ireland	34.0
United Kingdom	8.1
New Zealand	55.8
EU-15	10.7
Australia	19.5
Luxembourg	4.6
Greece	13.3
France	17.3
Iceland	11.0
Portugal	10.5
Switzerland	10.8
Japan	1.5
Turkey	6.8
Germany	6.2
Finland	8.2
Poland	5.1
Hungary	5.8
Czech Republic	3.3

1. Korea and Mexico are not included.
Note: See Annex Table 1.
Sources: OECD Secretariat; UNFCCC (1999); EUROSTAT (1997); Turkish Ministry of Environment (1998).

Canada, Denmark, Italy, the Netherlands, Norway, Sweden and the United States, however, agricultural emissions have increased since 1990-92.

Although the contribution of agriculture in total national gross emissions of GHGs is small (Table 2), agriculture is one of the major sources of CH_4 and N_2O, contributing around 40 and 58 per cent of total gross national emissions of these gases respectively in OECD countries as a whole (Figure 3). The share for N_2O would be even higher if data could be provided by more countries since at this stage a limited number of countries report N_2O emission from livestock waste, while CH_4 emission from the same source is reported by most countries. The share of agriculture in total CO_2 emissions, mainly from fossil fuel combustion, is under 1 per cent. CO_2 emissions from and removals by agricultural soil as a result of land use and land use change, which can be significant in some countries, are not included due to limited data availability.

Table 2.   **Greenhouse gas emissions in carbon dioxide equivalent: 1995-97**[1]

Type of Greenhouse gas	OECD total emissions[2]	Share of each gas in OECD total	Emissions from agriculture[3]	Share of each gas in agriculture	Share of agriculture in total of each gas
	Million tonnes	%	Million tonnes	%	%
Carbon dioxide (CO_2)[4]	11 552	82	59	5	1
Methane (CH_4)	1 437	10	557	47	39
Nitrous oxide (N_2O)	929	7	560	48	60
Others: (HFCs, PFCs, SF_6)[5]	224	2	0	0	0
Total	14 142	100	1 176	100	8

1.   For CO_2, 1996 data for EU countries, and 1995 data for non-EU countries. For CH_4 and N_2O, 1996-97 average for Poland and Sweden, average of 1995 and 1997 for Turkey, 1994-96 average for Australia, Belgium, Greece, Hungary, Ireland and the Netherlands, and 1993-94 average for Portugal. For "Others", 1995 data are used except 1994 for Germany.
2.   Korea and Mexico are not included. In general, UNFCCC data are used, except that EUROSTAT data are used for CO_2 emission from agricultural fuel combustion in EU countries, and national data are used for all emissions from Turkey.
3. CO_2 emission is not included for Australia, Austria, the Czech Republic, Hungary, Japan, New Zealand, Poland, Switzerland, Turkey and the United States.
4. CO_2 emission in agriculture covers fossil fuel combustion only (fossil fuel combustion in forestry and fisheries is included for non-EU countries).
5.   Other GHGs are not included for Hungary, Ireland, Luxembourg, Poland, Portugal, Spain and Turkey, and only partial emission of other GHGs is included for Australia, Austria, Denmark, Finland, Greece, Iceland, Japan, Sweden and the United Kingdom.
Sources: OECD Secretariat; UNFCCC (1999); EUROSTAT (1997); Turkish Ministry of Environment (1998).

Figure 3.   **Main sources of methane and nitrous oxide emissions: 1995-97**[1]

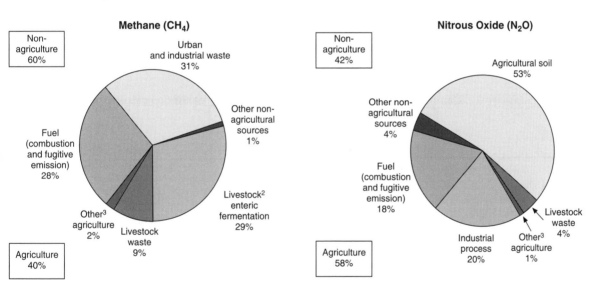

1.   Korea and Mexico are not included. 1996-97 average for Poland and Sweden; average of 1995 and 1997 for Turkey; 1994-96 average for Australia, Belgium, Greece, Hungary, Ireland and the Netherlands; 1994-95 average for Italy, Luxembourg, Iceland and Spain; 1993-94 average for Portugal.
2.   Livestock enteric fermentation for Turkey includes livestock waste.
3.   "Other agriculture" consists of rice cultivation, grassland and crop residue burning for both CH_4 and N_2O as well as agricultural soil for CH_4 only.
Sources: OECD Secretariat; UNFCCC (1999); EUROSTAT (1999); Turkish Ministry of Environment (1998).

The contribution of different agricultural sources of GHG emissions for the OECD as a whole (Figure 4), and for individual countries (Figure 5), indicate the following key points:

- Livestock farming contributes almost half of the total agricultural emissions for the OECD countries as a whole, with CH_4 emissions from livestock enteric fermentation the main component, contributing one-third of total agricultural emissions.

279|

Figure 4. **Contribution of main sources in total OECD agricultural greenhouse gas emissions: 1995-97[1, 2]**

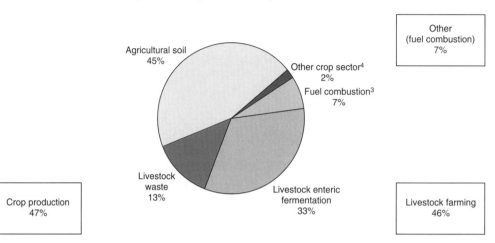

1. Korea and Mexico are not included.
2. For CO_2, 1996 data for EU countries, and 1995 data for others. For CH_4 and N_2O, 1996-97 average for Poland and Sweden; average for 1995 and 1997 for Turkey; 1994-96 average for Australia, Belgium, Greece, Hungary, Ireland and the Netherlands; 1994-95 average for Iceland, Italy, Luxembourg and Spain; 1993-94 average for Portugal.
3. For fuel combustion, Australia, Austria, Iceland, Japan, Mexico, New Zealand, Poland, Switzerland, Turkey and the United States are not included. Fuel combustion of Canada, the Czech Republic, Hungary and Norway includes fuel combustion in forestry and fisheries.
4. "Other crop sector" consists of rice cultivation and grassland and crop residue burning.
Sources: OECD Secretariat; UNFCCC (1999); EUROSTAT (1997); Turkish Ministry of Environment (1998).

Figure 5. **Contribution of main sources in agricultural greenhouse gas emissions for OECD countries: 1995-97[1, 2]**

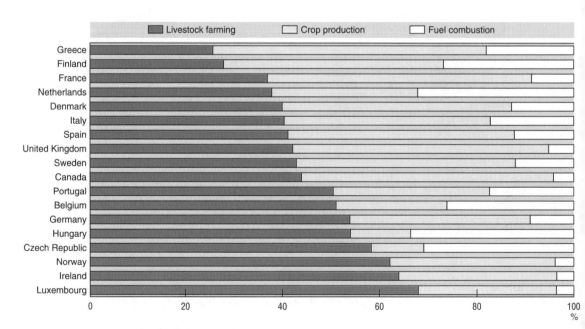

1. Countries for which fuel combustion data are not available are not included.
2. See notes of Figure 4.
Sources: OECD Secretariat; UNFCCC (1999); EUROSTAT (1997); Turkish Ministry of Environment (1998).

- Crop production, mostly N_2O emissions from agricultural soils, contributes almost half of the agricultural emissions. N_2O emissions from agricultural soils is the main source in this sub-category for most countries, although grassland burning is a significant part in Australia and rice cultivation in Japan.

- The share of CO_2 emissions from fuel combustion in total OECD agricultural GHG emissions is 7 per cent, but this share varies considerably between countries, exceeding 20 per cent for Belgium, the Czech Republic, Finland, Hungary and the Netherlands.

Interpretation and links to other indicators

The limitation of the current UNFCCC inventory, on which the calculation of the GHG indicator is based, should be noted. Because of many uncertainties in the mechanisms of GHG emissions, the reporting methodology is continuously under review. Changes in the indicator calculation could result from improvement in the methodology. In the most recent exercise of inventory updates, many countries modified the numbers in earlier submissions, due to applying the updated methodology, while other countries only added the data for recent years. This implies possible inconsistency among countries and/or over years within a country in reporting methodology. The discussion in the Subsidiary Body of Scientific and Technical Advice under IPCC, will improve the quality of the inventory, subsequently providing a better basis for the indicator.[19]

Another problem in the inventory is the substantial difference in data availability among countries. More than half of OECD countries have reported data up to the year 1997 by early 1999, but in some countries, the data is not available for recent years. Only the data for the reference period is available for a few countries. With regard to CO_2 emissions from fuel combustion in agriculture, only the data aggregated with forestry and fisheries sectors are available for many countries, and many others have no data at all.

The CO_2 emissions from agricultural soils is not included in the calculation (even though it is the essential part) because only a few countries have reported the data. A limited number of countries have reported N_2O emissions from livestock waste, which should correspond to the situation for CH_4 emissions from the same source, reported by almost all countries. The improvement of such reporting may reveal the greater importance of livestock waste in N_2O emissions. In addition, national emission estimates made by individual member countries may vary depending on which factors are included in their own calculations.

Trends in the current GHG indicator mainly reflect changes in agricultural production (*e.g.* number of cattle) but they are also affected by farm management practices, which can reduce GHG emissions from agriculture. For example, improvements in livestock feeding and rice paddy water management may reduce CH_4 emissions; more efficient use of nitrogen fertilisers can contribute to limiting N_2O emissions; and improved management of animal waste may cut overall GHG emissions. Thus, analysing trends in gross agricultural GHG emissions will be enhanced by linking them to farm management indicators, and also those which relate to nutrient use, land use and soil quality.

3. Related information

Agriculture as a sink of greenhouse gases

Emissions of CO_2 from agricultural soils is an area of increasing research, examining the links between soil quality, farm management practices and soil organic carbon retention. The factors affecting soil organic carbon retention include soil type, temperature, moisture, soil cover and crop growth. Management practices are also important, such as methods of planting, fertiliser application, tillage, grazing and application of organic material (Lal *et al.*, 1995c; Li, 1995).

While there are, as yet, no systematic estimates of agriculture's role as a sink for GHGs across OECD countries, a number of studies have been made which reveal the extent to which changes in farm management practices and land use affect net GHG emissions from agriculture.

A study in *France* has calculated net CO_2 emissions related to changes in agricultural land use in 1990 (Table 3). There was an increase in CO_2 emissions by converting grassland to other uses and clearing forest, while agricultural land left uncultivated acted as a sink for CO_2. Overall, the emissions exceeded the removals (IFEN, 1997).

Table 3. **Net carbon dioxide emissions related to agricultural land use changes: France, 1990**

	Forest clearing	Grassland converted to other uses	Agricultural land not cultivated	Total
	Million tonnes (carbon dioxide)			
Source	4 737	9 240	..	13 977
Sink	..	..	−1 797	−1 797
Balance	4 737	9 240	−1 797	12 180

Notes: Positive numbers indicate emissions and negative numbers represent removals. Total balance will be negative if the net carbon dioxide fixation by forestry is taken into account.
.. Not available.
Source: IFEN (1997).

Agricultural sources and sinks of GHGs in *Australia* were estimated in order to analyse the effects of reducing emissions of GHGs on broadacre agriculture. A mathematical programming model which employs farm level data was used (Table 4). Soil cultivation and cropping is a major source of GHG emissions in Australia, while improved pastures, reduction of stubble burning and the fertiliser effect influence GHG sinks.

Table 4. **Estimates of agricultural greenhouse gas sources and sinks: Australia, 1990**

Source		Sink	
Thousand tonnes of carbon dioxide equivalent		Thousand tonnes of carbon dioxide equivalent	
Carbon dioxide		Carbon dioxide	
Soil cultivation and cropping	15 000	Improved pastures	30 000
Net deforestation and land disturbance	10 000	Wildfire suppression and reduced stubble burning	23 000
Biomass burning	..	Shrub encroachment	5 000
		Fertiliser effect	0 to 110 000
Methane		Methane	
Enteric emissions from animals	2 456	Soil sink	1 682
Animal wastes	288		
Crop stubble burning	40		
Grazing land burning	455		
Rice cultivation	12		
Nitrous oxide			
Legume pastures	10		
Biomass burning	13		
Animal wastes	155		
Clearing	..		
Soil cultivation and cropping	38		
Fertilisers	4		

Note: Fertiliser effect refers to additional carbon fixation at higher carbon dioxide level.
.. Not available.
Source: Phipps and Hall (1994).

The marginal cost of reducing greenhouse gas emissions from *Australian* broadacre agriculture by 20 per cent was estimated by running model simulations. A reduction of 20 per cent was achieved by reducing CH_4 and N_2O emissions and increasing the net absorption of CO_2. The marginal cost of a 20 per cent reduction was estimated to be A$20 per tonne of CO_2 equivalent (US$16, in 1990 values).

Some OECD countries have undertaken computer-modelling exercises to estimate carbon exchanges between soil carbon and atmospheric CO_2.[20] The results suggest that improvements of tillage practices, cover cropping and crop-residue management, can increase soil carbon and reduce CO_2 emissions. Research in *Canada*, for example, shows that emissions are considerably reduced from such changes in farm management practices (Figure 6).

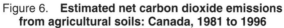

Figure 6. **Estimated net carbon dioxide emissions from agricultural soils: Canada, 1981 to 1996**

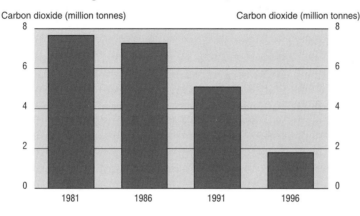

Source: Janzen *et al.* (1999).

Agriculture and renewable/inexhaustible energy

Agriculture's contribution to renewable energy, through energy crops and biofuel production, is attracting growing interest in a number of OECD countries. Energy crop production, such as perennial herbaceous crops and fast-growing woody crops, could reduce CO_2 emissions substantially. A market is being established in the *United Kingdom*, for example, through the Non Fossil Fuel Obligation (NFFO), which requires regional electricity companies to obtain a proportion of their power from renewable resources (MAFF, 1998).

Although production and use of biofuel is limited at this stage, its potential is not negligible (European Parliament, 1993). Some countries have already made an effort to maximise the use of livestock wastes for energy to reduce fossil fuel consumption. For example, in the *United Kingdom* poultry manure is used for heat and power generation and the feasibility of using pig slurry and straw is also being studied.

Agricultural land can also contribute to providing sites for wind energy turbines, while farming or cattle grazing can be continued on the same land. Local power demands can be met, and in addition, wind-origin electricity can be transformed to hydrogen by electrolysing water and provide transport fuel. Some OECD countries, such as *Denmark, Germany, the Netherlands* and *the United States*, have been developing wind energy on agricultural land, in relation with their policy of CO_2 emission reduction (Brown, 2000).

4.   Future challenges

The further *refinement of the measurement of agricultural greenhouse gas emissions and sinks* would improve accuracy, in particular through close co-ordination and co-operation with national efforts and the IPCC. While research to improve agricultural GHG emission estimates continues under the IPCC, refining livestock enteric fermentation CH_4 emission factors and analysing the role of agricultural soils as a sink, for example, would enhance emission and sink estimates. Such efforts would allow for a better understanding of the sink functions of agriculture, and could focus on the need to enhance sink capacity by improvements in tillage practices, crop cover, crop residue management and other agricultural practices. The development of a more comprehensive indicator incorporating sink capacity would show the net affect of agriculture on GHG emissions.[21]

Many OECD countries have engaged in the work related to *energy use and efficiency in agriculture*, including biofuel and wind energy production. It may be possible to develop indicators that could monitor developments in the renewable energy area related to agriculture. These include indicators of the area of agricultural land planted with energy crops, and the quantity of non-wood biofuel produced by agriculture, for example ethanol made from maize and crop residues burnt for energy. In addition, the reduction in CO_2 emission from fossil fuel combustion through replacement by biofuel burning (or "GHG savings") could be directly incorporated into a comprehensive indicator covering all agricultural GHG sources and sinks.

Indicators in terms of GHG emissions per unit of output could also be developed, which would add to information on the *economic efficiency of energy use in agriculture*. The development of such indicators should consider an appropriate choice of units, *e.g.* monetary, energy or weight of dry matter. *Canada*, for example, has reported the compilation of an energy balance of inputs and outputs within agriculture, concluding that the growth rate of energy outputs was higher than inputs, while the direction and magnitude of changes in specific energy use varied (MacGregor *et al.*, 2000).

NOTES

1. The changes during the period from about 1750 to 1992 are estimated by IPCC (1996a) as: Carbon dioxide (CO_2) from about 280 to almost 360 parts per million by volume (ppmv), methane (CH_4) from 700 to 1 720 parts per billion (thousand million) by volume (ppbv), and nitrous oxide (N_2O) from 275 to 310 ppbv.

2. UNFCCC requires the countries listed in its Annex I to have specific commitments on GHG emission levels. The list covers 35 countries including most OECD countries, except Korea and Mexico. All OECD countries have ratified the Convention, except Turkey.

3. The Kyoto protocol specified in its Annex A the six targeted GHGs subject to commitments: carbon dioxide (CO_2), methane (CH_4), nitrous oxide (N_2O), hydrofluorocarbons (HFCs), perfluorocarbons (PFCs) and sulphur hexafluoride (SF_6). The three fluoride gases are not related to agricultural activities.

4. Commitment levels are listed in Annex B of the Kyoto Protocol. The list covers 38 countries, including all OECD countries except Korea, Mexico and Turkey.

5. See Hedger (1996) for policy and technical options for net GHG reduction in agriculture, and Symbiotics Environment Research and Consulting (1996) for technologies to reduce GHG emissions from agriculture. OECD (1998, pp. 193-203), also discusses economic policies in general to reduce GHG emissions.

6. Further information on the Kyoto Protocol, the COP3 (Kyoto, 1997), COP4 (Buenos Aires, 1998), COP5 (Bonn, 1999), COP6 (The Hague, 2000) and activities of subsidiary bodies is available at *www.unfccc.de*.

7. The impact of global warming and climate change on agriculture is not further discussed in this Report. For further information on the effects of climate change on agriculture in general see Enquete Commission (1995), IPCC (1996b) and Parry and Swaminathan (1992). For the effects in particular countries, see Adams *et al.* (1999), Council on Environmental Quality (1997), Phipps and Hall (1994) and USDA (1996).

8. This includes a general shift of agricultural production toward higher latitudes with substantial regional variations.

9. Acceleration of plant growth by higher concentration of CO_2, under satisfactory soil and water conditions and nutrient supply, is known as the "fertiliser effect". On the other hand, responses of crop yields to higher temperatures is not simple, as an increase in the minimum temperature may result in higher yields, while too high temperatures may reduce yields (Nicholls, 1997).

10. See IPCC (1996c) and IPCC (1997) for further information on the process of GHG emissions in general, and EPA (1993) for CH_4 emissions.

11. Emission factors of enteric fermentation (Kg CH_4 per head per year) are 100 for dairy cattle, 48 for beef cattle, 8 for sheep and 1.5 for pigs (IPCC, 1997).

12. For further information on soil management and greenhouse gases, see Lal *et al.* (1995b).

13. Land use change has a large potential affect on greenhouse gas sources and sinks, although there remain substantial uncertainties on the magnitude of these changes (IPCC, 2000b). Carbon credit trading, a Kyoto-protocol mechanism allowing flexibility for countries in meeting their commitments, has already started to encourage tree-planting projects outside the committing countries, which may affect land use change from and to marginal agricultural land (see an example in Australia at: *www.carbontrading.com.au/*).

14. The contribution to global warming of upstream/downstream agro-food industries is not discussed in this Report.

15. For example, methane emission from intermittently drained paddy fields is less than half of that from continuously flooded fields (Yagi, 1997).

16. The "default" methodologies for estimation of greenhouse gas emissions and removals are provided in the IPCC Guidelines (IPCC, 1997), while countries are encouraged to provide information to replace the minimum default methods where possible.

17. The Global Warming Potentials (GWPs) reflect the different potential of each gas to contribute to global warming relative to CO_2 (see the table below). GWPs depend on the time span concerned because each GHG has a different atmospheric lifetime and consequently the cumulative radiative absorption of gases varies. Due to the alteration of atmospheric composition, GWPs also change over time, however, estimates of GWPs involve considerable uncertainties due to limited scientific knowledge.

Gas/Time span	20 years	100 years	500 years
Carbon dioxide (CO_2)	1	1	1
Methane (CH_4)	56	21	6.5
Nitrous oxide (N_2O)	280	310	170

Source: IPCC (1996c).

18. The sources of agricultural fossil fuel combustion include vehicle traction, grain drying and horticultural greenhouse heating (IPCC 1997). For EU countries, data on CO_2 emissions from fossil fuel combustion in agriculture (i.e. those in forestry and fisheries are excluded) are available from EUROSTAT (1997).

19. A recent report (IPCC, 2000a) provides detailed technical guidance in reporting national GHG emissions for the IPCC inventories.

20. For a comparison of different simulation models on trends in soil organic carbon, see Smith et al. (1997). See also Mitchell et al. (1996) for such a modelling approach in the United States, and Orthofer (1999), and Schipmann (1999) in Europe.

21. The economics of agricultural soil carbon sequestration is discussed by Antle et al., 2000.

Annex Table 1. **Total national emissions of agricultural greenhouse gases:**[1] **1990-92 to 1995-97**

	Emissions from agriculture in carbon dioxide equivalent			Total national emissions in carbon dioxide equivalent		Share of agriculture in total national emissions
	Million tonnes		% change[4]	Million tonnes		%
	1990-92[2]	1995-97[3]		1990-92[2]	1995-97[3]	1995-97[4]
Australia	86	85	−2	412	433	19.5
Austria	5	5	1	75	76	7.0
Belgium	13	15	11	141	147	10.0
Canada	58	65	12	592	661	9.8
Czech Republic	8	5	−38	175	152	3.3
Denmark	18	18	1	77	85	21.7
Finland	7	6	−14	72	75	8.2
France	98	95	−3	565	551	17.3
Germany	70	65	−8	1 148	1 051	6.2
Greece	15	14	−2	104	109	13.3
Hungary	6	4	−30	85	78	5.8
Iceland	0	0	−5	3	3	11.0
Ireland	20	20	−1	57	59	34.0
Italy	50	51	1	533	529	9.6
Japan	21	19	−6	1 195	1 279	1.5
Luxembourg	1	1	−2	13	11	4.6
Netherlands	26	27	4	212	224	12.2
New Zealand	42	41	−1	72	74	55.8
Norway	5	5	0	46	52	9.9
Poland	28	22	−20	449	431	5.1
Portugal	8	8	−5	71	72	10.5
Spain	43	43	0	305	320	13.5
Sweden	10	10	0	69	73	13.7
Switzerland	6	6	−6	54	53	10.8
Turkey	18	17	−7	207	251	6.8
United Kingdom	55	54	−1	719	668	8.1
United States	442	474	7	5 904	6 400	7.4
EU-15	439	432	−2	4 162	4 051	10.7
OECD[5]	1 160	1 176	1	13 356	13 918	8.4

1. Gross emissions of CH_4 and N_2O from agricultural sources, and CO_2 from fossil fuel combustion in agriculture (fossil fuel from forestry and fisheries is included for non-EU countries). CO_2 emission is not included for Australia, Austria, the Czech Republic, Japan, New Zealand, Poland, Switzerland, Turkey and the United States.
2. 1990 data for Finland, Italy, Luxembourg and Sweden. For CH_4 and N_2O, average of 1990 and 1992 for Poland and Turkey.
3. For CO_2, 1996 data for EU countries, and 1995 data for others. For CH_4 and N_2O, 1996-97 average for Poland and Sweden; average of 1995 and 1997 for Turkey; 1994-96 average for Australia, Belgium, Greece, Hungary, Ireland and the Netherlands; 1994-95 average for Iceland, Italy, Luxembourg and Spain; 1993-94 average for Portugal.
4. Calculated from unrounded data.
5. Korea and Mexico are not included.
Sources: OECD Secretariat; UNFCCC (1999); EUROSTAT (1997); Turkish Ministry of Environment (1998).

BIBLIOGRAPHY

Adams, R.M., B.H. Hurd and J. Reilly (1999),
Agriculture and global climate changes, A *review of impacts to* US *agricultural resources*, Pew Center on Global Climate Change, Arlington, United States. Available at: *www.pewclimate.org/* [> Projects and Reports].

Antle, J.M, S.M. Capalbo, S. Mooney, E. Elliot and K. Paustian (2000),
Economics of Agricultural Soil Carbon Sequestration in the Northern Plains, Research Discussion Paper No. 38, Trade Research Center, Montana State University, Bozeman, Montana, United States. Available at: *www.trc.montana.edu/* [Publications > Research Discussion Papers].

Brown, L.R. (2000),
US *farmers double cropping corn and wind energy*, Worldwatch Issue Alerts, Worldwatch Institute, Washington, DC. United States. Available at: *www.worldwatch.org/chairman/* [> Issue Alerts].

Council on Environmental Quality (1997),
Environmental Quality 1994-95 Report, 25th Report of the United States Council on Environmental Quality, Washington, DC., United States. Available at: *www.whitehouse.gov/CEQ/* [News and Information > Publications].

Desjardins, R.L. and R. Riznek (2000),
Agricultural Greenhouse Gas Budget, pp. 133-140, in T. McRae, C.A.S. Smith and L.J. Gregorich (eds.) *Environmental Sustainability of Canadian Agriculture: Report of the Agri-Environmental Indicator Project*, Agriculture and Agri-Food Canada (AAFC), Ottawa, Ontario, Canada. Available at: *www.agr.ca/policy/environment/publications list.html*.

Enquete Commission (1995),
"Protecting Our Green Earth: How to manage global warming through environmentally sound farming and preservation of the world's forests", in Enquete Commission, *Protecting the Earth's Atmosphere*, Bundestag, Verlag, Bonn, Germany.

EPA [Environmental Protection Agency] (1993),
Options for Reducing Methane Emissions Internationally Volume II: International Opportunity for Reducing Methane Emissions, Report to Congress, EPA 430-R-93-006B, October 1993, Washington, DC., United States. Available at: *www.epa.gov. ghginfo/* [> Reports].

European Parliament (1993),
Energy and Biomass, Scientific and Technical Options Assessment, Project paper No. 1, revised version, Stuttgart Germany.

EUROSTAT [Statistical Office of the European Communities] (1997),
Carbon Dioxide Emissions from Fossil Fuels, Luxembourg.

Hedger, M.M. (1996),
Agriculture and Forestry, Identification of Options for Net GHG Reduction, "Policies and Measures for Common Action" Working Paper 7, Annex I Expert Group on the UNFCCC, edited by the OECD, OECD General Distribution document [OCDE/GD(97)74], Paris, France. Available at: *www.oecd.org/* [Documentation > 1997 > Reference Components > OCDE > OCDE/GD].

IEA [International Energy Agency] (1998),
Renewable Energy Policy in IEA Countries, Volume II: Country Reports, Paris, France. Available at: *www.iea.org.* [Publications > Studies published 1998 and before].

IFEN [Institut français de l'environnement] (1997),
Agriculture et environnement: les indicateurs (only in French, "Agriculture and the Environment: Indicators"), édition 1997-1998, Orléans, France. Available at: *www.ifen.fr/* [> Publications].

IPCC [Intergovernmental Panel on Climate Change] (1996a),
Climate Change 1995: IPCC Second Assessment Synthesis of Scientific-technical Information Related to Interpreting Article 2 of the UN Framework Convention on Climate Change 1995, Bracknell, United Kingdom. Available at: *www.ipcc.ch/* [Publications > Reports].

IPCC (1996*b*),

Climate Change 1995: Impacts, Adaptations and Mitigation of Climate Change: Scientific-Technical Analyses. Contribution of Working Group II to the Second Assessment report of the IPCC, R.T. Watson, M.C. Zinyowera and R.H. Moss (eds.), Cambridge University Press, United Kingdom. Available at: *www.ipcc.ch/* [Publications > Reports].

IPCC (1996*c*),

Climate Change 1995: The Science of Climate Change, Contribution of Working Group I to the Second Assessment of the Intergovernmental Panel on Climate Change, J.T. Houghton, L.G. Meira Filho, B.A. Callender, N. Harris, A. Kattenberg and K. Maskell (eds.), Cambridge University Press, United Kingdom. Available at: *www.ipcc.ch/* [Publications > Reports].

IPCC (1997),

Revised 1996 IPCC Guidelines for National Greenhouse Gas Inventories , Reporting Instructions, Workbook and Reference Manual, Bracknell, United Kingdom. Available at: *www.ipcc.ch/* [Publications > Guidelines and Methodologies].

IPCC (2000*a*),

Good Practice Guidance and Uncertainty Management in National Greenhouse Gas Inventories, Bracknell, United Kingdom. Available at: *www.ipcc.ch/*.

IPCC (2000*b*),

Land Use, Land-Use Change, and Forestry, Special Report of the IPCC, R.T. Watson, I.R. Noble, B. Bolin, N.H. Ravindranath, D.J. Verardo and D.J. Dokken (eds.), Cambridge University Press, United Kingdom. Available at: *www.ipcc.ch/* [Publications > Reports].

Janzen, H.H., R.L. Desjardins, J.M.R. Asselin and B. Grace (eds.) (1999),

The Health of Our Air – Toward sustainable agriculture in Canada, Agriculture and Agri-Food Canada (AAFC), Ottawa, Canada. Available at: *www.agr.ca/* [English > Site Index > Environment and Resource Management].

Johnson, M.G. (1995),

"The Role of Soil Management in Sequestering Soil Carbon", pp. 351-363, in R. Lal, J. Kimble, E. Levine and B.A. Stewart (eds.), Advances in Soil Science: Soil Management and Greenhouse Effect, Lewis Publishers, London, United Kingdom.

Lal, R., J. Kimble and B.A. Stewart (1995*a*),

"World Soil as a Source or Sink for Radiatively-Active Gases", pp. 1-7, in R. Lal, J. Kimble, E. Levine and B.A. Stewart (eds.), Advances in Soil Science: Soil Management and Greenhouse Effect, Lewis Publishers, London, United Kingdom.

Lal, R., J. Kimble, E. Levine and B.A. Stewart (eds.) (1995*b*),

Advances in Soil Science: Soil Management and Greenhouse Effect, Lewis Publishers, London, United Kingdom.

Lal, R., N.R. Fausey and D.J. Eckert (1995*c*),

"Land Use and Soil Management Effects on Emissions of Radiatively Active Gases from Two Soils in Ohio", pp. 41-59, in R. Lal J. Kimble, E. Levine and B.A. Stewart (eds.), Advances in Soil Science: Soil Management and Greenhouse Effect, Lewis Publishers, London, United Kingdom.

Li, C. (1995),

"Modelling Impact of Agricultural Practices on Soil C and N_2O Emissions", pp. 101-112, in R. Lal, J. Kimble, E. Levine and B.A. Stewart (eds.), Advances in Soil Science: Soil Management and Greenhouse Effect, Lewis Publishers, London, United Kingdom.

MacGregor, R.J., R. Lindenbach, S. Weseen and A. Lefebvre (2000),

"Energy Use", Chapter 17, pp. 171-177, in T. McRae, C.A.S. Smith and L.J. Gregorich (eds.), Environmental Sustainability of Canadian Agriculture: Report of the Agri-Environmental Indicator Project, Agriculture and Agri-Food Canada (AAFC), Ottawa, Ontario, Canada. Available at: *www.agr.ca/policy/environment/publications/list.html*.

MAFF [Ministry of Agriculture, Fisheries and Food] (1998),

Developing a Set of Indicators for Sustainable Agriculture in the United Kingdom, Consultation Document, London, United Kingdom.

MAFF (2000),

Towards Sustainable Agriculture – A Pilot Set of Indicators, London, United Kingdom. Available at: *www.maff.gov.uk/* [Farming > Sustainable Agriculture].

Mitchell, P.D., P.G. Lakshminarayan, T. Otake and B.A. Babcock (1996),

The Impact of Soil Conservation Policies on Carbon Sequestration in Agricultural Soils of the Central United States, Working Paper 96-WP 170, Center for Agriculture and Rural Development (CARD), Iowa State University, Ames, Iowa, United States.

Nicholls, N. (1997),

"Have recent climate trends increased Australian crop yield and value?", Climate Change News Letter, Vol. 9, No. 3, pp. 11-13, Bureau of Resource Science, Kingston, Australia. Available at: *www.brs.gov.au/* [Greenhouse and Climate Change > Climate Change Newsletter].

OECD (1994),
   Energy and the Environment: Biofuel, Paris, France.

OECD (1998),
   OECD *Economic Outlook*, No. 63, Paris, France.

Orthofer, R (1999),
   "An Integrative Carbon Balance for Austrian Agriculture", pp. 121-136, in A. Freibauer and M. Kaltschmitt (eds.),
   Approaches to Greenhouse Gas Inventories of Biogenic Sources in Agriculture, Proceedings of the Workshop at Lökeberg,
   Sweden, 9-10 July 1998.

Parry, M.L. and M.S. Swaminathan (1992),
   "Effects of Climate Change on Food Production", in I.M. Mintzer (ed.), *Confronting Climate Change, Risk, Implications
   and Responses*, Cambridge University Press, United Kingdom.

Phipps, S. and N. Hall (1994),
   Reducing Greenhouse Gas Emissions from Australian Agriculture – A Regional Analysis, Australian Bureau of Agricultural
   and Resource Economics, Research Report 94.5, Canberra, Australia.

Schipmann, R. (1999),
   "A European Model for Carbon-Turnover in Agricultural Soils (SOMMS 1.0)", pp. 183-186, in A. Freibauer and
   M. Kaltschmitt (eds.), *Approaches to Greenhouse Gas Inventories of Biogenic Sources in Agriculture*, Proceedings of the
   Workshop at Lökeberg, Sweden, 9-10 July 1998.

Smith, P., J.U. Smith, D.S. Powlson, W.B. McGill, J.R.M. Arah, O.G. Chertov, K. Coleman, U. Franko, S. Frolking,
   D.S. Jenkinson, L.S. Jensen, R.H. Kelly, H. Klein-Gunnewiek, A.S. Komarov, C. Li, J.A.E. Molina, T. Mueller, W. J. Parton
   J.H.M. Thornley and A.P. Whitmore (1997),
   "A comparison of the performance of nine soil organic matter models using data sets from seven long term
   experiments", *Geoderma*, Vol. 81, pp. 153-225.

Sneath, R.W., D.R. Chadwick, V.R. Phillips and B.F. Pain (1997*a*),
   A U.K. *Inventory of Methane Emissions from Farmland Livestock*, Silsoe Research Institute, Devon, United Kingdom.

Sneath, R.W., D.R. Chadwick, V.R. Phillips and B.F. Pain (1997*b*),
   A U.K. *Inventory of Nitrous Oxide Emissions from Farmland Livestock*, Silsoe Research Institute, Devon, United Kingdom.

Symbiotics Environmental Research and Consulting (1996),
   Inventory of Technologies to Reduce Greenhouse Gas Emissions from Agriculture, Ottawa, Canada.

Turkish Ministry of Environment (1998),
   National Report on Climate Change, Ankara, Turkey.

UNFCCC [United Nations Framework Convention on Climate Change] (1998),
   Review of the Implementation of Commitments and of Other Provisions of the Convention, National Communications from Parties
   Included in Annex I to the Convention, Second Compilation and Synthesis of Second National Communications
   [FCCC/CP/1998/11/Add.1], General distribution paper presented at the Fourth Session of the Conference of the
   Parties, 2-13 November, Buenos Aires, Argentina. Available at: *http://cop4.unfccc.de* [Official Documents > COP4].

UNFCCC (1999),
   Report on National Greenhouse Gas Inventory Data from Annex I Parties for 1990 to 1997, National Communications from
   Parties Included in Annex I to the Convention, Greenhouse Gas Inventory Data, 1990-1997, [FCCC/SBI/1999/12]
   General distribution paper presented at the Eleventh Session of the Subsidiary Body for Implementation
   25 October – 5 November, Bonn. Available at: *http://cop5.unfccc.de* [Official Documents > SBI Reports 1999] Also
   related searchable database is available at: *www.unfccc.de/*.

USDA [United States Department of Agriculture] (1996),
   Agricultural Adaptation to Climate Change, Issues of Longrun Sustainability, Agricultural Economic Report No. 740
   Washington, DC., United States. Available at: *www.ers.usda.gov/epubs/pdf/aer740/*.

USDA (1997),
   "Global Climate Change: Could US Agriculture Adapt?", *Agricultural Outlook*, January-February 1997, Economic
   Research Service, Washington, DC., United States.

Yagi, K. (1997),
   "Methane Emissions from Paddy Fields", *Bulletin of the National Institute of Agro-Environmental Sciences*, No. 14,
   pp. 96-207, Tsukuba, Japan.

Chapter 5

BIODIVERSITY

HIGHLIGHTS

Context

Agriculture as the human activity occupying the largest share of the total land area for nearly all OECD countries, plays a key role with regard to biodiversity which is highly dependent on land use. The expansion of farm production and intensification of input use are considered a major cause of the loss of biodiversity, while at the same time certain agro-ecosystems can serve to maintain biodiversity. Farming is also dependent on many biological services, such as the provision of genes to develop improved crop varieties and livestock breeds, crop pollination, and soil fertility provided by micro-organisms. In some cases non-native species cause damage to crops from alien pests and competition for livestock forage.

The main focus of policy actions in the area of biodiversity has been to protect and conserve endangered species and habitats, but some countries have also begun to develop more holistic national biodiversity strategy plans. These plans usually incorporate the agricultural sector in biodiversity conservation. At the international level a range of agreements are also important in the context of agriculture and biodiversity, most notably, the International Convention on Biological Diversity.

Indicators and recent trends

A number of biodiversity indicators are being established by OECD within the general framework of genetic, species and ecosystem diversity (the latter is covered under Wildlife Habitat indicators). The indicators provide a coherent, but initial, picture of biodiversity in relation to agriculture.

Concerning *genetic diversity*, three indicators cover the diversity of crop varieties and livestock breeds used by agriculture. Overall these indicators reveal that diversity has increased for many OECD countries since the mid-1980s, in terms of the share of varieties/breeds in total crop production/livestock numbers. This suggests agriculture has improved its resilience to environmental changes through diversifying the number of varieties/breeds used in production.

A fourth genetic diversity indicator provides information on the extent of genetic erosion and loss of agricultural plants and livestock. While information on genetic erosion or loss is incomplete, evidence for a limited number of countries suggests significant losses and/or the endangerment of loss of genetic resources in agriculture over recent decades. The collections in genebanks, however, in general continue to grow, both public and private collections.

Indicators for *species diversity* cover trends in population distributions and numbers of: *i*) wildlife species dependent on or affected by agriculture, and *ii*) non-native species threatening agricultural production and agro-ecosystems.

While information on the *impact of agriculture on wild species* is limited for many OECD countries, it appears agricultural land provides an important habitat area for the wildlife that remains following the conversion to agricultural land use, but especially birds, vascular plants and some invertebrates, such as butterflies. Also, the population trends of wildlife species using agricultural land as habitat indicate in most cases a reduction over the past decade. This represents the continuation of a longer-term trend, although the decline has slowed or even reversed over recent years in some countries. Even so considerable numbers of wildlife species using agricultural land as habitat are under threat of being lost.

For *non-native species*, there is no systematic time series available across OECD countries, although their harmful effects on agricultural production and agro-ecosystems are reported for many countries. There has been a long history of non-native species introductions across countries, with the extent of economic losses to farming and damage to native biodiversity from their introduction varying widely.

I. Background

Policy context

The preservation and enhancement of biodiversity poses a major challenge for agricultural policy decision makers, as world population and demand for food increase. It is estimated that, with current population trends, food production will have to increase by 24 per cent by the year 2020 just to maintain the existing levels of food consumption and without any significant expansion of agricultural area. Policy makers will therefore need to find ways of minimising the conflicts between expanding production and biodiversity conservation, enhancing the many complementarities between agriculture and biodiversity, and finding ways to prevent the loss of biodiversity on agricultural land (Pagiola and Kellenberg, 1997).

Most agricultural policy affects, directly or indirectly, biodiversity. For a growing number of OECD countries, protecting and enhancing biodiversity is becoming an important part of their domestic and international agri-environmental policy objectives and actions. These policy actions are in response to a growing public concern over the increasing pressure and harmful impacts on natural and semi-natural ecosystems brought about through a variety of causes, including agricultural activity. There is also the perceived threat that damage to biodiversity could be highly detrimental to human welfare over the long term, although the consequences are complex and poorly understood (Smith, 1996).

In practice, implicitly or explicitly, government policy towards biodiversity involves balancing the trade-offs between socio-economic values and biodiversity conservation. Typically policy target options with a low level of ambition (such as target 1 in Figure 1, the threshold level below which species are endangered), can avoid short-term costs but may potentially lead to costs over the long term, such as risks to agricultural production due to genetic erosion. Different policy options and targets with a higher level of ambition toward biodiversity conservation (such as targets 2 and 3 in Figure 1), will require scientific research, including developing biodiversity indicators. Indicators can help support the decision-making process by providing information about the risks and degrees of sustainability associated with these different options.

Figure 1. **Policy target options for biodiversity**

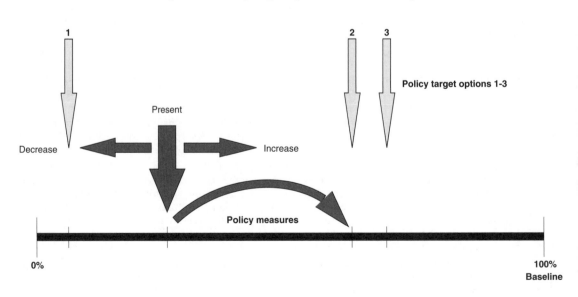

Source: Adapted from Ed Van Klink (National Reference Centre for Agriculture, The Netherlands), presentation to the OECD Workshop on Agri-environmental Indicators, York, United Kingdom, September, 1998.

Up to present the main focus of policy actions in the area of biodiversity has been to protect and conserve endangered species and habitats. Many OECD countries have introduced legislation for the protection of specific endangered species and habitats, and also designated certain areas as biosphere reserves, nature parks, and other protected sites.

In moving toward a more holistic approach, some OECD countries have begun to develop national biodiversity strategy plans, which usually incorporate the agricultural sector as a key player in biodiversity conservation. These strategy plans set out the relevant policy objectives and targets for managing and sustaining biodiversity. They also provide a starting point for establishing policy relevant biodiversity indicators to measure the performance of national policies and help monitor progress in fulfilling international obligations.

In most OECD countries a wide spectrum of organisations are also involved in the conservation of plant and animal genetic resources. However, the way these conservation efforts are organised varies across countries, ranging from involvement of governmental and non-governmental organisations, and from amateur collections to commercial companies. Some countries have national genebanks, others have several specialised agricultural research institutes responsible for the maintenance of agricultural genetic resources, while some countries work together in regional genebank networks.

At the international level a range of agreements and conventions are also important in the context of agriculture and biodiversity, most notably the International Convention on Biological Diversity (CBD) agreed at the UN Conference on Environment and Development at Rio in 1992 (Box 1). Recognition has been given by the CBD to the significance of biodiversity for agriculture. This has led the FAO to request member countries to negotiate, through the FAO inter-governmental Commission on Genetic Resources for Food and Agriculture (CGRFA), the revision of the international undertaking on plant genetic resources in agriculture in harmony with the CBD (Box 1).[1] In addition, in January 2000 within the overall context of the CBD, the Biosafety Protocol was agreed by 130 nations. This was the first major international agreement to control trade in genetically modified organisms (GMOs), covering food, animal feed and seeds.[2]

Other related international conventions include, for example, the Convention on International Trade in Endangered Species of Wild Fauna and Flora (CITES, 1973), the Convention on Wetlands (Ramsar Convention, 1971), the Convention on Migratory Species of Wild Animals (Bonn, 1983), the North American Waterfowl Management Plan (see Box 6), and the Canada-United States Migratory Birds Convention (1995).[3] The Commission for Environmental Cooperation, created by *Canada, Mexico* and the *United States* to examine the environmental provisions of the North America Free Trade Agreement, has begun to develop a strategy for improving biodiversity in North America, including the role of agriculture (CEC, 2000).

Environmental context[4]

The effects of agriculture on biodiversity are of considerable importance because farming is the human activity occupying the largest share of the total land area for many OECD countries. Even for countries where the share of agriculture in the total land area is smaller, agriculture can help by increasing the diversity of habitat types. The expansion of agricultural production and intensive use of inputs over recent decades in OECD countries is considered a major contributor to the loss of biodiversity.

At the same time certain agricultural ecosystems can serve to maintain biodiversity, which may create conditions to favour species-rich communities, but that might be endangered by fallowing or changing to a different land use, such as forestry.[5] Agricultural food and fibre production is also dependent on many biological services. This can include, for example, the provision of genes for development of improved crop varieties and livestock breeds, crop pollination and soil fertility provided by micro-organisms.

The interactions between agriculture and biodiversity are complex and diverse. This complexity is, to a major extent, reflected in the large range of services that biodiversity provides to society as, for

---

Box 1.   The International Convention on Biological Diversity

The Convention on Biological Diversity (CBD), was "open for signature" at the UN Conference on Environment and Development at Rio de Janeiro, Brazil, in 1992. The objectives of the Convention, "are the conservation of biodiversity, the sustainable use of its components and the fair and equitable sharing of the benefits arising out of the utilisation of genetic resources, including by appropriate access to genetic resources and by appropriate transfer of relevant technologies, taking into account all rights over those resources and to technologies, and by appropriate funding."

According to the CBD, "biological diversity means the variability among living organisms from all sources including, inter alia, terrestrial, marine and other aquatic ecosystems and the ecological complexes of which they are part; this includes diversity within species, between species and of ecosystems". The term "biodiversity" thus refers to the variety of all life on earth, and explicitly recognises how the interaction of the different components of ecosystems results in the provision of essential ecosystem services on the one hand, and social and recreational opportunities on the other, including being a source of inspiration and cultural identity.

At the third Conference of the Parties meeting of the CBD in 1997, it was agreed that countries should be encouraged to develop national strategies with respect to agriculture that would:

- identify key components of biological diversity in agricultural production systems that are responsible for maintaining natural processes and cycles;

- monitor and evaluate the effects of agricultural practices and technologies on biological diversity in agriculture and encourage the adoption of repairing practices;

- develop and promote the application of methods and indicators to monitor and evaluate *ex ante* and/or *ex post* impacts of agricultural development projects on biological diversity, especially in developing countries;

- study the positive and negative impacts on ecosystems and biomass of the intensification or extensification of production systems.

In the assessment of relevant ongoing activities and existing instruments under the CBD, indicator development, monitoring, and assessment are identified as major areas for consideration in programmes and action plans. The CBD Secretariat and FAO have identified the further development of the programme of work on agricultural biological diversity to:

- identify, develop and document indicators for assessment and monitoring and to improve understanding of the causes of and changes in agricultural biological diversity;

- focus on indicators for assessing changes at the agro-ecosystem level and on the economic forces that influence these changes; and

- link indicators and assessment with particular dimensions of agricultural biological diversity, such as sustainable production, biological conservation, ecological or life support functions and social services.

Note: For details of the CBD Convention see the CBD Secretariat website at: *www.biodiv.org/* Concerning aspects of the CBD related to agriculture see also the website: *www.biodiv.org/agro/*.

Source: Adapted from OECD (1999).

example, illustrated in Box 2 for *New Zealand*. The importance of biodiversity for agriculture involves (OECD, 1996, p. 20):

- facilitating the functioning of ecosystems, such as nutrient cycling, protection and enrichment of soils, pollination, regulation of temperature and local climates, and watershed filtration;

- providing the source of most of the world's food and fibre products, including the basis for crop and livestock genetic resources, their improvement, and the development of new resources; and,

- offering a range of scientific, health/medicinal, cultural, aesthetic, recreational and other intangible (and non-monetary values) and services from biodiversity richness and abundance.

Box 2.   **The Value of Biodiversity to New Zealand**

Biodiversity is New Zealand's biological wealth. New Zealanders base much of their economy on the use of biological resources, and benefit from the services provided by healthy ecosystems (such as raw materials, water purification, waste decomposition). Yet these services tend to be taken for granted because they are provided "free of charge" by nature.

A 1997 study by economists estimated that the annual value provided by New Zealand's indigenous biodiversity (including direct uses, indirect uses of ecosystem services, passive value, and marine ecosystems) at about NZ$ 230 billion (US$ 152 billion), compared with a Gross Domestic Product (GDP) of NZ$ 84 billion (US$56 billion). Aside from the use of biological resources used, New Zealand's biodiversity represents a pool of untapped opportunities. There are almost certainly other species with potentially useful and commercially valuable components yet to be discovered.

New Zealand's land-based primary production – farming, forestry, and horticulture – is reliant on the protection and management of biological systems. Maintaining the genetic diversity of the small number of introduced species on which these industries are based is crucial to their resilience to environmental change and usefulness for the nation's primary industries.

In addition to New Zealand's productive systems being underpinned by healthy ecosystems, a "clean and green" environment is a major selling point in itself and will reap increasing rewards as the country enters the 21st century. New Zealand primary producers target customers who enjoy high-quality products that come from a healthy and unpolluted environment. This is also the foundation of the tourist industry. However, increasingly critical international clients expect the green image to be backed up by reality.

Apart from the value of biodiversity in sustaining the present quality of life, to many people biodiversity has intrinsic value – the value of the variety of life itself. The responsibility of people towards other living things, and our obligations to future generations, provide a strong moral basis for their conservation and underlie the international requirements in the Convention on Biological Diversity.

Source: Adapted from: Ministry for the Environment, *Environmental Performance Indicators: Summary of Proposed Indicators for Terrestrial and Freshwater Biodiversity*, November 1998, Wellington, New Zealand.

Biodiversity, as it relates to agriculture, can be considered in terms of three levels, drawing on the Convention on Biological Diversity definition of biodiversity (Box 1):

- *genetic diversity* ("within species"): the diversity of genes within domesticated plants and livestock species and wild relatives;

- *species diversity* ("between species"): the number and population of wild species (flora and fauna) affected by agriculture, including soil biota and the effects of non-native species on agriculture and biodiversity;

- *ecosystem diversity* ("of ecosystems"): the ecosystems formed by populations of species relevant to agriculture or species communities dependent on agricultural habitats.

The survival of these three levels of diversity is dependent on the health of each other, as genetic diversity fosters the survival of species, enabling it to adapt to changing ecosystem conditions (see also Box 1 in the Wildlife Habitats chapter). A loss of species or the introduction of non-native species, can disturb the ecosystem diversity and alter its resilience to further changes (OECD, 1997).

Genetic diversity

Genetic diversity provides the means for agriculture to improve crop and livestock yields. Selective plant and animal breeding programmes in all OECD countries, drawing on a variety of genetic material, has helped to increase agricultural production with fewer inputs. In the United States it is estimated that over the past 60 years, half of agriculture's productivity increases can be attributed to genetic improvements.

Traditionally farmers have relied on "landraces", that is, varieties of crops or livestock breeds developed over many generations to raise yields. As these "landraces" have been adapted for specific environmental conditions and farming systems, the genetic diversity is usually very high. With the advent of modern "hybrid" breeding methods, which selects for specific desirable traits such as pest and disease resistance, maturation and stature, the yields of crops and livestock have been raised substantially. This process is likely to be accelerated with recent developments in biotechnology, such as those involving genetic modification, cloning, and other such technologies. These "new" technologies, however, have also raised concerns about their possible effects on human health, wild species, genetic erosion, the environment and development of genes resistant to pesticides.[6]

While more recent advances in genetic improvements have helped raise agricultural productivity, the short-term strategy of relying on a "relatively" small number of varieties/breeds has raised concerns about the greater susceptibility to the risks of pests and diseases spreading through a crop variety or livestock breed. Often quoted examples include the 15 per cent reduction in United States maize yields due to the southern maize leaf blight in the early 1970s causing an estimated loss to producers and consumers of more than US$2 billion. Also, the citrus canker led to the loss of 12 million orange and grapefruit trees in Florida, United States, in the mid-1980s.

Breeding commercial species with wild relatives, however, has played a critical role in combating pests and diseases (Perrings, 1998). A Mexican maize variety led to the recovery of the United States maize crop following losses from the maize leaf blight in the early 1970s and a gene from an Ethiopian barley variety has provided protection for the barley crop in Canada and the United States (California). In general, hybrid crop varieties developed for a specific pest or disease resistance trait retain their resistance for an average of 5 to 8 years, while it usually takes 8 to 11 years to develop new varieties.

Farmers usually react quickly to the financial returns on the crops they cultivate and this can result in rapid changes in the areas of different crops and crop varieties under cultivation. Hence, plant and livestock breeders need to continually search for infusions of new genetic material to maintain and improve yields. In this context, national and international efforts to collect, preserve and utilise plant and animal genetic resources from landraces and "wild" relatives are of vital importance.

Species diversity

While estimates of the global total number of species vary greatly, it is clear that the total number is very large.[7] In the context of agriculture, biodiversity "richness" can differ according to specific climatic and agro-ecosystem conditions, and the type of farming management practices and systems adopted. Farming systems based on multiple crops and livestock with natural pasture areas are richer in biodiversity than monocultural farms. However, regardless of the type of farming system, agriculture by seeking to maximise the yield of a limited number of plant and animal species, inevitably weakens and reduces competition from other unwanted species (Debailleul, 1997).

Species diversity and its relationship with agriculture is important in a number of different ways, which can be categorised as follows:

- *Species supporting agricultural production systems*, the so called "life-support-system", that is crypto-biota, including soil micro-organisms, earth worms, pest controlling species and pollinators.

- *Species related to agricultural activities*, covering *a*) wild species using agricultural land as habitat ranging from marginal use to complete dependence on agro-ecosystems, and *b*) wild species that use other habitats but are affected by farming activities, such as the impact of farm chemical run-off on marine life in coastal waters.

- *Non-native species* that can threaten agricultural production and agro-ecosystems, such as invasion of weeds and pests that are alien to indigenous biodiversity.

Important amongst the *species that support agricultural production systems* are soil micro-organisms or soil biodiversity, although soil life covers an extremely wide range of forms from viruses to mammals.[8] The main functions of soil micro-organisms are in processing part of the nitrogen and carbon cycle, and thereby, safeguarding soil fertility, although research in this area is still at an early stage (see Soil Quality chapter).

For insect pests the presence of predators is important to agriculture, but where pesticide use has been poorly managed, this has led to the reduction of predator populations, leading to more serious pest outbreaks. Pollinators, mainly insects, are also vital to the production of some agricultural crops. The recent outbreak of a parasitic mite, varroa, in bee populations in North America and Europe, for example, has reduced yields for some crops in affected areas. Bee colonies are also adversely affected, not only by parasitic mites or infectious bee diseases, but from the poor management of pesticides.

Wild species are also affected by agricultural activities, especially in OECD countries where agriculture usually occupies the major part of the national land surface area and thereby provides a key habitat for wild species. Even where agriculture's share of the total land area is small, agriculture can increase the diversity of habitat types. The degree to which wild species use agricultural land as habitat range from marginal use, for example some migratory birds, to complete dependence on agro-ecosystems, such as certain insects and plants.

Agriculture may also affect wild species that use other habitats that are in close proximity to farming areas, such as adjacent forest and coastal areas. In addition, there are wild species that have the possibility to provide potential benefits for agriculture in the future, either to be harvested or serve as inputs in improving the breeding stock, as previously described.

The relationship between *agriculture and non-native species* concerns their impact on agricultural production and indigenous ecosystems. Non-native species cover alien, exotic or non-endemic species, including plants, vertebrates, invertebrates and pathogens, and can be divided into three categories: intentional introductions, intentional introductions with subsequent escape, and unintentional introductions (Mac *et al.*, 1998, p. 118). Intentional introductions can have positive benefits to agriculture, such as introductions of alien varieties and breeds to increase food production or for biological control purposes. The introduction of non-native species, either escaped species from intentional introductions and/or unintentional introductions, can result in biodiversity destruction by predation, habitat alteration and the out-competing of native species. This can also lead to economic costs to farmers through damage to crops from alien pests and weeds and competition for livestock forage, such as rabbits in Australia.[9]

Ecosystem diversity

Ecosystem diversity and its relation to agriculture is manifest through:

- changes in farming practices and systems;
- changes in land use between agricultural and other land uses; and the
- interaction between agriculture and adjacent ecosystems.

In some cases agricultural land use patterns and practices support the conservation and sustainable use of biodiversity, while in others they cause serious threats. In this context, agriculture generates both benefits and pressures on biodiversity, which vary across different regions and countries depending on local farming practices, biogeography, grazing periods, climate and other factors. Farming communities have an intrinsic interest in ensuring that land use practices are sustainable and contribute to the conservation and sustainable use of biodiversity. Some semi-natural agricultural habitats can be preserved only if appropriate farming activities are continued. In many situations where agriculture production is a key element to sustain certain ecosystems, the change in land use from agriculture to other uses can lead to the degradation of some ecosystems.

It is evident that both within and across different OECD countries there is considerable ecosystem diversity in agriculture, and that in some cases certain types of biodiversity in semi-natural habitats are dependent on specific farming practices (*e.g.* low inputs, transhumance) and systems (*e.g.* alpine pasture, agro-forestry). In Scandinavia, for example, "traditionally" managed hay meadows are one of the most species-rich habitat types to be found in the region, with estimates of 50-60 plant species per square metre not uncommon (Norderhaug, 1987). Also in Britain, 40 species of butterfly (over 70 per cent of the butterfly fauna) breed entirely or mainly in agricultural ecosystems of open grassland and hedgerows (Thomas, 1984). Similarly, in a sub-alpine region of Central *Switzerland*, Erhardt (1985) recorded over 30 butterfly species in unfertilised mown meadows, compared with only five species in heavily fertilised mown meadows.

While agriculture can have a positive impact on biodiversity the displacement of mixed farming, agro-forestry and intercropping by monocultural systems, and the conversion of natural habitats to agricultural land can result in the loss and destruction of biodiversity. For example, the Clouded Yellow (*Colias croceus*) is the only butterfly in the *United Kingdom* which is capable of breeding on improved pasture (it uses clover as its food plant), compared with 28 species which breed on the more diverse unimproved pasture which has declined in area (Dennis, 1992).

The inappropriate use of pesticides, for example, can also have a negative effect on the conservation of biodiversity not only in the place where they are applied but also in other ecosystems (*i.e.* by pesticide run-off, see the Pesticide Use and Risks chapter). Moreover, the expansion of agricultural land can also lead to fragmentation of "natural" ecosystems and, where agricultural land is adjacent to other ecosystems, this can adversely affect diversity through the escape of farmed plants and animals.

The negative impacts of agriculture on biodiversity must also be considered in terms of the benefits agriculture brings to society through providing food and fibre, employment and incomes. A better understanding of the processes and trade-offs involved between agricultural production, biodiversity loss and agriculture's role in some situations to maintain biodiversity are, nevertheless, critical to improving land use decision making.[10]

The difficulty for scientists at present, is to quantify the critical thresholds of biodiversity resilience to stress, and identify the measures and likely costs of restoring biodiversity stability. Equally the different forms in which agriculture impacts on biodiversity, while widely recognised, vary in their intensity and effects across countries. There are also other influences on biodiversity besides agricultural activity, such as from natural processes, for example, fires; non-indigenous species; other economic activities, for example, forestry and industry; and global climate change (European Commission, 1998; Mac *et al.*, 1998).[11] For policy makers to improve their responses in reducing biodiversity loss associated with agriculture, this will require a better understanding and measurement of the driving forces and state of biodiversity in agriculture.

2. Indicators

While the set of indicators to monitor biodiversity are potentially very large, a smaller and policy relevant set are being established by OECD, structured within the general framework of genetic, species, and ecosystem diversity, described in Figure 2. Together the indicators establish the initial steps in providing a coherent picture of biodiversity in relation to agriculture.[12]

It is the impact of agriculture on biodiversity which is the emphasis in this chapter, and not the effects on agriculture of biodiversity and related ecosystem services. An exception is the indicator concerning the impacts of non-native species on agriculture and agro-ecosystems. In examining the relationship between agriculture and biodiversity, the discussion here is also limited to biodiversity that is either dependent on agricultural activities and/or affected by it. The range of agriculture's impact on biodiversity mainly concerns the area of ecosystems that are in the immediate vicinity and bordering on agricultural land. However, this is not to exclude the possibility that agriculture's impact on other ecosystems may extend further than the area adjacent to agricultural land, although this issue is not covered in the chapter.

For *genetic diversity* three indicators are reviewed in this chapter that monitor the diversity of crop varieties/livestock used in agricultural production. These indicators help to reveal the resilience of agricultural production to environmental changes and risks which occur through diversifying the number of varieties/breeds in production. A fourth genetic diversity indicator provides information on the extent of genetic erosion and the loss of domesticated agricultural plant varieties and livestock breeds.

Figure 2. **Coverage of biodiversity indicators in relation to agriculture**

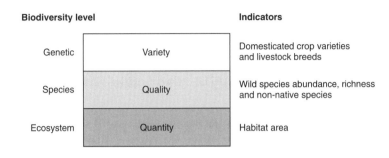

Source: Adapted from Ed Van Klink (National Reference Centre for Agriculture, The Netherlands), presentation to the OECD Workshop on Agri-environmental Indicators, York, United Kingdom, September, 1998.

Indicators for *species diversity* cover trends in population distributions and numbers of *a*) wild species dependent and/or affected by agriculture, and *b*) non-native species threatening agricultural production and agro-ecosystems. E*cosystem diversity* is covered in the Wildlife Habitat chapter.

Genetic diversity

Definitions

1. For the main crop/livestock categories (*e.g.* wheat, rice, cattle, pigs) the total number of crop varieties/livestock breeds that have been registered and certified for marketing.

2. The share of key crop varieties in total marketed production for individual crops (*e.g.* wheat, rice, rapeseed, etc.).

3. The share of the key livestock breeds in respective categories of livestock numbers (*e.g.* the share of Friesian, Jersey, Charolais, etc., in total cattle numbers).

4. The number of national crop varieties/livestock breeds that are endangered.

Method of calculation

The first three indicators track the extent of diversity in the range of crop varieties and livestock breeds used for agricultural production. These indicators require data covering the total registered or marketed number of crop varieties/livestock breeds, and total crop production/livestock numbers for the main categories of crops (*e.g.* wheat, rice, etc) and livestock (*e.g.* cattle, sheep, etc).

The fourth indicator, on endangered crop varieties/livestock breeds, provides information on the extent of genetic erosion and loss of domesticated varieties/breeds from the much wider genetic pool than just those varieties/breeds marketed for production. Sources for species data include national genebanks and breeding organisations, although the FAO has begun to develop internationally co-ordinated databases for genetic resources in agriculture.

Recent trends

General

There seems broad consensus that global losses of genetic resources for food and agriculture have been substantial over the past 100 years. Even so, trends in the populations and numbers of "wild" relatives of domesticated agricultural plants and livestock are poorly documented.

To a larger extent national definitions, systems of classification and monitoring of the state and trends of genetic diversity in agriculture, are based on the approaches being developed through the Convention on Biological Diversity (CBD), and the related work of the FAO inter-governmental Commission on Genetic Resources for Food and Agriculture (see endnote 1 and the example of Greece in Box 3). In addition, many OECD countries have major genebanks of crop and livestock genetic material (see section on *Crop Genebanks* below; and FAO, 1996 and 1998).

Box 3. National System for the Protection and Utilisation of Genetic Resources for Agriculture: Greece

The Greek National System for Protection and Utilisation of Plant Genetic Resources, established in 1990 by Presidential Decree 80/1990, provides for ecosystem surveying to monitor the distribution of domesticated crops and wild relatives, assessment of the degree of genetic erosion, and collection of the threatened germplasm. It also provides for implementing schemes for on-farm and *in-situ* protection. Data on ecosystem distribution are maintained at the Greek Gene Bank's Database, but they actually reflect these degree each region of the country has been surveyed and the distribution of the target species in these surveys.

These surveys are near complete for certain staple crops and their relatives (*e.g.* cereals, grapes, forage) and very weak for other crops, particularly vegetables. Reports/case studies on the ecosystem distribution of certain species (brassica, cereals etc.) have been presented to scientific fora. Data for the distribution of this germplasm in Greece are also available in the appropriate databases of FAO and the EU. A major attempt to record genetic diversity of domesticated crops in Greece has been undertaken by the Greek Ministry of Agriculture (Directorate of Environmental Protection) between 1995-1998 as a preliminary step towards the implementation of measures for its protection under the provisions of EU Regulation No. 2078/92.

As regards the genetic diversity of domesticated animals, the system used in Greece to classify their genetic diversity is based on the assessment of breeds, made according to the number of the female animals registered by the relevant authorities and in stipulation with EU Regulation No. 2078/92.

Source: Adapted from Greece's reply to the OECD Agri-environmental Indicators Questionnaire, 1999.

For *European Union* countries EU Regulation No.1467/94 provides a programme for the conservation, characterisation, collection and utilisation of genetic resources in agriculture, while in principle conservation of agricultural genetic resources can be supported through EU Regulation No. 2078/92 (European Commission, 1998, pp. 48-50). The latter EU regulation is applied to promote conservation of threatened farm animal species through provision of support for farmers who undertake to rear local livestock breeds in danger of extinction and to cultivate crops threatened by genetic erosion.[13]

Crops

Overall, there has been an *increasing number of crop varieties* registered for marketing and as a share in crop production over the past 13 years in OECD countries (Figure 3). This trend suggests that for many countries arable farming has improved its resilience to environmental change and risk through diversifying the number of crop varieties used in production.

The trend in the share of the one to five dominant varieties in the total marketed production for specific crops has also declined in a large number of cases. The share of these dominant crop varieties, however, is still in excess of 70 per cent for most crop categories, although for some countries the dominance of major varieties in crop production is lower, for example, in *Germany, Italy, Poland, Portugal* and *Sweden* (Figure 4). These trends are supported by other research, that reveals, over a longer time period than shown in Figure 4, the percentage share of the total area of wheat planted to the dominant cultivar has declined in *France, Hungary, Italy*, the *Netherlands* and the *United Kingdom* (Smale, 1997, p. 1261).

Figure 3. Number of plant varieties registered and certified for marketing: 1985 to 1998

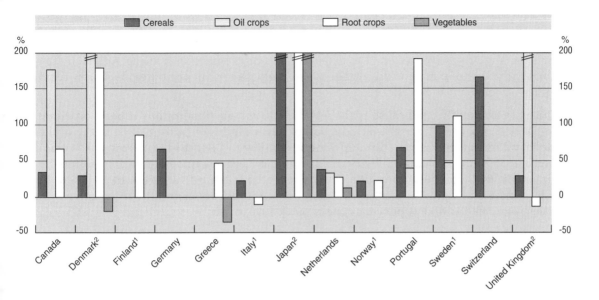

1. Percentages are zero or close to zero per cent for Finland (cereals, oil crops, vegetables), Italy (oil crops), Norway (oil crops), Sweden (vegetables).
2. Percentages are greater than 200% for Denmark (oil crops), Japan (cereals, root crops, vegetables), United Kingdom (oil crops).
Notes: See Annex Table 1. Data are not available for all crop categories and all countries.
Source: OECD Agri-environmental Indicators Questionnaire, 1999.

Figure 4. Share of the one to five dominant varieties in total marketed crop production: 1985 to 1998

Change in the share of the one to five dominant varieties in total marketed production

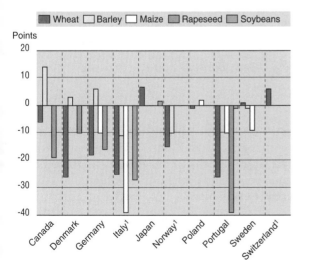

Percentage share of the one to five dominant varieties in total marketed production: 1998

	Wheat	Barley	Maize	Rape-seed	Soybeans
Canada	74	60	..	75	..
Denmark	70	71	..	82	..
Germany	41	67	47	54	..
Italy	63	42	56	100	60
Japan	83	..	..	..	50
Norway	85	80	..	100	..
Poland	59	..	37	..	..
Portugal	32	..	20	26	4
Sweden	55	58	44	..	..
Switzerland	90	..	..	90	90

1. Percentages are zero or close to zero per cent for Italy (rapeseed), Norway (rapeseed), Switzerland (rapeseed, soybeans).
Notes: See Annex Table 2. Data are not available for all crop categories and all countries.
Source: OECD Agri-environmental Indicators Questionnaire, 1999.

301

Australia has developed an index of agricultural plant species diversity to track trends in the regional diversity, or genetic diversity of cultivated agricultural plant species (Commonwealth of Australia 1998). The index is based on the number of different species grown (for major plant groups such as oilseeds, cereals, legume pasture), the area of each species and the number of farms growing each species over the period 1989-1994. An increase in the number of species grown reveals the greater resilience of farming systems to adapt to economic and environmental changes. Although the span of years was too short to draw conclusions about the biological resilience of regional agro-ecosystems there is no suggestion that diversity has declined in any region.

The most frequently cited cause of the *loss of genetic diversity* from country reports provided to the FAO (FAO, 1996, pp. 13-14), was the introduction of new varieties of crops leading to the replacement and loss of traditional, highly variable crop varieties. In *Korea* 74 per cent of varieties of 14 crops grown on farms in 1985 had been replaced by 1993.[14] In the *United States*, a study drawing on information about varieties grown by US farmers in the 19th century revealed that most varieties can no longer be found either in commercial agriculture or any US genebank, with 91 per cent of field maize varieties lost, 81 per cent of tomatoes, and 94 per cent of peas (FAO, 1996, p. 14).

Livestock

The overall trend for livestock, like that for crops, shows an *increasing number of breeds* registered for marketing and as a share of total livestock numbers in OECD countries since 1985. This indicates a growing diversity of the breeds used for livestock production for most categories of livestock and OECD countries. Examination of changes from 1985 to 1998 in the number of livestock breeds, registered or certified for marketing, shows an increase for nearly all major livestock categories and for most OECD countries, although data for poultry are extremely limited (Figure 5).

These trends are also reflected in the reduction in the share of the three major livestock breeds in total livestock numbers for respective livestock categories (Figure 6). Differences across OECD countries and between livestock categories exist, in particular, the increasing share of the three major breeds of sheep and cattle in respective total numbers of sheep and cattle, in some countries. Also, the dominance of a few breeds in total livestock numbers for respective categories is, in general, higher than for crops, in excess of 80 per cent in most cases.

In the case of the *loss of livestock genetic diversity*, FAO estimates that globally for over 3 800 breeds of cattle, goats, pigs, sheep, horses and donkeys that existed 100 years ago, 16 per cent have become extinct and 15 per cent are threatened. In cattle breeding, where the Holstein-Friesian breed has become the dominant breed for milk production world-wide, the number of sire-lines is decreasing and for the pig and poultry sectors only a small number of breeds dominate global production. Estimates for *Germany* show that in 1997 the number of endangered breeds was 12 out of a total of 77 for cattle, 14 out of 41 for sheep, 3 out of 16 for goats, 12 out of 103 for horses, but with no endangered breeds for pigs.[15]

Interpretation and links to other indicators

Preventing the erosion of genetic diversity and dependence of agricultural production on a relatively small number of varieties/breeds is important for agriculture. Genetic dependence on a small number of varieties/breeds can heighten the risks associated with changes in environmental conditions and susceptibility to pests and disease. Genetic erosion could impair the future potential to raise crop and livestock yields, as genetic material loss is generally irreversible.

The baseline from which this loss should be measured is yet to be determined, although initially the early 1980s is being used as a suitable baseline. Tracking *in situ* conservation of rare crop varieties/ livestock breeds can be important for conservation of certain specific ecosystems. This is also of significance for within-species diversity and the consequent adaptability of the species.

In some cases the increase in particular national varieties/breeds, shown in Figures 3 to 6, is the consequence of the expanding international trade in varieties/breeds. The Hereford cattle breed, for

Figure 5. **Number of livestock breeds[1] registered or certified for marketing:[2] 1985 to 1998**

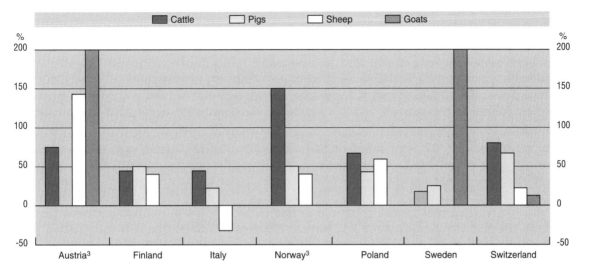

1. Poultry are not included in the figure as there was no change in the number of breeds registered or certified for marketing between 1985 and 1998, except for Poland, minus 1%.
2. Greece and the Netherlands are not included in the figure as there was no change in the number of breeds registered or certified for marketing between 1985 to 1998, except for cattle, minus 11% in the Netherlands.
3. Percentages equal zero for Austria (pigs), Norway (sheep, goats).
Notes: See Annex Table 3. Data are not available for all livestock categories and all countries.
Source: OECD Agri-environmental Indicators Questionnaire, 1999.

Figure 6. **Share of the three major livestock breeds in total livestock numbers: 1985 to 1998**

Change in the share of the three major livestock breeds in total livestock numbers

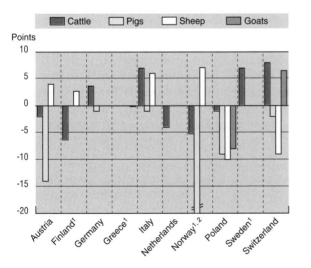

Percentage share of the three major livestock breeds in total livestock numbers: 1998

	Cattle	Pigs	Sheep	Goats
Austria	93	71	79	..
Finland	67	95	97	100
Germany	90	94	..	..
Greece	98	93	68	100
Italy	94	98	89	..
Netherlands	91	..	..	..
Norway	91	36	86	100
Poland	98	84	68	64
Sweden	92	95	..	95
Switzerland	98	98	82	74

1. Percentages are zero or close to zero per cent for Finland (pigs, goats), Greece (goats), Norway (goats), Sweden (goats).
2. Percentage is greater than –20% for Norway (pigs).
Notes: See Annex Table 4. Data are not available for all livestock categories and all countries.
Source: OECD Agri-environmental Indicators Questionnaire, 1999.

example, while previously a dominant breed in the United Kingdom, is now becoming more common in Norway.

Some caution is required, however, in using and interpreting indicators that measure genetic diversity by the trends in numbers of *crop varieties*, shown in Figures 3 and 4. First, the genetic structure of the varieties in current use is likely to be similar, independent of the number of varieties grown. In other words, twenty main varieties grown in 1998, for example, may not have more genetic diversity than two main varieties grown in 1985. Second, varieties for certain crops are not registered in some OECD countries, in particular, this applies to fruit and vegetables and forage plants. Third, and perhaps most importantly, these indicators only account for what is grown or registered for marketing at any given time. The available gene pool is much wider.

For some countries the information on *livestock breeds* in Figures 3 and 6 may underestimate the "real" situation, as not all livestock are registered, and in some cases registered animals represent the elite breeding population and not "commercial" animals. These indicators could also be improved by providing a breakdown by sex, which registration statistics often neglect, and providing information on the number of livestock breeds considered threatened because of low population numbers. The FAO is now in the process of developing the international Domestic Animal Diversity Information System (DAD-IS) database to address the issue of the loss of animal genetic resources and their better use and development (FAO, 1998).[16]

The genetic diversity between livestock breeds, as well as within breeds, is also important. So far exterior characteristics, *e.g.* coat colour, have been used to distinguish breeds. This is, however, a rather crude measure and does not sufficiently distinguish within breeds. Productivity levels may also be used as breed characteristics, but that would not represent genetic progress in production potential made for example, in rare breeds. Moreover, productivity levels also fail to take account of other desirable traits in domestic animals such as hardiness to cold or drought, behavioural traits, meat quality (*e.g.* taste, nutritional value, etc.).

Indicators of ecosystem diversity are also important in assessing genetic resources, because the plant varieties and livestock breeds have generally developed within specific agro-ecosystems. It is the adaptation of these breeds to these ecosystems that can make their conservation desirable. Ecosystem structure may, in this respect, not be an assessment variable, but a descriptive variable, linking adaptation traits with specific ecosystems.

Related information

Crop genebanks

Ex *situ* crop gene banks, which are now well established for crop genetic resources. They preserve and make available samples of heritage and unused cultivars, traditional landraces, wild and weedy relatives of cultivated varieties, and special genetic stocks (including many breeders' lines and mutants), in addition to the cultivated varieties in current use. All of this genetic diversity is readily available for use in plant breeding programmes. It is a well established practice that when a variety or landrace is no longer grown by farmers, for whatever reason, efforts are made to preserve that genetic diversity *ex situ*.

The world-wide number of genebanks has grown rapidly since the early 1970s, when there were fewer than 10 genebanks holding about a half million plant genetic accessions. Now there are more than 1 300 collections with in excess of 5 million accessions, and the major part of these accessions are held in the collections of OECD countries (FAO, 1996, pp. 20-25). Even so, it has recently been estimated that about 90 per cent of plant breeding material used by private breeding companies are from their own or other private company collections (Kate and Laird, 1999, pp. 135-37).

There are also examples, in some OECD countries, of *in situ* conservation of plant genetic resources (*e.g.* farmers fields and uncultivated pasture), such as in Germany (fruit trees), Mexico (Maize),[17] and Turkey (wild relatives of cereal plants), and the European Union which provides support to *in situ* conservation (see previous discussion). *Switzerland* also has a national *in situ* programme based on the FAO plan of action (FAO, 1996, pp. 16-19). Most *in situ* programmes are more limited than the development of *ex situ* genebanks, although often countries link programmes covering the two.

Transgenic crops[18]

The new and increasing use of *transgenic crops*, developed through genetic engineering, has raised concerns that this could threaten landraces and wild relatives of the world's plant genetic resources for agriculture and also adversely affect other wild plant species (Table 1). However, genetically modified crops also present the possibility of improving agriculture's environmental performance by, for example, making plants more pest resistant, thereby, reducing reliance on pesticides.

Table 1. **Agricultural area under transgenic crops: late 1990s**

	1996	1997	1998	1999	Share of arable land 1999[1]	Share of global transgenic crop area 1999[2]
	Million hectares				%	%
Australia	< 0.03	0.05	0.1	0.1	< 1	< 1
Canada	0.1	1.3	2.8	4	9	10
France	0	0	< 0.1	< 0.1	< 1	< 1
Mexico	0	0	< 0.1	< 0.1	< 1	< 1
Portugal	0	0	0	< 0.1	< 1	< 1
Spain	0	0	< 0.1	< 0.1	< 1	< 1
United States[3]	1.5	8.1	20.5	28.7	16	72

1. Arable land area data refer to 1998 except for Australia (1997), Portugal and Spain (1999).
2. The global area of transgenic crops in 1999 was approximately 40 million hectares.
3. The US Department of Agriculture estimates differ from the above industry estimates as follows: 1996: 3.2 million hectares; 1998: 20.23 million hectares.
Sources: James (1997, 1998, 1999); OECD Agri-environmental Indicators Database, 1999.

There is now a considerable research programme underway in a number of OECD countries to determine the effects of genetically engineered crops. Several *European* governments have called a moratorium on commercial planting of these crops pending further assessment of possible health and ecological risks.

Farmers in the *United States* sowed their first transgenic crops in 1994, followed by other OECD and non-OECD countries in 1996 (Table 1). By 1998, nine countries world-wide were growing transgenic crops, and that number is expected to reach 20 to 25 countries by 2000 (Brown *et al.*, 1999, pp. 122-123). While there are more than 60 marketed transgenic crops, the principal crops in terms of the total area under transgenic crops include maize, soyabeans, canola and cotton.

Species diversity

Wild species

Definition

Trends in population distributions and numbers of wild species related to agriculture.

Method of calculation

OECD countries have applied different approaches to describe and assess the state and trends in population distribution and numbers of wild species associated with agriculture. To a large extent this reflects differences in policy priorities, availability of data, and varying stages of scientific research on biodiversity issues. Thus, at this stage of the work it is not possible to develop a consistent method of calculation across OECD countries. Instead, it is only possible to report on the state and trends of wild species in relation to agriculture, according to different country approaches, such as in terms of measuring species abundance, species richness, species distribution, key species, endangered species, or groups of species having similar functions (*i.e.* species guilds). These different approaches have varying advantages and disadvantages in terms of accuracy, sensitivity, feasibility and cost.

Most OECD countries do not have specific monitoring systems to track wild species populations and numbers on agricultural land. Background information is available, however, for a number of species and species groups related to agriculture, but usually this is not collected in a systematic manner. Many OECD countries, and some international organisations, however, report on a regular basis the total number of known and threatened species of mammals and birds, and to a lesser extent fish, reptiles, amphibians invertebrates, vascular plants, mosses, lichens, fungi and algae, but none of this information relates specifically to agriculture (OECD, 1998).[19]

In some countries, *Norway*, *Sweden* and the *United Kingdom*, for example, biological records are maintained by government organisations and volunteer groups for various species groups, typically mammals, birds and vascular plants.[20] More commonly nearly all countries have Red Lists of endangered species, although these lists are not specific to agriculture, but some countries have been able to identify Red List species particularly associated with agriculture (*e.g.* Finland, Germany, Netherlands, Norway, Switzerland).

A few countries have begun to establish monitoring systems specifically to track wild species trends in agro-ecosystems. *Canada*, has started to examine the issue of monitoring wild species on agricultural land (Box 4). Some countries also use hunting statistics as proxies for the likely impact of agriculture on wild species (*e.g. Denmark*, hares; *Norway*, roe deer, rooks, blackheaded gull and partridge since the 1940s). *Germany*, is developing a system that will involve monitoring the occurrence and frequency of 100 selected species through periodic sampling for defined ecological areas, including agro-ecosystems.

In the *Netherlands*, for example, a monitoring programme exists, and is being further developed, covering plants, birds, butterflies, dragonflies, amphibians, mammals, fish, aquatic macro fauna and soil

---

Box 4. Canadian System to Monitor Wild Species Diversity

There is no comprehensive national system in place in Canada to monitor the diversity of wild species on agricultural land. Available data focus on economically important species (such as selected beneficial and pest species in agriculture), economically valuable species for which specific management programmes are in place (*e.g.* waterfowl; see also the North American Waterfowl Management Plan, see Box 6), some songbirds, and migratory birds subject to the Canada-US Migratory Birds Convention. In cases where population and diversity data exist, species are usually also influenced by factors other than agriculture or even factors in other countries (*Mexico, United States*).

Information is collected by the Committee on the Status of Endangered Wildspecies in Canada (COSEWIC) on endangered, threatened and vulnerable species. A study conducted for Agriculture and Agri-Food Canada (AAFC), completed in May 1998, found that 223 of the 268 species then classified by COSEWIC as endangered, threatened or vulnerable overlap into the Canadian agricultural landscape. The results of this study do not indicate a cause-effect relationship between agriculture and species at risk.

In part, due to sparse data, the difficulty of determining "key" species, and because in most cases factors other than agriculture also affect species populations, AAFC has not developed a national indicator of wild species diversity on farmland. Instead, AAFC has developed an indicator that combines information on agricultural land use and information on how different vertebrate species use agricultural land as habitat to develop an indicator of habitat availability on farmland (see the *Habitat matrix indicator* in the Wildlife Habitats chapter).

Source: Adapted from Neave *et al.* (2000).

fauna (*e.g.* nematodes, worms, mites, fungi etc.). Measurable species within these groups are selected, providing a representative cross-section of the agro-ecosystem, and consist of rare species as well as more common species. Species are measured under the Dutch system in various units, such as distribution, presence/absence, density, total numbers, breeding pairs, or area coverage, depending on what is feasible in sample areas or plots. The *United Kingdom* is another example, involving a national periodic random stratified sample survey of plant species, including agro-ecosystems.

There remains an active discussion amongst biologists as to the merits of using the species abundance or species richness in monitoring biodiversity. *Species abundance* measures both the decline or increase of populations, which may result from human activities, such as agriculture. *Species richness* refers to the total number of a specific taxonomic group or functional groups associated with key ecosystems per site. Species richness measures presence/absence of species and is, therefore, a relatively insensitive variable compared to species abundance (Figure 7).

The decrease in abundance of three original species, symbolised by the three oval shapes in time period t_0 in Figure 7, and the introduction and increase of one other species in one particular area over time t_1–t_2 is typically a common process of biodiversity loss, resulting from changing farming practices in a particular agro-ecosystem. The decrease of species abundance is a far more sensitive indicator than species richness, as the latter initially increases from 3 to 4 (in t_1) while the average species abundance of the "traditional" species dramatically decreases in t_1 and t_2 (Figure 7). As a result the policy message could be the opposite of what is expected. While traditional species may become extinct at the local level they may not be extinct nationally (*e.g.* due to conservation of specific habitats), while new species are easily introduced. The result is an increase of species richness at the national level while the loss of species abundance is totally ignored.

Figure 7. **Theoretical change in species abundance and richness over time**

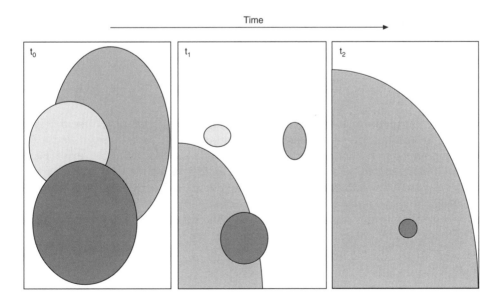

Note: Shaded areas show different species, "species richness" (*e.g.* 3 species in t_0) while area of each shaded part shows "species abundance" (*e.g.* decline of species ▮ from t_0 to t_2).
Source: Adapted from Ed Van Klink (National Reference Centre for Agriculture, The Netherlands), presentation to the OECD Workshop on Agri-environmental Indicators, York, United Kingdom, September, 1998.

Figure 8. **Share of selected wild species categories that use agricultural land as habitat:[1] 1998**

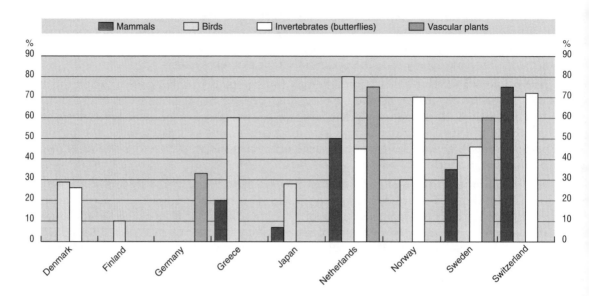

1. This figure should be interpreted with care as definitions of the use of agricultural land as habitat by wild species can vary. Species can use agricultural land as "primary" habitat (strongly dependent on habitat) or "secondary" habitat (uses habitat but is not dependent on it).
Notes: See Annex Table 5. Data are not available for all categories of wild species for all countries.
Source: OECD Agri-environmental Indicators Questionnaire, 1999.

The species richness of agricultural areas may rank in the order of tens of thousands of species, and it is not feasible to measure them all. Thus, choices will be necessary with regard to, specific taxonomic groups or functional groups, and spatial scales taking into account that species richness at the national level as an indicator has a different meaning than the average species richness per unit area of agricultural land. Moreover, data on the presence of species or taxonomic groups in the baseline state may be hard to find, especially on smaller spatial scales, while monitoring the current state on larger spatial scales is a costly activity and the sensitivity can be extremely low.

Recent trends

The information on the impact of agriculture on wild species, that either use agricultural land as habitat or use other habitats but are affected by farming activities, is limited for OECD countries although two key points emerge from the data and research material that does exist. *First*, agricultural land provides an important habitat area for "remaining" wild species (*i.e.* wild species that exist following the conversion of "natural" habitat to agricultural land use), but especially birds and vascular plants (Figure 8).[21] *Second*, the population trends of wild species using agricultural land as habitat indicate in most cases a reduction over the period from 1985 to 1998, representing the continuation of a longer term trend. There is some evidence, however, that the decline has slowed or even reversed over recent years in some countries, although from a low base, *i.e.* wild species population on agricultural land are increasing (Figure 9).

Europe[22]

Concerning population trends for wild species using agricultural land as habitat, there is considerable work completed on the status of birds on agricultural land, especially in *Europe* (Figure 9 and Box 5). A comparison of different habitat types (*e.g.* agriculture, forests, wetlands, etc.) reveals that

Figure 9. **Population trends for selected wild species using agricultural land as habitat: Denmark, Poland and the United Kingdom, 1985 to 1998**

Index 1985 = 100

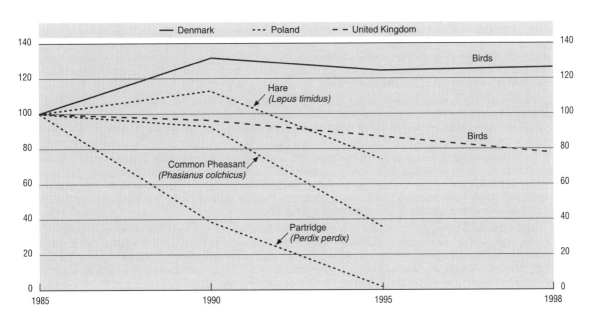

Note: See Annex Table 6.
Source: OECD Agri-environmental Indicators Questionnaire, 1999.

across Europe agricultural habitats account for the highest proportion of birds with an unfavourable conservation status (Tucker and Heath, 1994; and Tucker and Evans, 1997). Much of the adverse impact of agriculture on bird populations has been attributed to pesticides (EEA, 1998, p. 166; and see also the Pesticide Use and Risks chapter) and changing land use patterns in agriculture, especially the loss of extensive grazing land (see Contextual Indicators and Wildlife Habitat chapters).

In *Finland*, over one-third of the country's vascular plants are found on pasture (MAF Finland, 1996, pp. 4-6). With the reduction in the pasture area in Finland over the past few decades and large-scale structural changes in the agricultural sector, it is estimated that these changes have threatened the disappearance of almost 290 species of flora and fauna, and, in addition, thousands of other species have declined (Table 2).

Table 2. **Number of species threatened to disappear and dependent on agricultural habitats: Finland, early 1990s**

Agricultural habitat	Vertebrates[1]	Invertebrates[2]	Vascular plants	Cryptogams[3]	Total
Fresh meadows	1	18	8	6	33
Woodland pastures	0	34	13	22	69
Dry meadows	1	122	27	23	173
Fields	4	7	3	0	14
Total	6	181	51	51	289

1. Mammals, birds, fish, etc.
2. Annelids, molluscs, butterflies, beetles, and other insects, arthropods, and invertebrates.
3. Non-flowering plants, such as algae, mosses, ferns, etc.
Source: MAF Finland (1996).

Box 5. Biodiversity and Agriculture in the European Union

The complex ecology of flora and fauna have adapted to and been influenced by farming activities in Europe over thousands of years. The result is that many species are dependent for their lifecycle on the continuation of farming practices. Thus, once-common birds now confined to a few breeding areas in Europe, such as the Chough (*Pyrrhocorax pyrrhocorax*), rely on traditional grazed pastures. Another example is the globally threatened steppic bird, the Great Bustard (*Otis tarda*), which thrives in extensive mosaics of cereal fallow and pasture in *Portugal* and *Spain*.

European Union environment policy ensures that especially valuable habitats are identified and designated under the EU Habitats and Wild Birds Directives. These require member States to assure the necessary conservation measures, which often require the continuation of farming. The ensuing network of sites is known as NATURA 2000.

Farm-dependent biodiversity is not confined to the NATURA 2000 sites. Over 70 per cent of threatened vascular plant species in *Sweden*, for example, depend on open farmed landscapes. Throughout Europe, the centuries-old practice of haymaking has produced diverse field flora that has adapted to a rapid growing season and seeds before mowing takes place. Both the decline of, and earlier, haymaking have inevitably led to a corresponding decline in the populations of field flora.

While the links between intensification and biodiversity are the subject of continuing research in the EU, the main agents of change include, farming practices such as the use of chemical fertilisers and pesticides, land drainage and irrigation; loss of field margins and non-farmed habitat areas such as wet areas, farm woodlands, and hedgerows; and the replacement of traditional practices, such as haymaking replaced by silage production and temporary fallow by continuous cereals.

The combination of some of the above practices is believed, for example, to have contributed to the decline in numbers of farmland birds. However, it should be noted that there are cases where farm land was taken out of agriculture for nature conservation without subsequently achieving the protection objectives. As a consequence, well-adjusted farm practices had to be reintroduced in order to create suitable conditions for birds.

In most member States, agri-environment measures have been implemented under Regulation (EEC) No. 2078/92 to preserve biodiversity, for example, by reducing or ceasing the use of fertiliser and pesticides on the maintenance of rotational practices. Examples include the introduction of organic farming, integrated crop management, set aside of field margins, and specific measures aimed at particular habitats. Measures are also in place to manage farm woodlands, wetlands and hedgerows to benefit flora and fauna.

Source: Adapted from Commission of the European Communities (1999, pp. 16-18).

A study has been undertaken in *Germany*, by the Federal Ministry for the Environment, to examine the various human and natural factors that have caused declines in plant species over the past 10 years, including the impact of agriculture (Figure 10). Intensified agricultural land use, cessation of use, fallowing and natural succession, appears to have been the major cause of the decline in plant species, although the destruction of habitats and afforestation also has been important. It is also evident from Figure 10 that the causes of plant species decline in agriculture have had less effect in recent years.

Monitoring of the Peregrine Falcon (*Falco peregrinus*) population in *Ireland*, showed a decline in numbers between the 1940s to the 1970s because of contamination by organochlorine pesticides. With restrictions on the use of these pesticide compounds there has been a recovery in the population from 225 breeding pairs in 1981 to 350 in 1991 (Environmental Protection Agency, 1999).

The destruction and fragmentation of habitat of agricultural land in *Luxembourg* is considered to have had a negative impact on biodiversity in the country (OECD, 2000b). The eutrophication of rivers and lakes caused by agricultural inputs has also threatened amphibian species.

Almost a half of the bird species using farmland as habitat in the *United Kingdom* have declined in population size over the past 20 years (UK Department of the Environment, 1996, pp. 120-121). Within

Figure 10. **Decline in plant species due to various human and natural factors: Germany, 1998**

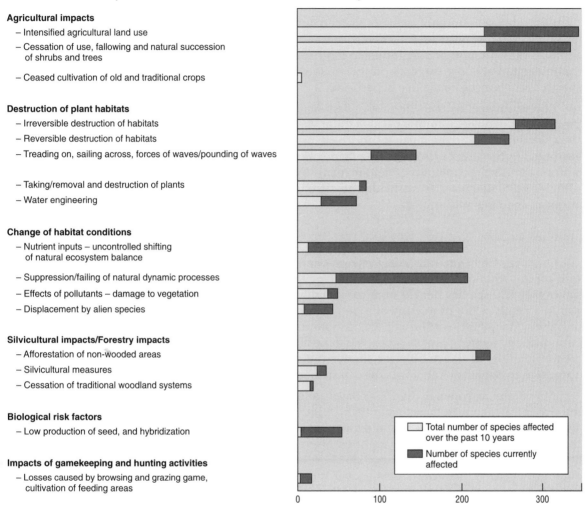

Causes of decline in species

Agricultural impacts
– Intensified agricultural land use
– Cessation of use, fallowing and natural succession of shrubs and trees
– Ceased cultivation of old and traditional crops

Destruction of plant habitats
– Irreversible destruction of habitats
– Reversible destruction of habitats
– Treading on, sailing across, forces of waves/pounding of waves
– Taking/removal and destruction of plants
– Water engineering

Change of habitat conditions
– Nutrient inputs – uncontrolled shifting of natural ecosystem balance
– Suppression/failing of natural dynamic processes
– Effects of pollutants – damage to vegetation
– Displacement by alien species

Silvicultural impacts/Forestry impacts
– Afforestation of non-wooded areas
– Silvicultural measures
– Cessation of traditional woodland systems

Biological risk factors
– Low production of seed, and hybridization

Impacts of gamekeeping and hunting activities
– Losses caused by browsing and grazing game, cultivation of feeding areas

Number of species affected

Total number of species affected over the past 10 years

Number of species currently affected

Notes: The horizontal bars indicate the number of species affected by each respective cause of endangerment. The dark blue parts of each bar show the number of those species for which respective causes of threat are still active or became more active over the past 10 years. (The assessment is based on 756 species/1 670 common names).
Source: German Federal Ministry for the Environment, Nature Conservation and Nuclear Safety.

farmland habitats the decline in numbers of species was higher on cultivated arable land (about 60 per cent of the bird species) than in grazing land (about 40 per cent). The decline in UK farmland birds shown in Figure 9 is a cause of concern. At the same time, some bird species benefit from intensive farming and their populations are not decreasing, for example, the stock dove (*Columba oenas*) and jackdaw (*Coruus monedula*) (MAFF, 2000). However, some rare species not included in the UK indicator, such as the corncrake (*Crex crex*), stone curlew (*Burhinus oedicnemus*) and cirl bunting (*Emberiza cirlus*), are responding well to conservation efforts.[23]

The marked reduction in UK bird populations occurred in the late 1970s and early 1980s and can partly be linked to the declines in farmland habitat quality as a result of intensification of agricultural practices. Pasture (a good source of invertebrate food) has been lost from the arable areas in the east and cereals from the pastoral areas in the west of the country. Most unimproved grassland has been lost since

311

the 1930s, thus reducing the variety and numbers of birds, especially in the west. Most cereal crops are now planted in the autumn, not the spring. As a result there are substantially fewer stubble fields, which are a good source of food for bird populations over the winter. Both hedgerow removal and the loss of other uncropped habitats have also reduced nesting and feeding opportunities for some species.

Pesticide use is another factor implicated in the decline of farmland birds in the UK. Concern has focused on whether pesticides, by removing insect pests and weed species, may have an indirect effect on some bird populations by reducing food sources. The UK Ministry of Agriculture has recently commissioned a 5-year research project, involving collaboration with various conservation bodies specifically to investigate the role of pesticides and other factors in the decline of farmland bird species.

Recent surveys by the United Kingdom Mammal Society, also reveal the reduction in mammal species that use agricultural land as habitat, such as voles (*Arvicola*), shrews (*Sorex*) and field mice (*Mus rylvaticus*).[24] The main causes for these declines over the period since the 1970s have been attributed to the loss of rough grazing land and small habitat features on farmland such as ditches, hedges, etc. Also the removal of field margins, by ploughing as close to field edges as possible, and spraying field margins with pesticides has also led to the reduction in habitat and feeding areas for mammals and other wild species.

North America

Over the past 15 years in *Canada*, many farmers have begun to replace conventional tillage practices with conservation tillage, including no-till (see the Soil Quality chapter).[25] In Canada, studies have shown that wild species benefit from conservation tillage. Invertebrate numbers have been shown to rise as a result of the protection afforded by crop residue cover and reduced mortality caused by ploughing. Many species of birds become more common as their prey, invertebrates, grow in numbers. Deer mice (*Hesperomys*), too, may become more abundant, possibly because of higher survival rates or greater mobility of the population than is the case in conventionally tilled fields. The impact of agriculture on Canadian waterfowl is also examined in Box 6.

Agricultural activities in the *United States* are considered to affect 380 of the over 660 wild species listed as threatened or endangered in 1995 (USDA, 1997, pp. 17-18). The main threats to wild species from agriculture in the US originate from converting land to cropland and grazing, with exposure to farm chemicals also important. The competition between agriculture and endangered species for land was heightened in the US with the introduction of the Endangered Species Act in 1973, which has the express objective of protecting ecosystems on which threatened and endangered species depend. Several agricultural programmes include measures that are designed to reduce the conflict between agriculture and biodiversity loss, including the Conservation Reserve Program and the Wetlands Reserve Program.

Interpretation and links to other indicators

Where agriculture is the dominant land use activity, as is the case for many OECD countries, then it is to be expected that agriculture is likely to provide the major habitat area for wild species. In this context Figure 8 needs to be interpreted with some care, as it is unclear if forests or other ecosystems were re-established on agricultural land what the relative share of wild species on different land uses would be.

The interpretation of wild species indicators is not straightforward, and caution is required in relating species reductions or increases to agriculture, where other external factors, such as changes in the weather or populations of natural living organisms and predators, may have an important influence. It will also be necessary to take care in interpreting such indicators across countries, as the number of species will tend to be greater in large countries than for small countries, hence, the possibility of expressing the indicator according to a standard area unit could be considered.

Defining baselines is an important step in calibrating, comparing and interpreting indicators of biodiversity, but in practical terms baselines will usually be limited by available data. Baselines can be useful as objective measures of status at a given point in time against which changes in status can be compared. However, irreversible ecosystem and climate changes may prevent restoration of pre-existing

---

Box 6.   **North American waterfowl and agriculture**

In the 1980s, waterfowl populations in North America began dropping at an alarming rate. Concern for this situation led Canada, United States, and Mexico to co-operate in restoring these birds to 1970 levels and improving the habitat for these and other wetland-dependent wildlife. Signed in 1986 and called the North American Waterfowl Management Plan, this agreement has resulted in a major conservation programme.

In Canada the plan focuses on the Prairies, which provide breeding habitat for almost 40 per cent of the North American duck population. Goals of the programme include the restoration and protection of wetlands and grasslands. To achieve these goals, a landscape approach is taken and agreements made with farmers to modify their land use and agricultural practices. Another major component of the programme is the reform of land use policy to remove the pressure to put marginal land into agricultural production.

Ten years into the programme, dabbling duck populations had nearly reached the 1970s average, and diving duck populations had far surpassed it. Provincial surveys of the socio-economic impact of the plan show that farmers and the general public have a positive attitude toward wetland and waterfowl conservation and that communities benefit economically through jobs associated with the plan and greater tourism opportunities.

Note: For the Canadian website of the North American Waterfowl Management Plan see: *www.cws-scf.ec.gc.ca/nawmp_e.html*; and for the United States website see: *http://northamerican.fws.gov/nawmphp.html*.

Source: Adapted from Neave *et al.* (2000).

---

species populations. In these cases progress towards agreed targets may be more useful for policy decision-making than measuring distance from baselines, especially when it is difficult to establish common baselines across OECD countries.

Setting baselines is a complex and often an arbitrary process, with many alternative baselines possible, and with each alternative generating different results and policy information. A number of baseline options with respect to wild species can be considered. These include first, setting the baseline at the time of the CBD's agreement in 1992; second, determining a baseline that represents the evolution of biodiversity in an ecosystem that has been unaffected by any significant human influence, *i.e.* the original "natural" state; and third, establishing a baseline, in the case of agriculture, prior to the intensive use of inputs in agriculture, which for many OECD countries is around the early 1950s.[26]

Measurement against the conditions at the time of CBD ratification is likely to be an attractive alternative, but assessing biodiversity using 1992 as a baseline would be perceived as giving a biased result, because at that time OECD countries had already achieved a high level of socio-economic and agricultural development partly at the expense of biodiversity.

Comparing an agricultural area with the original "natural" baseline, *e.g.* a forest or wetland, is of little value in that it will simply show that the majority of the original biodiversity has disappeared. However, the original natural state baseline is the relevant baseline in the case of clearing additional forests for agricultural use. It can also be of interest to potential resilience, if an area is no longer cultivated or if agriculture becomes less intensive. The so-called "climax" baseline, on the other hand, characterises the developing natural state after human activities on an area have ceased, and can be an important baseline in the case of a potential change in land use from agriculture to another use.

Establishing a baseline for agriculture in terms of the period before the intensive use of inputs, also raises a number of questions. For example, how to define "intensification", at what point this is considered to begin (which can also vary for regions across a country), and what are the impacts of agriculture on biodiversity under different systems of input intensity (*e.g.* intensive use of machinery and chemicals, organic, and extensive "low" input farming systems, etc.)?[27] For many countries, which

---

have only just begun to establish wild species monitoring systems, the only practical baseline will be the first year of the monitoring programme.

In terms of species diversity, links to the wildlife habitat indicator area are clearly critical, in particular, the habitat matrix indicator, which is a surrogate for species diversity. Farm management indicators also are of importance in terms of the choices farmers make in their use of farm chemicals, especially pesticides. Farm management practices are also important to wild species in terms of soil cover and crop harvesting practices. An example is the different influences of early grass silage production as opposed to haymaking later in the year on the development of insects and dependent bird populations.

Non-native species

Definition

Trends in population distributions and numbers of key "non-native" species threatening agricultural production and agro-ecosystems.

Method of calculation

Indicators of non-native species threatening agricultural production and ecosystems are being developed in some countries (Saunders *et al.*, 1998, p. 23; and New Zealand Ministry for the Environment, 1998, pp. 56-58). This can cover the abundance and distribution of non-indigenous species identified as pests, *i.e.* plants, vertebrates, invertebrates and pathogens, that cause economic losses to agriculture by damaging crops and competing for forage.

These indicators are being developed in terms of tracking the changing pressures on agricultural production, and biodiversity more widely. This involves collecting information about the distribution or range, and abundance where possible, of different invasive species. In general, the range of non-native species is the aspect most important for agriculture.

Recent trends

Non-native species have been reported as a concern across European countries, causing problems for agriculture as well as forestry and fisheries, and nature conservation (EEA, 1998, p. 152). In *Denmark*, mink are a menace to poultry and fish farms and in *Germany*, the muskrat (*Fiber zibethicus*) has damaged water banks and endangered cultivated plants. Problems elsewhere include those from rats and locusts in *Greece*; crabfish (*Procambarus clarkii*) in rice fields, and the *Norwegian* rat (*Rattus norvegicus*) in *Portugal*.

Certain invasive weeds are also common across Europe, including in *Denmark* damage to pasture by *Heracleum pubescens* and *rosa rugosa*; in *Germany*, imported crop species, such as tobacco, potatoes and tomatoes have been accompanied by specific pests and viruses. *Greece* has reported *Ipomoea hederacea* (ivy-leaf morning glory) and *Eleusine indica* (wire grass); while in *Portugal*, there is concern with *Microphiulum aquaticum* and *Eichhornia crassipes*; and in *Switzerland* with *Lyriomyza spp.*

Invasion by non-indigenous species is considered in the *United States* as one of the most important issues at present in natural resource management and conservation biology (Mac *et al.*, 1998, pp. 117-129). The major concern in the US has been the loss of native biodiversity, ecosystem changes due to alien species invasions, and economic losses resulting from the introduction of non-indigenous species, although some of these species can be beneficial. A US government study estimated that of the 6 500 non-indigenous taxa in the US, about 15 per cent are considered economically or ecologically harmful (Office of Technology Assessment, 1993). Economic losses were conservatively estimated over the 20th century at US$97 billion, and this does not include damage from agricultural weeds for which there is little or no data.

Australia and *New Zealand* are acutely affected by the impact of non-native species on agriculture and ecosystems because of the evolution of their distinctive biota prior to European settlement. About 17 per cent of the total flora in *Australia* are non-native species, with about a quarter of these having potential to be serious environmental weeds (Commonwealth of Australia, 1995, pp. 40-47). Also at least

18 exotic mammals have established feral populations in Australia, such as cats, dogs, foxes and rabbits. They have inflicted economic losses to farmers through damage to crops and competition for livestock forage, and through predation leading to the destruction and decline of native species.

While exotic mammals damage agricultural production and harm ecosystems, in part, these species have spread and become abundant in *Australia* because of agriculture itself. This has occurred through clearing native habitat and, with respect to feral animals, through cropping and grazing activities providing them forage and water (Commonwealth of Australia, 1996, p. 23). *New Zealand* has also had a similar experience to that of Australia with respect to non-native species and their effects on agriculture and native ecosystems (New Zealand Ministry for the Environment, 1998, pp. 56-58).

Interpretation and links to other indicators

For non-native species an increase (decrease) in abundance or range of the species would be interpreted as increasing (decreasing) the threat of damage to agricultural production. However, any changes in the number of non-native species must be interpreted with care, as it may indicate either an increase in the number of threatening species or research that has found more pests exist (ANZECC, 1998, p. 26). Also, it is not always evident from different studies whether non-native species, or instead native pest species, are being monitored. Further information is required here to identify the key non-native species that are causing significant problems or threats to agricultural production and ecosystem balance.

A significant constraint in developing both non-native and wild species indicators, is that surveys of species populations can be very expensive and may require highly specialised skills. Methods for cost-effective and statistically reliable sampling have yet to be established for many species groups. Even so, databases both nationally and internationally, have been, or are being, established that may help to provide information on species distributions and population trends (see endnote 19).

Ecosystem diversity

Indicators of ecosystem diversity include the proportion of semi-natural and uncultivated natural habitats on agricultural land, and the extent of changes in agricultural land use. Ecosystem diversity indicators represent the "quantity" aspect of biodiversity shown at the base of the rectangle in Figure 2. These indicators are examined in the Wildlife Habitats chapter, and the Contextual Indicators chapter under the section concerning agricultural land use.

3. Related information

Biomass production

An important aspect to the link between biodiversity and agriculture, is the relationship between biomass production from agriculture (*i.e.* crops and forage) and species diversity as set out in the CBD Box 1). This relationship is important as it can have implications for future sustainable land use management decisions, for example, determining how much of the world's land surface can be set aside for conservation.[28]

There is evidence to suggest that in agricultural systems plant biomass production increases rapidly with the first 5 to 10 crop species, and adding more species may bring diminishing returns. However, in grasslands there is mostly a negative relationship between biomass and biodiversity. Also on semi-natural agricultural habitats, under low intensive systems of management, there can be an "optimum" biodiversity and not a one-dimensional relationship. Research into the relationship between biomass and biodiversity, however, is still at an early stage of development.

There are also important links between biomass production in agriculture and productivity, such as the possibilities of increasing plant biomass through technology to provide energy.[29] In other cases data on biomass production are also of use in evaluating agricultural production potential under different environmental conditions. *Norway*, for example, through its Agro-Ecology Programme, is collecting geographically referenced data on altitude, climate and soils and, in the longer term, data from plant biomass experiments will be included. The aim is to develop a standardised and objective means of measuring agricultural production potential to enable evaluation of agricultural land in cases of expropriation, for example, compensation payments for loss of agricultural land during road and rail development.

4. Future challenges

Understanding the relationship between agriculture and biodiversity is still in an early phase of development and requires further research of the basic conceptual issues concerning the complex and multidimensional nature of biodiversity. This work will also benefit in the future from further co-operation internationally with efforts concerning biodiversity and agriculture underway in FAO, and more broadly through the Secretariat to the Convention on Biological Diversity. However, considerable research has been undertaken on the effects of agriculture on biodiversity, while there are now a range of databases established or being developed that are of relevance to the area.

While the emphasis of indicators of *genetic diversity* in agriculture, has been on the *in situ* diversity of domesticated crops and livestock, further work could examine *in situ* indicators of wild relatives for genetic improvement, especially for cultivated crops. As *in situ* indicators measure only a very small proportion of existing and available genetic diversity and can severely underestimate real available genetic diversity *ex situ* indicators might be further developed. The key to future work on *ex situ* indicators should involve drawing on FAO work already underway in this area (see FAO 1996; and 1998). Also, in the future, using molecular "fingerprint" genetic marker data to measure genetic diversity could allow more precise assessment of genetic diversity of domesticated species. For example, using different named varieties of maize could be misleading, as they may have very similar germplasm.

To improve monitoring of the state and trends in *wild species diversity* in agriculture across OECD countries may require developing a standardised methodology for indicators of wild species on agricultural land. One possibility, being explored by some countries, is to develop species diversity indicators for agriculture through a *Natural Capital Index* (NCI) framework. The NCI is calculated as the product of the quantity of the ecosystem (*e.g.* agro-ecosystems) multiplied by the quality of the ecosystems (*i.e.* the average of changes in wild species numbers from a baseline period).[30] This approach has similarities with the habitat matrix indicator discussed in the Wildlife Habitats chapter.

Comprehensive data on species distribution and population numbers are unavailable for most countries, although certain indicative wild species (*e.g.* birds) could serve as a useful proxy of biodiversity quality in agriculture. A pragmatic approach will be needed to choose indicative (endemic) species, or groups of species that are important to the functioning of particular agricultural ecosystems. In this context, it will also be necessary to distinguish between indicators of wild species that help support agricultural production, such as pollinators and pest controlling organisms and predators, and wild species that use agricultural habitat or are affected by farming but use other habitats (especially for those farming systems that have been established over long periods of time).

Baselines from which to interpret changes in biodiversity, can be important for valuing the state and trends in biodiversity. A number of baseline options can be considered for biodiversity, and setting such a baseline is a complex and often a relatively arbitrary process. Many countries are in the process of developing criteria and thresholds to interpret biodiversity indicators, and in many cases the only practical baseline will be the first year from the beginning of when programmes are monitored. However, given the difficulties in determining suitable baselines across OECD countries, it may be more useful for policy makers to measure progress towards agreed targets.

As targets and baselines are established it will also be useful for policy makers to improve understanding of the *spatial distribution of biodiversity in agriculture.* This may also require better understanding of the significance of particular species distribution patterns and how to interpret changes in these distributions over time. Knowledge is also poor of species numbers and distribution patterns in relation to different agricultural land use types and farm management practices and systems. A feasible approach o this is to link biodiversity and agro-ecosystems into a matrix, an approach that is discussed further in he Wildlife Habitat chapter.

Biodiversity has an economic value to society operating at many different levels, but mainly in terms of biodiversity's use value, such as providing a life supporting system to agricultural production; and non-use values, for example, the knowledge of the continued existence of a particular species which others might enjoy or benefit.[31] Placing a monetary value on biodiversity is especially difficult as in many instances no markets exist for biodiversity, and also market prices fail to properly reflect the many non-market benefits of biodiversity.[32]

This area of work is of considerable importance to policy makers and society in assessing the costs and benefits of biodiversity conservation, and in helping determine which policies might best achieve biodiversity goals in agriculture, as recognised in the CBD (Box 1 and also see the discussion on the valuation of wildlife habitats and landscapes in the relevant chapters of this report). While there is work underway in this area, further studies are required to estimate the economic benefits of biodiversity, and the costs and benefits of the trade-offs between increased agricultural production and biodiversity loss.[33]

NOTES

1. Further details of the FAO inter-governmental Commission on Genetic Ressources for Food and Agriculture are available on the FAO website at : *www.fao.org/ag/cgrfa/*.

2. For details of the Biosafety Protocol visit the CBD Secretariat website at: *www.biodiv.org/*.

3. Further details are available on the websites at: *www.cites.org/* (for CITES); *www.ramsar.org/* (for the Ramsar Convention); *www.wcmc.org/uk/cms* (for the Convention on Migratory Species); and *http://migratorybirds.fws.gov/* (for the Canada-United States Migratory Birds Convention).

4. This section on the environmental context of biodiversity draws, in particular, on Day (1996) and Pagiola and Kellenberg (1997).

5. The impacts on biodiversity from changing agricultural land use to other land uses is discussed in the Wildlife Habitats chapter, but see also Fjellstad and Dramstad (1999); Hunziker (1995); and Ihse (1995).

6. The recent developments in biotechnology as they relate to agriculture are also discussed below, but for an examination of biotechnology in relation to plant genetic resources see Spillane (1999); and in relation to animal genetic resources see Cunningham (1999). Also for an examination of the commercial use of genetic resources from agriculture, see Kate and Laird (1999).

7. Estimates of world species numbers range from 5 to 100 million, moreover, the richness of individual countries in biodiversity varies greatly according to the parameter chosen. Some E*uropean* countries and Turkey are rich in wild and local varieties of livestock and food crops, while A*ustralia*, M*exico* and the US are amongst the world's top ten countries in terms of species richness (in part because of their size and location). J*apan* and New Zealand, however, are not high in terms of species richness, but they have a distinctive fauna and flora (OECD, 1996, pp. 25-28).

8. In A*ustralia*, for example, the biological condition of the soil is also considered to cover elements such as, feral animal and pest invasions, woody shrub infestations and clearance of native vegetation (Industry Commission, 1996).

9. For a further discussion of the problem of non-native species see: ANZECC (1998, p. 26); Commonwealth of Australia (1995); Office of Technology Assessment (1993); Mac *et al.* (1998); and the New Zealand Ministry for the Environment (1998, pp. 56-58).

10. The trade-off between agriculture, production and biodiversity and improved wildlife management practices are discussed by Wossink *et al.* (1999). See also Montgomery *et al.* (1999) concerning the concept of biodiversity management policies to help inform decision-making to prioritise biodiversity conservation efforts.

11. For a bibliographic review of the impact of climate change on biodiversity, see Burns (2000).

12. Unless stated otherwise the information in this section draws from the responses to the OECD Agri-environmental Indicator Questionnaire 1999. For reviews of possible indicators related to biodiversity see Reid *et al.* (1993) and specifically related to agriculture see Tucker and Evans (1997).

13. For a discussion of the EU Regulation with respect to rare breeds, see European Commission (1999, p. 131) and ECNC (2000) for a broader assessment of the EU Agricultural Action Plan for Biodiversity.

14. The data on genetic erosion of crop plants in K*orea* are drawn from Ahn *et al.* (1996).

15. The list of endangered domesticated breeds in G*ermany* are those for which support under EU Regulation No. 2078/92 would be granted.

16. FAO is developing a monitoring system, the Domestic Animal Diversity Information System (DAD-IS), to track the state of the world's animal genetic resources, see: *www.fao.org/dad-is/*.

17. The M*exican* experience of conservation of maize varieties is examined by CEC (1999, pp. 163-167).

18. For a recent review of economic issues related to genetically modified crops see OECD (2000a).

19. There is an increasing availability of data and information related to biodiversity at an international level, see for example, the IUCN, the UNEP, BirdLife International, the European Environment Agency Topic Centre on Nature Conservation, and in the U*nited States* the Smithsonian Society databases.

20. Other examples here include: *Greece*, mid-winter counts of waterfowl since 1969; *Denmark* populations of certain birds since 1976; *Norway*, breeding bird survey, since 1995; *Sweden*, a breeding bird survey established in the 1970s and a project "flora guardians" monitoring mainly vascular plants; *Switzerland*, regular bird surveys; and *United Kingdom* a breeding birds survey established in 1970.

21. Figure 8 should be interpreted cautiously as definitions and the measurement of wild species using agricultural land as habitat vary across countries.

22. A detailed study of agriculture and biodiversity, with emphasis on the policy aspects in *Europe*, has recently been prepared for the IUCN (1999).

23. Trends in UK bird species, including those on farmland, are annually monitored by the RSPB (1999).

24. Information regarding UK mammal population trends can be found at the UK Mammal Society website at: *www.abdn.ac.uk/mammal/*.

25. This text draws from Neave *et al.* (2000).

26. The baseline of 1950 has been chosen in the *Netherlands* because first, data from that period are available or can be derived from research; second, in 1950 agricultural ecosystems are considered as having still a very high biodiversity; third, from 1950 industrial management practices were rapidly introduced and the loss of biodiversity was accelerating fast; and, fourth, 1950 has been proposed by the CBD as a postulated pre-industrial baseline to provide a common denominator across countries.

27. Increasingly in the public policy debate on environmental issues, including biodiversity, the precautionary principle and the safe minimum standard, are being invoked as a policy guideline to help ensure that the level of biodiversity that future generations inherit is no less than that available to present generations. The precautionary principle and safe minimum standard in relation to biodiversity is examined by Barbier (1997).

28. These issues are discussed by Holmes (1998), and see Lewandrowski *et al.* (1999) for an estimate of the cost of setting aside land to protect ecosystem diversity.

29. This issue has been explored by, for example, Haberl (1997). For an estimate of biomass production in *Switzerland* see Paulsen (1995). *Australia* is also considering developing an indicator of the net primary productivity of biomass, see Hamblin (1998, pp. 79-80). The biomass for energy issue is also discussed in the Greenhouse Gases and Wildlife Habitat chapters.

30. The *Netherlands*, for example, have been actively researching the possibilities of developing a NCI for agriculture, see RIVM (1998).

31. For a more complete discussion of the use and non-use values of biodiversity, see OECD (1999).

32. Work by Cooper (1999) has attempted to develop indicators of the economic value of plant genetic resources for agriculture, but on this subject see also Smale (1998) and Zohrabian and Traxier (1999).

33. See, for example, OECD (1997, pp. 42-45); OECD (2001, forthcoming); and Steffens and Hoehn (1997).

Annex Table 1. Total number of plant varieties registered and certified for marketing: 1985 and 1998

	Cereals		Oil crops		Dried pulses/beans		Root crops		Fruit		Vegetables		Industrial crops		Forage	
	1985	1998	1985	1998	1985	1998	1985	1998	1985	1998	1985	1998	1985	1998	1985	1998
Austria	..	160	..	27	..	31	..	83	..	..	..	4	..	..	..	38
Canada[1]	539	725	120	332	35	130	76	127	..	..	..	54	27	32	276	549
Denmark[2]	84	109	33	107	16	46	62	173	7	19	67	..	..	..	102	119
Finland[3]	57	57	7	7	11	4	22	41	..	..	..	..	2	2	58	34
Germany[4]	272	454	..	..	33	43	..	..	..	..	..	..	..	..	418	653
Greece[5]	..	323	..	..	..	..	17	25	27	36	104	68	15	56	..	95
Italy[6]	589	723	1	1	15	42	20	18	..	..	..	..	..	..	..	..
Japan[7]	54	308	..	..	11	42	5	42	157	574	173	656	19	87	19	117
Netherlands[8]	110	152	3	4	23	20	211	269	45	63	274	309	14	30	245	566
Norway	27	33	3	3	..	..	13	16	..	..	..	..	..	..	8	10
Portugal[9]	124	209	10	14	10	19	12	35	..	12	-	164	..	..	23	12
Sweden[10]	66	131	19	28	13	22	41	87	..	..	2	2	-	-	81	154
Switzerland	74	197	..	..	..	..	..	..	..	..	..	..	..	..	..	..
United Kingdom[11]	228	295	55	184	59	103	188	164	..	..	..	..	-	-	1	1

4. For each crop category (e.g., cereals), the number of varieties for specific crops (e.g., wheat, rice, barley, maize, etc) are added together to form total number of varieties.
.. Not available.
- Negligible.
1. Data for 1985, 1998 refer respectively to 1986, 1995. Number of varieties registered for sale. A registered variety does not mean that the seed of each variety is sold annually.
2. Data for 1998 refers to the year 1999. Forage: Seeds for sowing (perennial ryegrass, red fescue, smooth meadow grass). The species included in each category are the 3 dominant species in terms of area in 1997.
3. Forage: seeds for sowing (ryegrass, fescue, meadow grass, etc.) and nitrogen fixators (clover, alfalfa, etc).
4. Data are for registered and certified varieties. Forage: seeds for sowing (ryegrass, fescue, meadow grass, etc) and nitrogen fixators (clover, alfalfa, lupin, vetch).
5. Vegetables: data for 1985 refer to the year 1990.
6. Oil crops: data refer to rapeseed. Dried pulses/beans: data for 1985 refer to the year 1990.
7. Number of varieties registered for Plant Variety Protection at the end of the year.
8. Fruit: data for 1985 are number of varieties grown.
9. Oil crops, Root crops: data for 1985 refer to the year 1990.
10. Vegetables: data refer to brown kidney beans.
11. Forage: data refer to velvet bent and redtop.
Source: OECD Agri-environmental Indicators Questionnaire, 1999.

Annex Table 2. **Share of the one to five dominant varieties in total marketed crop production: 1985 and 1998**

	Canada[1]			Denmark[2]			Germany[3]			Greece			Italy[4]			Japan			Norway			Poland[5]			Portugal[6]			Sweden[7]			Switzerland		
	Nb	1985	1998	Nb	1985	1998	Nb	1985	1998	Nb	1985	1998	Nb	1985	1998	Nb	1985	1998	Nb	1985	1998	Nb	1985	1998	Nb	1985	1998	Nb	1985	1998	Nb	1985	1998
Cereals																																	
Wheat	3	80	74	3	96	70										5	76	83				7	60	59	5	58	32				5	84	90
Spring																			3	100	80							1	50	68			
Winter							5	59	41										3	100	85							1	54	55			
Bread	3	85	76							4	..	64	5	44	53																		
Durum										4	..	34	5	88	63																		
Barley																																	
Spring	3	46	60	3	68	71	5	61	67	5	..	53	5	53	42				5	90	80							5	59	58			
Winter				3	99	98	5	63	45																			1	86	81			
Maize							5	57	73				5	95	56	5	46	64				5	35	37	5	30	20	1	53	44			
Rice							5	57	47	1	..	80	5	63	53										5	85	92						
Rye (spring)	4	86	83				5	100	100				2	86	76*													1	71	61			
Rye (winter)	3	58	69				5	99	69																			3	81	60			
Oats							5	75	64				5	87	86				5	85	50							2	100	87			
Triticale													1/5	100	69																		
Oil crops																																	
Rapeseed	3	94	75				5	70	54				1	100	100				3	100	100				5	65	26				2	90	90
Spring				3	92	82																											
Winter				3	96	70																											
Oil flax	4	83	87	3	100	100																											
Swede rape – winter																												2	99	68			
Swede rape – spring																												2	86	91			
Turnip rape – winter																												1	89	99			
Turnip rape – spring																												1	73	98			
Dried pulses/Beans																																	
Field peas				3	95	68																						3	97	65			
Broad beans				3	100	100																											
Field beans																												1	70	88			
Soybeans										5	4	2	3/5	87	60										5	5	4						
Root crops																																	
Potatoes							5	31	23				5	79	81	5	84	78							5	88	84	5	71	57	2	90	90
Sweet potatoes																5	82	83										2	70	40			
Sugarbeet										5	70	55																					
Fruit																																	
Apples										5	79	58	5	84	87	5	84	87													5	65	69
Pears										3	66	63																					
Peaches (table)										5	79	51																					
Peaches (industrial)										5	74	76																					
Nectarines										5	54	52																					
Cerises										3	45	53																					
Apricot										3	95	69																			5	63	61

Annex Table 2. **Share of the one to five dominant varieties in total marketed crop production: 1985 and 1998** (cont.)

	Canada[1]			Denmark[2]			Germany[3]			Greece			Italy[4]			Japan			Norway			Poland[5]			Portugal[6]			Sweden[7]			Switzerland		
		% share			% share			% share			% share			% share			% share			% share			% share			% share			% share			% share	
	Nb	1985	1998	Nb	1985	1998	Nb	1985	1998	Nb	1985	1998	Nb	1985	1998	Nb	1985	1998	Nb	1985	1998	Nb	1985	1998	Nb	1985	1998	Nb	1985	1998	Nb	1985	1998
Vegetables																																		
Tomatoes										5	50	30																			5	80	80
Cucumbers										5	30	20																					
Watermelons										5	6	4																					
Lettuce																															5	50	50
Melons										5	8	5																					
Asparagus										5	4	3																					
Aubergine										5	3	3																					
Pepper										5	3	3																					
Brown kidney beans																												1	94	56			
Industrial crops																																	
Tobacco										5	70	80																					
Forage																																	
Perennial ryegrass				3	34	29*																											
Red fescue				3	90	30*																											
Smooth meadow grass				3	92	71*																											
Lucerne										1	..	80																					
Vetch										3	..	86																					
Red clover																			3	100	95												
Timothy																			3	90	90												
Fodder clover																									5	41	34	5	76	73			
Grasses																												10	70	57			

Notes: See Annex Table 1. Table shows, for Canada and wheat for example, that for 3 wheat varieties their share in total production declined by 6 points from 80% in 1985 to 74% in 1990.

.. Not available.

* 1995 data.

Nb Number.

1. Data for 1998 refer to 1990.
2. Data are on weight basis for cereals and on an area basis for other crop categories.
3. In Germany, the cultivated area or the share of the varieties in total marketed production is not directly recorded: the numbers are calculated by seed multiplication areas.
4. Triticale: one crop variety in 1985 and five crop vrarieties in 1998. Soybeans: data for 1985 refer to 1990.
5. Data for 1998 refer to 1995.
6. Data for 1985 refer to 1990.
7. Oats refers to spring oats; triticale refers to triticale winter and data for 1985 refer to 1990; soybeans 1998 refers to 1995; sugar beet 1985 refers to 1995.

Source: OECD Agri-environmental Indicators Questionnaire, 1999.

Annex Table 3. Number of livestock breeds registered or certified for marketing: 1985 and 1998

	Cattle		Pigs		Poultry		Sheep		Goats		Horses		Other	
	1985	1998	1985	1998	1985	1998	1985	1998	1985	1998	1985	1998	1985	1998
Austria	12	21	5	5	..	..	7	17	4	12	15	38	..	..
Canada[1]	..	31	..	8	..	..	..	32	..	10	..	25	1	1
Finland[2]	9	13	2	3	..	8	5	7	1	..	10	12	1	..
Germany	..	77	..	14	..	..	..	41	..	16	..	103	..	..
Greece	8	8	4	4	1	1	21	21	5	5	6	6	..	..
Italy[3]	18	26	9	11	..	..	34	23	..	..	..	..	1	1
Netherlands[4]	9	8	3	3	5	5	3	3	2	2	20	20	1	1
Norway[5]	4	10	2	3	..	..	7	7	1	1	..	..	..	..
Poland[6]	9	15	7	10	71	70	22	35	..	..	..	..	2	5
Portugal	..	16	..	8	..	..	..	11	..	4	..	..	..	..
Sweden[7]	17	20	4	5	6	6	..	..	1	3	..	..	..	..
Switzerland	10	18	3	5	..	..	9	11	8	9	3	21	..	..

.. Not available.
1. Data for 1998 refer to 1997.
2. Cattle: dairy cattle and beef breeds. Pigs: numbers refer to purebred, excluding cross-bred categories. Poultry: chicken, duck, goose, quail, and turkey. Goats: data for 1985 refer to 1995. Other: reindeer.
3. Data for 1985 refer to 1991.
4. Cattle: dairy cattle and beef breeds. Poultry: layer and boiler breeds, turkey, and guinea fowl. Other: mink.
5. Pigs: numbers refer to purebred, excluding cros-bred categories. Other: reindeer.
6. Poultry: data for 1985 refer to 1995. Others: goats, reindeer, shaanene and other livestock.
7. Data for 1985 refer to 1990.
Source: OECD Agri-environmental Indicators Questionnaire, 1999.

Annex Table 4. Share of the three major livestock breeds in total livestock numbers: 1985 and 1998

	Cattle			Pigs			Poultry			Sheep			Goats			Horses		
	% share		Points change	% share		Points change	% share		Points change	% share		Points change	% share		Points change	% share		Points change
	1985	1998	1985 to 1998	1985	1998	1985 to 1998	1985	1998	1985 to 1998	1985	1998	1985 to 1998	1985	1998	1985 to 1998	1985	1998	1985 to 1998
Austria[1]	95	93	-2	85	71	-14	..	..	..	75	79	4	..	..	..	75	81	6
Canada[2]	..	99	..	..	96	..	..	..	..	..	56	..	..	67	..	..	49	..
Finland[3]	74	67	-6	95	95	0	..	99	..	99	97	3	100	100	0	..	92	..
Germany[4]	86	90	4	95	94	-1	..	..	..	..	..	..	..	..	..	..	..	..
Greece[5]	..	98	..	..	93	..	..	100	..	..	68	..	100	100	0	89	86	-3
Italy[6]	87	94	7	99	98	-1	..	..	..	83	89	6	..	..	..	..	..	..
Netherlands	95	91	-4	90	..	..	..	..	..	79	86	7	100	100	0	100	100	0
Norway[7]	96	91	-5	90	36	-54	..	..	..	78	68	-10	100	100	0	100	100	0
Poland[8]	99	98	-1	93	84	-9	..	..	..	..	..	..	72	64	-8	..	..	..
Portugal	..	59	..	..	6	..	..	..	..	..	5	..	95	5	..	..	..	..
Sweden[9]	85	92	7	..	95	..	..	99	..	..	..	..	95	95	0	100	..	..
Switzerland[10]	90	98	8	100	98	-2	..	..	..	91	82	-9	67	74	7	100	94	-6

.. Not available.
1. Cattle and Horses: data for 1998 refer to 1995.
2. Data for 1998 refer to 1997.
3. Cattle: beef breeds. Pigs: percentages include purebred and cross-bred categories. Poultry: chicken, duck, goose, quail, and turkey and percentages are estimated from breeding animals. Goats: percentage for 1998 refers to 1995.
4. Cattle and Pigs: data for 1998 refer to 1997. Pigs: data for 1985 refer to 1987.
5. Goats and Horses: data for 1985 refer to 1990. Goats: as percentages for 1985 and 1998 refer respectively to 99.9% and 99.8%, the change equals -0.2.
6. Data for 1985 refer to 1991.
7. Cattle: data for 1985 refer to 1990. Pigs: percentages include purebred and cross-bred categories. Horses: reindeer.
8. Data refer to the major two breeds. Goats: percentages refer to one breed of goat.
9. Cattle: data for 1985 refer to 1990.
10. Pigs: data refer to the major two breeds.
Source: OECD Agri-environmental Indicators Questionnaire, 1999.

Annex Table 5. **Percentage share of all wild species that use agricultural land as habitat:[1] 1998**

	Mammals	Birds	Reptiles	Invertebrates (butterflies)	Amphibians	Fish	Vascular plants	Other
Denmark	..	..	..	29	..	..	26	..
Finland	5-10	10	0	..	0	0	..	..
Germany[2]	..	..	..	..	..	..	33	..
Greece	20	60	10	..	10	..	..	..
Japan[3]	7 (0)	28 (25)	42 (20)*	..	50 (45)	37 (37)*	..	..
Netherlands[4]	50	80	0	45	40	20	75	75
Norway[5]	..	30	..	70	..	..	..	16/25
Sweden[6]	35	42	75	46	78	0	60	29/27/33
Switzerland	75	70	..	72	..	..	..	..

.. Not available.
* Except marine species.
1. This table should be interpreted with care as definitions of the use of agricultural land as habitat by wild species can vary. Species can use agricultural land as "primary" habitat (strongly dependent on habitat) or "secondary" habitat (uses habitat but is not dependent on it).
2. It is estimated that about 50% of all wild species (animals and plants) depend on agricultural habitats.
3. Figures in brackets show species that use paddy rice fields as habitat. Japan does not have scientifically reliable data on invertebrates and vascular plants.
4. Share of all wild species on agricultural land classified into high, moderate, and low dependence. Mammals: including rodents. Birds: breeding birds. Other: dragonflies.
5. Percentages refer to the number of species that are associated with agricultural land but degree of dependence can vary. Birds: 30% of 250 species depend on agricultural habitats of which 3% are believed to have declined due to changes in agricultural landscapes. Invertebrates: day-flying butterflies, 70% of 94 species. Other: threatened mosses, 16% of 250 threatened moss species/red-listed fungi, 25% of 763 red-listed species.
6. Invertebrates: butterflies, beetles, aculeata hymenoptera, a number of smaller groups, plus an estimate of flies (diptera) and other hymenoptera. Overall the Swedish estimate is based on about one third of the known number of invertebrate species in Sweden. Other: mosses/fungi/lichens.

Source: OECD Agri-environmental Indicators Questionnaire, 1999.

325

Annex Table 6. **Population trends for selected wild species using agricultural land as habitat: 1985 to 1998**

Numbers of species

		1985	1990	1995	1998
Denmark[1]	Birds	57	75	71	72
Poland	Hare (*Lepus timidus*)	31 000	35 000	23 000	..
	Partridge (*Perdix perdix*)	4 462 000	1 727 000	73 000	..
	Common Pheasant (*Phasianus colchicus*)	14 000	13 000	5 000	..
United Kingdom[2]	Birds	82	79	71	64
	Vascular plants:				
	– Cropland	7	6	..	..
	– Fertile Grassland	11	11	..	..
	– Infertile Grassland	22	19	..	..

.. Not available.
1. Denmark
  Birds: Measured as abundance of 7 key bird species.
2. United Kingdom
  Birds: Population index (1970 = 100) for 20 breeding birds associated with farmland.
  Vascular plants: Average number of species per 200 m² random plots. Data for 1985 refer to 1978.
Source: OECD Agri-environmental Indicators Questionnaire, 1999.

BIBLIOGRAPHY

Ahn, W.S., J.H. Kang and M.S. Yoon (1996),
"Genetic Erosion of Crop Plants in Korea", pp. 41-55, in Y.G. Park and S. Sakamoto (eds.), *Biodiversity and Conservation of Plant Genetic Resources in Asia*, Japan Scientific Societies Press, Tokyo, Japan.

ANZECC [Australia and New Zealand Environment and Conservation Council] (1998),
Core Environmental Indicators for Reporting on the State of the Environment, State of the Environment Reporting Task Force, ANZECC Secretariat, Canberra, Australia.

Barbier, E.B. (1997),
"Ecological Economic, Uncertainty and Implications for Policy Setting Priorities for Biodiversity Conservation", pp. 115-140, in OECD, *Investing in Biological Diversity: The Cairns Conference*, Paris, France.

Brown, L.R., M. Renner and B. Halweil (1999),
Vital Signs 1999: The Environmental Trends that are Shaping Our Future, Worldwatch Institute, Washington, DC., United States.

Burns, W. (2000),
Bibliography: Impacts of Climate Change on Flora and Fauna Species and Associated Ecosystems, Pacific Institute for Studies in Development, Environmental Security, Oakland, California, United States. Available at: *www.pacinst.org/ccbio.pdf*.

CEC [Commission for Environmental Cooperation] (1999),
"Maize in Mexico: Some Environmental Implications of the North American Free Trade Agreement", Issue Study 1, pp. 65-182, in CEC, *Assessing Environmental Effects of the North American Free Trade Agreement (NAFTA): An Analytic Framework (Phase II) and Issue Studies*, Montreal, Canada. Available at: *www.cec.org/* [English > Publications and Information Resources > CEC Publications > Environment, Economy and Trade].

CEC (2000),
Securing the Continent's Biological Wealth: Towards Effective Biodiversity Conservation in North America, Commission for Environmental Cooperation, Montreal, Canada. Available at: *www.cec.org/programs_projects/conserv_biodiv/baseline.cfm?varlan=eng lish*.

Commission of the European Communities (1999),
Directions Towards Sustainable Agriculture, Communication from the Commission to the Council, The European Parliament, The Economic and Social Committee and the Committee of the Regions, COM(1999)22Final, Brussels. Available at: *http://europa.eu.int/comm/dg06/envir/index_en.htm*.

Commonwealth of Australia (1995),
Sustaining the Agricultural Resource Base, 12th Meeting of the Prime Minister's Science and Engineering Council, Office of the Chief Scientist, Department of the Prime Minister and Cabinet, Canberra, Australia.

Commonwealth of Australia (1996),
Australia State of the Environment 1996 Executive Summary, State of the Environment Advisory Council, Canberra, Australia.

Commonwealth of Australia (1998),
Sustainable Agriculture – Assessing Australia's Recent Performance, A Report to the Standing Committee on Agriculture and Resource Management (SCARM) of the National Collaborative Project on Indicators for Sustainable Agriculture, SCARM Technical Report No. 70, CSIRO Publishing, Victoria, Australia.

Cooper, J.C. (1999),
The Sharing of Benefits Derived from the Utilisation of Plant Genetic Resources for Food and Agriculture, Internal Memorandum, US Department of Agriculture, Washington, DC., United States.

Cunningham, E.P. (1999),
Recent Developments in Biotechnology as they Relate to Animal Genetic Resources for Food and Agriculture, Background Study Paper No. 10, FAO Commission on Genetic Resources for Food and Agriculture, Eighth Session, 19-23 April, Rome, Italy. Available at: *www.fao.org/ag/cgrfa/docs8.htm*.

Day, K. (1996),
"Agriculture's Links to Biodiversity", *Agricultural Outlook*, December, 1996, Economic Research Service, US Department of Agriculture, Washington, DC., United States.

Debailleul, G. (1997),
"Economic Incentives for Biodiversity Conservation in the Agricultural Sector", pp. 235-52, in OECD (1997) *Investing in Biological Diversity: The Cairns Conference*, Paris, France.

Dennis, R.L.H. (ed.) (1992),
The Ecology of Butterflies in Britain, Oxford University Press, Oxford, United Kingdom.

ECNC [European Centre for Nature Conservation] (2000),
Stimulating Positive Linkages between Agriculture and Biodiversity: Recommendations for the EC Agricultural Action Plan o Biodiversity, Tilburg, The Netherlands. Available at: *www.ecnc.nl/*.

EEA [European Environment Agency] (1998),
Europe's Environment: The Second Assessment, Office for Official Publications of the European Communities Luxembourg. Available at: *http://themes.eea.eu.int/* [> all available reports].

Environmental Protection Agency (1999),
Environment in Focus – A Discussion Document on Key National Environmental Indicators, Wexford, Ireland. Available at *www.epa.ie/pubs/default.htm*.

Erhardt, A. (1985),
"Diurnal Lepidoptera: sensitive indicators of cultivated and abandoned grassland", *Journal of Applied Ecology* Vol. 22, pp. 849-861.

European Commission (1998),
First Report on the implementation of the Convention on Biological Diversity by the European Community, Brussels, Belgium.

European Commission (1999),
Agriculture, Environment, Rural Development: Facts and Figures – A Challenge for Agriculture, Office for Official Publication of the European Communities, Luxembourg. Available at: *http://europa.eu.int/comm/dg06/envir/report/en/index.htm*.

FAO [United Nations Food and Agriculture Organisation] (1996),
Report on the State of the World's Plant Genetic Resources for Food and Agriculture, prepared for the International Technica Conference on Plant Genetic Resources, Leipzig, Germany, 17-23 June. Available at: *http://193.43.36.6/wrlmap_e.htm*.

FAO (1998),
The State of the World's Animal Genetic Resources for Food and Agriculture, First Session, 8-10 September of the International Technical Working Group on Animal Genetic Resources for Food and Agriculture, Rome, Italy Available at: *www.fao.org/ag/cgrfa/docs8.htm*.

Fjellstad, W.J. and W.E. Dramstad (1999),
"Patterns of change in two contrasting Norwegian agricultural landscapes", *Landscape and Urban Planning*, Vol. 45 No. 4, pp. 177-191.

Haberl, H. (1997),
"Human appropriation of net primary production as an environmental indicator: Implications for sustainable development", *Ambio*, Vol. 26, No. 3, pp. 143-146.

Hamblin, A. (1998),
Environmental Indicators for National State of the Environment Reporting – The Land, Australia: State of the Environmen (Environmental Indicator Reports), Department of the Environment, Canberra, Australia. Available at *www.environment.gov.au/soe/* [Environmental Indicators > Land under "Environmental Indicator Reports"].

Holmes, B. (1998),
"Life Support – Why bother to save every last species on the planet?", *New Scientist*, 15 August, pp. 30-34.

Hunziker, M. (1995),
"The spontaneous reafforestation in abandoned agricultural lands: perception and aesthetic assessment by locals and tourists", *Landscape and Urban Planning*, Vol. 31, No. 3, pp. 399-410.

Ihse, M. (1995),
"Swedish agricultural landscapes – patterns and changes during the last 50 years, studies by aerial photos" *Landscape and Urban Planning*, Vol. 31, No. 1, pp. 21-37.

Industry Commission (1996),
Land Degradation and the Australian Agricultural Industry, Staff Information Paper, Australian Government Publishin Service, Canberra, Australia.

IUCN [World Conservation Union] (1999),
Background study for the development of an IUCN Policy on Agriculture and Biodiversity, Report prepared by P. Nowicki, C. Potter and T. Reed, Wye College, University of London, United Kingdom. Available at: *www.iucn.org/places/europe/eu/docs/Agriculture_Biodiversity.pdf*.

ames, C. (1997-1999),
"Global Review of Transgenic Crops", ISAAA Briefs, 1997-1999, The International Service for the Acquisition of Agri-biotech Applications (ISAAA), Ithaca, United States. Available at: www.isaaa.org/.

Kate, K. ten and S.A. Laird (1999),
The Commercial Use of Biodiversity – Access to Genetic Resources and Benefit Sharing, Earthscan Publications Ltd., London, United Kingdom.

Lewandrowski, J., R.F. Darwin, M. Tsigas and A. Raneses (1999),
"Estimating costs of protecting global ecosystem diversity", Ecological Economics, Vol. 29, No. 1, pp. 111-125.

Mac, M.J., P.A. Opler, C.E.P. Haecker and P.D. Doran (1998),
Status and Trends of the Nation's Biological Resources, Two Volumes, United States Department of the Interior, United States Geological Survey, Reston, Virginia, United States. Available at: http://biology.usgs.gov/pubs/execsumm/page2.htm.

MAF Finland (1996),
Renewable Natural Resources and Biological Diversity, Ministry of Agriculture and Forestry (MAF), Helsinki, Finland.

MAFF [Ministry of Agriculture, Fisheries and Food] (2000),
Towards Sustainable Agriculture – A Pilot Set of Indicators, London, United Kingdom. Available at: www.maff.gov.uk/ [Farming > Sustainable Agriculture].

Montgomery, C.A., R.A. Pollak, K. Freemark and D. White (1999),
"Pricing Biodiversity", Journal of Environmental Economics and Management, Vol. 38, No. 1, pp. 1-19.

Neave, P., E. Neave, T. Weins and T. Riche (2000),
"Availability of Wildlife Habitat on Farmland", Chapter 15, in T. McRae, C.A.S. Smith and L.J. Gregorich (eds.), Environmental Sustainability of Canadian Agriculture: Report of the Agri-Environmental Indicator Project, Agriculture and Agri-Food Canada (AAFC), Ottawa, Ontario, Canada. Available at: www.agr.ca/policy/environment/publications/ list.html.

New Zealand Ministry for the Environment (1998),
Environmental Performance Indicators: Proposals for Terrestrial and Freshwater Biodiversity, Wellington, New Zealand.

Norderhaug, A. (1987),
"De urterike slåtteengene" (only in Norwegian "Hay meadows rich in herbal plants"), Fortidsvern, Vol. 3, pp. 12-13.

OECD (1996),
Saving Biological Diversity, Paris, France.

OECD (1997),
Investing in Biological Diversity: The Cairns Conference, Paris, France.

OECD (1998),
Towards Sustainable Development: Environmental Indicators, Paris, France.

OECD (1999),
Handbook of Incentive Measures for Biodiversity – Design and Implementation, Paris, France.

OECD (2000a),
OECD Agricultural Outlook 2000-2005, Paris, France.

OECD (2000b),
Environmental Performance Reviews: Luxembourg, Paris, France.

OECD (2001),
Handbook on the Applied Evaluation of Biodiversity, Paris, France, forthcoming.

Office of Technology Assessment (1993),
Harmful nonindigenous species in the United States, United States Congress, OTA-F-565, US Government Printing Office, Washington, DC., United States. Available at: www.ota.nap.edu/pdf/1993idx.html.

Pagiola, S. and J. Kellenberg (1997),
Mainstreaming Biodiversity in Agricultural Development – Toward Good Practice, World Bank Environment Paper No. 15, World Bank, Washington, DC., United States.

Paulsen, J. (1995),
Der Biologische Kohlenstoffvorrat der Schweiz, (only in German "Biological Carbon Sinks in Switzerland"), Verlag Ruegger, Zurich, Switzerland.

Perrings, C. (1998),
The Economics of Biodiversity Loss and Agricultural Development in Low Income Countries, paper prepared for the American Association of Agricultural Economists International Conference, "Agricultural Intensification, Economic Development and the Environment ", 31 July-1 August, Salt Lake City, Utah, United States.

Reid, W.V., J.A. McNeely, D.B. Tunstall, D.A. Bryant and M. Winograd (1993),
Biodiversity Indicators for Policy-makers, World Resources Institute, Washington, DC., United States.

RIVM [State Institute of Public Health and the Environment] (1998),
  Leefomgevingsbalans, voorzet voor vorm en inhoud, Bilthoven (only in Dutch "Balance for the Natural Environment") The Netherlands.

RSPB [Royal Society for the Protection of Birds] (1999),
  The State of the UK's Birds 1999, RSPB Annual Report, Sandy, Bedfordshire, United Kingdom. Available at *www.rspb.org.uk/* [> Conservation Issues].

Saunders, D.A., C. Margules and B. Hill (1998),
  Environmental Indicators For National State of the Environment Reporting – Biodiversity, State of the Environmen (Environmental Indicator Reports), Department of the Environment, Canberra, Australia.

Smale, M. (1997),
  "The Green Revolution and Wheat Genetic Diversity: Some Unfounded Assumptions", *World Development* Vol. 25, No. 8, pp. 1257-1269.

Smale, M. (ed.) (1998),
  Farmers, Gene Banks and Crop Breeding: Economic Analysis of Diversity in Wheat, Maize, and Rice, International Maize and Wheat Improvement Centre, Mexico, Kluwer Academic Publishers, Boston, United States.

Smith, F. (1996),
  "Biological diversity, ecosystem stability and economic development", *Ecological Economics*, Vol. 16, No. 3 pp. 191-203.

Spillane, C. (1999),
  Recent Developments in Biotechnology as they Relate to Plant Genetic Resources for Food and Agriculture, Background Stud Paper No. 9, FAO Commission on Genetic Resources for Food and Agriculture, Eighth Session, 19-23 April Rome, Italy. Available at: *www.fao.org/ag/cgrfa/docs8.htm*.

Steffens, K. and J.P. Hoehn (1997),
  Valuing Biodiversity: Issues and Illustrative Example, Staff Paper (97-7), February, Department of Agricultura Economics, Michigan State University, East Lansing, Michigan, United States.

Thomas, J.A. (1984),
  "The conservation of butterflies in temperate countries: past efforts and lessons for the future", in R.I. Vane-Wrigh and P.R. Ackery (eds.), *The Biology of Butterflies*, Symposium of the Royal Entomological Society of London, No. 11 pp. 333-353, Academic Press, London, United Kingdom.

Tucker, G.M. and M.F.Heath (1994),
  Birds in Europe: their conservation status, BirdLife Conservation Series No. 3, BirdLife International, Cambridge United Kingdom.

Tucker, G.M. and M.I. Evans (1997),
  Habitats for Birds in Europe: A Conservation Strategy for the Wider Environment, BirdLife Conservation Series No. 6 Birdlife International, Cambridge, United Kingdom.

UK Department of the Environment (1996),
  Indicators of Sustainable Development for the United Kingdom, London, United Kingdom. Available at: *www.environment.detr.gov.uk/* [> Indicators of Sustainable Development for the UK]

USDA [United States Department of Agriculture] (1997),
  Agricultural Resources and Environmental Indicators, 1996-97, Agricultural Handbook No. 712, Natural Resources and Environment Division, Economic Research Service, Washington, DC., United States. Available at: *www.ers.usda.gov* [Briefing Rooms > Agricultural Resources and Environmental Indicators].

Wossink, A., J. van Wenum, C. Jurgens and G. de Snoo (1999),
  "Co-ordinating economic, behavioural and spatial aspects of wildlife preservation in agriculture", *European Review of Agricultural Economics*, Vol. 26, No. 4, pp. 443-460.

Zohrabian, A. and G. Traxier (1999),
  Valuing Plant Genetic Resources: An Economic Model of Utilisation of the US National Crop Germplasm Collection, pape presented to the Annual Meeting of the American Association of Agricultural Economics, 8-11 August, Nashville Tennessee, United States.

Chapter 6

WILDLIFE HABITATS

HIGHLIGHTS

Context

All land, including agricultural land, provides habitat for wildlife (flora and fauna), but its composition and quality is highly variable. Agricultural activities can impact on wildlife and their habitats directly by the conversion of uncultivated natural habitats to crops or forage, and indirectly through disturbances of these habitats, such as the effects of elevated pollutant discharges.

OECD countries are paying greater attention to improving the quality of habitat on farmland because of the growing value society is placing on such habitats as sites of environmental and recreational value. Policy actions have focused on protecting endangered agricultural habitats and encouraging farmers to adopt management practices beneficial for habitat improvement, with some policy initiatives part of international commitments, such as the Convention on Biological Diversity.

Indicators and recent trends

Six indicators are being developed by OECD related to agriculture and wildlife habitat. Five indicators monitor the state and trends in intensively farmed, semi-natural, and uncultivated natural habitats. The importance of these habitats for wildlife differ widely. Intensively farmed land can be important for biodiversity where hedges, etc., are maintained, while semi-natural habitats are often rich in biodiversity. A sixth indicator is a habitat matrix, which identifies and relates the ways in which wild species use different agricultural habitat types.

For most countries since the mid-1980s the decline in the *intensively farmed land area* (arable and permanent crops), has been more rapid than for extensively farmed land (pasture), with production on the remaining intensively farmed land increasing through improving productivity. These developments have in many cases led to the conversion of habitat to cropped land and increased pollution levels threatening and endangering wildlife species. Since the late 1980s, however, the introduction of agri-environmental and land diversion schemes has helped improve certain highly valued agricultural habitats, led to the recovery of some wildlife species, and reduced diffuse pollution. But it is too early to know the extent and permanence of these changes.

Changes in the area of *semi-natural habitats on agricultural land* show considerable variation, for the few OECD countries where data are available. For certain countries these habitats cover more than 50 per cent of the total agricultural land area and have increased since the mid-1980s, partly because land diversion schemes have led to the shift from arable land to fallow and pasture. Semi-natural agricultural habitats that have been converted to other land uses, especially to forestry, is often because of their location in marginal farming areas.

Concerning *uncultivated natural habitats*, in the case of the conversion of aquatic ecosystems and natural forests for agricultural use, there is little comprehensive data across OECD countries. For the countries where data is available, over the past decade more aquatic ecosystems are being restored than are being converted to agriculture, although for a few countries there has been a net conversion of aquatic ecosystems to farm land. The conversion of agricultural land to woodland and forest represents a significant share of total agricultural land conversion over the past decade, but it is not clear whether these changes represent the conversion to natural or semi-natural wooded areas or commercial forest.

Some countries are starting to establish a *habitat matrix* to examine the impact of agricultural land use changes on wildlife, with initial results showing that all agricultural land offers a variety of habitats for wildlife, but some types are superior to others. Also changes in land use from less to more intensive practices, such as bringing marginal land into crop production, create pressures on wildlife, such as by reducing the availability of breeding areas.

1. Background

Policy context

Information about habitats and the way they change over time, in terms of both their quantity (area) and quality (ability to support a "rich" and abundant biodiversity) are an important element in agri-environmental policy decision making. Many OECD countries are paying greater attention to the conservation and restoration of habitat on agricultural land. This is because of the increasing value society is placing on wildlife habitats as sites of environmental and recreational importance and in their provision of other amenity values to society related to landscape.

Government policy actions have focused on protecting endangered habitats in agricultural areas, designating certain areas as nature reserves, and in other cases encouraging farmers to adopt farm management practices that are beneficial for habitat conservation and improvement. A number of countries have also begun to develop a more holistic approach to habitat protection by establishing national biodiversity strategy plans. These strategy plans usually incorporate the agricultural sector as a key player in biodiversity and habitat conservation.

These various policy actions provide the basis for developing policy relevant wildlife habitat indicators as one tool to help monitor the performance of national policies and establish a solid basis for informed policy decision-making. Such indicators can also help countries to monitor progress in fulfilling international obligations, in particular, under the International Convention on Biological Diversity, which recognises the need for countries to develop indicators and assess changes in agro-ecosystems (see Box 1 in the Biodiversity chapter).

There are also other international conventions and regional agreements of relevance to agriculture and wildlife habitats including, for example, the Convention on Wetlands (Ramsar Convention, 1971), the Convention on the Conservation of Migratory Species of Wild Animals (Bonn, 1983), the North American Waterfowl Management Plan (see Box 6 in the Biodiversity chapter), and the European Union's Habitat Directive and Natura 2000 network.[1]

Environmental context

All land, including agricultural land, provides habitat for wildlife. Habitats are used by wildlife as areas for breeding, shelter and feeding, but the composition and quality of habitat on agricultural land is highly variable. Certain habitats have the effect of maintaining the ecosystem's biological processes of self-regulation by improving the survival chances of beneficial species that are natural enemies of crop pests. Habitats can also serve as buffer-zones that protect natural resources, for instance by reducing soil erosion and protecting water quality. In addition, some agricultural habitats can help improve the amenity value of the landscape and increase its recreational value, for both the population in general and, in certain cases, for tourism.

Agriculture impacts on wildlife and their habitats directly by the conversion of semi-natural or uncultivated natural habitats to cultivation or grazing. This occurs through elevated nutrient and pollutant discharges into the environment, crop and livestock husbandry practices, and other farm management practices, such as the management of soils and water. Indirect impacts can also occur through increased disturbances of uncultivated habitats on and/or bordering agricultural land (e.g. forests, wetlands).

Habitats are a small part of a biome, which is defined as a broad grouping of unique flora and fauna maintained by a particular climate, for example, prairies (Box 1). Biomes consist of various bio-regions (or eco-zones), defined by social, biological and geographic criteria, rather than geopolitical boundaries. Bio-regions are composed of different ecosystems consisting of a plant and animal community and its environment functioning as an ecological unit.

The agricultural ecosystem can be in contact with five other major ecosystem types bordering agricultural land, including forest, aquatic, steppe, rocky and urban ecosystems. A habitat is a small part of an ecosystem and includes both living and non-living aspects, but is limited to an area where a

---

Box 1.   **The concept of "habitat" in the context of biodiversity**

Ecosystems	**Species**	**Genes**
Biomes	Kingdom	Population
Bio-region	Phylum	Individual
Ecosystem	Family	Chromosomes
Habitat	Genus	Genes
	Species	Nuclei
	Sub-species	

Source: Adapted from UNEP (1995).

---

certain number of ecological factors are quite homogeneous. For example, a field of wheat, a meadow or a hedge are habitats, which form components of an agricultural ecosystem.

There is considerable research concerning definitions and systems to classify agricultural habitats covering, for example, habitats on agricultural land that are defined as semi-natural, natural, uncultivated, "small" habitats (*e.g.* farm yards), intensively and extensively managed land, organic farming areas, etc. As a result there are now a large number of habitat definitions and classification systems that meet the varying purposes users require. The users range from research biologists operating perhaps at a fairly local scale, to policy makers concerned with monitoring domestic measures related to habitat (*e.g. Canada*, see Annex Table 1) or operating on a broader international scale (*e.g.* the *European* CORINE Land Cover Directory, see Annex Table 2).[2]

A key issue with developing highly detailed and disaggregated classification systems for habitats on agricultural land is whether data exist to reveal the trends in both the quantity and quality of the specific habitat types defined. Also, importantly, whether such classification systems can provide valuable information that is relevant to policy makers.

Whatever definitions or classification systems are used, it is important to consider all agricultural land as habitat. At the same time, the quality of specific habitat types in agriculture will vary according to a number of factors, in particular, soil, climate, farm management practices and the ownership pattern of the land (Lowe and Whitby, 1998). One way to measure the impact of agriculture on wildlife habitats is to consider agricultural land in terms of three broad categories, which have wide applicability across all OECD countries,[3] as follows:

- *Intensively farmed agricultural habitats.*

- *Semi-natural agricultural habitats.*

- *Uncultivated natural habitats.*

The quality and function of agricultural habitats vary between one category or type of habitat and another. Moreover, many animal species, in contrast to plant species, are located in more than one type of habitat. Even if a habitat is the main activity centre of a species, the abundance of its population will depend on a suitable mix of different habitats, representing together a landscape mosaic.

Intensively farmed agricultural habitats

While no generally agreed definition exists of the term "intensively farmed agricultural habitats" it is widely interpreted as concerning agricultural areas which are used to produce arable crops and improved grassland for food, feed, and renewable raw materials (Tucker and Evans, 1997, pp. 267-325). These areas are commonly treated with fertilisers and pesticides and subject to farm management practices, such as ploughing, sowing, weeding, and harvesting.

333|

Intensively farmed areas are artificial habitats subject to regular disturbance of the soil and dominated by annual and perennial crop species. While the value of these areas as wildlife habitat is generally low, because of the paucity of non-crop vegetation combined with the use of pesticides, they do provide habitat for some vascular plants, invertebrates, small mammals and birds. Often they are temporarily valuable habitats for migratory birds. The richness and abundance of wildlife on intensively farmed land will vary according to the:

- *Type of crops cultivated*: cereals, oilcrops, improved grassland, etc.
- *Methods of production*: farm management practices covering nutrients, soil, water, etc., and the farming system, such as "conventional", "integrated", "organic", etc.
- *Spatial composition of the cultivated areas*: field size, cropping patterns, etc.
- *Proximity to other categories of habitats*: semi-natural and uncultivated natural habitats.

In terms of the *type of crops* cultivated under an intensively farmed system, any type of crop can, to some extent, support wildlife, although the degree to which one crop is more supportive than another is unclear. A Canadian study showed, however, that the diversity of vertebrates was higher in cereal crops relative to oilcrops (Figure 2). The same study also showed that some crops may rank highly for a species in terms of a nesting site (for example fruit trees), but can be less important as a site for feeding (Annex Table 3).

With regard to the *methods of production* used on intensively cultivated land, this is well documented as a critical factor affecting wildlife (see the Farm Management chapter). Important in this context is the type of farming system used to produce crops ranging from "conventional" systems typified by widespread use of farm chemicals to "organic" systems where these inputs are not used. There is also the extent to which farm management practices retain or remove non-farmed marginal features such as field margins, hedges, and ditches, which provide crucial habitat sites for wildlife.

The *spatial composition of cultivated areas*, concerns the effects on wildlife of the cropping patterns ranging from monocultural systems to more diverse systems of cropping, and rotation patterns, with interspersed patches of non-crop vegetation. High levels of spatial crop heterogeneity, however, is not necessarily a beneficial indicator for all wildlife, for example, improved grassland habitats can provide a species rich and abundant habitat (Tucker and Evans, 1997).[4]

Proximity to other categories of habitats can be both beneficial and harmful depending on the proximity of intensive habitats to semi-natural and uncultivated habitats. Also important in this context are the types of farm management practices and systems under which each habitat type is maintained.

Semi-natural agricultural habitats

Semi-natural agricultural habitats can be characterised in terms of areas of farmland where the use of farm chemicals is either totally absent or they are applied at considerably lower rates per unit area than in more intensively cultivated areas. Also these habitats are relatively undisturbed by farming practices, such as from ploughing, mowing, and weeding. Typically, semi-natural habitats arise through interaction with other ecosystems, and can be broadly classified as follows:[5]

- *Semi-natural habitats typical of agricultural ecosystems*, such as extensive grassland and pasture; fallow land; extensive margins in cropped land; and "low intensity" permanent crop areas, including certain fruit orchards and olive groves.
- *Semi-natural habitats arising from the interaction between agricultural and aquatic ecosystems*, including some types of wetlands exploited for agricultural use, such as grazing in marshes and water meadows.
- *Semi-natural habitats arising from the interaction between agricultural and forest ecosystems*, including agro forestry and pastoral woodland.
- *Semi-natural habitats arising from the interaction between agricultural and mountain ecosystems*, including alpine pastures and grass patches.
- *Semi-natural habitats arising from the interaction between agricultural and steppe ecosystems*, ranging from semi-arid to desert steppe and including dry meadows and dry pastureland.

The value of semi-natural agricultural habitats for wild flora and fauna varies according to the individual type of habitat. In general these habitats are considered to have systematically better conditions for wildlife than intensively farmed habitats. They also include some important sites for nature conservation, with frequently a high level of species richness of botanical and entomological value. Moreover, the interspersion of intensively farmed areas by semi-natural habitat do enhance the quality of the entire agricultural ecosystem, both from the viewpoint of biodiversity and also in terms of the amenity value of a varied landscape.

Uncultivated natural habitats

No commonly accepted definition of "uncultivated natural habitats" exists, but it is generally considered to include those habitats that are on, crossing, or bordering agricultural areas. The main examples include:

- Small ponds, lakes and rivers, unexploited wetlands, bogs and other aquatic habitats.
- Natural woodlands and forests.
- Rocky outcrops.

Certain uncultivated habitats, such as unexploited wetlands and forests, are subject to the risk of damage from agriculture, such as through their transformation into farmland, and run-off from farm chemicals. These impacts of farming can result in the biological potential of many types of uncultivated habitats being considerably reduced as well as a loss of the amenity and recreational values attributed to such habitats.

Some countries include man-made features, which can provide wildlife habitat, under their definition of uncultivated habitats, although for others these are included as part of semi-natural habitat or landscape features (*e.g.* hedges, see Landscape chapter). The main types of man-made habitats related to agriculture include hedges, shelterbelts, ditches and woodland planted on farms, and farm-yards, buildings and stone walls, which might also provide habitat.

2. Indicators

There are four categories of indicators discussed here. The first three categories draw on the classification of agricultural land into intensively farmed, semi-natural, and uncultivated natural habitats. The fourth category involves developing an integrated approach by considering the entire agricultural landscape, including "man-made" features on agricultural land (*e.g.* hedges, farm buildings) which can provide wildlife habitat and combining this with information on biodiversity. This is usually termed a "habitat matrix", and is used to examine the linkages between agriculture, biodiversity and habitat.

Intensively farmed agricultural habitats

Definitions

1. The share of each crop in the total agricultural area.
2. The share of organic agriculture in the total agricultural area.

Method of calculation

The first indicator, *percentage of the agricultural area covered by each crop type*, requires annual agricultural census data on the respective areas of individual crops and/or major cropping areas, *i.e.* arable crops (*e.g.* cereals, oilcrops), permanent crops (*e.g.* fruit trees, vines), and pasture. Information on the trends in major cropping areas is included in the Report under the section on Land Use in the Contextual Indicators chapter. To date no comprehensive cross country analysis of the environmental impact of changing cropping patterns on intensively farmed agricultural habitat has been completed.

The second indicator, *share of organic farming in the total agricultural area*, also requires data from the annual agriculture census. This information is collected as part of the section on Whole Farm Management indicators, see Figure 3, in the Farm Management chapter.

Recent trends

Intensively farmed crops – General

The overall decline in the total agricultural land area for most OECD countries since the early 1980s (and over a longer time scale for many countries) has been associated with the conversion of highly productive agricultural land usually to urban, industrial and road development, and a large share of marginal farming land converted to forest (Figure 8). In many cases, such as in the *European Union* and the *United States*, the decrease in the area of intensively farmed land, *i.e.* for arable and permanent crops, has proceeded at a faster rate than for extensively farmed land, *i.e.* permanent pasture. At the same time agricultural production on the remaining intensively farmed agricultural land has increased through improving productivity by, for example, the greater use of farm chemicals and the removal of boundary features such as field border strips, to increase field size for larger farm machinery.

These developments in agricultural land use over the past 20 years are largely recognised as having had a harmful impact on the environment in most OECD countries, both through the conversion of habitat features, such as shelterbelts, and the effects of diffuse pollution. This pattern of change however, began to alter from a period around the late 1980s/early 1990s, with the introduction of agri environmental and land diversion schemes in many countries (Box 2). This started to improve farm management practices on intensively farmed land, such as the adoption of conservation tillage, and to lead to an increase in the area of land under more extensive farming practices, organic farming systems or land diverted to non-agricultural uses (*e.g.* long term fallow, forested).

While evidence is still limited, these changes in farm management practices and the pattern of land use, have led to the conservation and restoration of certain high nature value habitats on agricultural land. This has helped the recovery in some populations of wildlife species, and reduced diffuse pollution. Even so, it is still too early to be sure about the extent of these changes within or across OECD countries, or the permanence of the increase in some wildlife populations using agricultural land as habitat.

A further development in some OECD countries affecting cropping patterns in intensively farmed areas and the environment, is the expansion of *biomass production* as a source of renewable energy. Overall the production levels of renewable energy from agricultural sources are low in most OECD countries. There is increasing research in this area, however, with the use of some oilcrops for energy purposes, in addition to the production of energy from farm and agro-food industry waste.[6]

North America

A study of the Northeast part of the *United States*, reflects the more general trends described above over the past 20 years (Mac *et al.*, 1998, pp. 192-195). With the continuing expansion of urban communities, significant areas of prime agricultural land in the region were converted to housing, commercial development and roads. This led to the rise in agricultural land prices and encouraged more intensive farming on remaining land, including the removal of hedgerows, field-border strips, wetlands and woodland, and the greater use of farm chemicals. As a result of the removal of these habitats wildlife populations declined.

An examination of the major sources of threats to endangered and threatened wild species in the United States found that agriculture was the major source of threat (USDA, 1997, pp. 17-18). Of the different sources of agricultural threats to endangered species, the conversion of land to agricultural production threatens the most species. Grazing and the use of pesticides are also important, but fertilisers less so (Figure 1). This pattern of different agricultural threats is broadly reflected for vertebrates, invertebrates and plants, although for invertebrates pesticide use is a key threat.

Box 2. Agricultural land diversion schemes in OECD countries

Many OECD countries have implemented land diversion schemes that pay farmers to take land, usually cereals, out of production, or shift it to alternative uses. The land use change induced by these schemes often aims to achieve a combination of supply control and environmental objectives, with the latter objective becoming more important (*e.g.* compulsory ecological compensation areas in *Switzerland*). The environmental objectives under land diversion commonly include improving soil organic matter, lowering farm chemical use and soil erosion, and providing greater diversity of plant species and other wildlife. These effects can be temporary, however, where land is eventually returned to production.

In the *European Union*, over 7 million hectares were diverted from cereal and oilseed production under short-term set-aside schemes in 1995/96 (European Commission, 1999). In 1994/95, total short-term set-aside ranged from just over 1 per cent of the national base area in *Greece* to almost 17 per cent in the *United Kingdom* (the base area is equal to average plantings of cereals, oilseeds, linseed and protein crops over the period from 1989-1991, including land fallowed during that time). *Germany, France, Italy* and *Spain* had more than 15 per cent of their base area idled, whereas in *Belgium, the Netherlands* and *Portugal*, only 6 per cent was set aside. Farmers have to ensure crop coverage on the compulsory set-aside areas, where the use of machinery is also limited. The EU set-aside policy also aims to re-introduce fallow lands in more arid regions in the EU.

The Arable Area Payments Scheme (AAPS) introduced in 1992 in the *United Kingdom* includes a compulsory set-aside requirement for all except the smallest farms. Farmers are not eligible for payments under the AAPS for land which in 1991 was under permanent crops, permanent grass, woodland or non-agricultural use. This acts as a disincentive to those farmers who claim under the Scheme (the vast majority are arable farmers) to plough up permanent pasture for arable crops. In 1995, there were some 640 000 hectares of arable land in set-aside in Great Britain (excluding Northern Ireland).

In *Japan*, 700 000 hectares of paddy fields (27 per cent of total paddy fields) were diverted from rice production during the 1992-96 period. Most of this land was planted to other annual crops, such as wheat, soybeans and feed crops, although a smaller share was idled and converted to pasture, forests, orchards, or fish breeding ponds. Environmental provisions are attached to this programme through which farmers manage diverted paddy fields so that the land conservation functions, served previously by the diverted paddy fields, can be maintained to prevent floods, soil erosion and landslides.

Around 520 000 hectares of cropland (1 per cent of total arable land) in *Canada* have been seeded to grass under the *Permanent Cover Program*. Most of the changes took place on cattle farms or on mixed farms, only 4 per cent of programme participants being cereal farmers. Hay production is the most common activity on the diverted land, followed by livestock grazing.

Nearly 15 million hectares of crop land (8 per cent of total arable land) in the *United States* were enrolled in the *Conservation Reserve Program* (CRP) in 1995 and almost 6 million hectares (3 per cent) were idled under annual set-aside programmes. The annual programmes were discontinued in 1996. Roughly 87 per cent of the CRP land has been seeded to grass. But the Conservation Reserve also contains 800 000 hectares of land managed in line with special wildlife practices, over 100 000 hectares of wetlands, and 1 million hectares of land planted to trees (USDA, 1997).

In a few OECD countries, *Norway*, for example, where agricultural land is a limited resource, diversion to other uses is restricted, often to meet national food security objectives.

Source: This box draws mainly from OECD (1997).

The introduction of measures in the mid-1980s such as the United States Conservation Reserve Program (Box 2) and the encouragement of farm management practices beneficial to reducing soil erosion, has helped to maintain and restore certain habitats on farmland (see Table 8 in the Farm Management chapter). Also the adoption of conservation tillage has increased the availability of crop residues for wildlife. The study of the Northeast region of the US has shown that numbers of wild turkeys and Canadian geese have increased because of the availability of crop residues in autumn and winter (Mac et al., 1998). Some mammals, such as possums, deer, racoons and skunks, have also taken advantage of residual maize and other crops.

Figure 1. **Number of wild species threatened and endangered by the main sources of agricultural threats: United States, 1995**

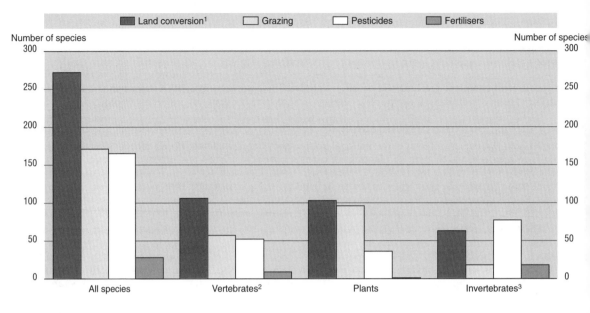

1. Conversion from non-agricultural land use to cropland.
2. Vertebrates: Amphibians, birds, fish, mammals and reptiles.
3. Invertebrates both on land and in aquatic ecosystems.
Source: USDA (1997).

Research has been undertaken to examine the effects of different types of cultivated crops on wild life. In *Canada*, a recent study has examined the use of agricultural land by vertebrates (Neave and Neave, 1998). Using the Canadian prairies eco-zone as an example, which represents over 80 per cent o the total national agricultural area, this revealed that all habitat types were used by some specie (Figure 2). However, while uncultivated habitats on agricultural land, especially wetlands, woodlands and "natural" pasture, supported the greatest number of species for breeding, feeding, cover and win tering; cropland was primarily used for feeding purposes only (Annex Table 4). Moreover, within the cropland category, cereal crops supported larger numbers of species than oilcrops.

Europe

The changes outlined in the US study, have also been broadly reflected by similar development in the *European Union* over the past two decades (European Commission, 1999). Crop production bot increased and intensified, with greater use of inputs and less diversified crop rotations, *i.e.* an increase in wheat, oilcrops and a reduction in secondary cereals, such as oats and rye. The area of permanen crops and pasture also declined, in some cases involving the ploughing up of meadows leading to the removal of habitat features such as hedges and other field boundaries. The overall consequence o these changes on the environment was an increase in diffuse pollution through the greater use o chemical inputs, and the removal of habitat, both to the detriment of wildlife.

The reform of the EU's Common Agricultural Policy and introduction of agri-environmenta measures in the early 1990s, has begun to encourage changes in farming practices, for example, the development of field margins on cropland and the maintenance of hedgerows. In addition, the policy o taking land out of production, "set-aside", has resulted in an increase in fallow land from arounc 1 million hectares in the early 1980s up to over 4 million hectares by the mid-1990s (Box 2, anc European Commission, 1999). While it is still too early to make any overall assessment of the impacts o

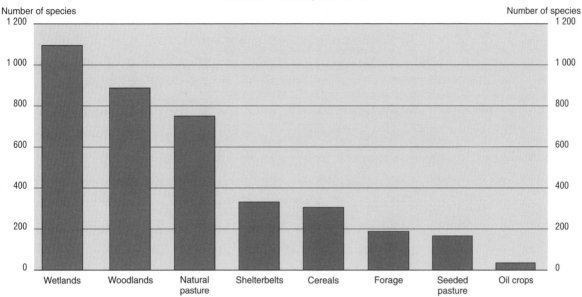

Figure 2. **Number of vertebrates[1] species using habitat[2] on agricultural land: Canadian Prairies, mid-1990s**

1. Vertebrates, including birds, mammals, amphibians and reptiles.
2. This includes the addition of species using the Prairies as a primary and secondary habitat for five activities, *i.e.* reproduction, feed, cover, wintering and staging (birds only).
Note: See Annex Table 3.
Source: Adapted from Neave and Neave (1998).

these changes on the environment in the EU, evidence from some member states would suggest that some environmental improvements have been achieved, especially the restoration of habitats.

Field margins surrounding intensively cropped areas can provide and enhance wildlife habitats without altering cropping patterns or the intensity of output on the remaining cropped land. As part of the United Kingdom's Biodiversity Action Plan, farmers are being encouraged under a Habitat Action Plan, to maintain and restore grass margins, conservation headlands, and uncropped field margins (MAFF, 2000). Recent trends show that the estimated area under cereal field margin management, that contributes to the targets in the Habitat Action Plan, has increased substantially in recent years (Figure 3).

A study of the corn bunting (*Miliaria calandra*) in Portugal concluded that extensively managed farmland appears to offer a preferable habitat to this bird than intensively managed areas (Stoate *et al.*, 2000). While the corn bunting is present on intensively managed areas, its population is in decline there.

Research completed in Switzerland, drew similar conclusions to the Canadian study examined above (Duelli *et al.*, 1999). The study, covering the use of agricultural land by arthropods (*e.g.* spiders, beetles, flies, bees), showed that the most beneficial crop for this species group was dry and low intensity meadows compared to wheat and maize crops (Figure 4).

Organic agriculture

The Swiss study, discussed previously, is further augmented by a considerable body of research revealing the higher abundance of arthropods (insects, spiders, mites, centipedes, millipedes, etc.) in organic agriculture systems, compared to similar production systems under non-organic or "conventional" agriculture (Figure 5).[7] This appears to be linked to the absence of pesticide use in organic farming, and the presence of a higher incidence of weeds providing a food source for arthropods. Also, the

Figure 3. **Area of cereal field margins under environmental management:
United Kingdom, late 1990s**

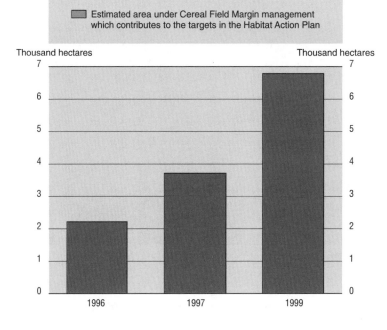

Source: MAFF (2000).

Figure 4. **Number of arthropod[1] species using intensive farmed land[2]
compared to semi-natural habitats:[3] Switzerland, 1987**

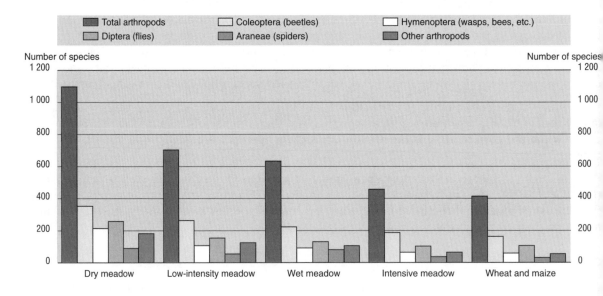

1. Arthropods recorded in this study were mainly spiders, beetles, flies, wasps and bees.
2. Intensive farmed land refers to wheat, maize and intensive meadow.
3. Semi-natural habitats refer to dry meadow, wet meadow and low-intensity meadow.
Note: See Annex Table 4.
Source: Adapted from Duelli et al. (1999).

Figure 5. **Differences in species diversity and abundance of arthropods and earthworms in organically and conventionally cultivated arable land, late 1980s and early 1990s**

Animal group	Sub group	Species diversity	Abundance[2]	Locations[3]
Coleoptera: (Beetles)	Carabidae[1]	ORG > CON	ORG > CON	Austria, Germany, Netherlands, Switzerland, United States
	Staphilinidae[1]	ORG > CON	ORG < CON	Germany
	Coccinellidae[1]	ORG >CON	ORG > CON	Germany
	Catopidae	ORG > CON	ORG > CON	Germany
	Chryomelidae	ORG > CON	ORG > CON	Germany
	Silphidae[1]	ORG = CON	ORG = CON	Germany
Hymenoptera: (Wasps, Bees)	Parasitic Hymen[1]		ORG > CON	Germany
Diptera: (Flies)	Nematocera		ORG < CON	Germany
	Brachycera		ORG > CON	Germany
	Syrphidae[1]	ORG = CON	ORG > CON	Germany
Hemiptera: (Aphids, etc.)	Heteroptera[1]	ORG > CON	ORG > CON	Germany
	Homoptera Cicadina	ORG = CON	ORG = CON	Germany
Arachnida: (Spiders)	Araneae[1]	ORG = CON	ORG = CON	Austria, Germany
	Opiliones[1]	ORG > CON	ORG > CON	Germany
	Acari[1]	ORG = CON	ORG = CON	Germany, Switzerland, United States
	Oribatidae	ORG > CON		Germany
Myriapoda: (Millipedes, centipedes, etc)	Diplopoda	ORG = CON	ORG = CON	Germany
	Chilopoda[1]	ORG > CON	ORG > CON	Germany
Crustacea: (Aquatic insects)	Isopoda	ORG > CON	ORG > CON	Germany
Collembola:	Springtails		ORG = CON	Germany, United States

Definitions:
ORG: organic farming; CON: conventional farming; >: Significantly higher value in the first mentioned farming system and vice versa; =: Higher and similar values in the first mentioned farming system; =: ORG same as CON.
1. Beneficial organisms in agricultural ecosystems.
2. Number of individuals.
3. For detailed references for each location see the source given below.
Source: Mäder et al. (1996).

usually lower density of crops in organic fields leads to a higher rate of microbial activity in the soil and an increase in earthworm populations (Pfiffner and Niggli, 1996).

The greater abundance of microbial activity, arthropods and weeds that appears to occur in organic systems, also encourages other wildlife higher up the food chain, such as birds. A study in *Denmark* showed a greater abundance of birds (31 bird species) on organic farms compared to farms with a similar production structure but using "conventional practices" (3 bird species) (Christensen *et al.*, 1996). A study in *Great Britain* confirmed these results (Fuller *et al.*, 1998).

Interpretation and links to other indicators

Interpreting the effects on the environment of changes in cropping patterns on *intensively farmed land* requires some care, as this can vary considerably not only with the type of crop, but also with the management system used to produce the crop. For example, organic wheat production with field margins can be expected to have very different implications for the environment than wheat produced without field margins using a high intensity of chemical inputs. Moreover, wildlife on intensively farmed land will also be affected by the extent of the spatial distribution across the farmed landscape of semi-natural and uncultivated habitat, and the extent of field boundaries or openness of the landscape.

The indicator of the changes in the *organically farmed area* should also be interpreted cautiously with respect to environmental impacts. Any farming system that lowers farm chemical use might be expected to reduce the potentially harmful effects on the environment. However, some organic farming systems can be intensive in terms of their output per unit area of land. For example, the environmental effects of using livestock manure in organic systems will depend on how the manure is stored and when and how it is applied.

Another issue, highlighted in the Farm Management chapter, is providing a consistent definition of organic agriculture, as standards differ across some countries. Within the European Union, Regulation 2092/91 harmonises organic farming, and under the International Federation of Organic Agriculture Movements (IFOAM), guidelines have been established for marketing organic products internationally.[8]

These indicators draw directly from information related to land use (see the Contextual Indicators chapter), and organic farming (see the Farm Management chapter). Other indicators related to farm management are also of importance in this context.

Semi-natural agricultural habitats

Definition

The share of the agricultural area covered by semi-natural agricultural habitats.

Method of calculation

The indicator requires data, from the annual agricultural census or national land inventory, covering the area of semi-natural agricultural habitats. A clear understanding and definition of the scope of semi-natural agricultural habitats is also necessary. Semi-natural agricultural habitats can be broadly defined as areas of land subject to "low intensity" farming practices, but this leaves open the difficulty of determining what is "low intensity" farming. For practical purposes, semi-natural agricultural habitats have been broadly defined in this chapter as covering grazing marshes and water meadows, pastoral woodlands, alpine pastures, and dry meadows and pasture, as discussed above.

Recent trends

Changes in the area of semi-natural habitats on agricultural land show considerable variation for the limited number of OECD countries for which data are available (Figure 6). For some countries semi-natural habitats as a share of the total agricultural land area is in excess of 50 per cent, but in Canada, Japan and Sweden the ratio is considerably lower than this. Also, for certain countries the area of semi-natural agricultural habitats has shown a modest increase since 1985, despite a reduction in the total agricultural land area (Figure 6). In some cases this can be explained by land diversion schemes leading to a shift from arable land to fallow and pasture (Box 2).

Semi-natural agricultural habitats have often been converted to other land uses because of their location, which is commonly in marginal farming areas, where both the physical terrain and climatic conditions result in low productivity and poor financial returns. This makes such areas especially unattractive for younger entrants into farming, particularly where higher income and less arduous employment opportunities exist.

A study of the Vejle county of Denmark (accounting for nearly two-thirds of the total national agricultural land area) from 1970-1995, revealed a number of important changes to semi-natural agricultural habitats and biodiversity in the area (IUCN, 1999, pp. 15-18).[9] Over this period semi-natural grasslands decreased by over 40 per cent, accompanied by a shift from low intensity pastoral farms to high intensity pig and cattle enterprises. Wild flora seed banks in arable fields declined by 60 per cent, while there were significant reductions in areas of wet and dry heathland and peat bogs. The intensification of agriculture was recognised as a major influence on these changes, although measures

Figure 6. **Area of total agricultural land, semi-natural agricultural habitats and uncultivated habitats: 1985 to 1998**

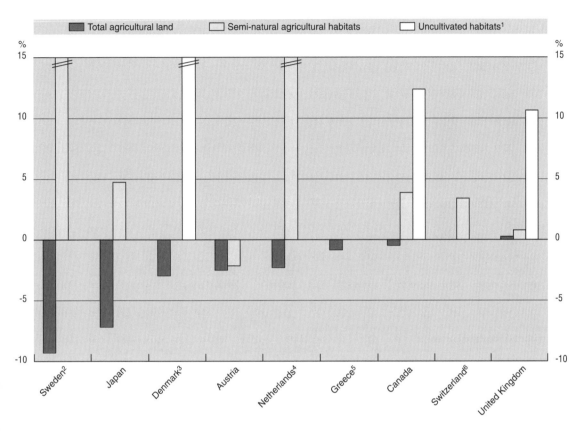

1. Uncultivated natural habitat (*e.g.* woodlands, small rivers, wetlands). For Canada, it includes man-made features (*e.g.* farm buildings, etc.) on and/or bordering agricultural land.
2. Area of semi-natural habitat showed an increase of 33%.
3. Area of uncultivated habitat includes only woodland which showed an increase of 21%.
4. Area of semi-natural habitat showed an increase of 547%.
5. Negligible change in semi-natural habitat area.
6. No change in agricultural land area.
Notes: See Annex Table 5. For some countries, the area of semi-natural or uncultivated habitats are unavailable, and not all data cover the period 1985 to 1998.
Sources: OECD Agri-environmental Indicators Questionnaire and Database, 1999.

introduced in the early 1990s, including agri-environmental management payments, are helping to maintain and restore semi-natural agricultural habitats.

Under new legislation on environmental protection, the creation of ecological farmland areas was introduced in *Poland* in 1999 to help restore semi-natural agricultural habitats such as water meadows, and agro-forestry areas (FAO, 1999, pp. 204-205). Agriculture is also included under measures to provide for national parks and landscape reserves, accounting for over 40 per cent of the total area of these parks/reserves in the late 1990s.

In the *United Kingdom* intensification of agricultural land use was considered to be one of the main contributors to the reduction in the area of semi-natural agricultural habitats over the past 50 years (this also applies to *Switzerland*). However, as a result of targeted agri-environment policies, reductions in price support, technological developments and consumer demand, trends towards extensification of agriculture may be emerging (Figure 7; and Stott and Haines-Young, 1998). The UK has also set targets for the maintenance and restoration of priority semi-natural grassland habitats, under the UK Biodiversity Action Plan (MAFF, 2000).

343|

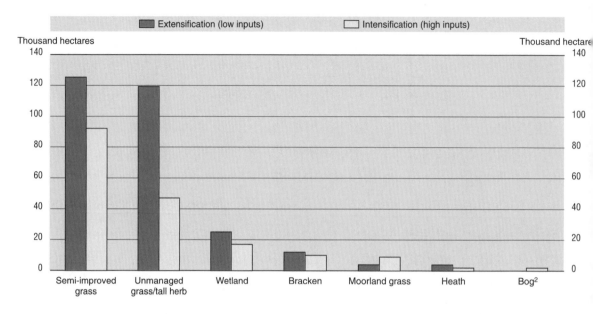

Figure 7. **Intensification and extensification of agricultural land use: Great Britain,[1] 1984 to 1990**

1. Great Britain, covers United Kingdom excluding Northern Ireland.
2. Extensification figure equals zero.
Note: Figure shows changes to (intensification) and from (extensification) intensive agricultural land use to other land uses.
Sources: Barr *et al.* (1993); Haines-Young *et al.* (1996).

The trend towards greater extensification in the UK is illustrated by the large net increase in the area of unmanaged grassland/tall herb, reflecting the introduction of arable set-aside (Figure 7 and Box 2 on UK arable set-aside). Intensification was associated largely with the agricultural improvement of grasslands, but this was more than balanced, in terms of area, by the reversion of previously improved agricultural land to unmanaged grassland. There was also a minor net gain in area of wetlands, resulting from the net conversion of intensive agricultural land to wetland, but small net losses in moorland and bogs. Figure 7 should be interpreted with caution, however, because of both sampling and possible observer error, and because it is unlikely that semi-natural habitats created by reversion or restoration compensate, in ecological terms, for the loss of semi-natural habitat of "high" nature conservation value.

Interpretation and links to other indicators

It is generally assumed that the larger the area covered by semi-natural agricultural habitats, the more beneficial are the effects on wildlife, as in general these habitats harbour a much greater variety and abundance of species than do intensively farmed agricultural areas. Semi-natural agricultural habitats are also characterised through their symbiotic relationship with surrounding habitats. However, as noted above, the reversion of intensively farmed land to semi-natural habitat is unlikely, in ecological terms, to fully compensate for the loss of semi-natural habitat of "high" nature value.

While the research literature clearly points to the sharp decline in the extent of certain types of semi-natural agricultural habitats, such as traditional terraced olive groves, alpine meadows, heathland and pastoral woodlands, it is extremely difficult to provide any systematic view due to the lack of consistent time series data.[10] Not only is data limited in terms of the extent of these habitats, but knowledge of their quality is also lacking. These problems are compounded by the absence of a clear definition of what constitutes a "traditional" semi-natural farmed habitat, although some attempts have been made to define low-intensity farming systems (Baldock *et al.*, 1995).

Uncultivated natural habitats

Definitions

1. Net area of aquatic ecosystems converted to agricultural use.
2. Area of "natural" forest converted to agricultural use.

Method of calculation

This chapter has defined the main categories of uncultivated natural habitats on and/or bordering agricultural land as covering the following habitat types: aquatic, forest and rocky. The indicators developed here focus on two of these habitat categories: aquatic ecosystems, in particular, wetlands; and "natural" forests.

The net area of **aquatic ecosystems**, such as unexploited wetlands, bogs, small ponds, lakes, and diverted rivers, converted to agricultural use gives an estimate of the loss of aquatic ecosystems through drainage or reclamation for farming offset by the restoration or reversion of these ecosystems from agricultural use. This approach is being used in the United States, for example, to help assess domestic wetland conservation policies (Heimlich et al., 1998). The conversion of agricultural land back into an aquatic ecosystem, may in some cases be part of efforts to help reduce flooding by the reclamation of farm land in order to increase the free flow of dammed rivers. In other instances this restoration has the objective of restoring the ecosystem as a valued aquatic environment.

The area of **natural forest** converted to agricultural use, encompasses both natural "primary" forest, such as areas of tropical rainforest in Australia and Mexico, and also "secondary" forests. Secondary forests are those forests which are, or have been commercially exploited, and in which the physical conditions and diversity closely resemble the natural state, having developed over a long time period. There is generally a contact zone with agriculture, where forests have been cleared for farming through cutting and burning.

Agricultural land is also restored back to use as woodland or forest, and a "net change" approach might be appropriate in these cases. However, this approach is not used here, as the main concern is the destruction of "natural" forest which even if restored could take hundreds of years, if not more, to return to its "original" state.

Recent trends

There is little comprehensive time series data on the net area of **aquatic ecosystems** converted to agricultural land across OECD countries. However, information is more widely available related to the conversion of agricultural land to aquatic ecosystems (Figure 8). For the limited of number countries where data is available, there has been, over the past ten years, a net conversion of agricultural land to aquatic ecosystems, *i.e.* more aquatic ecosystems are being restored than being converted to agricultural use (Annex Table 6). The two exceptions to this trend are in Japan and Korea, where the reverse is the case. However, proposals in Korea for large-scale reclamation of tidal flats for agriculture have been cut back drastically to safeguard estuarine habitats (OECD, 1998).

It is evident that in some countries agricultural expansion has not been the major cause of the decrease in the area of aquatic ecosystems. In the United States, for example, between 1982 and 1992 agriculture accounted for only 20 per cent of the total reduction in the area of wetlands, with conversion to urban development accounting for nearly 60 per cent over the same period (Heimlich et al., 1998).

Wetland conservation has been the focus of policy debate over recent years in the United States. The share of wetlands converted to agricultural use dropped from more than 80 per cent in the period 1954 to 1974 to 20 per cent during 1982 to 1992 (Heimlich, et al., 1998). The US appears to be reaching its goal, set through various wetland conservation measures, of "no net loss" of wetland area in the 1990s, that is conserving and restoring at least as much wetland as is lost. The study by Heimlich et al. (1998) observes

Figure 8. **Share of different land use types in land converted from agriculture to other uses: mid-1980s to mid-1990s**

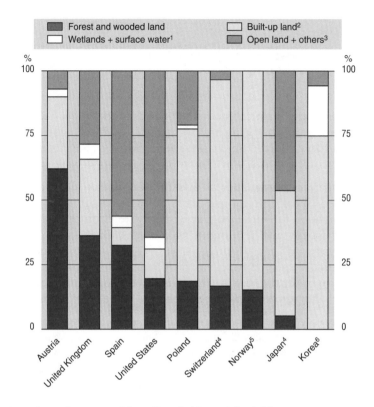

1. Wetlands + surface water: surface water covers mainly small ponds, lakes and diverted rivers.
2. Built-up land covers mainly land used for urban or industrial development and transport infastructure, *e.g.*, roads.
3. Open land + others: land not used for any of the above uses, such as barren land, exposed rocks and for some countries, *e.g.* Japan, farm land abandoned but not forested.
4. Data for wetlands + surface water areas are not available.
5. Data for wetlands + surface water areas and open land + others are not available.
6. Data for forest and wooded land are not available.
Note: See Annex Table 6.
Source: OECD Agri-environmental Indicators Questionnaire, 1999.

that while government policies are partly responsible for the decrease in wetland conversion, falling agricultural commodity prices also reduced the pressure on farmers to convert wetlands. Hence, it is difficult statistically to separate the policy and market factors responsible for decreased wetland conversion.

It should be noted that the share of total US wetlands converted during the period 1954 to 1992 is relatively small, and there remains a considerable area of wetland that could be converted to agricultural production. In addition, the slower rate of wetland conversion over the 1984-1992 period may reflect that most of the wetlands suitable to conversion were already converted to farmland prior to 1982.

In the *European Union* the area of *wetlands* in coastal zones decreased by between less than 1 per cent in *France* and up to 16 per cent in *Italy*, during the period 1975 to 1990 (EUROSTAT, 1999, pp. 50-51). Reduction in wetland areas are reported to be greater than this when comparing the period since the 1950s and 1960s, for example, a decrease of 60-65 per cent in *Finland*, 57 per cent in *Germany* (excluding marshes), and 55 per cent for the *Netherlands*. The conversion of agricultural land is identified as one of the major causes of wetland reduction in the EU, but other losses have occurred due to forestry, pollution and over-exploitation of aquifers.

For the few countries where data exist, the conversion of agricultural land to **woodland and forest** represents a significant share of agricultural land converted to other uses over the past decade (Figure 8). Moreover, forest and woodland also represent the main land use type of land converted to agricultural use (Figure 9). However, it is not clear whether these changes represent the conversion to "natural" wooded areas or commercial forest.

Interpretation and links to other indicators

These indicators reveal the extent of loss or conservation of uncultivated natural habitats – aquatic ecosystems and "natural" forest – on and/or bordering agricultural land. Where such habitats are converted to agricultural use, this is usually associated with a high diminution of wildlife and amenity value, especially in cases where the habitats may have taken several thousand years to evolve.

In any assessment of uncultivated habitat that has been restored from agricultural use, it is necessary to evaluate the conditions and type of restoration that has occurred. For example, whether agricultural land has been restored to a commercial or to a "natural" forest, and the period over which the change has occurred. Interpretation of these indicators may also require a regional and spatially disaggregated perspective. In some regions, an increase in the conversion of forest to agricultural land may involve the establishment of low intensity farming systems, which might have a positive impact on biodiversity depending on the type of forest converted, i.e. a "natural" or commercial area of forest.

Related information

Little disaggregated data seems to be available with respect to other types of uncultivated natural habitats, such as rocky outcrops.[11] A considerable area of agricultural land has been converted to urban, industrial and road infrastructure development (Figure 9). Even so, the share of the net change in agricultural land use in the total agricultural land area over the past 10 years has been less than 5 per cent for most OECD countries, although it was nearly 10 per cent in Japan.

Figure 9. **Share of different land use types in land converted from other uses to agricultural use: mid-1980s to mid-1990s**

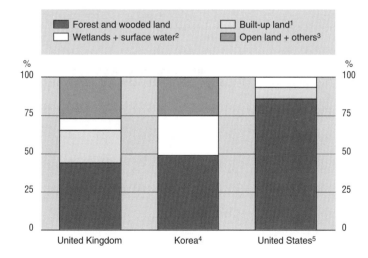

1. Built-up land covers mainly land used for urban or industrial development and transport infrastructure, *e.g.*, roads.
2. Wetlands + surface water: surface water covers mainly small ponds, lakes and diverted rivers.
3. Open land + others: land not used for any of the above uses, such as barren land, exposed rocks.
4. Data for built-up land are not available.
5. Data for open land + others are not available.

Source: OECD Agri-environmental Indicators Questionnaire, 1999.

347

Information from *Canada* reveals that "man-made" features on agricultural land (*e.g.* farm houses outbuildings, lanes, etc., Annex Table 1) represent about 2 per cent of the total agricultural land area Canadian research also shows these areas can provide important habitat for wildlife, especially fo breeding, feeding and cover (Annex Table 3). Moreover, some OECD countries are monitoring the importance of some of these "man-made" habitats as part of their development of agricultural land scape indicators (*e.g.* see the man-made objects (cultural features) indicator in the Landscape chapter).

Australia has recently developed a set of indicators to monitor the biodiversity and ecologica impacts of agriculture on remnant native vegetation on agricultural land, and on conservation reserves Assessment of the impact of agriculture on conservation reserves in Australia was achieved by linkins data for three variables (see Figure 10): the boundary length between conservation reserves anc

Figure 10. **Regional impact of agriculture on native vegetation in conservation reserves: Australia, 1993**

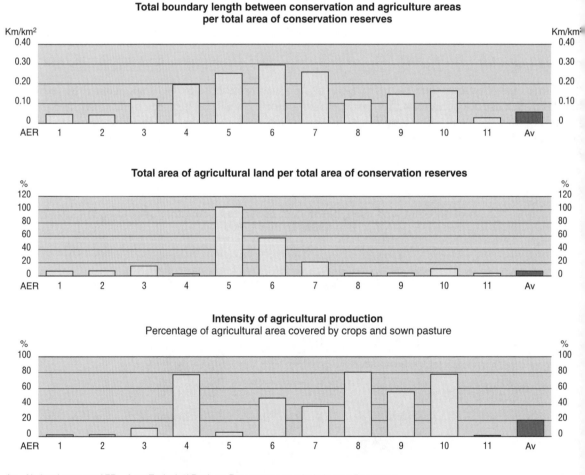

Av = National average; AER = Agro-Ecological Regions; Percentages may include rounding errors.
Note: For each agro-ecological regions, (..) indicates the percentage of each AER in the total national land area, and [..] indicates the percentage of each AER in the total agricultural land area.

AER - 1. North-west wet/dry tropics (9%), [9%]
AER - 2. North wet/dry tropics (5%), [4%]
AER - 3. North-east wet/dry tropics (5%), [6%]
AER - 4. Wet tropical coasts (0.2%), [0.2%]
AER - 5. Semi-arid tropical/subtropical plains (11%), [15%]
AER - 6. Subtropical slopes and plains (4%), [6%]

AER - 7. Wet subtropical coast (2%), [3%]
AER - 8. Wet temperate coasts (2%), [2%]
AER - 9. Temperate highlands (3%), [4%]
AER - 10. Temperate slopes and plains (9%), [12%]
AER - 11. Arid interior (49%), [40%]

Source: Commonwealth of Australia (1999).

agricultural land per total area of conservation reserves; the total area of agricultural land per total area of conservation reserves; and the intensity of agriculture in terms of the percentage area occupied by crops and sown pasture. Low values for all three variables indicate minimal impact of agriculture on conservation reserves, while high values indicate the maximum potential impact (Commonwealth of Australia, 1998, pp. 72-76).

At national level, it was found that agriculture potentially threatens native vegetation in all regions of *Australia*, but poses greater threats in some regions relative to others (Figure 10). In the semi-arid tropical and subtropical plains, and in intensively cropped agro-ecological regions of Australia, conservation of native vegetation requires urgent attention. Together these regions account for just over a third of the total land area in Australia.

Habitat matrix[12]

Definition

A habitat matrix identifies and relates the ways in which wild species use different agricultural habitat types.

Method of calculation

The habitat matrix identifies the ways in which various wild species use agricultural habitat types, ranging from cropped land to uncultivated habitat on agricultural land, and then relates this use to changes in the areas of these habitats. The indicator is then used to identify which habitat types on agricultural land support the most wildlife use and whether these habitat types are increasing, decreasing or remaining constant over time.

The methodology recognises that all farm land has some value as habitat. The matrix explicitly incorporates information on how various species use farmland to meet their habitat needs. It is also restricted to habitat change occurring within the agricultural land base only and not that due to other land uses. The agricultural land base is defined to include areas of uncultivated natural habitat (*e.g.* marshes) and man-made features on agricultural land (*e.g.* farm buildings).

To construct the matrix it is necessary to identify how different species use various agricultural habitats. To accomplish this, *habitat suitability matrices* are developed individually for the main agricultural ecozones across a country (or bio-regions, see Box 1). These matrices incorporate information on all flora and fauna, or more partial information where detail for all taxonomic groups does not exist. The particular use each species makes of agricultural land habitats in each ecozone (see below) is then identified. Each "habitat use" is ranked according to how dependent a species is on a certain habitat for this use, including:

- *Primary use*, meaning that a species is dependent on, or strongly prefers, a certain type of habitat (also called *critical habitat*).

- *Secondary use*, meaning that a species uses a certain habitat (*e.g.* to obtain food in the case of fauna) but is not dependent on it.

Matrices for each specified ecozone are then collected. This information might be assembled from a range of sources, depending on the quality and quantity of data available in any given country, including written sources, expert judgements by wildlife and agricultural specialists and, ideally, actual field survey data of wildlife species.

Once the matrices are completed, primary and secondary habitat use entries are summed separately into five main categories (this applies to fauna only), including first, breeding, nesting, and reproduction; second, feeding and foraging; third, cover, resting, roosting, basking, and loafing; fourth, wintering; and fifth, staging (for birds only). Each separate use of a habitat type by a species is recorded as a *habitat use unit*, that is not the number of species using the habitat, but the number of individual ways in which the habitat is used, such as, for feeding and nesting. Habitat use units are then summed by habitat type for each ecozone.

The habitat types can correspond to any classification system for which data is available, but for many countries, at present, this will generally correspond to the main land use categories defined in the annual Census of Agriculture (see Annex Table 1 in the case of *Canada*, for example). In general, the habitat matrix can provide an alternative or surrogate for the wild species diversity indicator (see the Biodiversity chapter). Where species population data is not available the matrix approach can provide a indirect measure for species diversity.

Recent trends

There are few attempts to provide an integrated holistic view of the impact on wild species of changes in the pattern of agriculture land use. A number of countries are now beginning to examine the possibility of establishing a habitat matrix to examine the impact of all agricultural land use changes (of the total land area including agriculture) on wildlife, for example, *Mexico*, *Switzerland*, and the *United Kingdom*. Possibly the most advanced work of this type has been developed in *Canada*, while some work has also been undertaken in *Finland*.

The results of the *Canadian* study concludes that all agricultural land offers a variety of habitats for wildlife, but some types are superior to others (Figure 2 and Neave *et al.*, 2000). The Canadian study suggests that changes in agricultural land use from less intensive to more intensive practices, such as bringing marginal land into crop production, create pressures on wildlife by making one or more of the resources they depend on more scarce or otherwise unavailable. On the other hand, the study indicates that reductions in summer fallow, and conversion of marginal cropland to other uses such as Tame or Seeded Pasture, will benefit wildlife, although these findings may not be valid for other countries.

In general, from 1981 to 1996 agricultural habitat for wildlife in Canada shows positive or neutral trends for wild species in all ecozones except, the Pacific Maritime and Mixedwood Plains (Figure 11). These two regions are noted for the intensity of their agriculture, although they account for less than 6 per cent of the total agricultural land area. The recent trend to reduce summer fallow in Canada and to convert cropland to permanent cover is a positive trend for wildlife, but one currently driven more by market forces, especially relatively low commodity prices, than by an apparent interest in wildlife.

Finland has begun to monitor the number of threatened species, flora and fauna, across different types of agricultural habitats (see Table 2 in the Biodiversity Chapter). Although this research has not yet provided any time series results, it does show that dry meadows are the agricultural habitat where the most threatened species can be found. However, this could reflect that in general more species use dry meadows as habitat relative to crop land.

A habitat matrix approach is also being used in *Korea* to examine the effects of different agricultural land use patterns and farm management practices on wild species. Preliminary and unpublished research by the Korean National Institute of Environmental Research has revealed that species diversity of birds was higher on farmland than on other habitat types studied (*e.g.* forest edges, mountain areas, forests). However, for certain species (*e.g.* small mammals), cropland might act as a barrier to species dispersal, limiting them to forest edges and other habitats.

Interpretation and links to other indicators

The habitat matrix approach allows changes in area of habitat to be monitored and mapped, and identifies which species are most likely to benefit from, or be adversely affected by, the change observed. The indicator is readily developed from standard agricultural land use data that is available in most countries. The matrix is able to track the trends in habitat area over time, identify areas where critical habitats are threatened, and provide a link to the species making use of different agricultural habitats.

Trends over time are calculated using land use data obtained through national Agricultural Censuses. In most countries this data covers all farms, is spatially detailed, undergoes extensive testing with respondents, and is usually validated prior to publication. The matrices can be based on the

Figure 11. **Share of habitat use units for which habitat area increased, decreased and remained constant: Canada, 1981 to 1996**

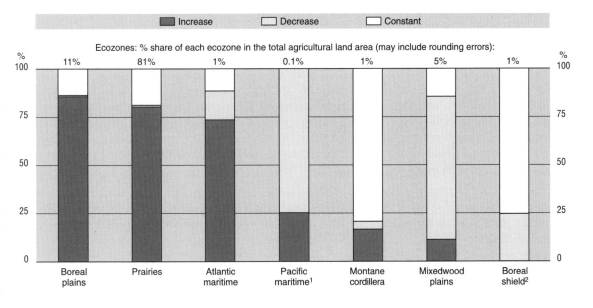

1. The share for which habitat area remained constant equals 0%.
2. The share for which habitat area increased equals 0%.
Source: Neave *et al.* (2000).

biological and ecological literature and on interviews and consultations with field biologists, or, where data exists, from field survey information.

Areas of different habitat types, and changes in those areas, can be mapped allowing policy efforts to target both valuable and/or vulnerable areas. Policy relevance is further enhanced because changes in habitat over time can be directly linked to the species making use of these habitats. In this way, species that may be affected by changes in land use and habitat can be identified, including species at risk. Moreover, because of the link to land use, the matrix can readily be linked to models which forecast agricultural land use trends.[13]

Notwithstanding the above points, there are several limitations to this approach, in particular, that the matrix records only information about the absence or presence of certain habitat uses, it does not reveal much about habitat and species quality. However, the matrix has the flexibility to use finer categories of habitats than provided from Census data where this data exists or where it is felt to be of value to collect such data. Related to this, the matrix does not always consider how successful is a particular habitat use, *i.e.* for reproduction or feeding.

The indicator does not examine the effects of various land management practices that can differ significantly for the same habitat unit. Using broad land-use categories also does not account for biological factors that may limit a species' use of a particular habitat type. For example, a species may not be able to use a habitat because one need may be met (*e.g.* food) while others are not (*e.g.* water, cover), the habitat may be fragmented, there may be behavioural barriers to use, or the species may be too widely dispersed.

A further limitation to the habitat matrix is that it does not distinguish between the conservation value of different species. That is to say, the indicator might not reflect the replacement of rare, protected or endangered species. Moreover, the local extinction of a rare species, whose ecological niche is then occupied by other opportunistic or non-native species, would be reflected as a positive

351

development in the matrix. To help better incorporate these aspects of species quality into the matrix different classes of species could be weighted by using, for example, national information on threatened species. Hence the respective parts of agricultural habitats used by such species could be singled out to avoid biases in the calculation of the matrix.

3. Future challenges

There are two key issues that face policy decision-makers in the possible future development of work on wildlife habitat indicators. *First*, habitats are highly diverse in their physical characteristics including their location, that determine the functions they perform. These functions include providing valued habitats for wildlife, a role in flood mitigation, sediment retention, and a filtering role for farm chemicals. *Second*, many of the services that habitats provide to society are not traded in markets, which means there are no quantitative measures of the social and economic value of their services as recreational sites or their aesthetic qualities.[14]

A key element in further developing habitat indicators may be the establishment across OECD countries of common *definitions* of the major types of habitat identified, namely: intensive, semi-natural and uncultivated habitats on agricultural land. This task might be helped by drawing on classification systems of different agricultural land use types already developed for most countries in annual agricultural censuses.

To help improve the analytical soundness and measurability of wildlife habitat indicators, further research could also be developed to examine the relationship between agricultural activity and habitats, covering *habitat fragmentation* (*i.e.* the degree to which a given habitat type is divided into separate patches), *heterogeneity* (*i.e.* average size of and variability of habitat types per monitoring area) and *vertical vegetation structure* (*i.e.* habitat strata, such as bushes and trees).

The *fragmentation*, or connectivity, of a habitat depends on both its abundance and spatial arrangement (Mac *et al.*, 1998, pp. 51-52). Land use changes generally alter both the area and configuration of habitats. Fragmentation of any habitat will aggravate the plant and animal communities using that habitat, and can result in the loss of species in single habitat patches, as well as loss from the regional landscape. The strength of these effects are species dependent, due to differences in dispersal abilities. For example, some butterfly species are known to take decades to colonise patches only a few kilometres from an existing population. Many questions remain about the effects of habitat fragmentation, especially as it affects species in different ways, and also because the impact on species of fragmentation of intensively cropped land may vary considerable from that of semi-natural agricultural habitats

Habitat *heterogeneity* is important, as many species require different habitats for their development feeding, over-wintering and reproduction. Approaches such as the Shannon diversity index and patch density, can help to express habitat heterogeneity (European Commission, 1999).[15] In the *Netherlands*, for example, the physical area of field patterns is monitored. However, interpretation of habitat heterogeneity indicators needs to be treated cautiously.

Whether habitat heterogeneity has a positive or negative effect on wild species will depend on the size of the habitat patch, the types of habitat in question, and the regional context. High heterogeneity over a small spatial scale may reflect a lack of core habitat, which will be negative for species dependent on such habitat. This will lower regional diversity, even if local diversity may appear high due to a large number of different habitat types. Illustrations include heathland habitats that need to extend over relatively large areas to allow an appropriate rotation of burning and cutting regimes for heath maintenance.

The abundance of *vertical vegetation structures* has been shown to be an important variable when correlated with the diversity of bird communities. The vertical habitat structure index (VHSI) describe habitat structure in terms of vertical layers based on empirical findings relating vegetation physiognomy to species richness.[16] The habitat strata that could be considered include sub-surface soil surface; shrub level; tree trunk level; and tree canopy level. There is a corresponding decrease in species richness associated with simplified habitats, in terms of few strata. As a consequence, the VHSI for cultivated land has usually a much simpler vegetative structure than land in uncultivated habitats, in particular forests, although agro-forestry ecosystems contain more strata than other farmed ecosystems.

Habitat indicators are integral components within biodiversity and landscape indicators, thus developing *linkages* between habitat indicators and other indicator areas will enhance their usefulness for policy makers. In this context farm management practices are viewed as a key element in farming's impact on habitat and wildlife. There are frequently private and public schemes that operate to maintain and enhance habitats on agricultural land, that require farmers to undertake certain farming practices in order to maintain or restore habitat features on agricultural land (see Table 1 in the Landscape chapter).[17]

Indicators that can capture *the demand for, and valuation of, agricultural wildlife habitats* might also be developed to better inform policy makers of the public demand for habitat, and measure the costs and benefits of habitat provision in agriculture. Already considerable work has been undertaken to provide economic values of the costs and benefits of habitat. Estimating the value of agricultural habitats, covering their value in producing marketed goods (*e.g.* crops), non-marketed goods (*e.g.* as recreational sites), and ecological and amenity value, may take considerable resources, however, to usefully inform cost/benefit considerations.[18]

Some semi-natural and uncultivated habitats on agricultural land are frequently the most difficult habitats for which to determine an economic value, because they are usually associated with the highest non-market values. In these cases it may be more pragmatic to estimate the economic value of such habitats in terms of the market value in their best alternative use.

NOTES

1. For details on the relevant web sites for the Ramsar and Bonn Conventions and the North American Waterfowl Plan see the Biodiversity chapter. The EU Habitat Directive as it relates to agriculture is discussed in the European Commission (1999, pp. 135-139), and a regular update of the Natura 2000 activities is provided in the newsletter available at the EU web site: *http://europa.eu.int/comm/environment/pubs_en.htm.*

2. The CORINE land cover system is now in the process of being replaced by the EUNIS habitat classification system, see EEA (1999).

3. To take account of the finer details in agricultural habitats, such as hedgerows, some OECD countries collect habitat data nationally at levels of disaggregation less than one hectare, including, for example, at a resolution of > 0.25 ha. for semi-natural and uncultivated habitats in *Denmark* and *Germany*. In *Norwegian* agricultural landscapes, for example, an area of 100 hectares can contain 15-20 fields and meadows and some 30 patches of semi-natural grassland, with data collected at a resolution of 0.2 ha and less.

4. Issues related to future research on habitat fragmentation, heterogeneity, and vertical structures are discussed in the final section of this chapter.

5. For a description of other semi-natural habitat classification systems relevant to agriculture see, for example Baldock *et al.*, (1995); Baldock (1999); Peco *et al.* (1999); and Tucker and Evans (1997).

6. The issue of biomass production for energy is also discussed in the Greenhouse Gas chapter. In the context of the *European Union*, see European Commission (1999, pp. 97-108); in the *United States* see USDA (1997, pp. 20, 137-141), and see a broader review in OECD (2000).

7. See, for example, the research by Mäder *et al.* (1996).

8. The IFOAM guidelines can be obtained online at the IFOAM website: *www.ifoam.org.*

9. The IUCN Report draws on the study undertaken by the Danish Ministry of Agriculture to examine the impact of agricultural change in a typical Danish county.

10. For a review of the literature in this area related to *Europe* see EEA (1998, p. 164).

11. The responses to the OECD Agri-environmental Indicators Questionnaire 1999 reveal very little data on uncultivated habitats, with only a few countries providing any disaggregated data, see Annex Table 6. However Norway has begun to collect information related to uncultivated natural habitat, which will become available in 2003.

12. The discussion under the habitat matrix heading draws, in particular, from work in *Canada* on this area see Neave *et al.* (2000), but for more detail of the Canadian approach see also Neave and Neave (1998). A similar approach is also under development in *Mexico* by the Mexican Ministry of Environment by linking different habitat types (landscape units) to the total number of species, including the total number of wild species, and races and varieties of domesticated species expressed as a biodiversity index for each landscape unit as follows:

$$BI_i = R_i \times S_i^{1/2}$$

where:

BI_i = Biodiversity index of landscape type I

R_i = Number of wild species, and domesticated varieties present in landscape type I

S_i = Surface area in thousands of hectares of landscape type I

For the total agricultural area (or land area) the BI is expressed as:

$$BI = (R_1 \times S_1^{1/2}) + (R_2 \times S_2^{1/2}) + (R_3 \times S_3^{1/2}) + ... + (R_n \times S_n^{1/2})$$

$$BI = \sum_i R_i \sqrt{S_i}$$

13. The importance of examining future land use changes on habitat and wild species is discussed by Mac *et al.* (1998, pp. 55-57).

14. This text here draws from the analysis of Crosson and Frederick (1999) in the context of their assessment of the impacts of *United States* policies on wetlands.

15. Wossink *et al.* (1999) have also examined the spatial aspects of wildlife preservation in agriculture from an economist's perspective.

16. The VHSI approach is examined by Flather *et al.* (1992); and Short (1988).

17. Linking wildlife species, habitat and farm management indicators, is discussed by Wenum *et al.* (1999).

18. Heimlich *et al.* (1998) provide a review of 33 studies from the literature on the economic valuation of wetlands, but see also Kline and Wichelns (1996) in this context.

Annex Table 1.   **Canadian Habitat Types used in the Habitat Matrix Indicator**

The Census of Agriculture database from Statistics Canada is the key national source of information for documenting areas of different land cover. Habitat types have been assembled around this database. The Census provides information for 5 main land cover types:

1. Cropland: subdivided into crop types.
2. Summerfallow.
3. Tame or Seeded Pasture.
4. Natural Land for Pasture.
5. All Other Land.

These 5 main Habitat types are very general, so some categories were subdivided into more detailed habitat types for the purposes of the Canadian habitat matrix (see endnote 12), distinguished both by species on the ground and by wildlife managers in the field as follows:

1. Cropland
   - any crop whose area is greater than 1% of total farm area for the ecozone will be considered as a separate habitat type;

   crops that are less than 1% of total farm area will be grouped into other categories such as:
   - other grains;
   - other oilseeds;
   - other crops;
   - fruits and vegetables.

2. Summerfallow.
3. Tame or Seeded Pasture.
4. Natural Land for Pasture:
   - natural land for pasture is divided into 2 types:
     A. Natural grassland.
     B. Pasture with shrubs/woodland. In the Prairie and the Montane Cordillera Ecozones, this type includes sagebrush/shrubs.

5. All Other Land: All other land is a variety of potential habitat types including farm buildings, barnyards, lanes, gardens, greenhouses, mushroom houses, idle land, woodlots, sugar bushes, tree windbreaks, bogs, marshes, sloughs, etc. This category is subdivided into a number of habitat types in the matrix:
   A. Farm houses and outbuildings: this category represents on average 2% of total farmland (farm buildings, barnyards, lanes, gardens, greenhouses, mushroom houses, feedlots).
   B. Shelterbelts/fencerows/ditches: with distinction between shelterbelts/fencerows/ditches with and without trees.
   C. Wetlands, with distinction between:
      a) riparian areas;
      b) shallow seasonal ponds with extensive margins;
      c) shallow seasonal ponds without extensive margins;
      d) deep permanent ponds with extensive margins;
      e) deep permanent ponds without extensive margins.
   D. Woodland, with distinction between:
      a) plantations;
      b) woodlot with interior habitat;*
      c) woodlot without interior habitat.*

---

* Woodland interior habitat is that habitat which falls at least 100 m from the edge of a woodlot.
Source: Neave and Neave (1998).

Annex Table 2. **The CORINE Land Cover Nomenclature and Aggregation**

1.1. Urban fabric	1.1.1 Continuous urban fabric 1.1.2 Discontinuous urban fabric	
1.2 Industrial, commercial and transport units	1.2.1 Industrial or commercial units 1.2.2 Road and rail networks and associated land 1.2.3 Port areas 1.2.4 Airports	**A** – Artificial surfaces
1.3 Mine, dump and construction sites	1.3.1 Mineral extraction sites 1.3.2 Dump sites 1.3.3 Construction sites	
1.4 Artificial, non-agricultural vegetated areas	1.4.1 Green urban areas 1.4.2 Sport and leisure facilities	
2.1 Arable land	2.1.1 Non-irrigated arable land 2.1.2 Permanently irrigated land 2.1.3 Rice fields	**B** – Homogeneous agricultural areas
2.2 Permanent crops	2.2.1 Vineyards 2.2.2 Fruit trees and berry plantations 2.2.3 Olive groves	
2.3 Pastures	2.3.1 Pastures	
2.4 Heterogeneous agricultural areas	2.4.1 Annual crops associated with permanent crops 2.4.2 Complex cultivation patterns 2.4.3 Land principally occupied by agriculture with significant areas of natural vegetation 2.4.4 Agro-forestry areas	**C** – Heterogeneous agricultural areas and pastures
3.1 Forests	3.1.1 Broad-leaved forest 3.1.2 Coniferous forest 3.1.3 Mixed forest	**D** – Forests
3.2 Shrub and/or herbaceous vegetation associations	3.2.1 Natural grassland 3.2.2 Moors and heathland 3.2.3 Sclerophyllous vegetation 3.2.4 Transitional woodland scrub	**E** – Semi-natural areas
3.3 Open spaces with little or no vegetation	3.3.1 Beaches, dunes, sand plains 3.3.2 Bare rock 3.3.3 Sparsely vegetated areas 3.3.4 Burnt areas 3.3.5 Glaciers and perpetual snow	
4.1 Inland wetlands	4.1.1 Inland marshes 4.1.2 Peat bogs	
4.2 Coastal wetlands	4.2.1 Salt marshes 4.2.2 Salines 4.2.3 Intertidal flats	**F** – Wetlands and water bodies
5.1 Continental waters	5.1.1 Water courses 5.1.2 Water bodies	
5.2 Marine waters	5.2.1 Coastal lagoons 5.2.2 Estuaries 5.2.3 Sea and ocean	

Source: EEA (1999).

357

Annex Table 3. **Number of vertebrates[1] species using habitat[2] on agricultural land divided into five categories of activity: Canadian Prairies, mid-1990s**

Cropland	Reproduction	Feed	Cover	Winter	Staging[3]	Total
Cereals	41	179	27	12	37	296
Spring wheat	10	39	6	2	6	63
Durum wheat	8	38	6	2	6	60
Oats	7	33	4	2	9	55
Barley	8	33	5	2	6	54
Other grains	8	36	6	4	10	64
Oil crops	2	28	1	1	2	34
Canola	1	9	0	0	0	10
Other oilseeds	1	19	1	1	2	24
Fruits and vegetables	12	29	11	1	0	53
Other arable crops	1	10	0	0	0	11
Forage	31	83	59	3	6	182
Alfalfa	11	38	25	1	3	78
Tame hay	20	45	34	2	3	104
Seeded pasture	35	62	46	14	3	161
Natural pasture	181	244	207	88	7	727
Woodlands	237	255	257	107	3	859
Shelterbelts	72	111	104	33	1	321
Wetlands	252	383	305	68	29	1 038
Others[4]	32	82	46	21	2	183
Total	864	1 384	1 017	327	88	3 865

1. Vertebrates, including birds, mammals, amphibians and reptiles.
2. This includes the addition of species using the Prairies as a primary and secondary habitat for five activities, *i.e.* reproduction, feed, cover, wintering and staging (birds only).
3. Activity only for birds.
4. "Others" mainly includes general crop use, summer fallow, and farm houses/outbuildings.
Source: Adapted from Neave and Neave (1998).

Annex Table 4. **Number of arthropod[1] species using intensive farmed land[2] compared to semi-natural habitats:[3] Switzerland, 1987**

	Dry meadow	Wet meadow	Low-intensity meadow	Intensive meadow	Wheat and maize
Araneae (spiders)	90	81	54	36	30
Coleoptera (beetles)	352	223	263	187	163
Diptera (flies)	258	131	154	103	106
Hymenoptera (wasps, bees, etc.)	214	92	107	65	59
Other Arthropods	182	106	125	65	55
Total	1 096	633	703	456	413

1. Arthropods recorded in this study were mainly spiders, beetles, flies, wasps and bees.
2. Intensively farmed land refers to wheat, maize, and intensive meadow.
3. Semi-natural habitats refer to dry meadow, wet meadow and low-intensity meadow.
Source: Duelli *et al.* (1999).

Annex Table 5. **Areas of semi-natural agricultural habitats and uncultivated habitats: 1985 to 1998**
Hectares

	1985	1990	1995	1998
Austria[1]				
Area of semi-natural habitats	2 023 512	1 992 765	1 976 011	1 980 370
Permanent Pasture	1 985 590	1 952 794	1 940 011	1 943 410
One cut meadows	104 283	89 159	56 366	58 060
Two and more cut meadows	852 024	844 634	861 444	870 560
Cultivated pastures	37 712	39 490	68 174	67 750
Litter meadows	13 805	10 734	15 806	15 730
Rough pastures	130 289	123 163	81 313	80 190
Total alpine meadows and pastures	847 477	845 614	856 908	851 120
Uncultivated grassland	37 922	39 971	36 000	36 960
Canada[2]				
Area of semi-natural habitats	19 219 680	20 104 520	19 961 298	..
Natural land for pasture	15 660 465	15 963 299	15 612 162	..
Tame or seeded pasture	3 559 215	4 141 221	4 349 136	..
Area of uncultivated habitats	6 155 300	6 220 452	6 914 200	..
All other land[3]	6 155 300	6 220 452	6 914 200	..
Denmark				
Area of semi-natural habitats	..	..	..	238 000
Dry grassland	..	..	..	26 000
Extensive pasture land	..	..	..	65 000
Meadows	..	..	..	104 000
Salt marshes	..	..	..	43 000
Area of uncultivated habitats	..	n.c.	n.c.	n.c.
Bogs	..	..	..	90 000
Woodland[4]	..	92 100	107 900	111 800
Heathland	..	..	..	82 000
Small rivers	..	..	16 341	..
Greece				
Area of semi-natural habitats	..	6 574 497	n.c.	n.c.
Extensive pasture	..	5 300 000	5 300 000	5 300 000
Grassland	..	60 000	60 000	60 000
Low intensity meadows	..	400	200	200
Wooded pasture	..	1 200 000	1 200 000	1 200 000
Fallow land	..	5 000	..	..
High trees in traditional orchards	..	9 097	..	..
Area of uncultivated habitats	..	299 600	..	..
Wet ditches, wetlands	..	299 600	..	..
Japan				
Area of semi-natural habitats	620 800	646 600	660 700	650 100
Meadow and pasture	620 800	646 600	660 700	650 100
Netherlands				
Area of semi-natural habitats	10 956	22 302	51 876	70 864
Extensive pasture land	6 000	16 363	40 411	57 993
Extensive field margins in cropped land	0	0	125	500
Fallow land	4 956	5 939	11 340	12 371
Area of uncultivated habitats	n.c.	n.c.	n.c.	n.c.
Forests	20 000	..	..	..
Wet ditches, wetlands	..	..	..	75 000
Norway				
Area of semi-natural habitats	..	..	..	2 163 986
Extensive grassland	..	..	..	128
Extensive pastureland	..	..	..	2 161 451
Other semi-natural habitats	..	..	..	2 407
Sweden				
Area of semi-natural habitats	668 967	760 680	891 721	n.c.
Extensive pasture land	..	..	..	374 200
Extensive pasture land + wooded pasture land	584 347	568 404	575 691	..
Fallow land[5]	84 620	192 276	316 030	194 000
Low intensity grassland	..	..	..	6 940

Annex Table 5. **Areas of semi-natural agricultural habitats and uncultivated habitats: 1985 to 1998** (*cont.*)

Hectares

	1985	1990	1995	1998
Switzerland[6]				
Area of semi-natural habitats	n.c.	603 036	601 704	623 468
Extensive grassland	..	20 419	26 078	46 244
Extensive alpine pasture	560 000	551 500	543 000	534 500
Fallow land	..	77	79	380
Low intensity grassland	..	31 040	32 547	42 344
United Kingdom[7]				
Area of semi-natural habitats	10 402 100	10 482 600	..	..
Extensive grassland	170 000	200 000	..	..
Extensive pasture land	3 880 000	3 820 000	..	..
Extensive field margins in cropped land	..	..	..	..
Fallow land	110 000	350 000	..	..
Low intensity grassland	170 000	200 000	..	..
Wooded pasture land	..	..	..	..
Rough grazing	6 072 100	5 912 600	..	..
Area of uncultivated habitats	660 000	730 000	..	..
Shrub	100 000	90 000	..	..
Uncultivated areas where weeds and wild plants grow freely	210 000	270 000	..	..
Wet ditches, wetlands	350 000	370 000	..	..

.. Not available.
n.c. Not calculated.
1. Data for 1998 refer to 1997.
2. Data for 1985 refer to 1986; data for 1990 refer to 1991 and data for 1995 refer to 1996.
3. "All other land" is defined as all land not included in the other census categories, such as land under farm buildings, barnyards, lanes, home gardens, greenhouses and mushroom houses, idle land, woodlots, sugar bushes, tree windbreaks, sugar bushes, tree windbreaks, bogs, marshes sloughs, etc.
4. Woodland, including small woodland areas on agricultural land.
5. Data are from Statistics Sweden, except for 1998 where the value is from the Swedish Board of Agriculture.
6. Data for 1990 refer to 1993 except for extensive alpine pasture where data for 1995 and 1998 are OECD estimates. Switzerland also has 2 million high trees in traditional orchards in 1990 and 1995 and 3 million in 1998.
7. Data for 1985 refer to 1984, and to Great Britain only.
Source: OECD Agri-environmental Indicators Questionnaire, 1999.

Annex Table 6. **Agricultural land use changes to (decrease) and from (increase) other land uses:**
mid-1980s to mid-1990s

Hectares

| | Land conversion period | Change from agricultural land use to other land uses, including to: | | | | | | |
		Forest and wooded land[1]	Built-up land[2]	Wetlands	Surface water areas[3]	Open land[4]	Others[5]	Total decrease
Austria	1987-96	77 457	34 701	..	3 729	8 887	..	124 774
Canada	1981-86	..	327 580	..	..	..	..	327 580
Finland	1985-97	101 746	..	..	..	..	..	101 746
France	1985-98	1 020 388	784 931	28 995	65 491	781 736	..	2 681 541
Japan	1985-98	33 050	308 200	..	..	..	293 950	635 200
Korea	1985-97/98	..	112 461	..	29 000	8 674	..	150 135
Norway	1985, 90, 95	493	2 745	..	..	..	..	3 238
Poland	1985-97	12 690	40 164	..	1 018	14 297	..	68 169
Spain	1985-94	362 553	76 730	..	50 082	628 433	..	1 117 798
Sweden	1990-95	..	2 700	..	..	..	..	2 700
Switzerland	mid-1990s	7 800	37 100	..	..	1 600	..	46 500
United Kingdom	1984-90	153 000	125 000	25 000	..	120 000	..	423 000
United States[8]	1982-92	4 602 380	2 681 500	187 000	879 670	15 125 880	..	23 476 430

| | Land conversion period | Change from other land uses to agricultural land use, including from: | | | | | | |
		Forest and wooded land[1]	Built-up land[2]	Wetlands	Surface water areas[3]	Open land[4]	Others[5]	Total increase
Austria	1987-96	..	..	..	..	..	..	..
Canada	1981-86	..	..	..	..	..	..	..
Finland[6]	1984-88	..	..	..	..	..	..	48 985
France	1985-98	721 209	321 001	18 203	29 220	486 584	..	1 576 217
Japan[7]	1985-98	135 750	..	..	1 730	..	6 390	143 870
Korea	1985-97/98	65 602	..	..	34 683	33 819	..	134 104
Norway[6]	1985-97	..	..	..	..	..	..	27 750
Poland	1980, 90, 96	2 671	..	..	..	..	..	2 671
Spain	1985-94	..	..	..	..	..	..	..
Sweden[6]	1990-95	..	..	..	..	..	..	15 579
Switzerland	mid-1990s	..	..	..	..	..	..	..
United Kingdom	1984-90	97 000	47 000	17 000	..	60 000	..	221 000
United States[8]	1982-92	1 741 700	154 290	138 000	..	..	..	2 033 990

Note: Changes shown in this table are cumulative (not annual) over the conversion period.
  .   Not available.
1.   Forest and wooded land: land used primarily for agricultural purposes such as grazing are included under agricultural land.
2.   Built-up land: land under houses, roads, mines and quarries and any other facilities, including their auxiliary spaces, deliberately installed for the pursuit of human activities. Included are also certain types of open land (non-built-up land), which are closely related to these activities, such as waste tips, derelict land in built-up areas, junk yards, city parks and gardens, etc. Land occupied by scattered farm buildings, yards, etc., is excluded. Land under closed villages or similar rural localities is included.
3.   Surface water areas: small ponds, lakes and diverted rivers.
4.   Open land: non-wooded land which is covered by low vegetation (less than 2 metres). Non-built-up land the surface of which either is not covered by vegetation or scarcely covered by vegetation, but which excludes it from other categories.
5.   Others: non-categorised land use such as abandoned farmland but not forest.
6.   The source of the increase in agricultural land is not available.
7.   The figure for forest and wooded land includes built-up land, wetlands, and open land.
8.   Data for wetlands are taken from Heimlich et al. (1998). Open land data include land under Conservation Reserves Program contracts, farmsteads, and other farm structures, field windbreaks, barren land such as salt flats or exposed rock, and marshland.
Source: OECD Agri-environmental Indicators Questionnaire, 1999.

BIBLIOGRAPHY

Baldock, D. (1999),
"Indicators for High Nature Value Farming Systems in Europe", Chapter 9, pp. 121-135, in F. Brouwer and B. Crabtree (eds.), *Environmental Indicators and Agricultural Policy*, CAB International, Wallingford, United Kingdom.

Baldock, D., G. Beaufoy and J. Clark (1995),
The Nature of Farming, Low Intensity Farming Systems in Nine European Countries, Institute for European Environmental Policy, London, United Kingdom.

Barr, C.J., R.G.H. Bunce, R.T. Clarke, R.M. Fuller, M.T. Furse, M.K. Gillespie, G.B. Groom, C.J. Hallam, DC. Howard and M.J. Ness (1993),
Countryside Survey 1990: Main Report, Department of the Environment, London, United Kingdom.

Christensen, D.K., E.M. Jacobsen and H. Nohr (1996),
"A comparative study of bird faunas in conventionally and organically farmed areas", *Dansk Ornitologisk Forening Tidsskrift*, Vol. 90, pp. 21-28.

Commonwealth of Australia (1998),
Sustainable Agriculture – Assessing Australia's Recent Performance, A Report to the Standing Committee on Agriculture and Resource Management (SCARM) of the National Collaborative Project on Indicators for Sustainable Agriculture, SCARM Technical Report No. 70, CSIRO Publishing, Victoria, Australia.

Crosson, P. and K. Frederick (1999),
Impacts of Federal Policies and Programs on Wetlands, Discussion Paper 99-26, Resources for the Future, Washington DC., United States of America. Available at: *www.rff.org/nat_resources/landuse.htm*

Duelli, P., M.K. Obrist and D.R. Schmatz (1999),
"Biodiversity evaluation in agricultural landscapes: above-ground insects", *Agriculture, Ecosystems and Environment*, Vol. 74, pp. 33-64.

EEA [European Environment Agency] (1998),
Europe's Environment: The Second Assessment, Office for Official Publications of the European Communities, Luxembourg. Available at: *http://themes.eea.eu.int/* [> all available reports].

EEA (1999),
EUNIS Habitat Classification: Towards a Common Language on Habitats, Copenhagen, Denmark. Available at: *http://themes.eea.eu.int/* [> all available reports].

European Commission (1999),
Agriculture, Environment, Rural Development: Facts and Figures – A Challenge for Agriculture, Office for Official Publications of the European Communities, Luxembourg. Available at: *http://europa.eu.int/comm/dg06/envir/report/en/index.htm*.

EUROSTAT [Statistical Office of the European Communities] (1999),
Towards Environmental Pressure Indicators for the EU, Environment and Energy Paper Theme 8, Luxembourg. The background documentation is available at: *http://e-m-a-i-l.nu/tepi/* and *http://esl.jrc.it/envind/*

FAO [United Nations Food and Agriculture Organisation] (1999),
Central and Eastern European Sustainable Agriculture Network, First Workshop Proceedings, REU Technical Series 61, FAO Subregional Office for Central and Eastern Europe, Rome, Italy. Available at: *www.fao.org/regional/europe/public-e.htm*.

Flather, C.H., S.J. Brady and D.B. Inkley (1992),
"Regional habitat appraisals of wildlife communities: a landscape-level evaluation of a resource planning model using avian distribution data", *Landscape Ecology*, Vol. 7, No. 2, pp. 137-147.

Fuller, R.J., R.W. Gregory, D.W. Gibbons, J.H. Marchant, J.D. Wilson, S.R. Baillie and N. Carter (1998),
"Population declines and range contractions among lowland farmland birds in Britain", *Conservation Biology*, Vol. 12, No. 9, pp. 1425-1441.

Haines-Young, R., C. Watkins, R.G.H. Bunce and C.J. Hallam (1996),
Environmental Accounts for Land Cover, Countryside 1990 Series, Vol. 8, Department of the Environment, London, United Kingdom.

Heimlich, R.E., K.D. Wiebe, R. Claassen, D. Gadsby and R.M. House (1998),
  Wetlands and Agriculture: Private Interests and Public Benefits, Agricultural Economic Report No. 765, Economic Research Service, US Department of Agriculture, Washington, DC., United States. Available at: *www.ers.usda.gov/epubs/pdf/aer765/*.

IUCN [World Conservation Union] (1999),
  Background study for the development of an IUCN Policy on Agriculture and Biodiversity, Report prepared by P. Nowicki, C. Potter and T. Reed, Wye College, University of London, United Kingdom. Available at: *www.iucn.org/places/europe/eu/docs/Agriculture_Biodiversity.pdf*.

Cline, J. and D. Wichelns (1996),
  "Measuring public preferences for the environmental amenities provided by farmland", *European Review of Agricultural Economics*, Vol. 23, pp. 421-436.

Lowe, P. and M. Whitby (1998),
  "The CAP and the European Environment", Chapter 13, in C. Ritson and D.R. Harvey (eds.) *The Common Agricultural Policy*, 2nd Edition, CAB International, Oxford, United Kingdom.

Mac, M.J., P.A. Opler, C.E.P. Haecker and P.D. Doran (1998),
  Status and Trends of the Nation's Biological Resources, Two Volumes, United States Department of the Interior, United States Geological Survey, Reston, Virginia, United States. Available at: *http://biology.usgs.gov/pubs/execsumm/page2.htm*.

Mäder, P., L. Pfiffner, A. Fließbach, M. von Lützow and J.C. Munch (1996),
  "Soil ecology – The impact of organic and conventional agriculture on soil biota and its significance for soil fertility", in T.V. Ostergaard (ed.), *Fundamentals of Organic Agriculture*, Proceedings of the 11th International Federation of Organic Agriculture Movements (IFOAM) Conference, Copenhagen, Denmark.

MAFF [Ministry of Agriculture, Fisheries and Food] (2000),
  Towards Sustainable Agriculture – A Pilot Set of Indicators, London, United Kingdom. Available at: *www.maff.gov.uk/* [Farming > Sustainable Agriculture].

Neave, P. and E. Neave (1998),
  Agroecosystem Biodiversity Indicator – Habitat Component: Review and Assessment of Concepts and Indicators of Wildlife and Habitat Availability in the Agricultural Landscape – Concept Paper, Report No. 26, Agri-Environmental Indicator Project, Agriculture and Agri-Food Canada, Regina, Canada.

Neave, P., E. Neave, T. Weins and T. Riche (2000),
  "Availability of Wildlife Habitat on Farmland", Chapter 15, in T. McRae, C.A.S. Smith and L.J. Gregorich (eds.), *Environmental Sustainability of Canadian Agriculture: Report of the Agri-Environmental Indicator Project*, Agriculture and Agri-Food Canada (AAFC), Ottawa, Ontario, Canada. Available at: *www.agr.ca/policy/environment/publications/list.html*.

OECD (1997),
  The Environmental Effects of Agricultural Land Diversion Schemes, Paris, France.

OECD (1998),
  Environmental Performance Reviews: Korea, Paris, France.

OECD (2000),
  Information Note on the Use and Potential of Biomass Energy in OECD Countries, Paris, France.

Peco, B., J.E. Malo, J.J. Onate, F. Suarez and J. Sumpsi (1999),
  "Agri-environmental Indicators for Extensive Land-use Systems in the Iberian Peninsula", Chapter 10, pp. 137-156, in F. Brouwer and B. Crabtree (eds.), *Environmental Indicators and Agricultural Policy*, CAB International, Wallingford, United Kingdom.

Pfiffner, L. and U. Niggli (1996),
  "Effects of bio-dynamic, organic and conventional farming on ground beetles (Col. Carabidae) and other epigaeic arthropods in winter wheat", *Biological Agriculture and Horticulture*, Vol. 12, pp. 353-364.

Short. H.L. (1988),
  "A habitat structure model for natural resource management", *Journal of Environmental Management*, Vol. 27, pp. 289-305.

Stoate, C., R. Borralho and M. Araujo (2000),
  "Factors affecting corn bunting *Miliaria calandra* abundance in a Portuguese agricultural landscape", *Agriculture, Ecosystems and Environment*, Vol. 74, pp. 33-64.

Stott, A.P. and R. Haines-Young (1998),
  "Linking land cover, intensity of use and botanical diversity in an accounting framework in the United Kingdom", pp. 245-262, in K. Uno and P. Bartelmus (eds.), *Environmental Accounting in Theory and Practice*, Kluwer Academic Publications, The Netherlands.

Tucker, G.M. and M.I. Evans (1997),
  Habitats for Birds in Europe: A Conservation Strategy for the Wider Environment, BirdLife Conservation Series No. 6, Birdlife International, Cambridge, United Kingdom.

UNEP [United Nations Environment Programme] (1995),
   Global Diversity Assessment – Summary for Policy Makers, Nairobi, Kenya. Available at: *www.unep.ch/iuc/*.

USDA [United States Department of Agriculture] (1997),
   Agricultural Resources and Environmental Indicators, 1996-97, Agricultural Handbook No. 712, Natural Resources and Environment Division, Economic Research Service, Washington, DC., United States. Available at: *www.ers.usda.gov* [Briefing Rooms > Agricultural Resources and Environmental Indicators].

Wenum, J., A.O. Lansink and A. Wossink (1999),
   Farm Heterogeneity in Wildlife Production, paper presented to the American Agricultural Economics Association Annual Meeting, 8-11 August, Nashville, Tennessee, United States.

Wossink, A., J. van Wenum, C. Jurgens and G. de Snoo (1999),
   "Co-ordinating economic, behavioural and spatial aspects of wildlife preservation in agriculture", *European Review of Agricultural Economics*, Vol. 26, No. 4, pp. 443-460.

Chapter 7

LANDSCAPE

HIGHLIGHTS

Context

Agriculture plays a key role in shaping the quality of landscape, as in many OECD countries farming is the major user of land. Agricultural landscapes are the visible outcomes from the interaction between agriculture, natural resources and the environment, and encompass amenity, cultural, and other societal values. Landscapes can be considered as composed of three key elements: *landscape structures* or appearance, including environmental features (*e.g.* habitats), land use types (*e.g.* crops), and man-made objects or cultural features (*e.g.* hedges); *landscape functions*, such as a place to live, work, visit, and provide various environmental services; *landscape values*, concerning the costs to farmers of maintaining landscapes and the value society places on agricultural landscape, such as recreational and cultural values.

Many OECD countries have legislation which recognises the importance of societal values embodied in landscapes and internationally some are also attracting attention, such as the designation by UNESCO of cultural landscape sites. The challenge for policy makers, because landscapes are often not valued through markets, is to judge the appropriate provision of landscape and which landscape features society values, and assess to what extent policy changes affect agricultural landscape.

Indicators and recent trends

OECD agricultural landscape indicators provide a tool to better inform policy makers by: recording the current state of landscape and how its appearance, including cultural features, is changing; establishing what share of agricultural land is under public/private schemes for landscape conservation; and measuring the cost of landscape provision by farmers and the value society attaches to landscapes.

Regarding the *current state and trends in the structure of agricultural landscapes* there does seem to have been a trend towards increasing homogenisation of landscape structures in OECD countries over the past 50 years, including the loss of some cultural features (*e.g.* stone walls). This trend appears closely related to the structural changes and intensification of production, linked with the degradation of the natural resource base in agriculture. There are signs, since the late 1980s, that the process toward increasing homogeneity of landscapes could be slowing or even in reverse in some regions. Since this period many OECD countries started to introduce a range of agri-environmental measures, including in some cases measures specifically seeking to maintain landscapes.

Public and private schemes for the conservation of agricultural landscapes are widespread across OECD countries, but are mostly publicly funded. Public expenditure on these schemes tends to be a minor share of total agricultural support, but for some countries expenditure has increased rapidly. In many cases the schemes cover multiple objectives, especially concerning biodiversity, habitat and landscape conservation; and focus on the biophysical and cultural features in a local context. Some countries are beginning to include public access requirements in landscape schemes.

Currently information on the *costs incurred by farmers in landscape improvement* is extremely limited. To establish the *value society places on landscape* some countries use public opinion surveys, although as with landscape related consumer expenditure, information is limited. Non-market valuation studies reveal that agricultural landscapes are highly valued in many cases, although there is a large variation in the values estimated. These studies also reveal that the landscape surveyed today is the preferred landscape, landscape's value decreases with greater distance from a particular site, heterogeneity and "traditional" elements are given a higher value over more uniform and newer landscapes, while landscapes perceived as overcrowded have a low value.

1. Background

Policy context

A large number of OECD countries have legislation which explicitly recognises the importance of the recreational, cultural, heritage, aesthetic and other amenity values embodied in agricultural and other landscapes. In the *United States* the National Environmental Policy Act of 1970, "assures[s] for all Americans aesthetically and culturally pleasing surroundings". Moreover, in some states, Maine for example, farmland protection law explicitly addresses scenic values (Nassauer, 1989).

The *Australian* 1996 State of the Environment Report states that, Australia's natural and cultural heritage is an integral part of its environment... natural landscapes with their biological and physical diversity – and cultural landscapes – with their diversity of cultural records and layers of meaning, objects and stories – collectively give us our uniquely Australian "sense of place" (Environment Australia, 1996, pp. 43).

Within the *European Union*, agri-environmental measures (EU Regulation 2078/92), include aid to farmers who adopt "farming practices compatible with the requirements of protection of the environment and natural resources, as well as maintenance of the countryside and the landscape". Within the EU, member States' national agricultural acts typically set objectives for the protection and restoration of landscapes and also to provide public access to these landscapes.

The 1995 Land Act in *Norway* makes provision that "consideration shall be taken of the landscape picture, natural diversity and cultural and historical values ... and the possibility for the public to experience natural and cultural history... The provision builds upon the fact that the cultural landscape is a public good that agriculture creates and is responsible for [and] .... takes into account that the cultural landscape changes over time according to developments in the agricultural sector".

Switzerland has also set out similar objectives for landscape to those of Norway, under its Federal Council Law of 1997 (OFEFP, 1998). While in *Germany* the Federal Nature Conservation Act (1998) defines certain landscape elements and characteristics (*e.g.* historic landscapes) for conservation and restoration.

Measures adopted by OECD countries for agricultural landscape conservation and restoration can be categorised in three main types:

- *Economic incentives*, such as through area payments (*e.g.* Norwegian area and cultural landscape payments, see Annex Table 1) and management agreements based on individual agreements between farmers and regional/national authorities, where payments are provided in compensation for restrictions on certain farming practices and maintenance of key landscape features (*e.g.* the EU Environmentally Sensitive Area Schemes, see Bonnieux and Weaver, 1996).

- *Regulatory measures*, which may set certain minimum standards on the whole agricultural area and can designate certain areas of "high" landscape value as national parks or reserves, and impose restrictions on certain management practices for farmers in these areas (*e.g.* the national park system created both in *France*, see Bonnieux and Rainelli, 1996; and *Poland*, see FAO, 1999, pp. 204-205), or protect specific landscape features (*e.g.* the Hedgerow Regulations in the *United Kingdom*).

- *Community and voluntary based systems*, which set out to devolve the responsibility and management of natural resources, the environment and landscapes to farm families, rural communities and local governments (*e.g.* the *Australian* Landcare programme, see OECD, 1998, and Frost and Metcalf, 1999; and the *New Zealand's* Resource Management Act, see Williams, 2000).

Internationally, landscapes are also attracting attention. UNESCO started in 1993 to inscribe cultural landscapes on the World Heritage List, following the revision of criteria for cultural properties adopted at the 16th session of the World Heritage Committee in Santa Fe, 1992. The designation of UNESCO cultural landscape sites is based on the notion of "cultural tradition".[1] Other international agreements are also indirectly relevant to landscape including the International Convention on Biological Diversity, and the Ramsar Convention which concerns wetlands of international importance (see the Biodiversity chapter), and the UN Framework Convention on Climate Change.

At the regional level the Council of Europe's Pan-European Biological and Landscape Diversity Strategy has been endorsed by 55 *European* countries at the Ministerial Conference "Environment for Europe" held in Sofia in 1995. The Ministers of Environment called for "...the effects of agriculture on the environment to be recognised, and for agricultural practices to be conducive to the conservation and enhancement of biological and landscape diversity" (Council of Europe, 1998). In October 2000 European countries signed the European Landscape Convention (Council of Europe, 2000).

A challenge for policy makers in many OECD countries is to match the apparent imbalance between the demand for, and supply of, landscape. That is to say there is an increasing public demand for landscape and associated amenity goods and services linked to rising disposable incomes, more leisure time and other factors. However, farmers tend to undersupply landscape, which is a public good arising from agricultural activity, as they are usually unable to charge for its provision and may be unwilling to bear the cost of landscape conservation. Even so, for many farmers the maintenance and enhancement of landscape can also be an important aspiration in common with non-farming interests.

The essence of this policy challenge concerning landscape and other amenity values associated with agriculture, is that there is no "right" or "correct" level for the supply of these amenities (Bromley, 1997). Figure 1 depicts landscape as a continuum from the least to the most desirable landscape. The current situation is defined by L^* which is a momentary assessment of the amenity attributes of the landscape, while L_u is the landscape desired by non-farming interests, and L_f is the level of landscape that farmers consider they should provide in the absence of any legal restrictions and/or remuneration. It is between the points L_f and L_u that the political process will refer to resolve its disagreements, although many farmers also seek to maintain and restore landscape irrespective of remuneration.

Figure 1. **The policy space for landscape and other amenity values associated with agriculture**

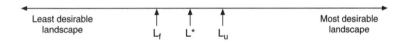

L_f: Level of landscape most farmers consider appropriate in the absence of any restrictions/remuneration.
L^*: Current momentary assessment of the amenity attributes of the landscape.
L_u: The landscape desired by non-farming interest.
Source: Bromley (1997).

The difficulty for policy makers is that there are few precise rules that indicate the "correct" or optimal provision of landscape. How much is optimal, precisely which landscape features does society value, and to what extent do changes in policies and policy mixes affect landscape? (Sinner, 1997). To help answer these questions indicators of agricultural landscapes provide a tool to better inform future policy decisions by recording the stock of landscape features, determining how these features are changing over time, establishing what share of agricultural land is under public/private schemes for landscape conservation, and measuring the cost of landscape provision by farmers and the value society attaches to agricultural landscapes.

Environmental context

Landscape definitions

Perceptions of landscape are rooted in history and local, regional and national cultures, and usually vary over time for the viewer and between different users of landscape, such as between farmers, environmentalists and urban dwellers (Cary, 2000). Agriculture plays a critical role in shaping and affecting the quality of the national "stock" of landscape, because in many OECD countries farming is

Figure 2. **Defining natural and cultural landscapes: the agricultural context**

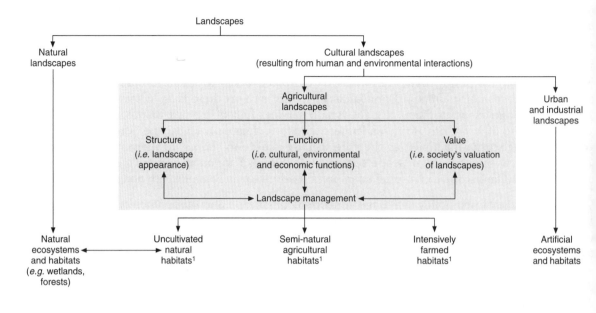

Field of main interest for OECD Agricultural Landscape Indicators.

1. These habitat categories are examined in the Wildlife Habitat chapter.

Source: OECD Secretariat and unpublished information from Dr. Hans-Peter Piorr (Center for Agricultural Landscape and Land Use Research Müncheberg, Germany).

the major user of land. What defines and constitutes an "agricultural landscape" varies greatly within and across OECD countries. A broad, all encompassing definition of agricultural landscapes is that the are the visible outcomes resulting from the interaction between agricultural commodity production natural resources and the environment, and encompass amenity, heritage, cultural, aesthetic and othe societal values.

Two broad types of landscape can be identified: first, "natural" landscape formed by various bio physical forces of nature (*e.g.* geology, soils, climate, habitat, etc); and second, man-made or "cultural" landscapes resulting from the interaction between human activity and the environment, in particula urban and agricultural landscapes (Figure 2). These interactions are dynamic: as technologies develop policies and economic forces change, cultural values evolve, and populations move. The fundamenta dynamic in creating and changing agricultural landscapes, however, is the need for agricultural products

Landscape structure, function and value

Despite the variety of individual, local, regional, and national interpretations of agricultura landscapes, three key elements are relevant to any landscape (Figure 3). These are:

- *structure*, including the interaction and relationship between various environmental feature (*e.g.* flora, fauna, habitats and ecosystems), land use patterns and distributions (*e.g.* crop type and systems of cultivation), and man-made objects (*e.g.* hedges, farm buildings);

- *function*, covering the provision of landscape functions for farmers and rural communities as place to live and work; for society at large as a place to visit and space for the enjoyment o various recreational activities; and also the function of landscape in providing variou environmental services, such as the provision of biodiversity, ecosystems, water supply, soi filtering and sink functions;

- *value*, concerning both the value society places on agricultural landscape, such as recreational, cultural, and other amenity values associated with landscape; and also, the costs of maintaining and enhancing landscape provision by agriculture.

The identification of these three elements can help to better organise the examination of agricultural landscapes to facilitate policy analysis and decision making. The *structural* landscape components provide the basis for landscape appearance and the connection to landscape functions. The latter have an important role in supporting the different societal *values* associated with landscape values.

There is no unique way in which the various structures and functions of landscapes shown in Figure 3 can be defined, classified and then valued. This will to a large extent depend on who is viewing the landscape and the purpose for which they wish to use and/or analyse landscape. Hence, the urban public tends to value the landscape from a general aesthetic, recreational and cultural perspective. The ecologist perceives landscape as primarily a provider of biodiversity and habitats. On the other hand, farmers, rural communities and ultimately consumers, are interested in, or at least benefit from, the economic value of a landscape related to the production of agricultural commodities and as a place to live and work.

Figure 3. **Key landscape elements: structure, function and value**

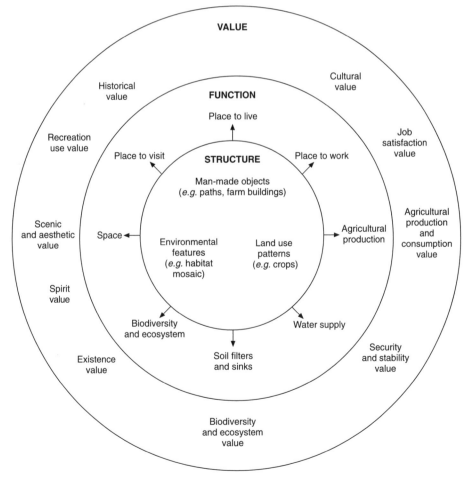

Source: Adapted from Bergstrom (1998).

Landscape typologies

Landscape typologies by drawing on various physical landscape descriptors – physical elements, environmental appearance, land use and man-made objects – can help to establish the basis for the spatial classification of landscape into homogenous units. Combining information from several descriptors can provide considerable interpretative power by highlighting landscape units with similar overall properties and potential for change. Landscape typologies can thus help to establish a useful holistic framework in which to examine the key elements and processes which affect landscape development, and also provide a useful benchmark against which to compare changes in landscapes. Even so, given that much research needs to be undertaken in developing landscape typologies, their potential use by policy makers is at a very early stage.

A considerable effort is underway in many OECD countries to develop landscape typologies in order to provide a framework and reference base for assessment and evaluation of landscapes by geographers, ecologists and land planners, in particular.[2] While national approaches vary in terms of objectives, scope and methodologies, they have a number of features in common, including:

- taking into account a large range of biophysical parameters, that can provide information to decision makers implementing and monitoring policies concerning agricultural landscape conservation;

- providing an information base for policy makers concerned with landscape conservation and land use planning issues;

- helping to resolve trade-off conflicts between "natural" habitat protection and agricultural development (*e.g.* wetlands); and,

- supplying information to help generate forecasts of future agricultural land use patterns.

With recent developments in geographical information systems, advances in information technologies, satellite land cover mapping, and multivariate statistical techniques, many countries are now able to build complex landscape typologies drawing on existing data sets. This has facilitated a better understanding of the relationship between geology, physical landforms, soil types, climate, biodiversity, habitats, and land use patterns.

Given the possibilities of developing complex land classification systems and the ability to analyse large quantities of data, this has also facilitated the assessment of land use and landscapes across a broad range of spatial scales from the field to the national level. Box 1 summarises the approach being adopted in *Canada* to the issue of examining landscape at different spatial scales.[3]

The geophysical characteristics of landscapes in terms of physical landforms (elevation, slopes, valley forms), soil types, surface water (ponds, rivers, lakes) and climate (temperature, precipitation) can be considered as stable features providing the first layer when developing a landscape typology. Farming systems are strongly influenced by these primary physical features of landscapes. Some countries are also trying to extend the biophysical data coverage of landscape typologies by including information on the socio-cultural and economic functions related to landscape, such as the impact of different farm management practices and systems.[4]

Combining various landscape descriptors into a single landscape typology will involve decisions, for example, about which data layers to include, whether to weight certain data layers, rules for locating unit boundaries, etc. This process is likely to be influenced by value judgements about which data are most important, for example, for a particular biological process or for the visual impression of the landscape. Illustrative, in this context, is how to determine the positive or negative impacts on agricultural landscapes of the conversion of agricultural land from/to other land uses, variations in cropping patterns on the visual appearance of the landscape, and changes in field structures, including alterations in the "openness" of the landscape. To a large extent, evaluation of whether changes are positive or negative will be dependent on local, regional and national targets.

The degree of subjectivity involved in a landscape typology will depend on the objective for establishing the typology. A typology that aims to indicate areas of similar crop production potential, for

---

Box 1. **The Canadian spatial ecological framework to classify agricultural landscapes**

Canada has developed a national spatial ecological framework, which is based on a nested hierarchy of spatial units that share similar geomorphologic, soil, vegetation and climate features. Each of these has subclassifications, for example, soils are classified by soil order group, geomorphology by physiographic or macro-landforms and vegetation by broad physiognomic types.

The Canadian framework comprises three levels of spatial detail: ecodistricts, ecoregions, and ecozones. Ecodistricts are broken down further by superimposing mapping units, called polygons, from Soil Landscapes of Canada (SLC) maps. A brief description of each level of this spatial hierarchy follows.

SLC *polygons*: These are mapping units from Agriculture and Agri-Food Canada's generalised soil maps of Canada (scale = 1:1 000 000). Polygon size varies throughout the country, being largest in the Prairies and smallest in Atlantic Canada. Data from the soil survey of Canada are stored at this level of detail.

Ecodistricts: These are groupings of soil landscape polygons that share similar climate and topography. Ecodistricts are a suitable level for storing generalised data about climate and cropping systems and sometimes for presenting the results of indicator calculations made at the more detailed SLC-polygon level.

Ecoregions: These are groupings of ecodistricts that share a similar range of regional climate and topography. Ecoregions have been used as the spatial level to summarise regional crop-management practices in order to estimate soil cover conditions through the year for all agricultural production systems in the country.

Ecozones: This broadest ecological class in the hierarchy is based on continental-scale topography and climate. Most agriculture in Canada is practised in two of Canada's 15 ecoregions: the Prairies and Mixed Wood Plain ecozones.

The Soil Landscape of Canada database holds detailed information on agricultural soil properties, as well as relevant information on agricultural production and management obtained from the national census of agriculture. The SLC database is used extensively for agri-environmental analysis in support of agricultural policy in Canada. For example, data are used to calculate agri-environmental indicators and to present areas at risk of degradation. Data are also used in many other applications, such as assessing vulnerable areas, as a basis for siting agricultural operations in suitable areas, etc.

Source: For a brief description of this system see Smith and McRae (2000) and for a more complete description see the CANSIS (Canadian Soil Information System) web site at: *http://res.agr.ca*/CANSIS/.

---

example, is likely to have a more solid theoretical and empirical basis and wider international applicability than a typology aiming to indicate areas of similar aesthetic appeal. To use a typology to describe the visual appearance of landscape it would seem preferable to define landscape units of homogeneous character without specifying whether these units are of high or low value.

The value of a landscape will often vary for different people, but the combination of physical features, land use, etc., that exist in the landscape are objective facts. Whatever the purpose of a typology, the process of combining data layers should be made transparent and repeatable, with the decision-rules for combining the fundamental physical data layers explicitly stated and open for discussion.

A limitation in the development of landscape typologies is the quantity of data required to build up the different layers that determine landscape appearance, although, as described above, the advent of new information technologies could greatly facilitate this task in future (Green, 2000). A further difficulty is encountered in trying to develop these data sets at an international level in terms of common definitions, data harmonisation and standardisation, in order to facilitate comparability of data sets. This problem could be eased by on-going efforts to establish harmonised terminology and definitions for different land cover nomenclatures and aggregations, such as the European CORINE Land Cover Directory (see Annex Table 2 in the Wildlife Habitats chapter).

371

Temporal considerations of landscapes

Temporal considerations are especially pertinent to policy makers concerned with the dynamics of the supply and demand for landscape, and with assessing the impacts on farmed landscapes of changes in policies and policy mixes. Moreover, the management of agricultural landscapes in terms of the different practices and systems used by farmers will have a considerable influence, not only on the structural appearance of landscape, but also on the type and composition of the functions and values associated with agricultural landscapes (*e.g.* ecosystems, recreational and scenic values, see Figure 3).

While there is a large spatial variation in landscape types within and across OECD countries reflecting variations in environmental and socio-economic conditions, a key difference between countries has been the rapidity with which landscapes have been modified over time (Figure 4). For *North America, Australia* and *New Zealand* the transformation of landscape from one impacted by hunter-gatherers to one dominated by modern agriculture has occurred within 200-400 years (Lefroy *et al.*, 2000). The same sequence of events over much of *Europe, Japan* and *Korea* took place over 10 000 years.

The transformation of agricultural landscapes over recent decades, however, has been subject to a set of new driving forces that are common to all OECD countries. Many of the socio-economic driving forces that are changing agricultural landscapes are external drivers, most importantly trade liberalisation, globalisation of trade and finance, vertical integration and concentration in the agro-food chain, new technologies, and greater population mobility and international tourism.

Landscape supply and demand

For most OECD countries there has been increasing demand from non-farming interests in the health of agricultural landscapes, for cultural, aesthetic, recreational and ecological reasons. Even so, different values may be placed on these aspects of landscape – locally, regionally, nationally and by

Figure 4. **A comparison across OECD countries of the progression from hunter-gatherer dominated landscapes through various historical stages of agricultural development**

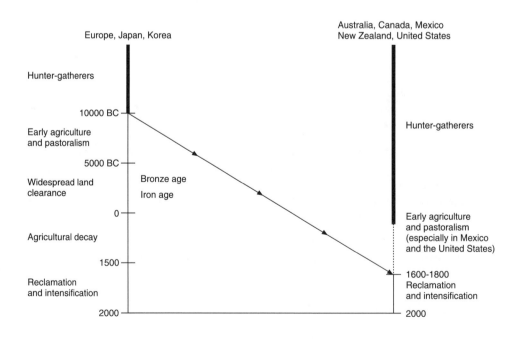

Source: Adapted from Lefroy *et al.* (2000).

each individual. Over recent decades the growing demand for landscape is mainly in response to rising incomes, increasing leisure time, greater personal mobility, and the impact of expanding urban areas stimulating demand for tranquillity and space in rural areas (Slangen, 1992).

At the same time, in the agricultural sector rising wages, technological progress and agricultural support levels have induced labour saving and production enhancing techniques. This has increased agricultural output and helped a smaller number of farmers to achieve incomes comparable to other sectors. These changes have been accompanied by a high level of mechanisation, intensification of land use, and specialisation of production at the farm and regional level (Oskam and Slangen, 1998).

The structural changes affecting agriculture have had two related, but highly different, consequences for agricultural landscapes over the past 50 years, in many OECD countries. Firstly, intensification of production has resulted in the widespread pollution of the environmental resource base and destruction of landscape features. Secondly, in marginal areas where farming is no longer remunerative agricultural landscapes have been transformed to other land uses and forms of landscape, especially forests (van Huylenbroeck and Whitby, 1999). Hence, as the supply and quality of biodiversity, wildlife habitats and landscape on agricultural land have been in decline, the demand for these amenities has increased.[5]

The inability of the market to match the supply and demand for landscape relates to the public good character of landscape and other rural amenities.[6] Most of the benefits of using and enjoying agricultural landscapes accrue to those who have not produced them, such as tourists. But it is usually difficult for farmers to charge for the costs of landscape provision, thus they may be unwilling to bear the cost of the conservation or restoration of landscapes that are most valued by society. For this reason markets tend to undersupply public goods, improving landscape quality in this case, relative to their demand (see also Figure 1). However, most farmers also enjoy living and working in an attractive landscape.

These longer term structural developments in OECD agricultural sectors over the past 50 years, have begun to show signs of changing since the late 1980s/early 1990s. From around this period many OECD countries started to introduce a range of agri-environmental measures, including certain schemes and measures addressing biodiversity, wildlife habitats and landscape concerns in agriculture (Annex Table 1).

Although it is still too early to fully assess the implications of these measures on landscape and related issues in agriculture, they would appear in some cases to have altered farm management practices and the pattern of land use. This has led to the conservation and restoration of certain high nature value habitats on agricultural land, the recovery in some populations of wildlife species, and the reduction in environmental impacts associated with farming, such as soil erosion and water pollution (see also the related discussion in the Soil Quality, Water Quality, Biodiversity and Wildlife Habitats chapters).

2. Indicators

The need for a holistic approach to develop indicators for analysing agricultural landscapes has been widely recognised by OECD countries. Toward this endeavour OECD is developing indicators that address the structural components, management and values associated with agricultural landscapes (Figure 2). In a field of research that is still at an early stage of development this approach is an initial step in establishing indicators as tools for policy monitoring and evaluation of agricultural landscape. The purpose of the OECD agricultural landscape indicators are to help:

- identify the main components that are commonly associated with agricultural landscapes *structure* (appearance);

- monitor the extent to which public/private *management* schemes have been introduced to maintain and restore these landscapes; and,

- measure the *value* society places on landscapes and the costs for farmers of maintaining or enhancing them.

The structure of landscapes

Environmental features and land use patterns

Definitions

1. *Environmental features*, encompassing mainly landscape habitats and ecosystems;

2. *Land use patterns*, including changes in agricultural land use patterns and distributions.

Method of calculation

Environmental features, concern the mosaic of habitats and ecosystems across a landscape. The presence of these elements and their spatial distribution can provide indirect information concerning the biodiversity and habitat functions of landscapes. This closely relates to other chapters in the Report on Biodiversity and Wildlife Habitats.

Land use patterns, include changes in total agricultural land use with other uses, such as forestry and urban development, which affects the total "stock" of agricultural landscapes. Also covered here is agricultural land use, describing the cropping patterns and systems on agricultural land. Agricultural land use is examined in both the chapters on Contextual Indicators and Wildlife Habitats.

Recent trends

It is not possible at this stage of development of landscape indicators to draw any firm conclusions regarding the current state and trends in the structure of agricultural landscapes across OECD countries. Even so, there does seem to be a widespread view that there has been a trend towards the increasing homogenisation of agricultural landscape structures over the past 50 years. For a large number of countries this trend appears closely related to the structural changes and intensification of agricultural production, linked with the degradation of the natural resource base in agriculture, especially water and soil, and the damaging impacts to biodiversity and wildlife habitats.[7] In some cases, however, the public may appreciate more homogenous agricultural landscapes, such as semi-natural grassland.[8]

There are signs, however, that the process toward an increasing homogeneity of agricultural landscapes could be slowing, or even in reverse in some regions of certain countries. As discussed previously, since the period around the late 1980s/early 1990s many OECD countries started to introduce a range of agri-environmental measures, including some that specifically seek to maintain and enhance biodiversity, wildlife habitats and landscapes in agriculture (Annex Table 1).

Interpretation and links to other indicators

A key aspect to developing indicators of landscape structure is determining at which spatial scale it is meaningful and policy relevant to collect and analyse such data. Approaches vary between countries as to how to tackle the issue of spatial scale, in some cases the emphasis is to focus on coarse-grained large spatial scales, while for others more attention is paid to smaller-scale dimensions and fine-grained landscape scales.

There are a number of attempts to interpret the spatial configuration of landscapes by using statistical measures of landscape structure (see for example, European Commission, 1999). This includes, for example, measuring patch density (the sum of the number of patches of each patch class on a per area basis), edge density (the length of borders between different patch types/classes related to a standard unit), and the Shannon diversity index (the number of different patch types/classes and the proportional distribution of area among patch types).[9] While these statistical measures of landscape can serve to describe the structure of landscape, they leave open the problem of interpreting changes in these indicators in terms of what is a positive/negative change in landscape structure.

Another possibility to establish structural landscape indicators is to define and measure the most important on-going processes by which agriculture affects landscape, including (an example of this approach, drawn from Sweden, is shown in Figure 5):

- Expansion-Contraction in the total area of agricultural land.
- Intensification-Extensification of agricultural production.
- Concentration-Marginalisation of farm holdings.

The on-going processes affecting landscape described above are usually linked, as in the case of agricultural marginalisation and land converted from agriculture to other uses, for example. They also operate on all scales from the farm to the national level. Such an approach enables landscape indicator

Figure 5. **National and regional physical landscape indicators: A Swedish approach, 1951 to 1995**

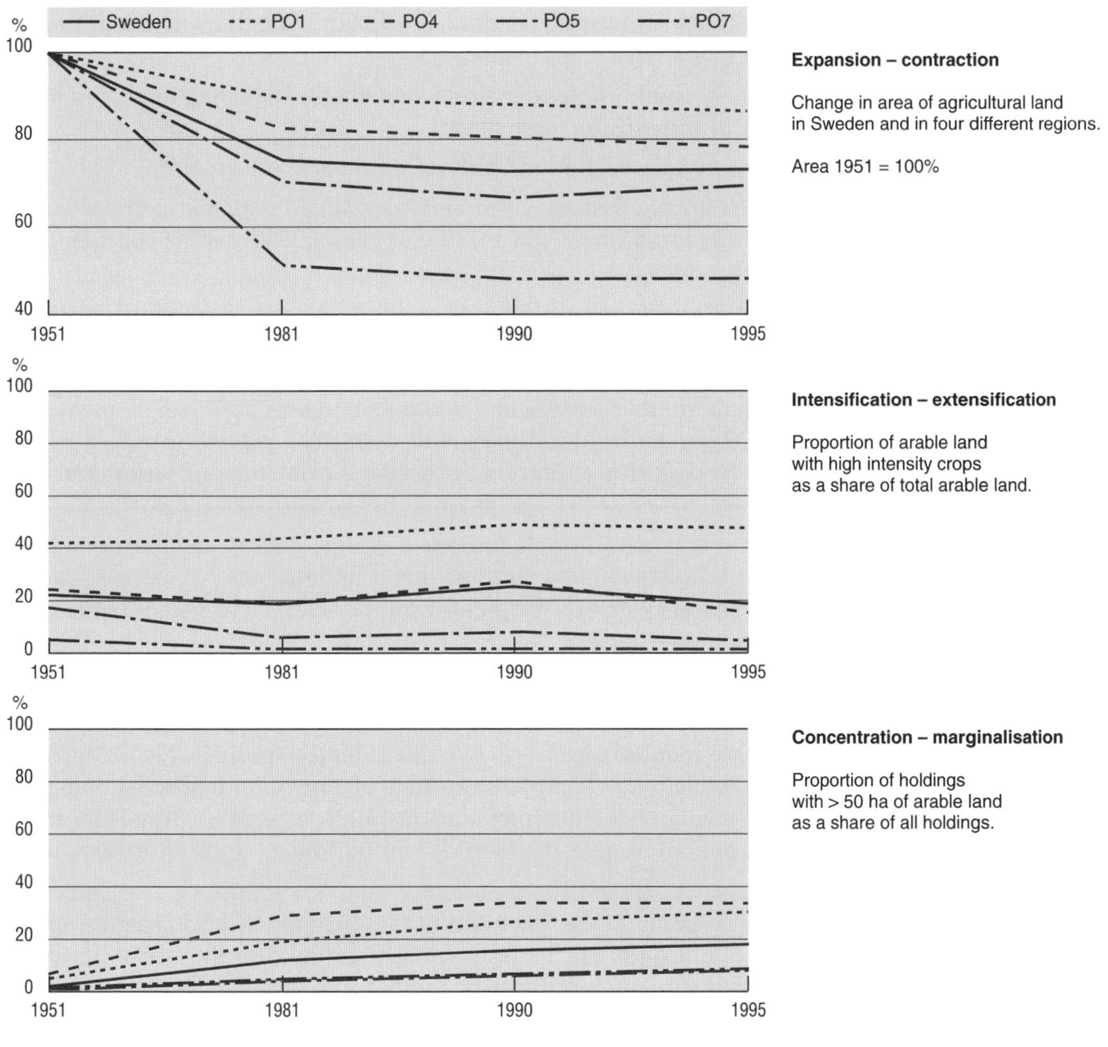

Legend: — Sweden · · · · PO1 – – PO4 — · PO5 — · · PO7

Expansion – contraction

Change in area of agricultural land in Sweden and in four different regions.

Area 1951 = 100%

Intensification – extensification

Proportion of arable land with high intensity crops as a share of total arable land.

Concentration – marginalisation

Proportion of holdings with > 50 ha of arable land as a share of all holdings.

Note: PO1, PO4, PO5, PO7, refer to regional areas of Sweden, respectively: Southern plain districts of Gotaland, Plain districts of Svealand, Forest region of Gotaland, and Lower Norrland.
Source: Drawn from a paper presented by Goran Blom (Swedish Environmental Protection Agency) to the OECD Workshop on Agri-environmental Indicators, York, United Kingdom, September 1998.

development to focus on some of the most policy relevant and significant impacts of agriculture on landscape, that can be determined on a country by country basis.

Much of the information required for the structural description of agricultural landscapes can be drawn directly from other indicator areas. This includes, in particular, the indicators related to wildlife habitats, but also contextual indicators concerning agricultural land use.

Man-made objects

Definition

Key indicative man-made objects (cultural features) on agricultural land resulting from human activity.

Method of calculation

This indicator provides the flexibility to be determined according to different regional and national situations and priorities, and provides an initial step to reflect the cultural functions and values of landscapes.[10] To help develop a more structured approach for this indicator, information can be collected in terms of the following groups, where applicable:

- *point elements*, such as "traditional" buildings and historic monuments on agricultural land and new buildings with a high ecological and architectural value;
- *linear elements*, for example dry stonewalls, hedges, and transhumance tracks; and,
- *area elements*, such as alpine meadows, historic sites, and specialised regional land use patterns, for example the Iberian dehesa (a traditional spaced tree agroforestry system of southern Portugal and Spain, see Ridley and Joffre, 2000).

An important consideration in identifying cultural features that are policy relevant, is that they should be clearly linked to an agricultural activity. Hedgerows on agricultural land are an example where the quality and quantity of hedges are affected by farm management practices and in some countries schemes have been implemented to restore and maintain hedges. Moreover, it might also be possible to distinguish between those cultural features with historical associations (*e.g.* old farm buildings) and those considered to be cultural features stemming from current farming activities (*e.g.* stonewalls).

Another aspect related to the cultural features of landscape concerns the recreational functions and values associated with landscape. For many OECD countries this is an important objective of national policy measures aiming to meet societal demands for greater public access and use of landscapes in agricultural areas for recreational and related uses.

Recent trends

A number of OECD countries are monitoring trends in cultural landscape features on agricultural land (Table 1). For some countries, Australia for example, they have just begun the process of establishing indicators in this area, by drawing together information from cultural heritage inventories (*e.g.* historic sites such as burial mounds), registers (*e.g.* old farm buildings) and other relevant data sources (Pearson *et al.*, 1998).

For those countries where it is relevant, hedgerows and other types of field boundaries, are used as cultural landscape indicators, as hedges are usually recognised as defining local agricultural landscape character with important historical, biodiversity and habitat linkages. Hedges are also the direct product of agricultural farming practices and their policy importance is high in view of a number of schemes that are now operating to protect and manage hedges. This is also an indicator that is relatively easily quantified, is rapidly changing, and has a public resonance.

The United Kingdom has taken this approach in monitoring changes in field boundary features including hedges (Box 2). Agricultural policy in the UK has moved from encouragement of boundary

Table 1. **Cultural landscape features on agricultural land: 1985 to 1998**

	Unit	1985	1990	1995	1998
Denmark[1]					
Quantity					
– Farm buildings, farm yards	Hectares	. .	. .	80 000	. .
– Hedgerows, ditches and field roads[2]	Hectares	. .	. .	c. 120 000	. .
– Burial mounds (tumuli)	Numbers	. .	. .	c. 30 000	. .
Greece					
Quantity					
– Terraces	Hectares	. .	. .	250 000	. .
Japan					
Quantity					
– Paddy fields (terraced + in valleys)	Hectares	220 000	. .	. .	. .
Norway					
Quantity					
– Buildings from before 1900 that are associated with agricultural activities	Numbers	. .	. .	. .	540 000
– Legally protected buildings associated with agricultural activities	Numbers	. .	. .	. .	c. 2 250
– Summer mountain farms with dairy production[3]	Numbers	. .	2 563	2 635	2 719
Poland					
Quantity					
– Group of trees	Numbers	2 611	3 193	4 222	4 482
– Old isolated trees	Numbers	10 035	18 876	26 423	30 811
– Tourist tracks	Km	25 873	28 355	26 725	. .
Spain					
Quantity					
– Dehesas[4]	Hectares	1 400 000	. .	. .	. .
– Transhumance tracks	Km	125 000	. .	. .	. .
United Kingdom[5]					
Quantity[6]					
– Banks/grass strips (GB)	Km	57 600	59 800	. .	. .
– Dry stone walls (GB)	Km	210 300	188 100	. .	. .
– Managed hedgerows (E&W)	Km	563 100	431 800	377 500	. .
– Relict hedgerows (GB)	Km	52 600	83 100	. .	. .
– Lowland ponds (GB)	Numbers	239 000	230 900	228 900	. .
Quality					
– Dry stone walls (E)[7]	% in poor condition	. .	. .	51	. .

. Circa.
. . Not available.
1. Denmark includes 14th and 15th century churches as cultural landscape features in agricultural areas.
2. Hedges are measured in terms of area, rather than length, as they usually consist of 3-7 rows of trees and large bushes.
3. Number of farms that own or have a share in a mountain farm are determined from the applications made for production subsidies for summer-mountain farming with dairy production with a minimum of 4 weeks.
4. Dehesas refer to wooded pastures and open grassland, used for grazing, crop cultivation and forest products.
5. E: England, W: Wales, GB: Great Britain.
6. Data for 1985 and 1995 refer respectively to 1984 and 1996. The data on length of linear features and number of ponds are net figures for the units defined, for example, for hedges the net figure is the balance between the numbers removed and the numbers of new hedges planted or restored.
7. The percentage refers to the year 1993.
Sources: Norwegian Grain Corporation (unpublished); OECD Agri-environmental Indicators Questionnaire, 1999.

removal to support for restoration (MAFF, 2000). The UK Biodiversity Action Plan has set targets to maintain the length and condition of ancient and species rich hedgerows and the number of hedgerow trees. This is supported by the UK Countryside Stewardship Scheme and Environmentally Sensitive Areas Scheme, which both include payments for the maintenance and restoration of landscape features.

Interpretation and links to other indicators

The downward trend in such an indicator would be considered an undesirable development and a diminution of the cultural function of agricultural landscapes. An example might be the loss of historic

Box 2. **Field boundaries as agricultural landscape indicators in the United Kingdom**

Field boundaries are often seen as defining features of landscape character in the UK, adding local distinctiveness, which is widely appreciated. As well as their contribution to the character of the landscape, field boundaries are important as a habitat for animals and plants, providing food and shelter and acting as corridors for the movement of some species. They are often the oldest remaining feature in the countryside, providing important evidence of the historic development of the landscape. Agriculture policy in the UK has shifted from encouragement of boundary removal to support for restoration and planting. Legislation was introduced in 1997 for the protection of important hedges.

Stock and change in agricultural field boundaries: 1984 to 1990

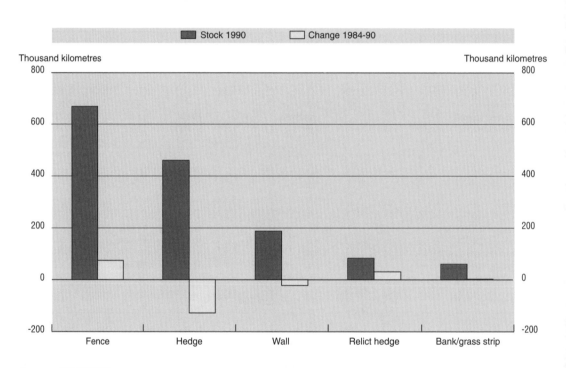

Source: MAFF (2000).

The estimated length of hedges and walls in Britain in 1990 were 462 000 km and 188 000 km, respectively. Between 1984 and 1990, an estimated 129 000 km of hedges and 22 000 km of walls were either removed, incorporated in development or changed to another boundary type. In detail, about 66% of hedges were unchanged between 1984 and 1990; 7% became relict hedges; 15% were converted to fence lines or other boundaries and 11% were removed or incorporated in development. For walls about 75% were unchanged; 14% were converted to fence lines or other boundaries and 9% were removed or incorporated in development. The total length of post and wire fence increased by 74 000 km and the total length of relict hedge increased by 31 000 km. It is too early to say whether changes in policy since the late 1990s will be sufficient to halt the trend of decline in traditional hedged landscapes in Britain.

Source: Adapted from a paper presented by Andrew Stott (UK Department of Environment) to the OECD Workshop on Agri-environmental Indicators, York, United Kingdom, September 1998; see also MAFF (2000).

monuments and sites on agricultural land. The interpretation of trends in this indicator, however, ultimately depends on what society determines are culturally important features on agricultural land which, in turn, is a reflection of public cultural and heritage values and aesthetic preferences. At present there are no systematic national efforts to measure these preferences and values, although some countries are exploring the use of public surveys and various valuation techniques to measure the importance and preferences the public attach to agricultural landscape, as discussed below.

The criteria by which countries have chosen to include the cultural features shown in Table 1 are not always clear, although the United Kingdom, for example, has set out such criteria as described above. Moreover, while in many cases the quantity of cultural features is recorded, information on the impact of agriculture on the quality of these features is more limited (*e.g.* point features such as buildings). In other cases, it may be uncertain the extent to which agricultural activity is the major cause of improvement or deterioration in certain cultural features (*e.g.* some linear features such as tracks and paths).

It is also important in interpreting changes in indicators of cultural features, to distinguish between reversible and irreversible changes. Hence, a loss in dry stone walls, for example, is potentially reversible as they can be replaced, but the loss of an historic building, monument or site is clearly irreversible, and thus, a permanent loss to a nation's cultural heritage.

Data layers on key indicative cultural features can be added to landscape typologies. Clearly, the more data layers that are added, the greater the complexity in interpreting and using a typology and the greater the number of decision-rules required (see above). However, cultural features are of obvious importance in any assessment of overall landscape character.

Certain cultural features on agricultural land, such as alpine meadows and lengths of hedgerows, are included by some countries as part of their surveys of agricultural habitats, as described in the Wildlife Habitats chapter. There is also a link here with the impact of farm management practices on cultural features in the landscape, in terms of their conservation and restoration.

Landscape management

Definition

The share of agricultural land under public and private schemes committed to landscape maintenance and enhancement.

Method of calculation

The information for this indicator includes the share of the total agricultural land area (or number of farms), covered by public/private schemes or plans that provide a commitment to landscape maintenance and enhancement. The indicator is calculated annually as a percentage share of the total area (number) of agricultural land (farms). In addition, it is important to know the objectives and annual expenditure (lump sum payments) of these schemes and plans. It is also useful to include those public/private initiatives intended to maintain/enhance agricultural landscapes that are based on regulatory measures and those using community/voluntary approaches (see discussion above).

Recent trends

Adoption of public and private schemes for the conservation and restoration of agricultural landscapes is now widespread across OECD countries, as summarised in Annex Table 1. For those countries that are engaged in such landscape management schemes, they are commonly funded through governments, although there are some exceptions to this with co-financing by both public and private sources.

The public expenditure on these schemes tends to be a minor share of total agricultural support levels (as measured by the OECD's Producer Support Estimate, see notes to Annex Table 1). However, in a number of cases the expenditure in this area has been increasing rapidly over recent years,

379

especially as in many instances landscape measures have only recently been implemented (see also the section on public and private agri-environmental expenditure in the Farm Financial Resource chapter). In a large number of cases the objectives of the schemes cover multiple aims, in particular concerning biodiversity, wildlife habitats and landscape conservation.

It is beyond the scope of this Report to provide an assessment of landscape management schemes, although it is possible to make a number of general observations concerning the operation of these schemes. Where areas under landscape schemes are designated for landscape and/or nature protection it is not always certain to what extent they are farmed or if farmers in these areas are subject to regulatory or other measures that limit farming practices that are detrimental to landscapes. The focus of many schemes is on biophysical and cultural features in agricultural landscapes, but some countries are beginning to include public access requirements in landscape programmes. It is also possible that community/voluntary based initiatives aimed an enhancing landscapes may go unreported. There are few cases where countries apply schemes or measures for landscape conservation that cover the total agricultural land area, instead they are usually applied to relatively small and selected areas (Annex Table 1).

Norway, however, has some measures for landscape conservation that cover the entire agricultural area, which include conditions that must be fulfilled in order to qualify for "Acreage and cultural landscape support" a type of financial support granted to all holdings with an area of at least 1 hectare. The measures include the prohibition of diverting rivers and streams and cultivating open ditches; the edges of woodland, ecotones and other residual uncultivated areas may not be cultivated; limits on removing, levelling or cultivating islands of natural vegetation in fields, dry-stone walls, cairns, old roads and footpaths; and ecotone vegetation shall not be sprayed with pesticides. The farmer is also required to comply with legislation aimed at restricting agricultural pollution, *e.g.* regulation requiring plans for fertiliser management, preserving cultural features, and a provision to require cattle to be on pasture for a minimum of 8 weeks each summer. Compliance with these conditions is monitored by checks of 5 per cent of agricultural holdings annually, and if a farmer is found to have contravened these provisions/regulations, grants may be withdrawn for up to three years.

In *Austria*, under the agri-environmental programme (EU Regulation 2078/92), a number of national measures affect landscape. These include: mowing in steep and mountainous areas, alpine and pastoral premiums, the conservation of ecologically valuable areas, landscape development on permanent fallow (20 years), and providing areas with ecological goals (see also Box 1 in the Farm Management chapter).

Interpretation and links to other indicators

It is assumed that the greater the area (or number) of farms covered by public and private landscape initiatives, the better will be the maintenance of, or improvement in, landscape quality. However, the absence of a public/private scheme for landscape conservation does not necessarily imply that a problem exists with landscape quality. Many farmers take a pride in the visual appearance of their farm, irrespective of whether such schemes exist. In addition, these schemes require empirical analysis in the light of their impact on landscape quality.

In the *United States*, for example, Nassauer (1989) suggests herbicide may be applied by certain farmers to achieve a weed free appearance, in excess of the margin required for crop protection, to make the farm look attractive. On the other hand, for some farmers the untidy appearance of perennial cover, at least in comparison with neat straight rows of maize, may influence farmers' decisions to participate in the US Conservation Reserve Program.

Moreover, these schemes frequently target more than just one area, and may cover, for example multiple biodiversity, wildlife habitats and landscape objectives (Annex Table 1). It might also be important to ascertain to what extent areas under government schemes are better managed in terms of landscape conservation compared with similar areas outside these schemes.

The management of landscape also relates to those indicators covering farm management; rural viability, such as the educational level of farmers influencing their choice and knowledge of certain practices; and the farm financial resources available to farmers to undertake landscape conservation and enhancement.

Landscape costs and benefits

Definitions

1. The cost of maintaining or enhancing landscape provision by agriculture.
2. The public valuation of agricultural landscapes.

Method of calculation

Measuring the **costs of landscape provision** can help policy makers determine the outlays by farmers in maintaining and/or restoring certain landscape elements. These costs may relate to cultural and heritage features, such as spending by farmers on the conservation of historic sites and/or buildings on farmland. However, expenditure could also involve costs incurred in hedge or stone wall maintenance that, while providing a positive externality in terms of the landscape, may also generate benefits for the farmer, for example, by providing a windshield for crops and livestock.

The costs incurred by farmers in maintaining and restoring landscapes are on occasions covered in the management schemes outlined in the previous section. For some European Union agri-environmental programmes, for example, provision is made to compensate for some of these costs (*e.g.* costs incurred in the restoration of farm buildings for use by tourists).

Establishing the **value society places on agricultural landscapes** can assist policy makers in determining the benefits of landscape conservation and restoration. Because of the lack of market prices to help value the public demand for landscape amenities, other methods must be employed to serve this purpose which usually include:

- *public opinion surveys*, to ascertain public preferences for landscapes;
- *consumer expenditure patterns*, covering expenditures by the public in using landscapes (*e.g.* expenditures for recreation and tourism purposes);
- *non-market valuation*, commonly employed by economists, including the hedonic price, travel cost and contingent valuation methods, to provide a monetary value of societal landscape preferences.

Public opinion surveys are used by governments for some OECD countries, to provide socio-economic information on public preferences for landscape and other environmental amenities. Such surveys are usually sample based interviews that aim to collect information related to, for example, the importance and preferences of one landscape type compared to another, the use and frequency of enjoying landscapes for recreational purposes such as walking.

In some cases systematic collection of data on *landscape related expenditures* are collected at sub-national or national levels to assist policy decision-makers in determining the economic value stemming from the public use of landscapes. Public expenditures related to landscape can include outlays on farm based tourist accommodation, entry costs to farmed national parks, and the costs of travelling to scenic areas in agricultural regions.

As landscapes are not normally traded in markets, economists have developed a number of techniques for estimating the *non-market economic value of landscape* and other non-marketed goods and services. These techniques help to estimate the various consumer values attached to landscape (Figure 3) and other non-marketed environmental goods and services. These values include: *"use" value*, which relates to how people are prepared to pay for an improvement in the landscapes which benefit them directly, such as for recreational purposes; *"option" value*, which is the value placed on the possibility of using a landscape benefit in the future; and, the *"existence" value* of landscape, which is the willingness to pay to ensure the landscape is maintained, irrespective of any independent expectation of ever using or seeing the landscape now or in the future (OECD, 1994).

The most commonly used techniques to value landscapes are the hedonic price, travel cost and contingent valuation method (CVM).[11] The first two techniques use a revealed preference approach that seeks to find some indirect reflection of landscape value in a market for other goods, while CVM uses an expressed preference approach where people express their hypothetical valuation of landscape.

The *hedonic price method* decomposes the observed value of goods, such as property, into various attributes including landscape amenity that may influence or be reflected indirectly in property prices. The *travel cost method* uses the cost incurred by people in visiting a particular landscape site, including lost earnings from the time visiting the site, travel costs and any entry fees to the site, as a revealed measure of the value users place on the landscape. The *contingent valuation method* is a more direct way of estimating people's valuation of landscape, by using a public opinion survey to measure the money use and non-use values that the people surveyed place on a particular landscape.

Recent trends

Data covering the labour and investment *costs incurred by farmers in landscape maintenance* and restoration is, however, extremely limited, only the *Netherlands* is known to collect this information. This absence of data could be an impediment to the future evaluation of the costs of landscape provision and also make it difficult to assess the level of payments that might be made to farmers under landscape conservation schemes.

The use of *public opinion surveys* and questionnaires to gauge societal preferences for agricultural landscapes are being employed by some OECD countries. For a number of countries this involve regular national government surveys to monitor the importance of biodiversity, wildlife habitats and landscape to society, as in *Canada*, for example (Environment Canada, 1999; and Smith and McRae, 2000 pp. 23-24). In other cases these surveys are conducted more irregularly (*e.g. Poland*), limited to local or regional investigations that focus on specific landscape types (*e.g. Japan*, see Tanokura *et al.*, 1999), or focus on specific programmes aimed at determining agricultural landscape preferences (*e.g. Finland* see Hietala-Koivu *et al.*, 1999).

Researchers have also investigated public perceptions of agricultural landscapes through interviews. In a study of rural residents in the Mid-West *United States*, Nassauer (1989) found three dominant themes that residents used to describe whether an agricultural landscape was viewed as attractive or unattractive. These included: *scenic quality*, such as expansive views, a mix of different land uses, including unfarmed areas; *neatness*, for example, the absence of weeds, mown roadsides, straight rows of crops; and *stewardship*, which like neatness reflects on the farmer, such as stripcropping and complex field or cropping patterns.

A similar study in *Australia* (Cary, 2000) gives support to the US research. It found that many people perceive agricultural landscapes that include patches of "native" vegetation and areas such as fallow that are left uncultivated, as uninteresting and mistakenly perceive them as illustrating a lack of care although such areas and patches on farmland may be encouraging a rich and diverse biodiversity.

A systematic framework to develop national level agricultural landscape indicators, using public opinion surveys, is under development in *Japan*. This framework involves essentially three steps: *i)* the classification of landscapes by using biophysical data; *ii)* evaluation of landscape types by conducting public surveys to identify perceptions and preferences for different landscapes; and *iii)* the development of indicators based on the previous steps to help determine landscape conservation and management strategies (Yokohari *et al.*, 1994).

There appears to be very limited information available on *landscape related consumer expenditures* across OECD countries. A few countries collect data related to public expenditures on rural tourism and cost of travelling to "scenic" landscapes (*e.g. Austria* and *Germany*).

A selective overview of studies regarding the *monetary valuation of agricultural landscape* and wildlife conservation is provided in Annex Table 2. The results shown in the table are based on the contingent valuation method (CVM), mainly drawing on the surveys made by Bonnieux and Weaver (1996); Oskam and Slangen (1998); and Santos (1998). The authors stress the need to interpret these CVM results with care, although it is possible to draw a number of conclusions from these studies.[12]

While there is a large variation of values displayed in Annex Table 2, it does reveal that agricultural landscapes are a valued externality arising from agricultural activity for a large number of countries. Moreover, the landscape surveyed "today" is the preferred landscape, while the willingness-to-pay (WTP) to maintain a particular landscape decreases with increasing distance from a particular site. Heterogeneity in landscapes is given a higher value over more uniform landscapes, while "traditional" elements in landscapes are valued more highly than new elements. As confirmed by the public opinion surveys discussed above, the CVM studies show that areas with a high biodiversity value are not always the most highly valued landscapes. These valuation studies also have a strong anthropocentric element, and accessible landscapes are valued more highly than inaccessible landscapes of the same quality.

The CVM studies in Annex Table 2 also reveal that landscapes perceived as overcrowded have a lower value. Increasing landscape and/or wildlife areas above a certain threshold reduces its per-hectare valuation, and wildlife areas under government schemes have a lower value than private wildlife areas, while expenditure on environmental goods, such as landscape, is more income elastic than expenditure on food. Some national CVM studies suggest the method is useful for long-run policy measures concerning landscapes, at least for a decade, although whether this conclusion is transferable between countries and future generations is unclear (Hasund, 1998).

Interpretation and links to other indicators

While all these methods of measuring consumer preferences for landscapes and their cost of provision have limitations, they do provide the foundation for the quantitative evaluation of the supply and demand for landscape. That is to say, such approaches and indicators can help provide subjective evaluations of landscapes based on economic costs and benefits expressed in monetary terms, with the exception of public opinion surveys. Developing landscape indicators in this way may assist policy makers to determine the importance attached to landscape values by society, and also help address the various trade-offs between the costs and benefits of encouraging farmers to maintain and improve the quality of landscapes.

Some caution, however, is required in interpreting valuation estimates for landscapes. In the case of *public opinion surveys* (which do not usually provide monetary estimates of landscape value) there may be a range of problems, including the sample size of the survey, the regularity with which the survey is repeated and how survey questions are phrased in affecting responses. Also such surveys are susceptible to public views that an agricultural landscape which appears not to be cared for may have a low value, but in terms of biodiversity and wildlife habitat it can have a high value.[13] In the case of *consumer expenditure* in using landscape, care is required to distinguish between landscapes in areas of high touristic value and more remote agricultural areas where consumer expenditure may be much lower.

While considerable progress has been made by economists in refining *non-market valuation techniques*, current evidence suggests that policy makers are still somewhat reluctant to use these methods in policy formulation, instead preferring to use them as only a contribution to inform the policy making process. This, in part, reflects concern that public preferences for landscapes may be transient and not take into account other objectives of agricultural policy such as rural development and food security.

It is also unlikely at present that these valuation estimates can be deployed rapidly enough and with sufficient sensitivity to fully inform cost-benefit considerations of landscape and other environmental amenities (Heimlich *et al.*, 1998, p. 17). Additionally, valuation estimates may be complicated by different attitudes in society towards monetary wealth superimposed on varying preferences for landscapes, which can make it impossible to use such estimates for purposes of international comparability.

The valuation of landscapes and the cost of their provision, is closely related to similar issue raised in the context of biodiversity and wildlife habitat indicators, while aspects concerning farm landscape expenditure are linked with the farm financial resources indicator.

3. Future challenges

The process of nationally and internationally establishing indicators to monitor the state and changes in agricultural landscapes is at an early stage of development. There is, however, an active process underway in many countries and international organisations to develop a better understanding of the agricultural landscape issue. To better inform policy decision making in the landscape context further research might be strengthened in a number of key directions outlined below.

Information and data sources being established in other indicator areas, in particular indicator covering changes in agricultural land use and land cover, biodiversity, wildlife habitats, and farm management, could be drawn upon to help develop landscape indicators. In this context identifying more precisely the *linkages* with other indicators, especially biodiversity and wildlife habitats, will be crucial to the development of a coherent set of landscape indicators. It is clear that biodiversity, wildlife habitat and landscape processes, structures, functions and values have critical linkages, but past research has given little attention to these relationships (Mac *et al.*, 1998, Vol. I, pp. 31-32). Linked to this effort is the importance of harmonising amongst countries landscape definitions and the standardisation of related databases.

Improving understanding of the linkages between the various elements that create landscapes – *i.e.* structure, function and value – will also help to better explain and identify the cause and effect relationships that are changing agricultural landscapes. Underlying this analysis, and an issue that deserves special attention in the policy sphere, is that the public demand for landscape in general is to maintain heterogeneity, while the process of expanding and improving the efficiency of agricultural production tends to lead to landscape homogeneity. In some cases, however, a homogenous landscape can be highly valued by the public (*e.g.* grassland).

There is an active discussion in the scientific community as to the consequences of altering the mix between heterogeneity and homogeneity in the context of biodiversity (Mac, *et al* 1998, Vol. I, pp. 32). This discussion might provide useful insights in the case of the landscape issue, so that it is possible to evolve beyond stereotyped "industrial agricultural" and "garden of Eden" views of landscape, to a more positive discussion of examining landscape in the wider context of sustainable agriculture (Williams, 2000).

The development of *landscape typologies and classification systems*, holds the possibility of providing a framework and reference base for landscape assessment and evaluation. This enables the spatial delineation of homogenous landscape units which can capture the site-specific character of landscape necessary in those cases where agri-environmental measures are used for landscape conservation. There are a number of limitations with this approach, especially the problem of developing complex databases that seek to summarise and standardise many elements of the landscape issue. One approach that could help overcome this limitation over the short term, could be, as described above, to identify and measure the most important on-going processes by which agriculture affects landscape such as changes in agricultural land use, intensification of production, and trends in the concentration of agricultural holdings.

Indicators of the *cultural features of agricultural landscape* reveal that there is the possibility to further develop these indicators, as many countries have inventories, registers and other data sources relevant to the area. Before these indicators can be become more widely accepted and comparable across countries, it will be necessary to develop criteria to help better establish which cultural features of agricultural land should be monitored. These criteria would mainly include determining whether the designated cultural feature: *i*) is commonly recognised as defining regional/national agricultural landscape character; *ii*) the direct product of agricultural activities or is clearly associated with agriculture; *iii*) is linked to a particular public/private landscape conservation initiative or measure; *iv*) can be easily quantified; and *v*) has public resonance.

Concerning indicators related to the *management of agricultural landscape*, this seems to be an area where existing information and data could be further exploited, especially those covering government measures that address landscape issues in agriculture. While information does exist concerning the payments to farmers for biodiversity, wildlife habitat and landscape conservation, it is not always clear as to the precise objectives of these measures, nor the methods by which they are being monitored and evaluated. Further information on regulatory measures, community/voluntary approaches and private initiatives in the landscape area would also be valuable, so that countries could share different experiences in addressing landscape conservation issues.

One way in policy makers in can determine the costs and benefits of agricultural landscape conservation is through the use of various *landscape valuation* techniques. While information on public landscape expenditures, such as on rural tourism and the labour and investment costs incurred by farmers in landscape maintenance and restoration, appear limited, this is an area where possibly data sources have not been fully investigated or systematically collected. Some caution would be required, however, in using data related to such expenditures between regions of high touristic interest and less accessible remote areas, and also because of significant differences in the level of income between OECD countries.

With regard to the *non-market valuation* of consumer landscape preference, there remain considerable limitations concerning methodologies and approaches to achieve this. For example, it may be difficult to separate the relative importance of attitudes to money, cultural expectations and norms in differing attitudes to valuing landscape.

The brief review of the contingent valuation method (CVM) studies in this chapter provides evidence that landscape valuation is possible at broad regional/national scales and that these studies can help to better inform the policy debate on landscape. A more comprehensive, consistent and systematic effort to review non-market valuations of agricultural landscapes could be undertaken to build on the work reviewed here. The utility of CVM and other such techniques might also be improved through an international effort to develop guidelines that would seek to harmonise data collection and valuation approaches. This would help to improve both the confidence and comparability of results from CVM studies within and across countries.

NOTES

1. The UNESCO World Heritage Convention can be found online at: *www.unesco.org/whc/* For a discussion of landscapes related to World Heritage Sites, see Mitchell and Buggey (2000).

2. In *Europe*, for example, the European Soil Bureau has undertaken extensive research concerning land use information systems as they relate to landscapes, see EEA (1995); Heineke *et al.* (1998); Meeus *et al.* (1990); van Mansvelt and van der Lubbe (1999); and Wascher (1997; and 2000). For *Norway*, see Puschmann (1998); and Countryside Commission (1993) for work on the countryside character of *England*. In the context of *Australia*, see Hamblin (2000) and for the *United States*, see Mac *et al.* (1998).

3. For further examination of technical issues related to the spatial description of landscape, see for example Haines-Young *et al.* (1996) in the UK context. Dramstad and Lagbu (2000) and Puschmann (1998) also examine the spatial issue in *Norway*, and discuss the various layers required to develop a landscape typology. Wrbka *et al.* (1999) also elaborates a set of indicators to reflect the spatial structure of landscapes in *Austria*.

4. *Germany*, for example, has developed a system of landscape maps consisting of 68 individually defined landscapes aggregated to five main landscape regions to cover the whole country. An extensive survey and mapping of agricultural landscapes in *Norway* has been made by Puschmann (1998) with associated socio-economic analysis by Nersten *et al.* (1999).

5. Examples of this process of structural change in agriculture over the past 50 years and its impact on biodiversity, habitats and landscape is discussed in the case of *Norway*, for example, by Olsson and Ronningen (1999, pp. 21-26); and in *Sweden* by Bjorklund *et al.*, (1999). See also the discussion on the process of increasing intensification of agriculture in the Wildlife Habitats chapter.

6. The literature on public goods and externalities related to agriculture is vast, but see for example Bromley (1997) and OECD (1994).

7. For evidence on the trend towards a less varied landscape in, for example, *Australia* see Lefroy *et al* (2000); the *United States*, see Mac *et al.*, (1998, Vol. 1, pp. 30-31); and for *European* OECD countries see the papers in Umstatter and Dabbert (1996). For a discussion of monitoring recent changes in agricultural landscapes in *Norway* see Fjellstad and Dramstad (1999); and in *Sweden* see Bjorklund *et al.* (1999); and Ihse (1995). See also the Wildlife Habitats chapter.

8. Porteous (1996), for example, has shown the public appreciation of more homogenous agricultural landscapes.

9. The 1999 OECD Agri-environmental Indicator Questionnaire has revealed that a number of countries are considering developing such statistical measures to describe spatial landscape configurations. But also relevant are the indicators being developed in *Australia*, for example, to monitor the impact of agriculture on native vegetation, see Figure 10 in the Wildlife Habitats chapter.

10. For a detailed examination of a methodology to develop cultural heritage indicators as part of state of the environment reporting, in *Australia*, see for example, Pearson *et al.*, 1998. The cultural heritage and amenity aspects of agricultural landscapes are also discussed in a *Norwegian* context by Romstad *et al.* (2000, pp. 37-42).

11. There is a vast literature on the description, development and use of these techniques, but for literature that examines these methods in the context of agricultural landscapes and related environmental goods and services, see for example, Dubgaard *et al.* (1994); Heimlich *et al.* (1998); Holstein (1998); OECD (1994); and Olsson and Ronningen (1999, pp. 16-20).

12. Some of the studies here relate to the evaluation of agricultural landscapes in national parks.

13. The issue of public perceptions of "tidy" agricultural landscapes and conflicts with "messy" biodiversity is examined by Ashworth *et al.*, (1999); Cary (2000); and Nassauer (1992).

Annex Table 1. Public and private schemes for conservation of biodiversity, habitats and landscape related to agriculture: 1998

Name of the scheme	Public/Private	Main objective	Area covered ('000 ha)	Share of total agricultural area	1998 Domestic currency ('000)	1998 US$ ('000)
Austria						
Landscape						
– Mountainous and less favoured areas	Federal/Provincial Government	Open farming landscape.	1 214	35%	2 906 600 (1997)	238 301
Canada						
Habitats						
– North American Waterfowl Management Plan	Federal Government	:	:	:	9 871 (1997-1998)	6 882
– North American Waterfowl Management Plan	Provincial Government	:	:	:	9 894 (1997-1998)	6 898
– North American Waterfowl Management Plan	Private	:	:	:	3 562 (1997-1998)	2 483
Denmark						
Biodiversity						
– Genetic diversity in farm animals	Public	Biodiversity.	:	:	1 600	239
Landscape						
– Nature management	Public	Nature protection.	1.251 (1995)	< 1%	124 500 (1995)	22 216
– Nature conservation	:	:	0.194 (1995)	< 1%	:	:
– Nature restoration project	:	:	0.552 (1995)	< 1%	:	:
– State owned areas	:	:	0.182 (1995)	< 1%	:	:
– Wildlife plantation scheme	Public 75%/Private 25%	To help wildlife in general.	0	< 1%	6 000	896
Finland						
Landscape						
– General Agricultural Environment Protection Scheme (GAEPS)	Public	Both these schemes (GAEPS and SPS) cover a range of objectives, including, for example, management of manure and pesticides, managing and enhancing biodiversity and landscape.	1 875	69%	1 372 000 (1997)	264 507
– Supplementary Protection Scheme (SPS)	Public		173	6%	195 000 (1997)	37 594
Germany						
Landscape						
– Landscape conservation areas	Public	:	8 798	51%	:	:
– Nature protection areas	Public	:	685	4%	:	:
– National parks	Public	:	727	4%	:	:
– Biosphere reserves	Public	:	1 249	7%	:	:
– Nature parks	Public	:	5 679	33%	:	:
Greece						
Landscape						
– Lanscape elements maintainance[1]	Public	Maintenance of terraces.	:	:	5 000 (1993 to 1997)	5 592
Japan[2]						
Landscape						
– Yusuhara village	Public/Private	Landscape, soil quality.	:	:	4 000 Yen/ha	31/ha
– Kiwa village	Public/Private	Landscape, soil quality.	:	:	3 000 Yen/ha	23/ha
– Wajima village	Foundation	Landscape, soil quality.	:	:	2 620 Yen/ha	20/ha
– Yuhuin village	Municipal	Landscape.	:	:	60 Yen/ha	0.458/ha

Annex Table 1. **Public and private schemes for conservation of biodiversity, habitats and landscape related to agriculture: 1998** *(cont.)*

Name of the scheme	Public/Private	Main objective	Area covered ('000 ha)	Share of total agricultural area	1998 Domestic currency ('000)	1998 US$ ('000)
Netherlands						
Habitats						
– Extensive pasture land	Public	Biodiversity conservation.	58	3%	41 000	20 660
– Extensive field margins in cropped land	Public	Biodiversity conservation.	0.5	< 1%	1 500	756
– Fallow land	Public	Biodiversity conservation.	12	1%	300	151
– Wet ditches, wetlands	Public	Biodiversity conservation.	75	4%	300	151
Landscape						
– Landscape conservation subsidy scheme	Public	Conservation of valuable landscape elements.	..	..	1 000 (1995)	623
– Landscape and farmyard planting scheme	Public	Planting new elements in the landscape on farms and in the farmyard.	0.150	< 1%	2 000 (1995)	1 246
– Provincial schemes for maintenance of landscape elements	Public	Support for farmers who maintain valuable landscape elements. The scheme operates at the provincial level.	..	..	4 700 (1995)	2 928
Norway[3]						
Habitats						
– Maintenance and development of agricultural landscape	..	Expenditure for biodiversity and semi-natural habitats.	17 (1998)	2%	14 600 (1995)	2 304
– Extensive grassland	..	Biodiversity.	0.128	< 1%	800	106
– Extensive pastureland	..	..	14	1%	14 500	1 922
– Hedges and woodlands	..	Investment grants for environmental measures.	49 areas	..	3 500	464
– Other semi-natural habitats types:	..	Expenditure for biodiversity and semi-natural habitats.	2 047 areas	..	6 500	861
e.g. Wetlands and mires for fodder, grazing...	..	Acreage not available at national level now.	146 areas	..	1 500	199
– Wet ditches, wetlands	..	Prevent runoff from agricultural land.	30 objects/areas	..	2 500	331
Landscape						
– Support for maintenance and development of agricultural landscape	Public/30-50% Private	Annual or/and lump sum expenditure. Conditions: usually no fertiliser or pesticide. Geographic and thematic priorities by the country authorities. Area data aggregated to national level from 1997.	2	< 1%	77 700	10 298
– Preservation of protected and listed farm buildings	Public 35%	Lump sum expenditure.	370 objects (1995)	..	15 (1995)	2
– Local management of areas given priority for landscape and environmental support	Public/Private	Lump sum expenditure for planning, information, coordination, maintenance plans. Coordination of support from other schemes for each area dependent on purpose. Areas of priority by the county authorities. Project period 3-5 years for each area. Bottom-up organisation and management. 10 projects 1993-96 in 4 counties, 3 mill kr/year (0.4 mill US$/year). 1998 start year for projects in all counties. Area not aggregated to national level.	c. 50 projects	..	12 000	1 590
– Information, research monitoring and education projects on agricultural landscapes	Public	Annual expenditure. Started with a campaign, "Living landscapes" 1988-89. Research programme from 1991-95.	..	..	6 500	861

Annex Table 1. **Public and private schemes for conservation of biodiversity, habitats and landscape related to agriculture: 1998** (cont.)

Name of the scheme	Public/Private	Main objective	Area covered ('000 ha)	Share of total agricultural area	1998 Domestic currency ('000)	1998 US$ ('000)
Norway (cont.)						
Landscape (cont.)						
– Projects for maintenance of agricultural landscapes	:	Lump sum expenditure. 2-3 year projects.	:	:	4 000	530
– Deficiency support for summer mountain farms	Public	Annual expenditure. Fixed payment per farm. Number of transhumance farms/summer mountain farms supported. Dairy production minimum 4 weeks each summer. Area not aggregated to national level.	2 719 farms	< 1%	19 800	2 624
– Support for livestock grazing on extensive pastureland		Annual expenditure. Grazing minimum 8 weeks each summer out of field land. No fertiliser, no spraying, natural vegetation with heather, shrubs, bushes and/or trees, low animal density. New scheme 1998. Included in acreage and cultural landscape scheme before 1998.	:	:	184 (support from 1999)	24
– Area and cultural landscape scheme	Public	Annual expenditure Cross-compliance scheme. Per-hectare payment aimed at reducing the intensity of production and conserving cultural landscapes. From 1991. Approximately ⅓ has landscape effect. Support for farming steep slopes and basic area support for organic farming are included.	1 050	102%	3 955 000	524 165
– Support to organic farming	Public	Annual expenditure. Objective is to enhance ecological farming. Effect on biodiversity and habitats? Assume there is an effect on biodiversity and habitats because of more crop rotation and no use of artificial fertiliser and pesticides. Since 1990, basic area support included in Area and Cultural Landscape Scheme. Information and research included.	11	1%	13 200	1 749
– Investment grants for environmental measures	Public/Private 30%	Lump sum expenditure or loan. Main objective is to prevent runoff from agricultural land. Totals reported here: 1. Support for planting vegetation to complete existing green structure and increase the variation in the landscape. 2. Support for ecological purification systems: Constructed wetlands and vegetation zones.	:	:	6 000	795
Poland						
Landscape						
– Restoration of agricultural land	Public/Private	Restoration wasteland and peatbogs into farm management.	2	< 1%	1 858	532
– Fertilisation of soil	Public/Private	Soil liming.	26	< 1%	2 510	719
– Measurement against erosion	Public/Private	Field amalgamation.	0.026	< 1%	90	26
– Small water retention	Public/Private	Building storage reservoir.	0.451	< 1%	2 231	639

Annex Table 1. **Public and private schemes for conservation of biodiversity, habitats and landscape related to agriculture: 1998** (cont.)

Name of the scheme	Public/Private	Main objective	Area covered ('000 ha)	Share of total agricultural area	1998 Domestic currency ('000)	1998 US$ ('000)
Portugal						
Biodiversity						
– Douro vineyards	Public	Protection of the douro vineyards landscape stone wall terraces.	9	< 1%	360 000 000 (1994-1996)	2
– Orchards of traditional varieties	Public	Protection of traditional orchards.	3	< 1%	161 000 000 (1994-1996)	1
– Traditional livestock breeds	Public	Support for traditional livestock breeds threatened by extinction.	..	..	1 037 000 000 (1994-1996)	7
– Traditional almond orchards	Public	Protection of traditional almond varieties to avoid loss of rural communities.	13	< 1%	198 000 000 (1994-1996)	1
Landscape						
– Maintenance of traditional agricultural systems	Public	Avoid loss of rural communities.	439	11%	8 141 000 000 (1997)	46
Spain						
Landscape						
– Leader and Proder	Public	Restoring traditional rural buildings.	..	..	2 750 (1999)	15
Sweden						
Biodiversity						
– Red beans	Public	Maintain traditional cultivation of local varieties.	0.974	< 1%	2 600	327
– Endangered local livestock breeds	Public	To guarantee the survival of livestock breeds.	..	..	3 100	390
Habitats						
– Extensive ley and mowed meadows	Public	Biodiversity, cultural, water quality.	7.5	< 1%	20 100	2 529
– Conservation in semi natural grazing land and maintenance of an open landscape[4]	Public	Biodiversity, cultural, open landscape.	382.5	12%	484 600	60 979
– Fallow land-area aid financed by EU	Public	..	194	6%	484 000	60 903
– Wetlands and ponds	Public	Biodiversity, water quality.	1.24	< 1%	5 800	730
Landscape						
– Nature conservation areas (agricultural land)	Public	Biodiversity, cultural.	..	< 1%	10 000	1 258
– Perennial ley farming	Public	Water quality, open landscape.	774	..	423 100	53 240
– Conservation of biodiversity and cultural heritage[4]	Public	Biodiversity, landscape.	1 583	51%	1 114 500	140 242
Switzerland						
Biodiversity						
– Gene banks	Public/Private	Conservation of genetic information.	..	..	300	207
– Conservation of local breeds	Public/Private	Conservation of cultivated plants diversity.	..	..	1 000	690
– Pest control (Pou de San José)	Public	Pest control (eradication through quarantine).	2	< 1%	400	276
Habitats						
– Ecological compensation, conservation of habitat diversity	Public	..	..	..	113 600	78 358
Landscape						
– Ecological compensation	Public	Conservation of species diversity and landscape diversity.	89	6%	100 900	69 598
– High fruit trees	Public	Conservation of species diversity and landscape diversity.	2 700 (trees)	< 1%	37 400	25 798
– Support for transhumance	Public	Support for transhumance on alpine pastures: conservation of biodiversity and landscape.	306	19%	66 900	46 146

Annex Table 1. Public and private schemes for conservation of biodiversity, habitats and landscape related to agriculture: 1998 (cont.)

Name of the scheme	Public/Private	Main objective	Area covered ('000 ha)	Share of total agricultural area	1998 Domestic currency ('000)	1998 US$ ('000)
United Kingdom						
Landscape						
– Environmentally Sensitive Areas	Public	Wildlife, Landscape, Historical.	501	3%	32 984	54 660

Note: The share of total expenditure on biodiversity, habitats and landscape as a percentage of the total Producer Support Estimate (PSE) for 1998 is as follows: Canada: < 1%; Norway: 20%; Poland: < 1%; Switzerland: 4% and EU: < 1% (the % for EU is higher than shown here as only 9 member States are included in this calculation, while the PSE covers 15 Member countries).

c. Circa.
.. Not available.
1. The domestic currency is the EURO.
2. Not a comprehensive list.
3. Figures refer to public expenditure only.
4. The same programmes are included for landscape and habitats.

Sources: OECD Agri-environmental Indicators Questionnaire, 1999; OECD (2000).

Annex Table 2. **Selected monetary valuation studies for agricultural landscape and wildlife conservation**

Author	Country	Geographical level	What has been measured	Aggregate WTP ECU ('000)	Aggregate WTP US$ ('000)	Average WTP ECU/ha	Average WTP US$/ha
1. Pruckner (1995)	Austria	National	WTP (willingness-to-pay) whether farmers or others should provide landscape services	53 884	70 437	..	..
2. Bonnieux and Rainelli (1995)	France	Regional	WTA (willingness-to-accept) compensation to change farming practices: 1. Decreasing intensification of dryland; 2. Decreasing stocking rate of cattle; 3. Joining an organic farming network.	.. .. ..	.. .. ..	519 145 353	437 122 297
3. Le Goffe and Gerber (1994)	France	Regional	Preservation of today's landscape.	803	621	144	111
4. Marinelli et al. (1990)	Italy	Regional	1. WTP to prevent a worsening of a natural park; 2. WTA refraining from a visit to the park.	.. ..	.. ..	300 751	253 633
5. Brouwer and Slangen (1995)	Netherlands	Regional	WTP for the preservation of wildlife and landscape within the cultivated area in the Alblasserwaard.	..	..	1 688	1 423
6. Spaninks (1993)	Netherlands	Regional	WTP to get a varied vegetation on ditch sides and an improvement of the situation of meadow birds.	..	..	76	64
7. Santos (1998)	Portugal	Regional	Visitors' WTP to keep agri-environmental measures currently applied in the Peneda-Geres National Park, as opposed to the landscape changes that would occur without the programme (general abandonment and scrub encroachment on terraced farmland, meadows and oak woods).	2 245 483	2 850 321	646	820
8. Rebolledo and Perez y Perez (1994)	Spain	Regional	Maintaining a natural park.	1 334	1 031	960	742
9. Drake (1992)	Sweden	National	WTP to prevent half of all agricultural land with: 1. Grain production; 2. Grazing; 3. Wooded pasture from being cultivated with spruce.	.. .. ..	.. .. ..	94 180 227	80 152 192
10. Hasund (1998)	Sweden	National	WTP for preserving landscape elements of cultivated land in Sweden.	..	..	153 – 207	129 – 174
11. Bateman et al. (1992)	United Kingdom	Regional	Preservation of the landscape from increased risk of flooding. 1. User value; 2. Non-use benefits.	8 620 137 163	6 663 106 375	288 4 590	223 3 548
12. Dillman and Bergstrom (1991)	United Kingdom	Regional	WTP to prevent conversion of prime agricultural land to urban-industrial use (a quarter of the whole area).	..	..	28 – 72	24 – 60

Annex Table 2. **Selected monetary valuation studies for agricultural landscape and wildlife conservation** (*cont.*)

Author	Country	Geographical level	What has been measured	Willingness-to-pay (WTP)			
				Aggregate WTP		Average WTP	
				ECU ('000)	US$ ('000)	ECU/ha	US$/ha
13. Santos (1998)	United Kingdom	Regional	Visitors' WTP to keep the Pennine Dales Environmentally Sensitive Area (ESA) scheme as opposed to the landscape changes that would occur without the scheme (decay of walls and barns and intensification of meadows).	7 958 175	10 402 844	309	404
14. Willis and Benson (1993)	United Kingdom	Regional	WTP for three nature reserves: 1. Derwent; 2. Skipwith Common; 3. Upper Teesdale.	.. .. ..	.. .. ..	652 2 961 569	549 2 496 480
15. Willis and Garrod (1994)	United Kingdom	Regional	WTP to preserve South Downs Environmentally Sensitive Area (ESA): 1. User value; 2. Non-use value (general public).	63 000 40 000	53 000 34 000	.. ..	.. ..
16. Adger and Whitby (1993)	United Kingdom	National	WTP 1. To retain the green belt in the United Kingdom; 2. To conserve wildlife in the United Kingdom.	.. ..	.. ..	423 54	356 46
17. Willis and Garrod (1993)	United Kingdom	National	WTP to preserve: 1. Today's landscape; 2. Conserved landscape.	54 000 52 000	46 000 44 000	.. ..	.. ..
18. Beasley *et al.* (1986)	United States	Regional	1. WTP to prevent moderate housing development from taking place on agricultural land; 2. WTP to prevent large housing development from taking place on agricultural land.	.. ..	.. ..	187 383	158 323

.. Not available.

Note: Exchange rates for references were as follows: Reference numbers 2, 4-6, 9-10, 12, 14–18 = 1994 exchange rate; 3, 8, 11 = 1992 exchange rate; 1 = 1995 exchange rate; 7, 13 = 1996 exchange rate.

Sources: Adapted from Bonnieux and Weaver (1996), Oskam and Slangen (1998), and Santos (1998). For detailed sources see following page.

Annex Table I. **Selected monetary valuation studies for agricultural landscape and wildlife conservation** (*cont.*)

Sources: Adger, W.N. and Whitby, M.C. (1993), "Natural resource accounting in the land-use sector: theory and practice," *European Review of Agricultural Economics*, Vol. 20, pp. 77-97.

Bateman, I., *et al.* (1992), *Recreation and Environmental Preservation Value of the Norfolk Broads: a contingent valuation study*, unpublished report to the National Rivers Authority, Environment Appraisal Group, University of East Anglia, Norwich.

Beasley, S.D., Workman, W.G. and William, N.A. (1986), *Non-market Valuation of Open Space and Amenities Associated with Retention of Lands in Agricultural Use*, Bulletin 71, Agricultural and Forestry Experiment Station, University of Alaska, Fairbanks.

Bonnieux, F. and Rainelli, P. (1995), "Contingent valuation and the design of agri-environmental measures", in Hofreither, M.F. and Vogel, S. (eds), *The Role of Agricultural Externalities in High Income Countries*, Wissenschaftsverlag Vauk, Kiel, pp. 91-108.

Brouwer, R. and Slangen, L.G.H. (1995), *The Measurement of the Non-Marketable Benefits of Agricultural Wildlife Management: The Case of Dutch Peat Meadow Land*, Department of Agricultural Economics and Policy, Agricultural University, Wageningen.

Dillman, B.L. and Bergstrom, J.C. (1991), "Measuring environmental amenity benefits of agricultural land", in Hanley, N. (ed.), *Farming and the Countryside*, CAB International, Wallingford, pp. 250-271.

Drake, L. (1992), "The non-market value of the Swedish agricultural landscape", *European Review of Agricultural Economics*, Vol. 19, pp.351-364.

Hasund, K. Per, (1998), "Valuable Landscapes and Reliable Estimates", in Dabbert, S., Dubgaard, A., Slangen, L. and Whitby, M. (eds), *The Economics of Landscape and Wildlife Conservation*, CAB International, Wallingford, pp. 65-83.

Le Goffe, P. and Gerber, P. (1994), *L'Espace Rural : Entre Protection et Contraintes*, Report to the French Government by the Conseil Economique et Social, Paris.

Marinelli, A., Casini, L. and Romana, D. (1990), "User-benefits and the economic regional impact of outdoor recreation in a natural park of Northern Tuscany", in Whitby, M.C. and Dawson, P.J. (eds), *Land Use for Agriculture, Forestry and Rural Development*, Department of Agricultural Economics and Food Marketing, University of Newcastle upon Tyne, Newcastle upon Tyne, pp. 179-193.

Pruckner, G.J. (1995), "Agricultural landscape cultivation in Austria: an application of the CVM", *European Review of Agricultural Economics*, Vol. 22, No. 22.

Rebolledo, D., and Perez y Perez, L. (1994), *Valoracion contingente de bienes ambientales: aplicacion al Parque Nacional de la Dehesa del Moncayo*, Gobierno de Aragon, Departamento de Agricultura, Ganaderia y Montes.

Santos, J. M. L. (1998), *The economic valuation of landscape change. Theory and policies for land use and conservation*, New horizons in environmental economics, Edward Elgar Press, Cheltenham, United Kingdom.

Spaninks, F.A. (1993), *Een Schatting van de Sociale Baten van Beheersovereenkomsten met Behulp van de Contingent Valuation Methode*, Scriptie, Vakgrope Algemene Agrarische Economie, Wageningen.

Willis, K.G. and Garrod, G.D. (1993), "Valuing landscape: a contingent valuation approach", *Journal of Environmental Management*, Vol. 37, pp.1-22.

Willis, K.G. and Benson, J.F. (1993), "Valuing environmental assets in developed countries", in Turner, R.K. (ed.), *Sustainable Environmental Economics and Management: Principle and Practice*, Belhaven Press, London, pp. 269-295.

Willis, K.G. and Garrod, G.D. (1994), "The ultimate test: measuring the benefits of ESAs", in Whitby, M. (ed.), *Incentives for Countryside Management: the Case of Environmentally Sensitive Areas*, CAB International, Wallingford, pp. 179-217.

BIBLIOGRAPHY

Ashworth, S.W., K. Topp, F. Newcombe, J.P. Boutonnet and G. Brunori (1999),
"The Demands of the Public from Agricultural Production, Landscape and the Environment", pp. 218-225, in ADAS, *Agriculture and the Environment – Challenges and Conflicts for the New Millennium*, Conference Proceedings, Wolverhampton, United Kingdom.

Bergstrom, J.C. (1998),
Exploring and Expanding the Landscape Values Terrain, Faculty Paper Series FS 98-20, August, Department of Agricultural and Applied Economics, University of Georgia, Athens, Georgia, United States.

Bjorklund, J., K.E. Limburg and T. Rydberg (1999),
"Impact of production intensity on the ability of the agricultural landscape to generate ecosystem services: an example from Sweden", *Ecological Economics*, Vol. 29, No. 2, pp. 269-291.

Bonnieux, F. and P. Rainelli (1996),
"Landscape and Nature Conservation – French Country Report", pp. 68-81, in J. Umstatter and S. Dabbert (eds.) (1996), *Policies for Landscape and Nature Conservation in Europe*, published as an inventory to the EU Concerted Action (AIR 3-CT93-1164) Workshop on Landscape and Nature Conservation, held on 26-29 September, University of Hohenheim, Germany.

Bonnieux, F. and R. Weaver (1996),
"Environmentally Sensitive Area Schemes: Public Economics and Evidence", Chapter 12, in M. Whitby (ed.), *The European Environment and CAP Reform – Policies and Prospects for Conservation*, CAB International, Oxford, United Kingdom.

Bromley, D.W. (1997),
"Environmental Benefits of Agriculture: Concepts", pp. 35-54, in OECD, *Environmental Benefits of Agriculture, Issues and Policies, The Helsinki Seminar*, Paris, France.

Cary, J. (2000),
"The aesthetics of remnant vegetation and rural landscape features", in A. Hamblin (ed.), *Visions of Future Landscapes*, Proceedings of the Australian Academy of Science Fenner Conference on the Environment 2-5 May 1999, Canberra, Bureau of Rural Sciences, Canberra, Australia (in press). Details on the Conference are available at: *www.brs.gov.au/* [Resources > Publications > Conference Proceedings].

Council of Europe (1998),
Council for the Pan-European Biological and Landscape Diversity Strategy, STRA-CO(98)8rev, April, Strasbourg, France. Available at: *www.strategyguide.org/fulltext.html*.

Council of Europe (2000),
European Landscape Convention. Available at: *www.conventions.coe.int/treaty/en/treaties/html/17b.htm*.

Countryside Commission (1993),
Landscape Assessment Guidance, Advisory booklet, United Kingdom.

Dramstad, W.E. and R. Lagbu (2000),
Landscape Indicators – Where to now?, Norwegian Institute of Land Inventory (NIJOS), Document 8/00, As, Norway.

Dubgaard, A., I. Bateman and M. Merlo (eds.) (1994),
Economic Valuation of Benefits from Countryside Stewardship, Proceedings of a Workshop organised by the Commission of the European Communities, Wissenschaftsverlag Vauk, Kiel, Germany.

EEA [European Environment Agency] (1995),
"Landscapes", Chapter 8, in EEA, *Europe's Environment: The Dobris Assessment*, Office for Official Publications of the European Communities, Luxembourg. Available at: *http://themes.eea.eu.int/* [> all available reports].

Environment Australia (1996),
State of the Environment Report 1996: Executive Summary, Report to the Commonwealth Minister for the Environment, Department of the Environment and Heritage, Canberra, Australia. Available at: *www.environment.gov.au/epcg/soe/soe96/soeexec2.html*.

Environment Canada (1999),
> The Importance of Nature to Canadians: Survey Highlights, Ottawa, Canada. Available at: www.ec.gc.ca/nature/splash.htm#s1.

European Commission (1999),
> "From Soil to Landscape: A Fundamental Part of the European Union's Heritage", Chapter 16, in European Commission, Agriculture, Environment, Rural Development: Facts and Figures – A Challenge for Agriculture, Office for Official Publications of the European Communities, Luxembourg. Available at: http://europa.eu.int/comm/dg06/envir/report/en/index.htm.

FAO [United Nations Food and Agriculture Organisation] (1999),
> Central and Eastern European Sustainable Agriculture Network, First Workshop Proceedings, REU Technical Series 61, FAO Subregional Office for Central and Eastern Europe, Rome, Italy. Available at: www.fao.org/regional/europe/public-e.htm.

Fjellstad, W.J. and W.E. Dramstad (1999),
> "Patterns of change in two contrasting Norwegian agricultural landscapes ", Landscape and Urban Planning, Vol. 45, No. 4, pp. 177-191.

Frost, F. and P. Metcalf (1999),
> "Landscape in the future: Using Landscaping now to design our futures", in A. Hamblin (ed.) Visions of Future Landscapes, Proceedings of the Australian Academy of Science Fenner Conference on the Environment 2-5 May 1999, Canberra, Bureau of Rural Sciences, Canberra, Australia (in press). Details on the Conference are available at: www.brs.gov.au/ [Resources > Publications > Conference Proceedings].

Green, D.G. (2000),
> "Environmental futures – the role of information technology", in A. Hamblin (ed.) Visions of Future Landscapes, Proceedings of the Australian Academy of Science Fenner Conference on the Environment 2-5 May 1999, Canberra, Bureau of Rural Sciences, Canberra, Australia (in press). Details on the Conference are available at: www.brs.gov.au/ [Resources > Publications > Conference Proceedings].

Haines-Young, R., C. Watkins, R.G.H. Bunce and C.J. Hallam (1996),
> Environmental Accounts for Land Cover, Countryside 1990 Series, Vol. 8, Department of the Environment, London, United Kingdom.

Hamblin A. (ed.) (2000),
> Visions of Future Landscapes, Proceedings of the Australian Academy of Science Fenner Conference on the Environment 2-5 May 1999, Canberra, Bureau of Rural Sciences, Canberra, Australia (in press). Details on the Conference are available at: www.brs.gov.au/ [Resources > Publications > Conference Proceedings].

Hasund, K.P. (1998),
> "Valuable Landscapes and Reliable Estimates", pp. 65-83, in S. Dabbert, A. Dubgaard, L. Slangen and M. Whitby (eds.), The Economics of Landscape and Wildlife Conservation, CAB International, Oxford, United Kingdom.

Heimlich, R.E., K.D. Wiebe, R. Claassen, D. Gadsby and R.M. House (1998),
> Wetlands and Agriculture: Private Interests and Public Benefits, Agricultural Economic Report No. 765, Economic Research Service, US Department of Agriculture, Washington, DC., United States. Available at: www.ers.usda.gov/epubs/pdf/aer765/.

Heineke, H.J., W. Eckelmann, A.J. Thomasson, R.J.A. Jones, L. Montanarella and B. Buckley (eds.) (1998),
> Land Information Systems – Developments for Planning the Sustainable Use of Land Resources, Research Report No. 4, European Soil Bureau, Official Publication of the European Communities, Luxembourg. Available at: http://esb.aris.sai.jrc.it/publications/.

Hietala-Koivu, R., L. Tahvanainen, L. Nousiainen, T. Heikkilä, A. Alanen, M. Ihalainen, L. Tyrväinen and J. Helenius (1999),
> A Visual Landscape in Monitoring of the Finish Agri-environmental Programme, paper presented at the Statistics Denmark Seminar, "How can agricultural statistics meet environmental information needs?", July, Copenhagen, Denmark.

Holstein, F. (1998),
> "The values of the agricultural landscape: a discussion on value-related terms in natural and social science and the implications for the contingent valuation method", pp. 37-52, in S. Dabbert, A. Dubgaard, L. Slangen and M. Whitby (eds.), The Economics of Landscape and Wildlife Conservation, CAB International, Oxford, United Kingdom.

Ihse, M. (1995),
> "Swedish agricultural landscapes – patterns and changes during the last 50 years, studies by aerial photos", Landscape and Urban Planning, Vol. 31, No. 1, pp. 21-37.

Lefroy, E.C., R. Hobbs and T. Hatton (2000),
> "Effects of changing vegetation on hydrology and biodiversity", in A. Hamblin (ed.) Visions of Future Landscapes, Proceedings of the Australian Academy of Science Fenner Conference on the Environment 2-5 May 1999, Canberra, Bureau of Rural Sciences, Canberra, Australia (in press). Details on the Conference are available at: www.brs.gov.au/ [Resources > Publications > Conference Proceedings].

Mac, M.J., P.A. Opler, C.E.P. Haecker and P.D. Doran (1998),
  Status and Trends of the Nation's Biological Resources, Two Volumes, United States Department of the Interior, United States Geological Survey, Reston, Virginia, United States. Available at: *http://biology.usgs.gov/pubs/execsumm/page2.htm*.

MAFF [Ministry of Agriculture, Fisheries and Food] (2000),
  Towards Sustainable Agriculture – A Pilot Set of Indicators, London, United Kingdom. Available at: *www.maff.gov.uk/* [Farming > Sustainable Agriculture].

Meeus, J.H.A., M.P. Wijermans and M.J. Vroom (1990),
  "Agricultural landscapes in Europe and their transformation", *Landscape and Urban Planning*, Vol. 18, No. 3-4, pp. 289-352.

Mitchell, N. and S. Buggey (2000),
  "Protected Landscapes and Cutural Landscapes: Taking Advantage of Diverse Approaches", *The George Wright Forum*, Vol. 17, No. 1, pp. 35-46. Available at: *www.georgewright.org/forum.html*.

Nassauer, J.I. (1989),
  "Agricultural policy and aesthetic objectives", *Journal of Soil and Water Conservation*, Vol. 44, No. 5, pp. 384-387.

Nassauer, J.I. (1992),
  "The appearance of ecological systems as a matter of policy", *Landscape Ecology*, Vol. 6, No. 4, pp. 239-250.

Nersten, N.K., O. Puschmann, J. Hofsten, A. Elgersma, G. Stokstad and R. Gudem (1999),
  The Importance of Norwegian Agriculture for the Cultural Landscape, Notat 11, Norwegian Institute of Land Inventory (NIJOS), Oslo, Norway.

OECD (1994),
  "Agricultural Policy Reform: Environmental Externalities and Public Goods", Part V, in OECD, *Agricultural Policy Reform: New Approaches the Role of Direct Income Payments*, Paris, France.

OECD (1998),
  Co-operative Approaches to Sustainable Agriculture, Paris, France.

OECD (2000),
  Agricultural Policies in OECD Countries: Monitoring and Evaluation 2000, Paris, France.

OFEFP [Office fédéral de l'environnement, des forêts et du paysage] (1998),
  Le paysage entre hier et demain (The landscape from yesterday to tomorrow, with English summary), Berne, Switzerland.

Olsson, G.A. and K. Rønningen (1999),
  Environmental Values in Norwegian Agricultural Landscapes, Report No. 10/99, Centre for Rural Research, Department of Botany, Norwegian University of Science and Technology, Trondheim, Norway.

Oskam, A. and L. Slangen (1998),
  "The financial and economic consequences of a wildlife development and conservation plan: A case study for the ecological main structure in the Netherlands", pp. 113-133, in S. Dabbert, A. Dubgaard, L. Slangen and M. Whitby (eds.), *The Economics of Landscape and Wildlife Conservation*, CAB International, Oxford, United Kingdom.

Pearson, M., D. Johnston, J. Lennon, I. McBryde, D. Marshall, D. Nash and B. Wellington (1998),
  Environmental Indicators for National State of the Environment Reporting – Natural and Cultural Heritage, Australia: State of the Environment (Environmental Indicator Reports), Department of the Environment, Canberra, Australia. Available at: *www.environment.gov.au/soe/indicators.html*.

Porteous, J.D. (1996),
  Environmental Aesthetics, Routledge Publishers, London and New York.

Puschmann, O. (1998),
  The Norwegian Landscape Reference System – use of different sources as a base to describe landscape regions, Norwegian Institute of Land Inventory (NIJOS), NIJOS Report 12/98, Norway.

Ridley, A.M. and R. Joffre (2000),
  "The Iberian dehesa: Unrealistic parkland or practical solution?", in A. Hamblin (ed.), *Visions of Future Landscapes*, Proceedings of the Australian Academy of Science Fenner Conference on the Environment 2-5 May 1999, Canberra, Bureau of Rural Sciences, Canberra, Australia (in press). Details on the Conference are available at: *www.brs.gov.au/* [Resources > Publications > Conference Proceedings].

Romstad, E. A. Vatn, P.K. Rorstad and V. Soyland (2000),
  Multifunctional Agriculture Implications for Policy Design, Report No. 21, Department of Economics and Social Sciences, Agricultural University of Norway, As, Norway. Available at: *www.nlh.no/ios/publikasjoner/melding/m-21.html*.

Santos, J.M.L. (1998),
  The economic valuation of landscape change – Theory and policies for land use and conservation, New horizons in environmental economics, Edward Elgar Press, Cheltenham, United Kingdom.

Sinner, J. (1997),
"New Zealand: Policy Considerations regarding Landscape Amenities and Biodiversity from Sustainabl Agriculture", pp. 229-235, in OECD, *Helsinki Seminar on Environmental Benefits from Agriculture – Country Case Studie* Paris, France. Available at: *www.oecd.org/agr/publications/index1.htm*.

Slangen, L.H.G. (1992),
"Policies for nature and landscape conservation in Dutch agriculture: An evaluation of objectives, mean effects and programme costs", *European Journal of Agricultural Economics*, Vol. 19, pp. 331-350.

Smith, C.A.S. and T. McRae (2000),
"Understanding and Assessing the Environmental Sustainability of Agriculture", Chapter 2, in T. McRae C.A.S. Smith and L.J. Gregorich (eds.), *Environmental Sustainability of Canadian Agriculture: Report of the Agr Environmental Indicator Project*, Agriculture and Agri-Food Canada (AAFC), Ottawa, Ontario, Canada. Availabl at: *www.agr.ca/policy/environment/publications/list.html*.

Tanokura, N., M. Yokohari, K. Yamamoto and Y. Kato (1999),
"Local residents impressions and perceptions on paddy field landscapes: A case study in Hiki region, Saitam Prefecture, Japan" (in Japanese with English summary), *Lando Skepu Kenkyu* (Journal of Landscape Research Vol. 62, No. 5, pp. 727-732.

Umstatter, J. and S. Dabbert (eds.) (1996),
Policies for Landscape and Nature Conservation in Europe, published as an inventory to the EU Concerted Actio (AIR 3-CT93-1164) Workshop on Landscape and Nature Conservation, held on 26-29 September, University Hohenheim, Germany.

van Huylenbroeck, G. and M. Whitby (eds.) (1999),
Countryside Stewardship: Farmers' Policies and Markets, Pergamon Press, Amsterdam, The Netherlands.

van Mansvelt, J.D. and M.J. van der Lubbe (1999),
Checklist for Sustainable Landscape Management, Final Report of a European Communities Concerted Actio Programme, Elsevier Press, Amsterdam, The Netherlands.

Wascher, D. (ed.) (1997),
European landscapes: Classification, evaluation and conservation, European Environment Agency, Environment Monograph Copenhagen, Denmark.

Wascher, D. (ed.) (2000),
Landscapes and Sustainability. Proceedings of the European Workshop on Landscape Assessment as a Policy Too 25-26 March 1999, Strasbourg, France, European Centre for Nature Conservation, Tilburg, The Netherlands.

Williams, J.M. (2000),
"Sustainable Development of Land uses in New Zealand: Utopian Vision or Realistic Goal?", in A. Hambl (ed.), *Visions of Future Landscapes*, Proceedings of the Australian Academy of Science Fenner Conference on th Environment 2-5 May 1999, Canberra, Bureau of Rural Sciences, Canberra, Australia (in press). Details on th Conference are available at: *www.brs.gov.au/* [Resources > Publications > Conference Proceedings].

Wrbka, T., E. Szerencsits, K. Reiter and A. Kiss (1999),
"Identifying sustainable land-use by describing landscape structure. A case study in alpine and lowlan agricultural landscapes of Austria", in C. Brebbia and J.L. Uso (eds.), *Ecosystems and Sustainable Development, WI* Press, Ashurst, United Kingdom.

Yokohari, M., R.D. Brown and K.Takeuchi (1994),
"A framework for the conservation of rural ecological landscapes in the urban fringe area in Japan", *Landscape ar Urban Planning*, Vol. 29, pp. 103-116.

GLOSSARY

This glossary provides definitions of key terms that appear repeatedly in the text. The list is not exhaustive and draws from many of the sources in this Report.

Agricultural land: Arable crops (*e.g.* cereals), permanent crops (*e.g.* orchards) and permanent pasture (*i.e.* land devoted to livestock grazing for orchards periods longer than 5 years)

Agri-environmental indicator: A summary measure combining raw data of an environmental driving force, state, risk, or change resulting from agricultural activities identified as important to OECD policy makers (*e.g.* soil erosion rates, see also *Risk indicator* and *State indicator*).

Agroecosystem: Ecosystem under agricultural management, connected to other ecosystems.

Biological diversity: Global variety of species and ecosystems and the ecological processes of which they are part, covering three components: genetic, species and ecosystem diversity.

Biomass: The quantity of living material of plant or animal origin, present at a given time within a given area.

Carbon dioxide: One of the greenhouse gases produced through the decomposition of organic matter in soils under oxidising conditions, also produced by the burning of fossil fuels.

Carbon dioxide equivalent: A measure used to compare the emissions from various greenhouse gases based upon their global warming potential. For example, the global warming potential for methane over 100 years is 21. This means that emissions of one million metric tons of methane is equivalent to emissions of 21 million metric tons of carbon dioxide

Carbon sequestration (carbon sink): Biochemical process by which atmospheric carbon is absorbed by living organisms, including trees, soil micro-organisms, and crops, and involving the storage of carbon in soils, with the potential to reduce atmospheric carbon dioxide levels.

Climate change: The changes that the global climate may undergo as a result of the effect of greenhouse gases, including global warming and changes in the amount and pattern of precipitation.

Compaction: The process whereby the density of soils is increased by tillage, livestock pressure and/or vehicular traffic. Such compaction gives rise to lower soil permeability and poorer soil aeration with resultant increases in erosion risk and lowered plant productivity.

Conservation tillage: A tillage system that creates a suitable soil environment for growing a crop and that conserves soil, water and energy resources mainly through the reduction in the intensity of tillage, and retention of plant residues.

Conventional tillage: A tillage system using cultivation as the major means of seedbed preparation and weed control. Typically includes a sequence of soil tillage, such as ploughing and harrowing, to produce a fine seedbed, and also the removal of most of the plant residue from the previous crop. In this context the terms cultivation and tillage are synonymous, with emphasis on soil preparation.

Cover crop: A temporary vegetative cover that is grown to provide protection for the soil and the establishment of plants, particularly those which are slow growing. Some cover crops are introduced by undersowing and in due course provide permanent vegetative cover to stabilise the area concerned. The term can include an intermediate crop that can be removed by the use of selective herbicides.

Crop residue: Plant material remaining after harvesting, including leaves, stalks, roots.

Driving force – State – Response Framework: A conceptual framework to describe environmental linkages, whereby "driving forces" are the factors that influence agricultural activities, the "states" are the outcomes of these activities, and "responses" are the actions by society to influence outcomes.

Evapotranspiration: Removal of moisture from soil by evaporation plus transpiration by plants growing in that soil.

Fallowing: The management practice of leaving land in an uncropped state for a period of time prior to sowing another crop. Its purpose is to allow for the accumulation and retention of water and mineralised nutrients in the soil, and generally to also allow for weed control.

Farm financial resources: or farm income consist of market returns on agricultural production, loans and equity capital, and transfers due to agricultural policies from taxpayers (government budgetary support) and consumers (through market price support).

Genetic modification (genetic engineering): Manipulation of the genetic material of an organism to produce desired traits, such as nutritional quality, photosynthetic efficiency and herbicide resistance.

Global warming: Rise in global temperatures resulting from changes in the levels of atmospheric greenhouse gases.

Integrated pest management: Control of pests using a combination of techniques such as crop rotations, cultivation, and biological and chemical pest controls.

Land conservation: concerns the flow of water resources across agricultural land (which can cause flooding and landslides) and the loss of soil sediment from agricultural land into rivers, lakes and reservoirs.

Nitrogen fixation: The conversion of free nitrogen to nitrogen combined with other elements; specifically regarding soils, the assimilation of atmospheric nitrogen from the soil air by soil organisms to produce nitrogen compounds that eventually become available to plants.

No-tillage (also zero tillage): A minimum tillage practice in which the crop is sown directly into soil not tilled since the harvest of the previous crop. Weed control is achieved by the use of herbicides and stubble is retained for erosion control. It is typically practised in arable areas where fallowing is important.

Nutrient: Substance required by an organism for growth and development. Key crop nutrients are nitrogen, phosphorus and potassium.

Organic farming: system of crop cultivation employing biological methods of fertilisation and pest control as substitutes for chemical fertilisers and pesticides.

Pasture: Grasses, legumes and/or other herbage used or suitable for the grazing of animals. The term also includes the land covered by such herbage, being used or suitable for grazing.

Pesticide: Chemical that kills or controls pests; mainly includes herbicide, insecticide and fungicide.

Precision farming: Farm management at a level that allows inputs to be tailored to variable conditions across short distances in a single field.

Risk indicator: Indicator that estimates the potential for some form of resource degradation using mathematical formulas or models.

Runoff: The portion of precipitation not immediately absorbed into or detained on soil and which thus becomes surface water flow.

Sediment: Material of varying size, both mineral and organic that is being, or has been, moved from its site of origin by the action of wind, water, gravity, or ice, and comes to rest elsewhere on the earth's surface.

Soil cover: Vegetation, including crops, and crop residues on the surface of the soil.

Soil degradation: Process(es) by which soil declines in quality and is thus made less fit for a specific purpose, such as crop production.

Soil organic matter: Carbon-containing material in the soil that derives from living organisms.

Soil quality: encompasses two distinct, but related parts: *inherent quality*, the innate properties of soils such as those that lead to soil formation; and *dynamic quality*, covering the main degradation processes (physical, chemical and biological) and farm management practices.

State indicator: Indicator that expresses an actual resource condition, usually based on direct field measurement.

Terracing: Steplike surface that breaks the continuity of a slope.

KEY WEBSITES RELATED TO AGRI-ENVIRONMENTAL ISSUES

Organisation for Economic Co-operation and Development (OECD) www.oecd.org/

Agri-environmental indicators	*www.oecd.org/agr/env/indicators.htm*
Agri-environmental policies	*www.oecd.org/agr/policy/ag-env/*
Agriculture	*www.oecd.org/agr/*
Environment	*www.oecd.org/env/*
Sustainable development	*www.oecd.org/subject/susdev/*
Territorial development	*www.oecd.org/tds/*

OECD Member Governments and Related Agencies:

Agriculture

Australia	Department of Agriculture, Fisheries and Forestry	*www.affa.gov.au/*
	Australian Bureau of Agriculture and Resource Economics	*www.affa.gov.au/outputs/economics.html*
	Bureau of Rural Science	*www.brs.gov.au/*
Austria	Federal Ministry for Agriculture and Forestry	*www.bmlf.gv.at/*
	Federal Institute for Agricultural Economics	*www.awi.bmlf.gv.at/indexe.htm*
Belgium	Ministry of Middle-class and Agriculture	*www.cmlag.fgov.be/*
	Centre for Agricultural Economics	*www.clecea.fgov.be/*
Canada	Agriculture and Agri-Food Canada	*www.agr.ca/*
Czech Republic	Ministry of Agriculture	*www.mze.cz/*
Denmark	Ministry of Food, Agriculture and Fisheries	*www.fvm.dk/*
	National Institute of Agricultural and Fisheries Economics	*www.sjfi.dk/*
Finland	Ministry of Agriculture and Forestry	*www.mmm.fi/*
	Research Institute for Agricultural Economy	*www.mttl.fi/*
France	Ministry of Agriculture and Fisheries	*www.agriculture.gouv.fr/*
	National Institute of Agricultural Research	*www.inra.fr/*
Germany	Federal Ministry for Food, Agriculture and Forestry	*www.bml.de/*
	Federal Research Institute for Agriculture	*www.fal.de/*
Greece	Ministry of Agriculture	*www.minagric.gr/*
Hungary	Ministry of Agriculture and Regional Development	*www.hvm.hu/*
Iceland	Ministry of Agriculture	*www.stjr.is/lan/*
Ireland	Department of Agriculture, Food and Rural Development	*www.irlgov.ie/daff/*
Italy	Ministry of Agriculture and Forestry Policies	*www.politicheagricole.it/*
	National Institute of Agricultural Economics	*www.inea.it/*
Japan	Ministry of Agriculture, Forestry and Fisheries	*www.maff.go.jp/eindex.html*
	National Institute of Agro-Environmental Sciences	*ss.niaes.affrc.go.jp/index_e.html*
Korea	Ministry of Agriculture and Forestry	*www.maf.go.kr/english/default.html*
Luxembourg	Ministry of Agriculture, Viniculture and Rural Development	*www.etat.lu/ONR/*
Mexico	Secretariat of Agriculture, Cattle and Rural Development	*www.sagar.gob.mx/*
Netherlands	Ministry of Agriculture, Nature Management and Fisheries	*www.minlnv.nl/international/*
	Agricultural Economics Research Institute	*www.lei.dlo.nl/*

New Zealand	Ministry of Agriculture and Forestry	*www.maf.govt.nz/mafnet/*
Norway	Ministry of Agriculture	*odin.dep.no/ld/engelsk/*
Poland	Ministry of Agriculture and Food Economy	*www.minrol.gov.pl/glowna-eng.html*
Portugal	Ministry of Agriculture, Rural Development and Fisheries	*www.min-agricultura.pt/*
Spain	Ministry of Agriculture, Fisheries and Food	*www.mapya.es/*
Sweden	Ministry of Agriculture	*jordbruk.regeringen.se/*
	Swedish Board of Agriculture	*www.sjv.se/english/default.htm*
Switzerland	Federal Office for Agriculture	*www.blw.admin.ch/*
	Federal Research Station for Agricultural Economics and Engineering	*www.admin.ch/sar/fat/*
Turkey	Ministry of Agriculture and Rural Affairs	*www.tarim.gov.tr/english/english.htm*
United Kingdom	Ministry of Agriculture, Fisheries and Food	*www.maff.gov.uk/*
United States	Department of Agriculture	*www.usda.gov/*
	Economic Research Service	*www.ers.usda.gov/*
	Natural Resource Conservation Service	*www.nrcs.usda.gov/*
EU	Directorate General for Agriculture	*europa.eu.int/comm/dg06/*
	Statistical Office of the European Communities	*europa.eu.int/comm/eurostat/*

Environment

Australia	Department of the Environment and Heritage	*www.environment.gov.au/*
	National Land and Water Resource Audit	*www.nlwra.gov.au/*
Austria	Federal Ministry for Environment, Youth and Family	*www.bmu.gv.at/*
	Federal Agency for the Environment	*www.ubavie.gv.at/*
Belgium	Ministry of Social Affairs, Public Health and the Environment	*www.minsoc.fgov.be/*
Canada	Environment Canada	*www.ec.gc.ca/*
	Natural Resources Canada	*www.nrcan.gc.ca/*
Czech Republic	Ministry of Environment	*www.env.cz/www/domino.nsf/*
Denmark	Ministry of Environment and Energy	*www.mem.dk/*
	Environmental Agency	*www.mst.dk/*
Finland	Ministry of the Environment	*www.vyh.fi/ym/ym.html*
	Finnish Environment Centre	*www.vyh.fi/syke/syke.html*
France	Ministry of Regional Planning and Environment	*www.environnement.gouv.fr/*
	French Institute for the Environment	*www.ifen.fr/*
Germany	Federal Ministry for Environment, Nature Protection and Reactor Security	*www.bmu.de/*
	Federal Office for Environment	*www.umweltbundesamt.de/*
Greece	Ministry for the Environment, Physical Planning and Public Works	*www.minenv.gr/*
Hungary	Ministry of Environmental Protection	*www.ktm.hu/*
Iceland	Ministry for the Environment	*www.stjr.is/umh/*
Ireland	Department of the Environment and Local Government	*www.environ.ie/*
	Environmental Protection Agency	*www.epa.ie/*
Italy	Ministry of Environment	*www.minambiente.it/*
	National Institute of Statistics	*www.istat.it/*
Japan	Environment Agency	*www.eic.or.jp/eanet/en/index.html*
	National Institute for Environmental Studies	*www.nies.go.jp/*
Korea	Ministry of Environment	*www.me.go.kr/english/eindex.html*
	National Institute of Environmental Research	*www.nier.go.kr/english/english.html*

Luxembourg	Ministry of Environment	*www.mev.etat.lu/*
Mexico	Secretariat for Environment, Natural Resources and Fisheries	*www.semarnap.gob.mx/*
Netherlands	Ministry of Housing, Regional Planning and Environment	*www.minvrom.nl/*
	State Institute of Public Health and the Environment	*www.rivm.nl*
New Zealand	Ministry for the Environment	*www.mfe.govt.nz/*
Norway	Ministry of Environment Protection	*odin.dep.no/md/engelsk/*
Poland	Ministry of Environmental Protection, Natural Resources and Forestry	*www.mos.gov.pl/index_main.shtml*
Portugal	Ministry of Environment	*www.dga.min-amb.pt/*
Spain	Ministry of Environment	*www.mma.es/*
Sweden	Ministry of Environment	*miljo.regeringen.se/*
Switzerland	Federal Department for Environment, Transport, Energy and Communication	*www.uvek.admin.ch/*
	Federal Office for the Environment, Forests and Landscape	*www.buwal.ch/*
Turkey	Ministry of Environment	*www.cevre.gov.tr/*
	Ministry of Energy and Natural Resources	*www.enerji.gov.tr/*
United Kingdom	Department of the Environment, Transport and the Regions	*www.detr.gov.uk/*
	Environment Agency	*www.environment-agency.gov.uk/*
United States	Environmental Protection Agency	*www.epa.gov/*
	Geological Survey	*www.usgs.gov/*
EU	Directorate General for Environment	*europa.eu.int/comm/environment/*
	European Environment Agency	*eea.eu.int/*

International Governmental Organisations:

Environmental Treaties and Resource Indicators (ENTRI)	*sedac.ciesin.org/pidb/*
Intergovernmental Panel on Climate Change (IPCC)	*www.ipcc.ch/*
International Standardisation Organisation (ISO)	*www.iso.ch/*
North American Commission for Environmental Cooperation (CEC)	*www.cec.org/*
Oslo and Paris Convention for the Prevention of Marine Pollution (OSPAR convention)	*www.ospar.org/*
United Nations :	*www.un.org/*
UN Commission on Sustainable Development (UNCSD)	*www.un.org/esa/sustdev/csd.htm*
UN Convention on Biological Diversity (UNCBD)	*www.biodiv.org/*
UN Convention to Combat Desertification (UNCCD)	*www.unccd.int/*
UN Educational, Scientific and Cultural Organisation (UNESCO)	*www.unesco.org/*
– World cultural and natural heritage sites	*www.unesco.org/whc/*
UN Environment Programme (UNEP)	*www.unep.org/*
– World Conservation Monitoring Centre	*www.unep-wcmc.org/*
UN Food and Agriculture Organisation (FAO)	*www.fao.org/*
– Sustainable development	*www.fao.org/waicent/faoinfo/sustdev*
UN Framework Convention on Climate Change (UNFCCC)	*www.unfccc.de/*
World Bank:	*www.worldbank.org/*
Rural Development and Agriculture	*www.worldbank.org/*
Environment	*www.worldbank.org/environment/*
Land Quality Indicators	*www-esd.worldbank.org/lqi/*

Non-Governmental Organisations:

BirdLife International	*www.wing-wbsj.or.jp/birdlife/*
Earth Council	*www.ecouncil.ac.cr/*
International Federation of Organic Agriculture Movements (IFOAM)	*www.ifoam.org/*
International Society for Ecological Economics (ISEE)	*www.ecologicaleconomics.org/*
International Soil Reference and Information Centre (ISRIC)	*www.isric.nl/*
Resources for the Future (RFF)	*www.rff.org/*
Wetlands International	*www.wetlands.agro.nl/Wetlands_ICU/*
World Conservation Union (IUCN)	*www.iucn.org/*
World Resource Institute (WRI)	*www.wri.org/*
World Wide Fund for Nature (WWF)	*www.panda.org/*
Worldwatch Institute	*www.worldwatch.org/*

INDEX

This Index is divided into three sections:

- OECD Member Countries
- Environmental Issues
- Other Related Agri–environmental Issues

Page numbers marked in **Bold** signify key references in the text, figures, tables, boxes or annexes, while other less important references are not bolded. For the OECD Member country section page numbering is divided under the main chapters of the report (full titles of these chapters are provided in the table of contents).

OECD MEMBER COUNTRIES

KOREA

(Contextual): 42-43; 45-46; 48; 52-53; 56-59 (Farm Financial): 66; 76 (Farm Management): **91**; 94; 103 (Nutrient): 123; **125**; 128; 134-135 (Pesticides): **146**; 147-148; 161; 166 (Water Use): 176-177; 179; 188-190 (Soil Quality): 203-204; 210; **212**; 217; 219 (Water Quality): 236; **239**; 248 (Land Conservation): 258-259; 261 (Biodiversity): **302** (Wildlife Habitats): 345-347; **350**; 361 (Landscape): 372 (Websites): 401-402.

LUXEMBOURG

(Contextual): 42-43; 46; 56 (Pesticides): 162; 166 (Water Use): 176; 188 (Soil Quality): 219 (Water Quality): 236; 249 (Greenhouse Gases): 278; 280; 287 (Biodiversity): **310** (Websites): 401; 403.

MEXICO

(Contextual): 42-44; 48; 52-53; 56-59 (Nutrient): 123-124; 128; 134-135 (Pesticides): **163**; 166 (Water Use): 176-177; 179; **185**; 188-190 (Soil Quality): **202**; 217; 219 (Land Conservation): 267 (Biodiversity): 296; 304-305 (Wildlife Habitats): 345; 350; **354** (Landscape): 372 (Websites): 401; 403.

NETHERLANDS

(Background): 24 (Contextual): 42-43; 45-46; 52-53; 56-59 (Farm Financial): 66; 69; 71; 73; 76-77 (Farm Management): 94; 96; 103; 107 (Nutrient): 118; 123; **124**; 128; 134-135 (Pesticides): 142; **146**; 147-148; 161; 162; 166 (Water Use): 176; 179; 185; 188-191 (Soil Quality): 205-206; 217; 219 (Water Quality): 236; **240**; **243**; 248-249 (Land Conservation): 259; 261; 267 (Greenhouse Gases): **278**; 280-281; 283; 287 (Biodiversity): 300-301; 303; 306; 308; 320; 323-325 (Wildlife Habitats): 337; 341; 343; 346; 352; 359 (Landscape): 382; 388; 392 (Websites): 401; 403.

NEW ZEALAND

(Background): 24 (Contextual): 42-43; 46; 48; 52-53; 56-59 (Farm Financial): **65-67** (Farm Management): 105 (Nutrient): 123-124; 126; 128; 134-135 (Pesticides): **146**; 147; 161; 163; 166 (Water Use): 176; 178-179; 188-190 (Soil Quality): **202-204**; 217; 219 (Water Quality): **239**; 243 (Greenhouse Gases): 274; 277-278; 287 (Biodiversity): **295**; **314-315** (Landscape): 366; 372 (Websites): 402-403.

NORWAY

(Contextual): 42-46; 48; 52-53; 56-59 (Farm Financial): 66; 69; 76; 77 (Farm Management): 95-97; 99; 103; 105 (Nutrient): 123; 128; 134-135 (Pesticides): 142; **146**; 147-148; 161; 163; 166 (Water Use): 176; 179; 188-190 (Soil Quality): 203; 205; 217; 219 (Water Quality): 235-236; **240**; 248-249 (Land Conservation): 258; 262; 267 (Greenhouse Gases): 274; 278; 280; 287 (Biodiversity): 301; 303-304; 306; 308; 314-315; 320-325 (Wildlife Habitats): 337; 346; 359; 361 (Landscape): 366; 377; **380**; 388-389 (Websites): 402-403.

POLAND

(Contextual): 42-43; 48; 52-53; 56-59 (Farm Management): 107 (Nutrient): 123; **124**; 128; 134-135 (Pesticides): **146**; 147; 163; 166 (Water Use): 175-179; 183; 188-190 (Soil Quality): 203; 205; **208**; 217; 219 (Water Quality): 236; 240; 243; 248-249 (Land Conservation): 259; 261; 267 (Greenhouse Gases): 274; **277**; 278; 287 (Biodiversity): 300-301; 303; 309; 321-324; 326 (Wildlife Habitats): 343; 346; 361 (Landscape): 366; 377; 380; 389 (Websites): 402-403.

PORTUGAL

(Contextual): 42-43; 45-46; 52-53; 56-59 (Farm Financial): 69-70; 73; 76-77 (Farm Management): 94; 101 (Nutrient): 123; 128; 134-135 (Pesticides): 166 (Water Use): 176; 179; 183; **185**; 188-191 (Soil Quality): 203; **206**; 217; 219 (Water Quality): 236; 248 (Land Conservation): 261 (Greenhouse Gases): 278; 280; 287 (Biodiversity): 300-301; 305; 310; 314; 320-324 (Wildlife Habitats): 337; 339 (Landscape): 376; 390; 392 (Websites): 402-403.

SPAIN

(Contextual): 42-43; 45-46; 52-53; 56-59 (Farm Financial): 69; 71; 76-77 (Farm Management): 93-94; 101 (Nutrient): 123; 128; 134-135 (Pesticides): 146-147; 162; 166 (Water Use): **174**; 175-177; **178**; 179-180; 183; **185**; 189-191 (Soil Quality): 203; **206**; 217; 219 (Water Quality): **240**; 248 (Land Conservation): 259; 261; 267 (Greenhouse Gases): 278; 280; 287 (Biodiversity): 305; 310 (Wildlife Habitats): 337; 346; 361 (Landscape): 376-377; 390; 392 (Websites): 402-403.

SWEDEN

(Contextual): 42-44; 46; 52-53; 56-59 (Farm Financial): 69; 71; 77 (Farm Management): 91; 92; 94-95; 103 (Nutrient): 123-124; 126; 128; 134-135 (Pesticides): 142; **146-147**; **158-159**; 162; 166 (Water Use): 176-177; 179; 188-190 (Soil Quality): 217; 21 (Water Quality): 236; **240**; **243**; 248-249 (Greenhouse Gases): 278; 280; 287 (Biodiversity): 300-301; 303; 306; 308; 310; 320 325 (Wildlife Habitats): 342-343; 359; 361 (Landscape): **375**; 390; 392 (Websites): 402-403.

SWITZERLAND

(Background): 24 (Contextual): 42-44; 46; 48; 52-53; 56-59 (Farm Financial): 69; 71-74; 76-77 (Farm Management): 91-94; 99; 101; **103-104**; 105 (Nutrient): 123-124; 128; **130**; 134-135 (Pesticides): **146**; 147-148; 161; 166 (Water Use): 176; 179; 183; 188-190 (Soil Quality): 203; **206**; 217; 219 (Water Quality): 235-236; 240; 243; 248-249 (Land Conservation): 261-26 (Greenhouse Gases): 274; 278; 287 (Biodiversity): 298; 301; 303; 305-306; 308; 314; 320-325 (Wildlife Habitats): 337; **339-340**; 341; 343; 346; 350; **358**; 360-361 (Landscape): 366; 390 (Websites): 402-403.

TURKEY

(Contextual): 42-43; 48; 52-53; 56-59 (Nutrient): 123-124; 128; 134-135 (Pesticides): 142; 148; 161; **163**; 166 (Water Use): 176; 179; **185**; 188-191 (Soil Quality): 203; **206**; 208; 217; 219 (Greenhouse Gases): 278; 287 (Biodiversity): 30 (Websites): 402-403.

UNITED KINGDOM

(Background): 24 (Contextual): 42-46; 52-53; 56-59 (Farm Financial): **69**; 71; **72**; 73; 77 (Farm Management): 94-97; 99 102; 107; **108** (Nutrient): 123-124; 127-128; 134-135 (Pesticides): 143; 146-147; **152**; **161-162**; 166 (Water Use): 176-177 179; **181-182**; 185-186; 188-191 (Soil Quality): 211; **212-213**; 217; 219 (Water Quality): **233-235**; 236; **237**; 242; **243**; 248-24 (Land Conservation): 261; 267 (Greenhouse Gases): 278; 280; 283; 287 (Biodiversity): 297-298; 300; 304; 306-307; **310-312** 320; 326 (Wildlife Habitats): **337**; **339-340**; 341; **343-344**; 346-347; 350; 360-361 (Landscape): 366; **376-378**; 379; 390-39 (Websites): 402-403.

UNITED STATES

(Background): 24 (Contextual): 42-46; 48; 52-53; 56-59 (Farm Financial): 66; **67-68**; 69-70; 73; 76-77 (Farm Management) 93-94; **97-99**; 101; **105-106**; 107-108 (Nutrient): 123-124; 126; 128; 134-135 (Pesticides): 142-143; 146-147; 149; **159-161** 163; 166 (Water Use): 174-177; **178**; 179-180; 183; **185**; 188-191 (Soil Quality): 200; **201-202**; 203; 205; **208-210**; 211; 217 219 (Water Quality): 236; **237-239**; 241; **242-244**; 248 (Land Conservation): 258; 267 (Greenhouse Gases): 274; 278; 283 287 (Biodiversity): 295-296; 301-302; **305**; **312**; 313; **314** (Wildlife Habitats): **336-338**; 341; **345-346**; 361 (Landscape) 366; 372; **380**; **382**; 392 (Websites): 402-403.

AGRI-ENVIRONMENTAL ISSUES

AMMONIA EMISSIONS
118; **128**

BIODIVERSITY
20; 24; 143; 162; 174; 200; 213-214; **291-330**; **333**

GREENHOUSE GASES
20; 25; 200; 214; **273-290**

HABITATS
20; 174; **183-184**; 186; **297-298**; 308; **309**; 315-316; **331-364**; **374-379**

LAND CONSERVATION (Agricultural land water retaining capacity and off-farm sediment flow)
255-271

LANDSCAPE
20; **365-398**

OTHER RELATED AGRI-ENVIRONMENTAL ISSUES